DYNAMICS OF RIGID BODIES

MacMillan's

THEORETICAL MECHANICS

STATICS AND THE DYNAMICS OF A PARTICLE

THE THEORY OF THE POTENTIAL

DYNAMICS OF RIGID BODIES

THEORETICAL MECHANICS

DYNAMICS
OF
RIGID BODIES

BY

WILLIAM DUNCAN MacMILLAN, A. M., Ph. D., Sc. D.

DOVER PUBLICATIONS, INC.
NEW YORK

Published in the United Kingdom by
Constable and Company Limited,
10 Orange Street, London, W.C. 2.

This new Dover edition, first published in 1960, is an unabridged and unaltered republication of the first edition originally published by the McGraw-Hill Book Company, Inc. in 1936.

Manufactured in the United States of America

Dover Publications, Inc.
180 Varick Street
New York 14, N.Y.

PREFACE

The present volume brings to a close the task undertaken some ten years ago of writing a series of volumes on various aspects of mechanics. The first volume dealt with the subject of statics and the dynamics of a particle, the second with the theory of the potential, and the present volume deals with the dynamics of rigid bodies. In this volume references to Statics and the Dynamics of a Particle are indicated by the roman numeral I followed by the section number, and to the Theory of the Potential by the numeral II and the section number.

It is assumed that by the time a student undertakes a study of the dynamics of rigid bodies his mathematical training is well advanced. The three laws of motion as given by Newton furnish the foundation for the entire structure. Two methods of development are in common use: the intuitive, or geometrical, method, leading to the invention and development of the theory of vectors, and the purely analytic method that results from the equations of Lagrange and of Hamilton. Both of these methods are used in the present work, as they were in studies in statics and the dynamics of a particle in the first volume. Analysis, however, is indispensable even in the intuitive method. But analysis by itself is incomplete without intuition. A mere mathematical formula is meaningless unless it is accompanied by an interpretation that makes it really worth while.

The subject of small oscillations, as it is called in many books, really infinitesimal oscillations, is extended here to the finite periodic oscillations, known as the periodic solutions of Poincaré. Lack of space forbids the development of solutions that are reentrant only after many periods, and of solutions that are asymptotic to periodic solutions. The same reason also forbids a treatment of the figures of equilibrium of rotating fluid masses, which, I think, properly belongs in this volume, for such bodies move just as though they were rigid.

My grateful appreciation is extended to Dr. R. W. Barnard for valuable suggestions and assistance, and particularly to Dr. Walter Bartky, not only for his kindness and assistance, which have been constant, but also for his permission to set forth his treatment of linear differential equations with constant coefficients in advance of his own publications on the subject.

THE UNIVERSITY OF CHICAGO,
January, 1936.

W. D. MACMILLAN.

CONTENTS

CHAPTER III

Systems of Free Particles

CHAPTER IV

General Theorems on the Motion of a Rigid Body

CHAPTER V

Motion Parallel to a Fixed Plane

One Degree of Freedom

CHAPTER IX

IMPULSIVE FORCES

CHAPTER X

THE DIFFERENTIAL EQUATIONS OF ANALYTICAL DYNAMICS

I. Holonomic Systems

II. Non-holonomic Systems

CHAPTER XI

The Canonical Equations of Hamilton

CHAPTER XII

The Method of Periodic Solutions

I. Certain Theorems Concerning Implicit Functions

II. The Solutions of Differential Equations as Power Series in a Parameter

III. Theorems on Matrices and Linear Differential Equations

IV. The Existence and Construction of Periodic Solutions

V. Illustrative Examples

An Unsymmetrical Top

DYNAMICS OF RIGID BODIES

DYNAMICS OF RIGID BODIES

CHAPTER I

ALGEBRA OF VECTORS

1. Introduction.—In the volume on "Statics and the Dynamics of a Particle" *vectors* were defined as directed magnitudes which combine in accordance with the parallelogram law, and were denoted by **bold face** type, thus **A, B, C, a, b, c,** etc. Graphically they are represented by arrows. Thus in Fig. 1, the sum of **A** and **B** is **C,** since **C** is the diagonal of the parallelogram of which the sides are **A** and **B.** The other diagonal **D** drawn from the terminus of **B** to the terminus of **A** is the difference between **A** and **B.** Thus

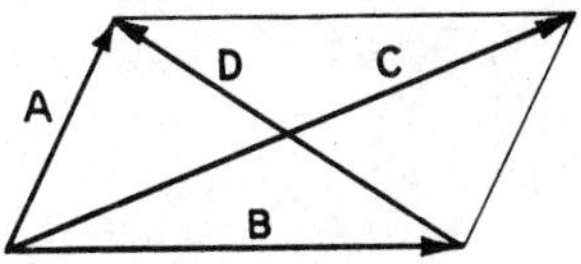

Fig. 1.

$$\mathbf{A} + \mathbf{B} = \mathbf{C},$$
$$\mathbf{A} - \mathbf{B} = \mathbf{D}.$$

C is said to be the vector sum of **A** and **B,** and **D** is the vector difference.

Inasmuch as the combinations of vectors in addition and subtraction obey the associative, commutative, and distributive laws of algebra, the usual notation of algebra for these operations can be used, and the vectors in these operations act like algebraic magnitudes.

A *scalar* is a quantity which possesses magnitude but not direction, like the numbers of arithmetic. Thus the length of the vector **A** (its tensor) is a scalar and, to distinguish between the vector **A** and its tensor, the tensor will be denoted by the *italic* letter A.

The multiplication of a vector by a scalar merely alters the length of the vector without changing its direction. Inasmuch as the vector character is not changed, the laws of algebra hold for vectors with scalar multipliers for the operations of addition and subtraction. For example, the equations

$$\mathbf{2A} + \mathbf{B} = \mathbf{M},$$
$$\mathbf{A} + \mathbf{2B} = \mathbf{N},$$

in which **M** and **N** are expressed in terms of **A** and **B**, can be solved for **A** and **B** in terms of **M** and **N**, just as though the vectors were algebraic quantities, giving

$$\mathbf{3A} = \ \ 2\mathbf{M} - \ \ \mathbf{N},$$
$$\mathbf{3B} = -\mathbf{M} + 2\mathbf{N};$$

for the solutions require only the operations of addition and subtraction, together with multiplication or division by scalars.

2. Scalar Multiplication of Vectors.—There are two types of vector products, one of which is a scalar and the other a vector. The *scalar* product is represented by a dot between the two vectors. Its value is the product of the tensor of one of the vectors into the tensor of the projection of the second vector upon the first; thus

$$\mathbf{A} \cdot \mathbf{B} = \mathbf{B} \cdot \mathbf{A} = AB \cos \widehat{\mathbf{AB}}. \qquad (1)$$

As an example, it will be remembered that the work done by a force **A** in a displacement **B** is

$$AB \cos \widehat{\mathbf{AB}} = \mathbf{A} \cdot \mathbf{B}.$$

From the definition of a scalar product it follows that

$$\cos \widehat{\mathbf{AB}} = \frac{\mathbf{A} \cdot \mathbf{B}}{AB};$$

and if **a** and **b** are any two unit vectors, it is seen that

$$\mathbf{a} \cdot \mathbf{b} = \cos \widehat{\mathbf{ab}}.$$

Consequently, if **i**, **j**, and **k** are three mutually perpendicular unit vectors,

$$\left.\begin{array}{l} \mathbf{i} \cdot \mathbf{i} = \mathbf{j} \cdot \mathbf{j} = \mathbf{k} \cdot \mathbf{k} = 1, \\ \mathbf{i} \cdot \mathbf{j} = \mathbf{j} \cdot \mathbf{k} = \mathbf{k} \cdot \mathbf{i} = 0. \end{array}\right\} \qquad (2)$$

Scalar Multiplication Obeys the Distributive Law.—Let **A**, **B**, and **C** be three vectors such that, Fig. 2,

$$\mathbf{A} + \mathbf{B} = \mathbf{C},$$

and let **D** be any fourth vector, not necessarily in the same plane. Let $\overline{oa}$, $\overline{ob}$, and $\overline{oc}$ be the projections of **A**, **B**, and **C** upon the line of **D**. Then $\overline{ob} = \overline{ac}$, since the projection of **B** upon the line of **D** is independent of the position of **B**. Now

$$\begin{aligned} \mathbf{D} \cdot \mathbf{C} &= DC \cdot \cos \widehat{\mathbf{DC}} = D \cdot \overline{oc} \\ &= D(\overline{oa} + \overline{ac}) = D(\overline{oa} + \overline{ob}) \\ &= DA \cos \widehat{\mathbf{AD}} + DB \cos \widehat{\mathbf{DB}} \\ &= \mathbf{D} \cdot \mathbf{A} + \mathbf{D} \cdot \mathbf{B}, \end{aligned}$$

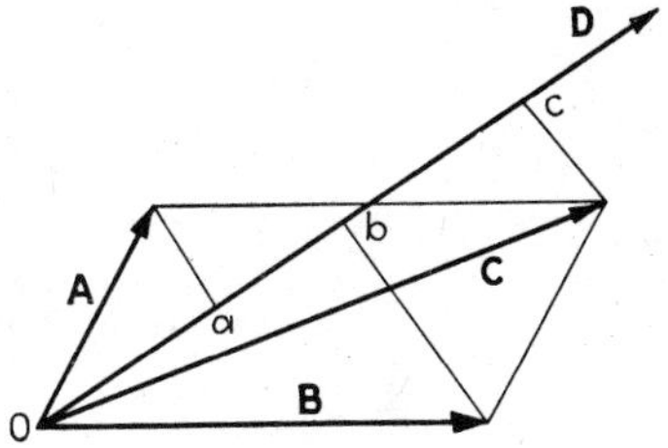

FIG. 2.

and therefore

$$\mathbf{D} \cdot \mathbf{C} = \mathbf{D} \cdot (\mathbf{A} + \mathbf{B}) = \mathbf{D} \cdot \mathbf{A} + \mathbf{D} \cdot \mathbf{B}, \tag{3}$$

which shows that the distributive law holds for scalar multiplication.

It is a simple matter to generalize and show that

$$\begin{aligned} (\mathbf{A}_1 + \mathbf{A}_2 + \cdots + \mathbf{A}_n) \cdot (\mathbf{B}_1 + \mathbf{B}_2 + \cdots \mathbf{B}_m) \\ = \mathbf{A}_1 \cdot \mathbf{B}_1 + \mathbf{A}_1 \cdot \mathbf{B}_2 + \cdots + \mathbf{A}_1 \cdot \mathbf{B}_m \\ + \mathbf{A}_2 \cdot \mathbf{B}_1 + \mathbf{A}_2 \cdot \mathbf{B}_2 + \cdots + \mathbf{A}_2 \cdot \mathbf{B}_m \\ + \cdots\cdots\cdots\cdots\cdots\cdots \\ + \mathbf{A}_n \cdot \mathbf{B}_1 + \mathbf{A}_n \cdot \mathbf{B}_2 + \cdots + \mathbf{A}_n \cdot \mathbf{B}_m. \end{aligned}$$

In particular, if **i**, **j**, and **k** are mutually perpendicular unit vectors, and if

$$\begin{aligned} \mathbf{A} &= x_1\mathbf{i} + y_1\mathbf{j} + z_1\mathbf{k}, \\ \mathbf{B} &= x_2\mathbf{i} + y_2\mathbf{j} + z_2\mathbf{k}, \end{aligned}$$

then

$$\left.\begin{aligned} \mathbf{A} \cdot \mathbf{B} = {} & x_1x_2\mathbf{i} \cdot \mathbf{i} + x_1y_2\mathbf{i} \cdot \mathbf{j} + x_1z_2\mathbf{i} \cdot \mathbf{k} \\ & + y_1x_2\mathbf{j} \cdot \mathbf{i} + y_1y_2\mathbf{j} \cdot \mathbf{j} + y_1z_2\mathbf{j} \cdot \mathbf{k} \\ & + z_1x_2\mathbf{k} \cdot \mathbf{i} + z_1y_2\mathbf{k} \cdot \mathbf{j} + z_1z_2\mathbf{k} \cdot \mathbf{k} \\ = {} & x_1x_2 + y_1y_2 + z_1z_2, \text{ by Eqs. (2).} \end{aligned}\right\} \tag{4}$$

Example.—Consider the triangle formed by the three vectors

$$\mathbf{A} - \mathbf{B} = \mathbf{C}.$$

On taking the scalar product of **C** into itself, there results

$$\mathbf{C} \cdot \mathbf{C} = (\mathbf{A} - \mathbf{B}) \cdot (\mathbf{A} - \mathbf{B}) = \mathbf{A} \cdot \mathbf{A} - 2\mathbf{A} \cdot \mathbf{B} + \mathbf{B} \cdot \mathbf{B}.$$

Hence

$$C^2 = A^2 + B^2 - 2AB \cos \widehat{\mathbf{AB}},$$

which is the cosine law of trigonometry.

3. The Vector Product of Two Vectors.—The vector (or cross) product of two vectors is indicated by the ordinary multiplication sign (×) placed between the symbols of the two vectors, thus

$$\mathbf{A} \times \mathbf{B} = AB \sin \widehat{\mathbf{AB}},$$

and, since the angle $\widehat{\mathbf{AB}}$ is opposite in sign to $\widehat{\mathbf{BA}}$, it is evident that

$$\mathbf{A} \times \mathbf{B} = -\mathbf{B} \times \mathbf{A}.$$

The commutative law is not obeyed, and careful attention must be paid to the order of the letters.

It is seen in Fig. 3 that $AB \sin \widehat{\mathbf{AB}}$ represents the area of the parallelogram of which the vectors **A** and **B** form two of the sides. Any plane area can be represented by a vector which is perpendicular to the plane and whose tensor is equal to that of the area. Hence $\mathbf{A} \times \mathbf{B}$ can be represented by a vector **C** which is perpendicular to the plane of **A** and **B** and whose tensor is

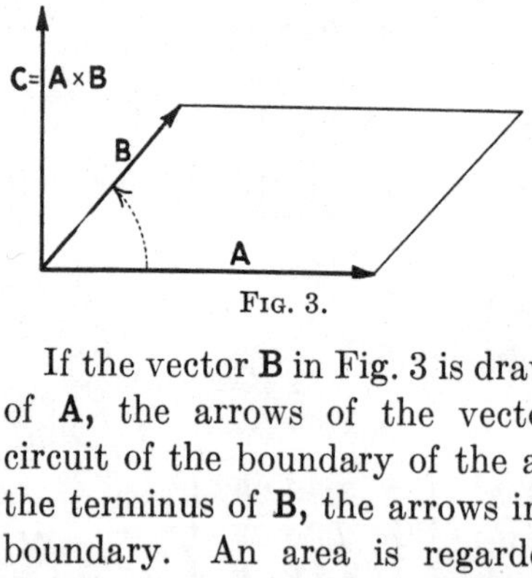

FIG. 3.

$$C = AB \sin \widehat{\mathbf{AB}}.$$

If the vector **B** in Fig. 3 is drawn with its origin at the terminus of **A**, the arrows of the vectors indicate a counterclockwise circuit of the boundary of the area; but, if the origin of **A** is at the terminus of **B**, the arrows indicate a clockwise circuit of the boundary. An area is regarded as positive if the circuit is counterclockwise, and negative if the circuit is clockwise. If a point describes a circuit in a plane, the area thus bounded is positive on one side of the plane, and negative on the other side. The plane can therefore be regarded as having a positive side and a negative side. This understanding is always implied in the statement that the projection of any closed surface upon any plane which does not intersect the surface is zero.

The projection of any plane area A upon any plane is the same as the projection of its vector **A** upon the normal to the plane, since the angle between the two planes is the same as the angle between the two normals. Consequently the vector sum of two plane areas is the projection of the two given areas upon a plane which is perpendicular to the vector sum of their two vectors.

Since the projection of any closed polyhedral surface upon any plane which does not intersect the surface is zero, it follows that the sum of the projections of the vectors $\mathbf{A}_i$, directed outward, which represent its plane faces, upon any line whatever is zero. Hence the vector which represents such a surface is zero; and, since a curved surface can be regarded as the limit of a sequence of polyhedral surfaces, the proposition holds for any closed surface.

The Distributive Law Holds for Vector Products.—It is desired to prove that

$$(\mathbf{A} + \mathbf{B}) \times \mathbf{D} = (\mathbf{A} \times \mathbf{D}) + (\mathbf{B} \times \mathbf{D}). \qquad (1)$$

In Fig. 4, let the vectors **A**, **B**, and **C** form a closed triangle, and let **D** be any other vector. Let **D** be placed first at the terminus of **A**, then at the terminus of **B**, and finally at the terminus of **C**. In these three positions the vector **D** defines a prism whose vector is zero since the prism with its two bounding triangles is a closed surface. Since the two triangles are equal and lie in parallel planes, their vector sum is zero. Therefore the vector sum of the three sides of the prism also is zero. That is, if $\mathbf{F}_A$, $\mathbf{F}_B$, $\mathbf{F}_C$ are the three vectors which represent these sides,

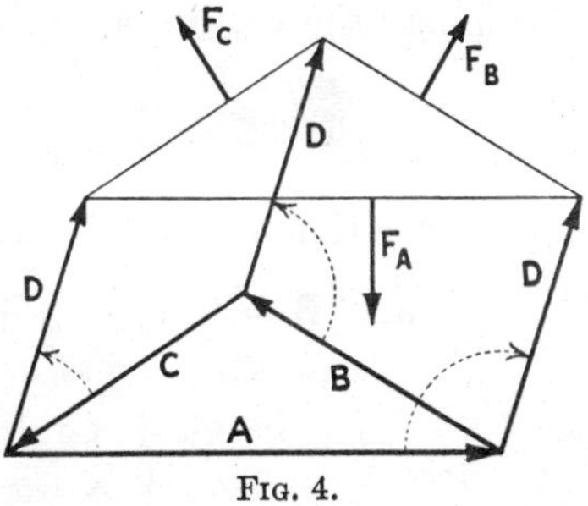

Fig. 4.

$$\mathbf{F}_A + \mathbf{F}_B + \mathbf{F}_C = 0.$$

This fact is otherwise obvious, since $\mathbf{F}_A$ is perpendicular to **A**, $\mathbf{F}_B$ to **B**, $\mathbf{F}_C$ to **C**, and

$$F_A:F_B:F_C::A:B:C;$$

and the three vectors are coplanar.

Now

$$\mathbf{F}_A = \mathbf{A} \times \mathbf{D},$$
$$\mathbf{F}_B = \mathbf{B} \times \mathbf{D},$$
$$\mathbf{F}_C = \mathbf{C} \times \mathbf{D};$$

so that, on taking the sum,

$$0 = (\mathbf{A} \times \mathbf{D}) + (\mathbf{B} \times \mathbf{D}) + (\mathbf{C} \times \mathbf{D}).$$

But

$$\mathbf{C} = -(\mathbf{A} + \mathbf{B}).$$

Hence

$$(\mathbf{A} + \mathbf{B}) \times \mathbf{D} = \mathbf{A} \times \mathbf{D} + \mathbf{B} \times \mathbf{D},$$

which is the theorem that was to be proved.

Three Mutually Perpendicular Unit Vectors.—Let **i**, **j**, and **k** be three mutually perpendicular unit vectors forming a right-handed system. Then

$$\mathbf{i} \times \mathbf{i} = \mathbf{j} \times \mathbf{j} = \mathbf{k} \times \mathbf{k} = 0,$$
$$\left.\begin{aligned} \mathbf{j} \times \mathbf{k} &= \mathbf{i}, \\ \mathbf{k} \times \mathbf{i} &= \mathbf{j}, \\ \mathbf{i} \times \mathbf{j} &= \mathbf{k}, \end{aligned}\right\} \quad \text{but} \quad \left\{\begin{aligned} \mathbf{k} \times \mathbf{j} &= -\mathbf{i}, \\ \mathbf{i} \times \mathbf{k} &= -\mathbf{j}, \\ \mathbf{j} \times \mathbf{i} &= -\mathbf{k}. \end{aligned}\right\} \tag{2}$$

Suppose the vectors **A** and **B** are expressed in the form

$$\mathbf{A} = x_1\mathbf{i} + y_1\mathbf{j} + z_1\mathbf{k},$$
$$\mathbf{B} = x_2\mathbf{i} + y_2\mathbf{j} + z_2\mathbf{k};$$

then, since the distributive law holds,

$$\begin{aligned} \mathbf{A} \times \mathbf{B} &= (x_1\mathbf{i} + y_1\mathbf{j} + z_1\mathbf{k}) \times (x_2\mathbf{i} + y_2\mathbf{j} + z_2\mathbf{k}) \\ &= x_1x_2\mathbf{i} \times \mathbf{i} + x_1y_2\mathbf{i} \times \mathbf{j} + x_1z_2\mathbf{i} \times \mathbf{k} \\ &\quad + y_1x_2\mathbf{j} \times \mathbf{i} + y_1y_2\mathbf{j} \times \mathbf{j} + y_1z_2\mathbf{j} \times \mathbf{k} \\ &\quad + z_1x_2\mathbf{k} \times \mathbf{i} + z_1y_2\mathbf{k} \times \mathbf{j} + z_1z_2\mathbf{k} \times \mathbf{k}, \end{aligned}$$

which reduces to

$$\mathbf{A} \times \mathbf{B} = (y_1z_2 - z_1y_2)\mathbf{i} + (z_1x_2 - x_1z_2)\mathbf{j} + (x_1y_2 - y_1x_2)\mathbf{k}; \tag{3}$$

or in the form of a determinant, which is convenient for the memory,

$$\mathbf{A} \times \mathbf{B} = \begin{vmatrix} \mathbf{i} & \mathbf{j} & \mathbf{k} \\ x_1 & y_1 & z_1 \\ x_2 & y_2 & z_2 \end{vmatrix}. \tag{4}$$

The coefficients of **i**, **j**, and **k** in this formula will be readily recognized as the projections of the parallelogram formed by **A** and **B** upon the **jk**, **ki** and **ij** planes respectively.

4. The Scalar Triple Product.—The product $\mathbf{A} \cdot \mathbf{B}\ \mathbf{C}$ must be understood to mean $(\mathbf{A} \cdot \mathbf{B})\mathbf{C}$, for the reading $\mathbf{A} \cdot (\mathbf{BC})$ has no meaning, since the combination **BC** has not been defined. Since $(\mathbf{A} \cdot \mathbf{B})$ is a scalar, the product $\mathbf{A} \cdot \mathbf{B}\ \mathbf{C}$, notwithstanding that it involves three vectors, is essentially a simple scalar product.

The product $\mathbf{A} \cdot (\mathbf{B} \times \mathbf{C})$ is called *the scalar triple product*, and, since $(\mathbf{A} \cdot \mathbf{B}) \times \mathbf{C}$ has no meaning, being the vector product of a scalar and a vector, the parentheses are not necessary, so that it can be written simply $\mathbf{A} \cdot \mathbf{B} \times \mathbf{C}$.

The interpretation of the scalar triple product $\mathbf{A} \cdot \mathbf{B} \times \mathbf{C}$ is simple. Since

$$\mathbf{B} \times \mathbf{C} = \mathbf{D}$$

is the area of the parallelogram defined by the vectors **B** and **C**, Fig. 5, and $\mathbf{A} \cdot \mathbf{D}$ is the product of D and the projection of **A** on **D**, it is readily seen that $\mathbf{A} \cdot \mathbf{B} \times \mathbf{C}$ is the volume of the parallelopiped defined by the vectors **A**, **B**, and **C**. The volume is positive if **A** and **D** lie on the same side of the **BC** plane, negative in the opposite case. It is positive if **A**, **B**, and **C** form a right-handed system as is the case in Fig. 5, and negative if they form a left-handed system. If any two of the vectors **A**, **B**, and **C** are interchanged, the system passes from a right-hand system to a left-hand system, and the volume changes sign.

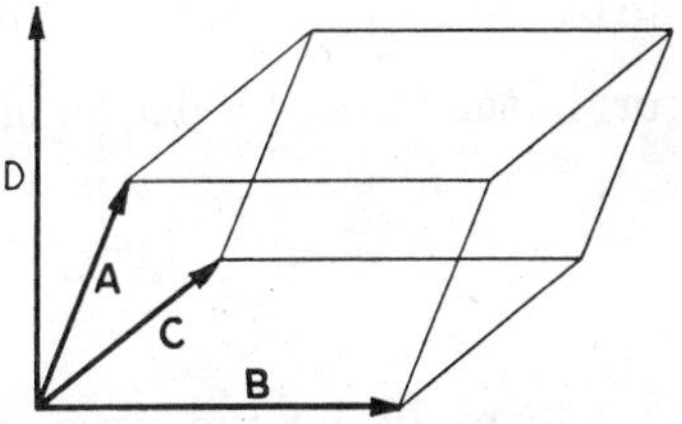

FIG. 5.

If merely the lettering is changed, the vectors themselves remaining unaltered, the volume of the parallelopiped is unaltered. The sign of the volume is unaltered if the change of lettering is cyclic, that is, in the order $\mathbf{A} \to \mathbf{B} \to \mathbf{C} \to \mathbf{A}$ or $\mathbf{A} \to \mathbf{C} \to \mathbf{B} \to \mathbf{A}$. But if only two of the letters are interchanged, the sign changes. It is evident therefore that

$$\left.\begin{aligned} \mathbf{A} \cdot \mathbf{B} \times \mathbf{C} &= \mathbf{B} \cdot \mathbf{C} \times \mathbf{A} \quad = \mathbf{C} \cdot \mathbf{A} \times \mathbf{B} \\ = -\mathbf{A} \cdot \mathbf{C} \times \mathbf{B} &= -\mathbf{B} \cdot \mathbf{A} \times \mathbf{C} = -\mathbf{C} \cdot \mathbf{B} \times \mathbf{A}. \end{aligned}\right\} \tag{1}$$

A comparison of these expressions shows that *the dot and the cross can be interchanged provided the cyclic order of the letters is preserved.* Since the commutative law holds for scalar products,

$$\mathbf{A} \cdot \mathbf{B} \times \mathbf{C} = \mathbf{B} \times \mathbf{C} \cdot \mathbf{A}.$$

As there are altogether six of these expressions which have the same value, they can all be denoted by the symbol

$$\left.\begin{aligned}[\mathbf{ABC}] &= \mathbf{A} \cdot \mathbf{B} \times \mathbf{C} = \mathbf{B} \cdot \mathbf{C} \times \mathbf{A} = \mathbf{C} \cdot \mathbf{A} \times \mathbf{B} \\ &= \mathbf{A} \times \mathbf{B} \cdot \mathbf{C} = \mathbf{B} \times \mathbf{C} \cdot \mathbf{A} = \mathbf{C} \times \mathbf{A} \cdot \mathbf{B},\end{aligned}\right\} \qquad (2)$$

and

$$[\mathbf{ABC}] = -[\mathbf{ACB}]. \qquad (3)$$

If $\mathbf{i}$, $\mathbf{j}$, $\mathbf{k}$ are mutually orthogonal unit vectors, and if

$$\begin{aligned}\mathbf{A} &= x_1\mathbf{i} + y_1\mathbf{j} + z_1\mathbf{k}, \\ \mathbf{B} &= x_2\mathbf{i} + y_2\mathbf{j} + z_2\mathbf{k}, \\ \mathbf{C} &= x_3\mathbf{i} + y_3\mathbf{j} + z_3\mathbf{k},\end{aligned}$$

then, by actually carrying out the operations indicated, it is found that

$$[\mathbf{ABC}] = x_1(y_2z_3 - y_3z_2) + y_1(z_2x_3 - z_3x_2) + z_1(x_2y_3 - x_3y_2); \qquad (4)$$

or, in the form of a determinant,

$$[\mathbf{ABC}] = \begin{vmatrix} x_1 & y_1 & z_1 \\ x_2 & y_2 & z_2 \\ x_3 & y_3 & z_3 \end{vmatrix}. \qquad (5)$$

Obviously, for the three mutually orthogonal unit vectors,

$$[\mathbf{ijk}] = -[\mathbf{ikj}] = +1. \qquad (6)$$

The scalar triple product vanishes if all three of the vectors are coplanar, if any two of them are collinear, or if any one of them vanishes.

5. The Vector Triple Product.—The vectcr triple product is written

$$\mathbf{A} \times (\mathbf{B} \times \mathbf{C}).$$

It is the vector product of two vectors, one of which is itself a vector product. The vector $\mathbf{B} \times \mathbf{C}$ is perpendicular to the plane which contains **B** and **C**, assuming that **B** and **C** have the same origin. The vector $\mathbf{A} \times (\mathbf{B} \times \mathbf{C})$ is perpendicular to **A** and to $(\mathbf{B} \times \mathbf{C})$ and therefore lies in the plane of **B** and **C**. If φ is the angle between **A** and the normal to the plane which contains **B** and **C**, then the tensor of $\mathbf{A} \times (\mathbf{B} \times \mathbf{C})$ is $ABC \sin \widehat{\mathbf{BC}} \sin \varphi$. Likewise the vector $(\mathbf{A} \times \mathbf{B}) \times \mathbf{C} = -\mathbf{C} \times (\mathbf{A} \times \mathbf{B})$ lies in the plane of **A** and **B**, and its tensor is $ABC \sin \widehat{\mathbf{AB}} \sin \varphi_1$, where φ_1 is the angle between **C** and the normal to the plane of **A** and **B**. Therefore in general

$$\mathbf{A} \times (\mathbf{B} \times \mathbf{C}) \neq (\mathbf{A} \times \mathbf{B}) \times \mathbf{C}.$$

The parentheses are important, and cannot be omitted.

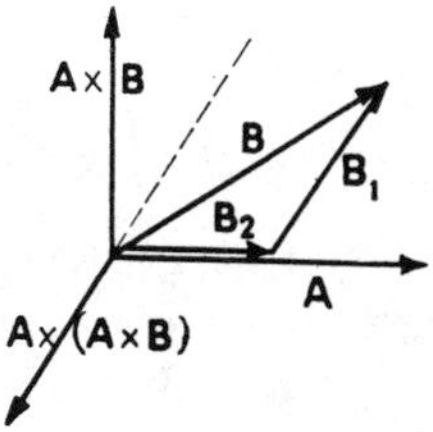

FIG. 6.

Consider first two coplanar vectors **A** and **B**. Let $\mathbf{B}_1$ and $\mathbf{B}_2$ be the components of **B** perpendicular to **A** and parallel to **A** respectively, Fig. 6. Since $\mathbf{B}_1/B_1$ is a unit vector perpendicular to **A**

$$\left.\begin{aligned}(\mathbf{A} \times \mathbf{B}) \times \mathbf{A} &= A^2B \sin \widehat{\mathbf{AB}}\ \frac{\mathbf{B}_1}{B_1}\\ &= A^2\mathbf{B}_1\\ &= \mathbf{A} \cdot \mathbf{A}\ \mathbf{B}_1.\end{aligned}\right\} \tag{1}$$

Hence the component of **B** which is perpendicular to **A** can be written

$$\mathbf{B}_1 = \frac{(\mathbf{A} \times \mathbf{B}) \times \mathbf{A}}{\mathbf{A} \cdot \mathbf{A}}. \tag{2}$$

The component of **B** which is parallel to **A** is

$$\mathbf{B}_2 = \frac{\mathbf{A} \cdot \mathbf{B}}{\mathbf{A} \cdot \mathbf{A}}\ \mathbf{A}. \tag{3}$$

Consequently

$$\mathbf{B}_1 + \mathbf{B}_2 = \mathbf{B} = \frac{(\mathbf{A} \times \mathbf{B}) \times \mathbf{A}}{\mathbf{A} \cdot \mathbf{A}} + \frac{\mathbf{A} \cdot \mathbf{B}}{\mathbf{A} \cdot \mathbf{A}}\ \mathbf{A}.$$

Whence

$$(\mathbf{A} \times \mathbf{B}) \times \mathbf{A} = \mathbf{A} \cdot \mathbf{A}\ \mathbf{B} - \mathbf{A} \cdot \mathbf{B}\ \mathbf{A}; \tag{4}$$

and similarly

$$\mathbf{B} \times (\mathbf{A} \times \mathbf{B}) = \mathbf{B} \cdot \mathbf{B}\ \mathbf{A} - \mathbf{A} \cdot \mathbf{B}\ \mathbf{B}.$$

Consider now three coplanar vectors $\mathbf{A}_2$, **B**, and **C**. Since they are coplanar (I, **15**),[1] there exist scalars b and c such that

$$\mathbf{A}_2 = b\mathbf{B} + c\mathbf{C}.$$

Hence

$$\begin{aligned} \mathbf{A}_2 \times (\mathbf{B} \times \mathbf{C}) &= b\mathbf{B} \times (\mathbf{B} \times \mathbf{C}) + c\mathbf{C} \times (\mathbf{B} \times \mathbf{C}) \\ &= +b\mathbf{B} \cdot \mathbf{C}\ \mathbf{B} - b\mathbf{B} \cdot \mathbf{B}\ \mathbf{C} + c\mathbf{C} \cdot \mathbf{C}\ \mathbf{B} - c\mathbf{C} \cdot \mathbf{B}\ \mathbf{C}, \end{aligned}$$

by Eq. (4).

Therefore

$$\mathbf{A}_2 \times (\mathbf{B} \times \mathbf{C}) = +\mathbf{A}_2 \cdot \mathbf{C}\ \mathbf{B} - \mathbf{A}_2 \cdot \mathbf{B}\ \mathbf{C}. \tag{5}$$

Finally let **A** be any vector in space. Let $\mathbf{A}_1$ be its component perpendicular to the plane of **B** and **C**, and $\mathbf{A}_2$ its component in the plane; so that

$$\mathbf{A} = \mathbf{A}_1 + \mathbf{A}_2,$$

and

$$\mathbf{A} \times (\mathbf{B} \times \mathbf{C}) = \mathbf{A}_1 \times (\mathbf{B} \times \mathbf{C}) + \mathbf{A}_2 \times (\mathbf{B} \times \mathbf{C}).$$

But

$$\mathbf{A}_1 \times (\mathbf{B} \times \mathbf{C}) = 0,$$

since $\mathbf{A}_1$ is parallel to $\mathbf{B} \times \mathbf{C}$. It can be written

$$\mathbf{A}_1 \times (\mathbf{B} \times \mathbf{C}) = \mathbf{A}_1 \cdot \mathbf{C}\ \mathbf{B} - \mathbf{A}_1 \cdot \mathbf{B}\ \mathbf{C}, \tag{6}$$

since

$$\mathbf{A}_1 \cdot \mathbf{C} = \mathbf{A}_1 \cdot \mathbf{B} = 0.$$

On taking the sum of Eqs. (5) and (6), it is seen that in general

$$\mathbf{A} \times (\mathbf{B} \times \mathbf{C}) = \mathbf{A} \cdot \mathbf{C}\ \mathbf{B} - \mathbf{A} \cdot \mathbf{B}\ \mathbf{C}. \tag{7}$$

The scalar triple product [**ABC**] is unaltered by cyclical permutations of the letters, but if the letters in the vector triple product are circularly permuted, the vector itself is altered; in such a way, however, that

$$\mathbf{A} \times (\mathbf{B} \times \mathbf{C}) + \mathbf{B} \times (\mathbf{C} \times \mathbf{A}) + \mathbf{C} \times (\mathbf{A} \times \mathbf{B}) \equiv 0,$$

[1] References to "Statics and the Dynamics of a Particle" will be denoted by the roman numeral I, the number following being the section number. References to the "Theory of the Potential" will be denoted by the roman numeral II.

as is readily verified by means of Eq. (7). That is, the sum of all the circular permutations of the vector triple product vanishes.

6. Any Vector in Terms of Three Reference Vectors.—Let **A, B,** and **C** be any three non-coplanar, non-vanishing vectors; then any other vector **R** can be expressed in terms of **A, B,** and **C** and certain scalars. Thus

$$\mathbf{R} = a\mathbf{A} + b\mathbf{B} + c\mathbf{C}, \tag{1}$$

if a, b, and c are properly chosen numbers (I, **17**).

Let Eq. (1) be multiplied by $\cdot\,(\mathbf{B} \times \mathbf{C})$. It then becomes

$$\mathbf{R} \cdot (\mathbf{B} \times \mathbf{C}) = a\mathbf{A} \cdot (\mathbf{B} \times \mathbf{C}) + b\mathbf{B} \cdot (\mathbf{B} \times \mathbf{C}) + c\mathbf{C} \cdot (\mathbf{B} \times \mathbf{C}).$$

Since the vector $\mathbf{B} \times \mathbf{C}$ is perpendicular to both **B** and **C,** the last two terms of this equation vanish, and there remains

$$\mathbf{R} \cdot \mathbf{B} \times \mathbf{C} = a\mathbf{A} \cdot \mathbf{B} \times \mathbf{C},$$

or

$$[\mathbf{RBC}] = a[\mathbf{ABC}].$$

Therefore

$$a = \frac{[\mathbf{RBC}]}{[\mathbf{ABC}]};$$

and similarly,

$$b = \frac{[\mathbf{RCA}]}{[\mathbf{ABC}]}, \qquad c = \frac{[\mathbf{RAB}]}{[\mathbf{ABC}]}.$$

If these values of a, b, and c are substituted in Eq. (1), there results

$$\mathbf{R} = \frac{[\mathbf{RBC}]}{[\mathbf{ABC}]}\mathbf{A} + \frac{[\mathbf{RCA}]}{[\mathbf{ABC}]}\mathbf{B} + \frac{[\mathbf{RAB}]}{[\mathbf{ABC}]}\mathbf{C}. \tag{2}$$

On multiplying through by [**ABC**] and taking all terms to the same side of the equality sign, there results the symmetric form

$$[\mathbf{ABC}]\mathbf{R} - [\mathbf{BCR}]\mathbf{A} + [\mathbf{CRA}]\mathbf{B} - [\mathbf{RAB}]\mathbf{C} = 0. \tag{3}$$

Now

$$[\mathbf{RBC}] = \mathbf{R} \cdot \mathbf{B} \times \mathbf{C}, \qquad [\mathbf{RCA}] = \mathbf{R} \cdot \mathbf{C} \times \mathbf{A},$$

and

$$[\mathbf{RAB}] = \mathbf{R} \cdot \mathbf{A} \times \mathbf{B},$$

so that Eq. (2) can also be written

$$\mathbf{R} = \left(\mathbf{R}\cdot\frac{\mathbf{B}\times\mathbf{C}}{[\mathbf{ABC}]}\right)\mathbf{A} + \left(\mathbf{R}\cdot\frac{\mathbf{C}\times\mathbf{A}}{[\mathbf{ABC}]}\right)\mathbf{B} + \left(\mathbf{R}\cdot\frac{\mathbf{A}\times\mathbf{B}}{[\mathbf{ABC}]}\right)\mathbf{C}. \tag{4}$$

If the **ABC** system of vectors is an **i, j, k** system, that is, a mutually orthogonal system of unit vectors, then

$$[\mathbf{ijk}] = 1, \qquad \mathbf{j}\times\mathbf{k} = \mathbf{i}, \qquad \mathbf{k}\times\mathbf{i} = \mathbf{j}, \qquad \mathbf{i}\times\mathbf{j} = \mathbf{k},$$

and Eq. (4) becomes

$$\mathbf{R} = (\mathbf{R}\cdot\mathbf{i})\mathbf{i} + (\mathbf{R}\cdot\mathbf{j})\mathbf{j} + (\mathbf{R}\cdot\mathbf{k})\mathbf{k}. \tag{5}$$

7. The Reciprocal System of Vectors.—The three vectors

$$\mathbf{a} = \frac{\mathbf{B}\times\mathbf{C}}{[\mathbf{ABC}]}, \qquad \mathbf{b} = \frac{\mathbf{C}\times\mathbf{A}}{[\mathbf{ABC}]}, \qquad \mathbf{c} = \frac{\mathbf{A}\times\mathbf{B}}{[\mathbf{ABC}]}, \tag{1}$$

which are perpendicular to the planes of **B** and **C, C** and **A,** and **A** and **B** respectively, are an interesting system of vectors that is associated with the system **A, B, C,** provided **A, B,** and **C** are non-vanishing and non-coplanar vectors. They are known as the *reciprocal system* of the system of vectors **A, B, C.** Using this system of vectors also, Eq. (6.4) becomes

$$\mathbf{R} = \mathbf{R}\cdot\mathbf{a}\ \mathbf{A} + \mathbf{R}\cdot\mathbf{b}\ \mathbf{B} + \mathbf{R}\cdot\mathbf{c}\ \mathbf{C}. \tag{2}$$

From the definitions, Eq. (1), it is readily seen that the scalar product of any two corresponding vectors of the two systems is

$$\mathbf{A}\cdot\mathbf{a} = \mathbf{B}\cdot\mathbf{b} = \mathbf{C}\cdot\mathbf{c} = 1; \tag{3}$$

and that the product of any two non-corresponding vectors is zero. That is,

$$\mathbf{A}\cdot\mathbf{b} = \mathbf{A}\cdot\mathbf{c} = \mathbf{B}\cdot\mathbf{a} = \mathbf{B}\cdot\mathbf{c} = \mathbf{C}\cdot\mathbf{a} = \mathbf{C}\cdot\mathbf{b} = 0; \tag{4}$$

and therefore **A** is perpendicular to the plane of **b** and **c, B** is perpendicular to the plane of **c** and **a,** and **C** is perpendicular to the plane of **a** and **b.**

Equations (3) and (4) show that if **a, b, c** is the reciprocal system of **A, B, C,** then **A, B, C** is also the reciprocal system of **a, b, c.** Suppose it were not so and that the reciprocal system of **a, b, c** were $\mathbf{A}_1, \mathbf{B}_1, \mathbf{C}_1$, different from **A, B, C.** Then the equations

$$\mathbf{A}_1\cdot\mathbf{a} = \mathbf{B}_1\cdot\mathbf{b} = \mathbf{C}_1\cdot\mathbf{c} = 1,$$

and

$$\mathbf{A}_1 \cdot \mathbf{b} = \mathbf{A}_1 \cdot \mathbf{c} = \mathbf{B}_1 \cdot \mathbf{a} = \mathbf{B}_1 \cdot \mathbf{c} = \mathbf{C}_1 \cdot \mathbf{a} = \mathbf{C}_1 \cdot \mathbf{b} = 0$$

also would hold. That is, $\mathbf{A}_1$ is perpendicular to the plane of **b** and **c**, and therefore collinear with **A**. Furthermore

$$\mathbf{A} \cdot \mathbf{a} = 1 \qquad \text{and} \qquad \mathbf{A}_1 \cdot \mathbf{a} = 1.$$

Hence

$$(\mathbf{A} - \mathbf{A}_1) \cdot \mathbf{a} = 0.$$

Therefore

$$\mathbf{A}_1 = \mathbf{A},$$

and is not different from it, as was supposed. One concludes therefore that a necessary and sufficient condition that the systems of vectors **A, B, C** and **a, b, c** be reciprocal systems is that they satisfy Eqs. (3) and (4).

8. Vector Equation of a Plane.—If **A** is a fixed vector and **R** is a variable vector which has the same origin as **A**, the equation

$$\mathbf{R} \cdot \mathbf{A} = a \tag{1}$$

obviously represents a plane if a is a fixed scalar. For

$$\mathbf{R} \cdot \frac{\mathbf{A}}{A} = R \cos \widehat{\mathbf{RA}} = \frac{a}{A} \tag{2}$$

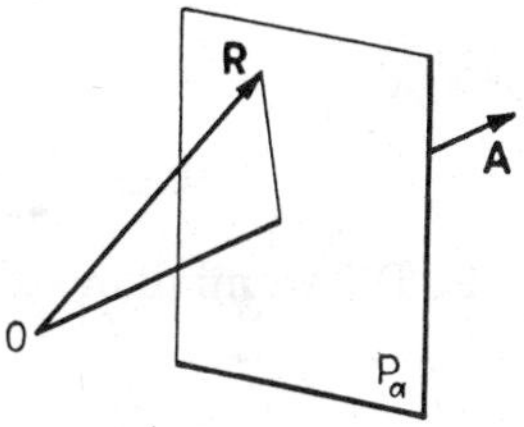

Fig. 7.

is the projection of **R** upon the line of **A**. If the plane P_a is perpendicular to **A** at a distance a/A from O, and if the terminus of **R** lies in P_a, it is evident that, Fig. 7,

$$\mathbf{R} \cdot \mathbf{A} = a.$$

This equation, therefore, can be regarded as a vector equation of the plane P_a.

Two such equations,

$$\mathbf{R} \cdot \mathbf{A} = a \qquad \text{and} \qquad \mathbf{R} \cdot \mathbf{B} = b, \tag{3}$$

however, can be satisfied only by the line of intersection of the two planes which the equations represent. Hence Eqs. (3) represent a straight line in space. If the vectors **A** and **B** are collinear, the planes P_a and P_b will be parallel and Eqs. (3) will be incompatible unless

$$\frac{a}{A} = \frac{b}{B},$$

in which case Eqs. (3) are essentially identical.

If three such equations are given, namely,

$$\mathbf{R} \cdot \mathbf{A} = a, \qquad \mathbf{R} \cdot \mathbf{B} = b, \qquad \mathbf{R} \cdot \mathbf{C} = c,$$

and if the vectors **A**, **B**, and **C** are non-coplanar, the vector **R** is restricted to the point of intersection of the three planes, and is completely determined.

If **a**, **b**, **c** is the system of vectors reciprocal to **A**, **B**, **C**, then, by Eq. (6.4),

$$\mathbf{R} = \mathbf{R} \cdot \mathbf{A}\ \mathbf{a} + \mathbf{R} \cdot \mathbf{B}\ \mathbf{b} + \mathbf{R} \cdot \mathbf{C}\ \mathbf{c},$$

or

$$\mathbf{R} = a\mathbf{a} + b\mathbf{b} + c\mathbf{c},$$

or again

$$\mathbf{R} = \mathbf{R} \cdot \mathbf{a}\ \mathbf{A} + \mathbf{R} \cdot \mathbf{b}\ \mathbf{B} + \mathbf{R} \cdot \mathbf{c}\ \mathbf{C}.$$

9. Differentiation of Vectors.—Suppose the vector **r** is a continuously varying vector, and that, its origin remaining fixed, its terminus describes a certain curve C, so that **r** is a function of the time. Let $\mathbf{r}_1$, Fig. 8, be the position of **r** at the time t_1, and let $\mathbf{r}_2$ be its position at some subsequent time t_2. If the time interval $t_2 - t_1 = \Delta t$ is small, the vector

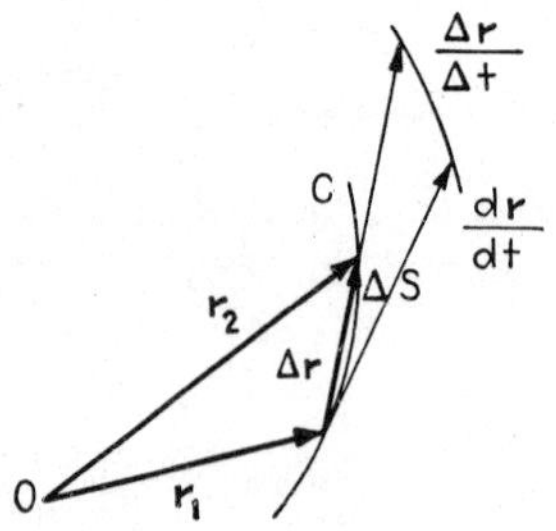

Fig. 8.

$$\Delta \mathbf{r} = \mathbf{r}_2 - \mathbf{r}_1 \tag{1}$$

also will be small. The quotient

$$\frac{\Delta \mathbf{r}}{\Delta t}$$

is the average rate of change of the vector **r** in the interval t_1 to t_2. In accordance with the usual methods of the calculus, the limit of this expression as t_2 tends toward t_1 is the derivative of $\mathbf{r}$ at the instant t_1. That is,

$$\lim_{t_2 \to t_1} \frac{\Delta \mathbf{r}}{\Delta t} = \frac{d\mathbf{r}}{dt} = \mathbf{r}'. \tag{2}$$

That this limit, which, when t is the independent variable, will be denoted by $\mathbf{r}'$, is a vector which has the direction of the tangent to the curve C at the position $\mathbf{r}_1$ is obvious.

Let $\mathbf{a}$, $\mathbf{b}$, $\mathbf{c}$ be any three non-coplanar, constant vectors and let

$$\mathbf{r} = r_1\mathbf{a} + r_2\mathbf{b} + r_3\mathbf{c}. \tag{3}$$

Since $\mathbf{r}$ varies with the time, and $\mathbf{a}$, $\mathbf{b}$, $\mathbf{c}$ do not, it is clear that r_1, r_2, and r_3 are functions of the time, and that

$$\mathbf{r}_2 = \mathbf{r}_1 + \Delta\mathbf{r} = (r_1 + \Delta r_1)\mathbf{a} + (r_2 + \Delta r_2)\mathbf{b} + (r_3 + \Delta r_3)\mathbf{c}. \tag{4}$$

Consequently, on subtracting Eq. (3) from Eq. (4),

$$\Delta\mathbf{r} = \Delta r_1\mathbf{a} + \Delta r_2\mathbf{b} + \Delta r_3\mathbf{c},$$

from which it follows at once that

$$\frac{d\mathbf{r}}{dt} = \mathbf{r}' = r_1'\mathbf{a} + r_2'\mathbf{b} + r_3'\mathbf{c}. \tag{5}$$

In a similar manner, it follows for the second derivative that

$$\frac{d^2\mathbf{r}}{dt^2} = \mathbf{r}'' = r_1''\mathbf{a} + r_2''\mathbf{b} + r_3''\mathbf{c}, \tag{6}$$

and so on, for derivatives of any order. In particular if $\mathbf{i}$, $\mathbf{j}$, and $\mathbf{k}$ are unit vectors having the directions of the x-, y-, and z-axes of a rectangular system

$$\begin{aligned} \mathbf{r} &= x\ \mathbf{i} + y\ \mathbf{j} + z\ \mathbf{k}, \\ \mathbf{r}' &= x'\,\mathbf{i} + y'\,\mathbf{j} + z'\,\mathbf{k}, \\ \mathbf{r}'' &= x''\mathbf{i} + y''\mathbf{j} + z''\mathbf{k}, \\ &\cdots\cdots\cdots\cdots\cdots\cdots \end{aligned}$$

Example.—Suppose a particle describes a space curve in such a way that its radius vector is

$$\mathbf{r} = \mathbf{a}\cos t + \mathbf{b}\sin t + nt\mathbf{c}. \tag{7}$$

Its velocity is (I, **28**)

$$\mathbf{r}' = -\mathbf{a}\sin t + \mathbf{b}\cos t + n\mathbf{c}, \tag{8}$$

and its acceleration is (I, **31**)

$$\mathbf{r}'' = -\mathbf{a}\cos t - \mathbf{b}\sin t + 0\mathbf{c}. \tag{9}$$

If n is zero, the curve described by the particle is a plane curve, which is evidently an ellipse; for if its coordinates parallel to **a** and **b** are A and B, referred to the same origin as **r**, it is seen that

$$A = a\cos t, \qquad B = b\sin t,$$

and therefore

$$\left(\frac{A}{a}\right)^2 + \left(\frac{B}{b}\right)^2 = 1,$$

which is the equation of an ellipse of which **a** and **b** are conjugate semidiameters.

If n is not zero, the particle can be regarded as moving in an ellipse, the plane of which is moving uniformly in the **c** direction, remaining always parallel to its initial position, with the velocity $n\mathbf{c}$. That is, Eq. (7) represents an elliptical helix.

By combining Eqs. (9) and (7), it is seen that

$$\mathbf{r}'' = -\mathbf{r} + nt\mathbf{c},$$

which is a vector differential equation, the right member being the component of $-\mathbf{r}$ which is in the **a**, **b** plane. Hence the acceleration of the particle is always toward the center of the moving ellipse.

10. Differentation of Vector Products.—Suppose **A** and **B** are vectors that vary with the time. The derivative with respect to the time of the scalar product $\mathbf{A}\cdot\mathbf{B}$ is

$$\frac{d}{dt}(\mathbf{A}\cdot\mathbf{B}) = \lim_{\Delta t = 0} \frac{(\mathbf{A}+\Delta\mathbf{A})\cdot(\mathbf{B}+\Delta\mathbf{B}) - \mathbf{A}\cdot\mathbf{B}}{\Delta t}.$$

Since

$$(\mathbf{A}+\Delta\mathbf{A})\cdot(\mathbf{B}+\Delta\mathbf{B}) = \mathbf{A}\cdot\mathbf{B} + \mathbf{A}\cdot\Delta\mathbf{B} + \mathbf{B}\cdot\Delta\mathbf{A} + \Delta\mathbf{A}\cdot\Delta\mathbf{B},$$

it is seen that

$$\frac{d}{dt}(\mathbf{A}\cdot\mathbf{B}) = \lim_{\Delta t = 0}\left[\mathbf{A}\cdot\frac{\Delta\mathbf{B}}{\Delta t} + \mathbf{B}\cdot\frac{\Delta\mathbf{A}}{\Delta t} + \frac{\Delta\mathbf{A}\cdot\Delta\mathbf{B}}{\Delta t}\right],$$

that is

$$\frac{d}{dt}(\mathbf{A} \cdot \mathbf{B}) = \mathbf{A} \cdot \mathbf{B}' + \mathbf{B} \cdot \mathbf{A}'. \tag{1}$$

Thus the derivative of the scalar product is formed just as the derivative of the product of two functions is formed in the differential calculus.

The same rule holds also for the derivative of the vector product of two vectors, only in this case the order of the factors must be preserved, since the vector product does not obey the commutative law. That is,

$$\frac{d}{dt}(\mathbf{A} \times \mathbf{B}) = (\mathbf{A}' \times \mathbf{B}) + (\mathbf{A} \times \mathbf{B}'). \tag{2}$$

Likewise

$$\frac{d}{dt}(\mathbf{A} \cdot \mathbf{B} \times \mathbf{C}) = (\mathbf{A}' \cdot \mathbf{B} \times \mathbf{C}) + (\mathbf{A} \cdot \mathbf{B}' \times \mathbf{C}) + (\mathbf{A} \cdot \mathbf{B} \times \mathbf{C}'), \tag{3}$$

and

$$\frac{d}{dt}[\mathbf{A} \times (\mathbf{B} \times \mathbf{C})] = \mathbf{A}' \times (\mathbf{B} \times \mathbf{C}) + \mathbf{A} \times (\mathbf{B}' \times \mathbf{C}) + \mathbf{A} \times (\mathbf{B} \times \mathbf{C}'), \tag{4}$$

their derivation being quite similar to that of Eq. (1).

11. Applications to Geometry.—The above results are valid whatever the independent variable may be, but the accents cannot be used to denote the derivatives with respect to other variables, since the notation would not indicate what the independent variable is.

Suppose s is the length of the arc of a curve described by the terminus of $\mathbf{r}$ measured from some convenient point. Then

$$\frac{d\mathbf{r}}{ds} = \lim_{\Delta s = 0} \frac{\Delta \mathbf{r}}{\Delta s} = \mathbf{t}. \tag{1}$$

Since, Fig. 8, $\Delta \mathbf{r}$ is the chord of the arc Δs, and, since the limit of the ratio of these two variables, as Δs diminishes, is unity, it follows that $\mathbf{t}$ is a unit vector tangent to the curve at the terminus of $\mathbf{r}$. It is not a constant vector notwithstanding that its length is always unity, for its direction changes as the terminus of **r** moves along the curve. The equation

$$\mathbf{t} \cdot \mathbf{t} = 1 \tag{2}$$

however holds at all points of the curve. On differentiating Eq. (2) with respect to s, there results

$$\mathbf{t} \cdot \frac{d\mathbf{t}}{ds} = 0.$$

Hence

$$\frac{d\mathbf{t}}{ds} = \frac{d^2\mathbf{r}}{ds^2}$$

is a vector which is perpendicular to **t**, since its scalar product with **t** vanishes, and, since it lies in the osculating plane of the curve, it is collinear with the principal normal.

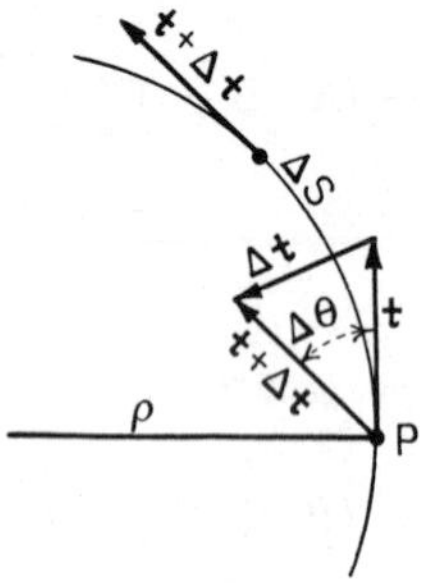

Fig. 9.

It is seen from Fig. 9 that, if $\Delta\theta$ is the angle through which the tangent has turned in the distance Δs, the length of $\Delta\mathbf{t}$ is 2 sin $(\Delta\theta/2)$, since the length of **t** is unity. Hence in magnitude

$$\frac{d\mathbf{t}}{ds} = \lim_{\Delta s = 0} \frac{2 \sin (\Delta\theta/2)}{\Delta s} = \frac{d\theta}{ds} = \frac{1}{\rho},$$

where ρ is the radius of curvature. Hence, if **n** is a unit vector directed from the terminus of **r** toward the center of curvature, then

$$\frac{d\mathbf{t}}{ds} = \frac{d^2\mathbf{r}}{ds^2} = \frac{\mathbf{n}}{\rho}, \tag{3}$$

and $d\mathbf{t}/ds = d^2\mathbf{r}/ds^2$ is called the curvature.

If **b** is a unit vector in the direction of the binormal, then **t, n,** and **b** is a right-handed rectangular system of unit vectors, and

$$\mathbf{b} = \mathbf{t} \times \mathbf{n}. \tag{4}$$

The Normal Derivative.—Suppose

$$\varphi(x, y, z) = C$$

is a certain surface. It was shown in II, **54** that the derivative of the function φ normal to this surface is the direction in which the values of the function φ are changing most rapidly, and the normal derivative is denoted by the symbol $d\varphi/dn$.

If the direction cosines of the normal are λ, μ, and ν, the derivatives of φ with respect to x, y, and z are related to the normal derivative by the equations

$$\frac{\partial\varphi}{\partial x} = \lambda\frac{\partial\varphi}{\partial n},$$
$$\frac{\partial\varphi}{\partial y} = \mu\frac{\partial\varphi}{\partial n},$$
$$\frac{\partial\varphi}{\partial z} = \nu\frac{\partial\varphi}{\partial n}.$$

Now let **i**, **j**, and **k** be unit vectors in the x-, y-, and z- directions respectively. Multiply the first of the above equations by **i**, the second by **j**, the third by **k**, and add. There results

$$\mathbf{i}\frac{\partial\varphi}{\partial x} + \mathbf{j}\frac{\partial\varphi}{\partial y} + \mathbf{k}\frac{\partial\varphi}{\partial z} = (\lambda\mathbf{i} + \mu\mathbf{j} + \nu\mathbf{k})\frac{\partial\varphi}{\partial n}.$$

But

$$\lambda\mathbf{i} + \mu\mathbf{j} + \nu\mathbf{k} = \mathbf{n}$$

is a vector which has the direction of the normal; and it is a unit vector, since the sum of the squares of its components is equal to unity. Hence

$$\mathbf{i}\frac{\partial\varphi}{\partial x} + \mathbf{j}\frac{\partial\varphi}{\partial y} + \mathbf{k}\frac{\partial\varphi}{\partial z} = \mathbf{n}\frac{\partial\varphi}{\partial n} \tag{5}$$

is a vector which has the direction of the normal and in magnitude is equal to the normal derivative. Or, if preferred, it is the derivative in the direction in which the function φ is changing most rapidly.

For the sake of brevity the operator

$$\mathbf{i}\frac{\partial}{\partial x} + \mathbf{j}\frac{\partial}{\partial y} + \mathbf{k}\frac{\partial}{\partial z}$$

is denoted by the symbol ∇ (an inverted Greek capital delta) which is called *del* in the vector analysis of Gibbs-Wilson. Thus

$$\nabla\varphi \equiv \mathbf{i}\frac{\partial\varphi}{\partial x} + \mathbf{j}\frac{\partial\varphi}{\partial y} + \mathbf{k}\frac{\partial\varphi}{\partial z}; \tag{6}$$

from its significance, it is obviously independent of the particular rectangular coordinate system which is used.

In particular, if $V(x, y, z)$ is a potential function, it is evident that the force which is acting at any point P is the vector ∇V at that point (see II, **27**). It will be observed that V is a scalar function of position (x, y, z), while ∇V is a vector function of position.

12. Applications to Kinematics.—Suppose an origin O is chosen. The position of a particle with respect to O can be defined by means of a vector $\mathbf{r}$, whose origin is at O and whose terminus is at the particle. The velocity of the particle was defined at I, **28** as the rate of change of its position. Hence, if $\mathbf{v}$ is its velocity,

$$\mathbf{r}' = \mathbf{v}, \tag{1}$$

since $\mathbf{r}'$ also is its rate of change of position.

Similarly, if $\boldsymbol{\alpha}$ is its acceleration, or the rate of change of its velocity (I, **31**), then

$$\boldsymbol{\alpha} = \mathbf{v}' = \mathbf{r}''. \tag{2}$$

If m is the mass of the particle, its momentum is

$$m\mathbf{v} = m\mathbf{r}',$$

and since force is the rate of change of momentum, by Newton's second law, the force acting on a free particle is

$$\mathbf{f} = m\mathbf{v}' = m\mathbf{r}'', \tag{3}$$

since the mass is assumed to be constant.

Consider the motion of a particle which is moving in a circle of radius r. Let $\mathbf{r}$ be its vector of position referred to the center of the circle. The equation of the circle is

$$\mathbf{r} \cdot \mathbf{r} = r^2, \tag{4}$$

where the scalar r is constant, although the vector $\mathbf{r}$ is not constant. If Eq. (4) is differentiated with respect to the time, there results

$$\mathbf{r} \cdot \mathbf{r}' = \mathbf{r} \cdot \mathbf{v} = 0. \tag{5}$$

If neither $\mathbf{r}$ nor $\mathbf{v}$ is zero, this equation states the geometrically obvious fact that the velocity $\mathbf{v}$ is perpendicular to the radius vector $\mathbf{r}$. If Eq. (5) is differentiated, it is found that

$$\mathbf{r} \cdot \mathbf{r}'' + \mathbf{r}' \cdot \mathbf{r}' = 0. \tag{6}$$

If the speed of the particle is constant,

$$\mathbf{r}' \cdot \mathbf{r}' = v^2, \qquad \text{and} \qquad \mathbf{r}' \cdot \mathbf{r}'' = 0.$$

The vectors $\mathbf{r}$ and $\mathbf{r}''$, therefore, are collinear, but oppositely directed, and

$$\mathbf{r} \cdot \mathbf{r}'' = -r\alpha;$$

so that Eq. (6) gives the result

$$\alpha = \frac{v^2}{r},$$

in agreement with the expression for the acceleration given for uniform circular motion in I, **39**.

In uniform circular motion the acceleration is always directed toward the center of the circle. In general the acceleration vector lies in the osculating plane (I, **256**), which coincides with the plane of motion when the curve described by the particle is a plane curve. If the acceleration is resolved into components along the tangent, normal and binormal, the binormal component is always zero.

In order to find the general expressions for the tangential and normal components, take the formula

$$\mathbf{r}' = \mathbf{v} = v\mathbf{t}, \tag{7}$$

where

$$v = s'$$

is the speed. On differentiating Eq. (7) with respect to the time, there results

$$\mathbf{r}'' = \mathbf{v}' = v'\mathbf{t} + v\mathbf{t}'.$$

Now

$$v' = s'', \qquad \text{and} \qquad \mathbf{t}' = \frac{dt}{ds}\frac{ds}{dt} = v\frac{\mathbf{n}}{\rho},$$

by Eq. (11.3). Hence

$$\alpha = \mathbf{r}'' = s''\mathbf{t} + \frac{v^2}{\rho}\mathbf{n},$$

which shows that, in magnitude, the component of the acceleration along the tangent is s'', and along the normal is v^2/ρ.

If a particle moves in such a way that its moment of momentum is constant, a case that is of much interest, its momentum is $m\mathbf{v}$, and its moment of momentum with respect to the origin O, is (I, **133**)

$$\mathbf{M} = m\mathbf{r} \times \mathbf{v}.$$

If $\mathbf{M}$ is a constant, there results by differentiation

$$m(\mathbf{r}' \times \mathbf{v} + \mathbf{r} \times \mathbf{v}') = 0.$$

Since $\mathbf{r}' = \mathbf{v}$, it is seen that $\mathbf{r}' \times \mathbf{v}$ is zero by itself. Hence

$$\mathbf{r} \times (m\mathbf{v}') = 0,$$

which reduces to

$$\mathbf{r} \times \mathbf{f} = 0,$$

since $m\mathbf{v}'$ is the rate of change of momentum, or the force. This result shows that the force which is acting always lies in the line of $\mathbf{r}$, or, stated otherwise, the force is a central force.

13. Integration of Vectors.—Integration, regarded as the inverse of differentiation, proceeds in much the same way as in the integral calculus, and difficulties of the same type are encountered. If

$$\mathbf{A}' = \mathbf{B}',$$

it is not difficult to understand that

$$\mathbf{A} = \mathbf{B} + \mathbf{C},$$

where $\mathbf{C}$ is a constant vector; that is, $\mathbf{C}$ is independent of the time. Of course, such an expression as

$$\mathbf{A}' = B$$

would have no sense, since a vector cannot equal a scalar. But if

$$\mathbf{A}' = \mathbf{B},$$

where **B** is a constant vector, the general integral is

$$\mathbf{A} = \mathbf{B}t + \mathbf{C},$$

where **C** is a constant vector.

Falling Bodies.—In the case of a falling body, for which the acceleration is constant, the equation of acceleration is

$$\mathbf{r}'' = \mathbf{g};$$

therefore

$$\mathbf{r}' = \mathbf{g}t + \mathbf{a},$$

and

$$\mathbf{r} = \tfrac{1}{2}t^2\mathbf{g} + \mathbf{a}t + \mathbf{b}, \tag{1}$$

where **a** and **b** are constant vectors that play the rôle of constants of integration. The vector **b** is the value of **r** at $t = 0$, and **a** is the value of **r′**, or the velocity, at $t = 0$. This result can be translated into the familiar form in rectangular coordinates by taking

$$\mathbf{r} = x\mathbf{i} + y\mathbf{j}, \qquad \mathbf{g} = -g\mathbf{j}, \qquad \mathbf{a} = x_0'\mathbf{i} + y_0'\mathbf{j}, \qquad \mathbf{b} = x_0\mathbf{i} + y_0\mathbf{j}.$$

Equation (1) then becomes

$$x\mathbf{i} + y\mathbf{j} = (x_0't + x_0)\mathbf{i} + (-\tfrac{1}{2}gt^2 + y_0't + y_0)\mathbf{j},$$

and therefore

$$x = x_0't + x_0,$$
$$y = -\tfrac{1}{2}gt^2 + y_0't + y_0.$$

Simple Harmonic Motion.—In simple harmonic motion the acceleration is always directed toward the origin and is proportional to the distance. In this case

$$\mathbf{r}'' = -k^2\mathbf{r}. \tag{2}$$

This is a linear vector differential equation of the second order. In analogy with the ordinary differential equation, one is led to suspect that the solution is

$$\mathbf{r} = \mathbf{A}\cos kt + \mathbf{B}\sin kt, \tag{3}$$

where **A** and **B** are any two constant vectors; and on substituting Eq. (3) in Eq. (2) it is found that the differential equation is satisfied. Equation (3) is therefore the general solution of Eq. (2), since it contains two arbitrary vectors. As was seen in Sec. 9, Eq. (3) represents an ellipse in which **A** and **B** are conjugate semidiameters.

Keplerian Motion.—If a free particle is attracted towards a fixed point by a force which varies inversely as the square of its distance from the point, its acceleration equation is

$$\mathbf{r}'' = -\frac{k^2}{r^3}\mathbf{r}, \tag{4}$$

where k^2 is the factor of proportionality. On multiplying both sides of this equation by $\mathbf{r}\times$, the right side vanishes, since

$$\mathbf{r}\times\mathbf{r} = 0.$$

The left side then gives

$$\mathbf{r}\times\mathbf{r}'' = 0.$$

To this, add

$$\mathbf{r}'\times\mathbf{r}' = 0,$$

and there results

$$(\mathbf{r}'\times\mathbf{r}') + (\mathbf{r}\times\mathbf{r}'') = 0,$$

or

$$(\mathbf{r}\times\mathbf{r}')' = 0.$$

Hence,

$$\mathbf{r}\times\mathbf{r}' = \mathbf{h}, \tag{5}$$

where **h** is a constant vector which represents the moment of the velocity, or twice the rate at which the radius vector sweeps over areas. Equation (5) shows that the particle moves in a fixed plane.

The vector product of Eqs. (4) and (5) gives

$$\begin{aligned}\mathbf{r}''\times\mathbf{h} &= -\frac{k^2}{r^3}\mathbf{r}\times(\mathbf{r}\times\mathbf{r}')\\ &= -\frac{k^2}{r^3}(\mathbf{r}\cdot\mathbf{r}'\ \mathbf{r} - \mathbf{r}\cdot\mathbf{r}\ \mathbf{r}'), \qquad \text{by Eq. (5.7).}\end{aligned}$$

But

$$\mathbf{r}\cdot\mathbf{r} = r^2,$$

and, by differentiation,

$$\mathbf{r} \cdot \mathbf{r}' = rr';$$

hence

$$\mathbf{r}'' \times \mathbf{h} = -\frac{k^2}{r^3}(rr'\mathbf{r} - r^2\mathbf{r}'),$$

which can be written

$$(\mathbf{r}' \times \mathbf{h})' = k^2\left(\frac{\mathbf{r}}{r}\right)'.$$

On integrating, this equation becomes

$$\mathbf{r}' \times \mathbf{h} = k^2\left(\frac{\mathbf{r}}{r} + e\mathbf{a}\right), \tag{6}$$

where $\mathbf{a}$ is a constant unit vector and e is an arbitrary scalar. The vector $\mathbf{a}$ lies in the plane of motion, as is indicated in Fig. 10.

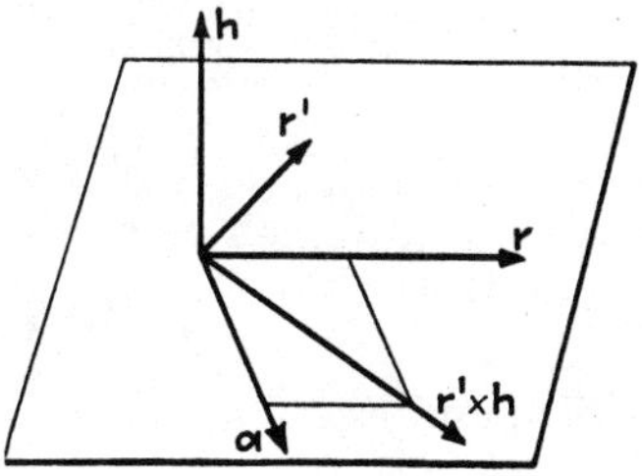

FIG. 10.

Now let Eq. (6) be multiplied by $\mathbf{r}\cdot$. There results

$$\mathbf{r} \cdot (\mathbf{r}' \times \mathbf{h}) = k^2\left(\frac{\mathbf{r} \cdot \mathbf{r}}{r} + e\mathbf{r} \cdot \mathbf{a}\right), \tag{7}$$

and since, Eq. (4.2),

$$\mathbf{r} \cdot \mathbf{r}' \times \mathbf{h} = \mathbf{r} \times \mathbf{r}' \cdot \mathbf{h} = \mathbf{h} \cdot \mathbf{h} = h^2,$$

and

$$\mathbf{r} \cdot \mathbf{r} = r^2,$$

Eq. (7) reduces to

$$h^2 = k^2(r + re \cos \widehat{\mathbf{ra}}).$$

If a new constant p is introduced by the relation

$$h^2 = k^2 p,$$

there results finally the general equation of a conic referred to its focus, namely,

$$r = \frac{p}{1 + e \cos \theta}, \qquad \text{where } \theta = \widehat{\mathbf{ra}}.$$

The vector **a**, evidently, is directed toward the perihelion point.

The Energy Integral.—In case there exists a potential function $V(x, y, z)$, the equation of motion of a single particle becomes [Eq. (11.6)]

$$m\mathbf{r}'' = \nabla V = \mathbf{i}\frac{\partial V}{\partial x} + \mathbf{j}\frac{\partial V}{\partial y} + \mathbf{k}\frac{\partial V}{\partial z}. \tag{8}$$

Multiply this equation by $\mathbf{r}'\,\cdot$, and it becomes

$$m\mathbf{r}' \cdot \mathbf{r}'' = \mathbf{r}' \cdot \nabla V. \tag{9}$$

Now

$$\mathbf{r}' \cdot \mathbf{r}'' = \tfrac{1}{2}(\mathbf{r}' \cdot \mathbf{r}')',$$

and

$$\begin{aligned} \mathbf{r}' \cdot \nabla V &= (x'\mathbf{i} + y'\mathbf{j} + z'\mathbf{k}) \cdot \left(\frac{\partial V}{\partial x}\mathbf{i} + \frac{\partial V}{\partial y}\mathbf{j} + \frac{\partial V}{\partial z}\mathbf{k}\right) \\ &= \frac{\partial V}{\partial x}x' + \frac{\partial V}{\partial y}y' + \frac{\partial V}{\partial z}z' \\ &= V', \end{aligned}$$

so that Eq. (9) can be written

$$\tfrac{1}{2}m(\mathbf{r}' \cdot \mathbf{r}')' = V',$$

which, on integration gives

$$\tfrac{1}{2}m\mathbf{r}' \cdot \mathbf{r} - V = E,$$

where E is the constant of integration. The negative of the potential function V is the potential energy; $\frac{1}{2}m\mathbf{r}' \cdot \mathbf{r}'$ is the kinetic energy; and E, the total energy, is a constant. For the Newtonian law of force with the center of force at the origin,

$$V = \frac{k^2}{r}.$$

14. The Differential Equation of the Orbit for a Central Force.—The method of the preceding section is particular in that it applies only to the inverse square law. But the differential equation of the orbit for any central force can be obtained by vector methods in the following manner.

Let f be any function of position, that is, in polar coordinates, a function of r and θ; and let $\boldsymbol{\rho}$ be a unit vector which has the direction of **r**. Then the differential equation of motion for any central force can be written

$$m\mathbf{r}'' = f\boldsymbol{\rho}. \tag{1}$$

If f is negative the force is attractive, and if f is positive the force is repellent. On multiplying both sides of Eq. (1) by $\mathbf{r} \times$ there is obtained

$$\mathbf{r} \times \mathbf{r}'' = 0, \qquad \text{since} \qquad \mathbf{r} \times \boldsymbol{\rho} = 0.$$

Hence, on integrating,

$$\mathbf{r} \times \mathbf{r}' = \mathbf{h}, \tag{2}$$

just as in Sec. 12. This equation shows that the motion is in a plane perpendicular to **h**. Now let

$$u = \frac{1}{r}.$$

Then, since

$$\mathbf{r} = \frac{1}{u}\boldsymbol{\rho}, \qquad \mathbf{r}' = -\frac{u'}{u^2}\boldsymbol{\rho} + \frac{1}{u}\boldsymbol{\rho}',$$

Eq. (2) becomes

$$\boldsymbol{\rho} \times \boldsymbol{\rho}' = u^2\mathbf{h}. \tag{3}$$

Let θ be the angle in the plane of motion which gives the direction of **r**. Then

$$\boldsymbol{\rho}' = \frac{d\boldsymbol{\rho}}{d\theta}\theta'.$$

In a unit circle, the ds of Eq. (11.1) is the same as $d\theta$. Hence

$$\boldsymbol{\rho}' = \theta'\mathbf{t},$$

where **t** is a unit vector in the plane perpendicular to $\boldsymbol{\rho}$, and, if **p** is a unit vector perpendicular to the plane of motion,

$$\boldsymbol{\rho} \times \boldsymbol{\rho}' = \theta'\boldsymbol{\rho} \times \mathbf{t} = \theta'\mathbf{p}.$$

Hence $\boldsymbol{\rho} \times \boldsymbol{\rho}'$ is the angular velocity, and Eq. (3) then gives

$$\theta' = hu^2, \qquad \text{since} \qquad \mathbf{h} = h\mathbf{p}. \tag{4}$$

The expression for $\mathbf{r}'$ can now be written

$$\begin{aligned}\mathbf{r}' &= -\frac{1}{u^2}\frac{du}{d\theta}\theta'\boldsymbol{\varrho} + \frac{1}{u}\frac{d\boldsymbol{\varrho}}{d\theta}\theta' \\ &= -h\frac{du}{d\theta}\boldsymbol{\varrho} + hu\frac{d\boldsymbol{\varrho}}{d\theta} \\ &= -h\frac{du}{d\theta}\boldsymbol{\varrho} + hu\mathbf{t},\end{aligned}$$

and

$$\mathbf{r}'' = \left[-h\frac{d^2u}{d\theta^2}\boldsymbol{\varrho} + hu\frac{d\mathbf{t}}{d\theta}\right]\theta'.$$

But, by Eq. (11.3),

$$\frac{d\mathbf{t}}{d\theta} = \mathbf{n} = -\boldsymbol{\varrho},$$

so that the expression for the acceleration reduces to

$$\mathbf{r}'' = -h^2u^2\left[\frac{d^2u}{d\theta^2} + u\right]\boldsymbol{\varrho}. \tag{5}$$

On comparing this expression with Eq. (1), it is seen that

$$-h^2u^2\left(\frac{d^2u}{d\theta^2} + u\right) = \frac{f}{m} \tag{6}$$

is the differential equation of the orbit, just as in I, **284.**

Problems

1. The vectors $\mathbf{A}_1$ and $\mathbf{B}_1$ have the same origin. $\mathbf{A}_2$ and $\mathbf{B}_2$ have the same origin, and likewise $\mathbf{A}_3$, and $\mathbf{B}_3$. If $\mathbf{A}_1 + \mathbf{A}_2 + \mathbf{A}_3 = 0$, and if

$$\begin{aligned}\mathbf{B}_1 &= t_1\mathbf{A}_1 + (t_1 - 1)\mathbf{A}_3, \\ \mathbf{B}_2 &= t_2\mathbf{A}_2 + (t_2 - 1)\mathbf{A}_1, \\ \mathbf{B}_3 &= t_3\mathbf{A}_3 + (t_3 - 1)\mathbf{A}_2,\end{aligned}$$

the condition that $\mathbf{B}_1$, $\mathbf{B}_2$, and $\mathbf{B}_3$ shall be concurrent is

$$t_1t_2t_3 = (1 - t_1)(1 - t_2)(1 - t_3).$$

2. $\mathbf{A}$ and $\mathbf{B}$ are two sides of a parallelogram and $\mathbf{C}$ and $\mathbf{D}$ are the diagonals. Prove that

$$C^2 + D^2 = 2(A^2 + B^2),$$

and

$$C^2 - D^2 = 4AB\cos\widehat{\mathbf{AB}}.$$

3. The condition that two non-vanishing vectors are parallel is that their cross product is zero; and the condition that they are mutually perpendicular is that their scalar product is zero.

4. If

$$\mathbf{A} = a_1\mathbf{L} + a_2\mathbf{M} + a_3\mathbf{N},$$
$$\mathbf{B} = b_1\mathbf{L} + b_2\mathbf{M} + b_3\mathbf{N},$$
$$\mathbf{C} = c_1\mathbf{L} + c_2\mathbf{M} + c_3\mathbf{N},$$

show that

$$[\mathbf{ABC}] = \begin{vmatrix} a_1 & a_2 & a_3 \\ b_1 & b_2 & b_3 \\ c_1 & c_2 & c_3 \end{vmatrix} [\mathbf{LMN}].$$

5. By regarding the scalar product of two vectors, each of which is a vector product of two vectors $(\mathbf{A} \times \mathbf{B}) \cdot (\mathbf{C} \times \mathbf{D})$, as a scalar triple product of the three vectors **A**, **B**, and $\mathbf{C} \times \mathbf{D}$, namely, $\mathbf{A} \times \mathbf{B} \cdot (\mathbf{C} \times \mathbf{D})$, show that

$$(\mathbf{A} \times \mathbf{B}) \cdot (\mathbf{C} \times \mathbf{D}) = \mathbf{A} \cdot \mathbf{C}\ \mathbf{B} \cdot \mathbf{D} - \mathbf{A} \cdot \mathbf{D}\ \mathbf{B} \cdot \mathbf{C}.$$

6. If **A**, **B**, **C**, and **D** are unit vectors with the same origin, they define a quadrilateral on a unit sphere. Let A be the terminus of **A**, B the terminus of **B**, etc., and, finally, let AB and CD be the diagonals of the quadrilateral. Show that the interpretation of the formula in Problem **5** leads to Gauss's theorem for the spherical quadrilateral, namely,

$$\sin AB \sin CD \cos I = \cos AC \cos BD - \cos AD \cos BC,$$

where I is the angle of intersection of the diagonals.

7. Show that

$$(\mathbf{A} \times \mathbf{B}) \times (\mathbf{C} \times \mathbf{D}) = [\mathbf{ACD}]\mathbf{B} - [\mathbf{BCD}]\mathbf{A} = [\mathbf{ABD}]\mathbf{C} - [\mathbf{ABC}]\mathbf{D}.$$

8. Show that, if **i**, **j**, and **k** are mutually orthogonal unit vectors,

$$\mathbf{i} \times (\mathbf{i} \times \mathbf{i}) = 0, \qquad \mathbf{i} \times (\mathbf{i} \times \mathbf{j}) = -\mathbf{j}, \qquad \mathbf{i} \times (\mathbf{j} \times \mathbf{k}) = 0.$$

9. Show that the **i**, **j**, **k** system of vectors is its own reciprocal system.

10. If **A**, **B**, **C** and **a**, **b**, **c** are reciprocal systems, show that

$$[\mathbf{ABC}] = \frac{1}{[\mathbf{abc}]}.$$

11. The equations

$$\mathbf{R} \cdot \mathbf{A} = aA, \qquad \mathbf{R} \cdot \mathbf{B} = bB,$$

represent two planes. Let $\mathbf{C} = \mathbf{A} \times \mathbf{B}$ so that $C = AB \sin \theta$, where $\theta = \widehat{\mathbf{AB}}$. Show that the vector equation of the straight line in which the two planes intersect is

$$\mathbf{R} = \frac{aA\mathbf{B} \cdot \mathbf{B} - bB\mathbf{A} \cdot \mathbf{B}}{[\mathbf{ABC}]}\mathbf{A} + \frac{bB\mathbf{A} \cdot \mathbf{A} - aA\mathbf{A} \cdot \mathbf{B}}{[\mathbf{ABC}]}\mathbf{B} + t(\mathbf{A} \times \mathbf{B})$$
$$= \frac{a - b \cos \theta}{\sin^2 \theta} \frac{\mathbf{A}}{A} + \frac{b - a \cos \theta}{\sin^2 \theta} \frac{\mathbf{B}}{B} + t(\mathbf{A} \times \mathbf{B}),$$

where t is a variable parameter.

12. The scalar triple product $[(\mathbf{A} \times \mathbf{B})(\mathbf{B} \times \mathbf{C})(\mathbf{C} \times \mathbf{A})]$ is equal to $[\mathbf{ABC}]^2$.

13. Also

$$[(\mathbf{A} \times \mathbf{P})(\mathbf{B} \times \mathbf{Q})(\mathbf{C} \times \mathbf{R})] + [(\mathbf{A} \times \mathbf{Q})(\mathbf{B} \times \mathbf{R})(\mathbf{C} \times \mathbf{P})] + [(\mathbf{A} \times \mathbf{R})(\mathbf{B} \times \mathbf{P})(\mathbf{C} \times \mathbf{Q})] \equiv 0.$$

14. The tortuosity of a curve T is the limit of the ratio of the angle through which the osculating plane turns to the length of the arc; that is, it is the magnitude of $d\mathbf{b}/ds$, taken negatively, however. Show that

$$T = \frac{\left[\dfrac{d\mathbf{r}}{ds}\,\dfrac{d^2\mathbf{r}}{ds^2}\,\dfrac{d^3\mathbf{r}}{ds^3}\right]}{\dfrac{d^2\mathbf{r}}{ds^2}\cdot\dfrac{d^2\mathbf{r}}{ds^2}}.$$

15. If the origin of the velocity vector is a fixed point, the locus of its terminus is called the hodograph. If $\mathbf{i}$ and $\mathbf{j}$ are unit vectors which have the directions of the x- and y-axis respectively, show that the hodograph for Keplerian motion is

$$\mathbf{r}' = \frac{h}{p}[-\sin\theta\mathbf{i} + (e + \cos\theta)\mathbf{j}]$$

and that this locus is a circle.

16. For simple harmonic motion the force equation is

$$m\mathbf{r}'' = -k^2\mathbf{r}.$$

Integrate this equation and show that the hodograph is an ellipse which is similar to the path of motion.

17. If $\boldsymbol{\rho}$ and $\mathbf{t}$ are unit vectors in the direction of $\mathbf{r}$ and perpendicular to it, show that the components of the velocity in plane motion along $\mathbf{r}$ and perpendicular to it, respectively, are

$$r'\boldsymbol{\rho} \qquad \text{and} \qquad r\theta'\mathbf{t};$$

and the components of the acceleration are

$$(r'' - r\theta'^2)\boldsymbol{\rho} \qquad \text{and} \qquad (r\theta'' + 2r'\theta')\mathbf{t}.$$

18. If $\mathbf{a}$, $\mathbf{b}$, and $\mathbf{c}$ are constant vectors, and t is a parameter which can be regarded as the time, show that the equation

$$\mathbf{r} = t\mathbf{a} + \mathbf{b}$$

represents a straight line, and that

$$\mathbf{r} = \tfrac{1}{2}t^2\mathbf{a} + t\mathbf{b} + \mathbf{c}$$

represents a parabola.

CHAPTER II

MOMENTS OF INERTIA

15. Definition of Moment of Inertia.—In treating the motion of finite bodies, or systems of particles, two types of integrals arise which belong essentially to the geometry of the body. The first type, which defines the center of gravity of the body, or system of particles, arises when the translation of the system is considered. These integrals were discussed at sufficient length in I, **75–91**; but the second type of integrals, *viz.*, the moments and products of inertia, which were discussed briefly in I, **91–99**, are worthy of further discussion. Both types belong to the general class of inertial integrals

$$\int_B \xi^i \eta^j \zeta^k \, dm$$

which was defined in II, **50**; i, j, and k being positive integers, or zero. For centers of gravity

$$i + j + k = 1,$$

and for moments or products of inertia

$$i + j + k = 2.$$

The moment of inertia of a system of particles with respect to a plane, line, or point is the sum of the products of the mass of the particle into the square of the perpendicular distance from the particle to the plane, line, or point (or merely the square of the distance in the case of a point). If m_i are the masses of the particles and p_i are the perpendicular distances mentioned, the moment of inertia has the form

$$I = m_1 p_1^2 + m_2 p_2^2 + \cdot \cdot \cdot + m_n p_n^2 = \Sigma m_i p_i^2.$$

If the system of particles forms a continuous body this sum passes over into the definite integral,

$$I = \int_B p^2 \, dm.$$

If I_{yz} is the moment of inertia with respect to the yz-plane, then

$$I_{yz} = \Sigma m_i x_i^2, \qquad \text{or} \qquad \int_B x^2\, dm,$$

and similarly,

$$I_{zx} = \Sigma m_i y_i^2, \qquad \text{or} \qquad \int_B y^2\, dm,$$

$$I_{xy} = \Sigma m_i z_i^2, \qquad \text{or} \qquad \int_B z^2\, dm.$$

The moments of inertia with respect to the x-, y-, and z-axes respectively are

$$I_x = \Sigma m_i(y_i^2 + z_i^2), \qquad \text{or} \qquad \int_B (y^2 + z^2)\, dm,$$

$$I_y = \Sigma m_i(z_i^2 + x_i^2), \qquad \text{or} \qquad \int_B (z^2 + x^2)\, dm,$$

$$I_z = \Sigma m_i(x_i^2 + y_i^2), \qquad \text{or} \qquad \int_B (x^2 + y^2)\, dm.$$

From these definitions it is evident that

$$I_x = I_{zx} + I_{xy},$$
$$I_y = I_{xy} + I_{yz},$$
$$I_z = I_{yz} + I_{zx}.$$

The moment of inertia with respect to the origin is

$$I_0 = \Sigma m_i(x_i^2 + y_i^2 + z_i^2), \qquad \text{or} \qquad \int_B (x^2 + y^2 + z^2)\, dm,$$
$$= I_{yz} + I_{zx} + I_{xy}$$
$$= \tfrac{1}{2}(I_x + I_y + I_z).$$

Since the choice of the coordinate system is entirely arbitrary, it is seen from these relations that:

The moment of inertia with respect to any line is the sum of the moments of inertia with respect to any two mutually perpendicular planes which pass through that line.

The moment of inertia with respect to any point is equal to the sum of the moments of inertia with respect to any three mutually perpendicular planes which pass through that point, or one-half the sum of the moments of inertia with respect to any three mutually perpendicular lines which pass through that point.

16. Products of Inertia.—Similar expressions which involve the products of the coordinates are called *products of inertia.* They are

$$\Sigma m_i y_i z_i, \qquad \Sigma m_i z_i x_i, \qquad \Sigma m_i x_i y_i,$$

or

$$\int_B yz\, dm, \qquad \int_B zx\, dm, \qquad \int_B xy\, dm;$$

and can be denoted by P_x, P_y, and P_z respectively. Since

$$(y - z)^2 \geqq 0,$$

it is evident that

$$(y^2 + z^2) \geqq 2yz,$$

and therefore

$$\int_B (y^2 + z^2)\, dm \geqq 2\int_B yz\, dm,$$

that is

$$I_x \geqq 2P_x;$$

and similarly,

$$I_y \geqq 2P_y,$$
$$I_z \geqq 2P_z,$$

and

$$I_0 > (P_x + P_y + P_z).$$

17. The Radius of Gyration.—Suppose that the entire mass M of the body, or system of particles, is concentrated into a single particle of mass M at a distance k from the plane, line, or point, with respect to which the moment of inertia is I. If k is chosen so that

$$Mk^2 = I,$$

it is called the *radius of gyration* with respect to that plane, line, or point.

The *principal radius of gyration* is the radius of gyration with respect to a parallel plane or line which passes through the center of gravity.

18. The Principal Radius of Gyration Is a Minimum.—Let I be the moment of inertia with respect to a given axis, which will be taken as the z-axis of a coordinate system. Let k be the radius of gyration of the body with respect to this axis and k_0 the radius of gyration with respect to a parallel axis through the center of gravity, so that k_0 is a principal radius of gyration. Let x_0, y_0, z_0 be the coordinates of the center of gravity, and

$$x = x_0 + \xi, \qquad y = y_0 + \eta, \qquad z = z_0 + \zeta;$$

so that ξ, η, and ζ are the coordinates with respect to the center of gravity. Then

$$Mk_0^2 = \Sigma m_i(\xi_i^2 + \eta_i^2),$$

and

$$\Sigma m_i \xi_i = \Sigma m_i \eta_i = \Sigma m_i \zeta_i = 0.$$

Also

$$\begin{aligned} Mk^2 &= \Sigma m_i(x_i^2 + y_i^2) \\ &= \Sigma m_i[(x_0 + \xi_i)^2 + (y_0 + \eta_i)^2] \\ &= \Sigma m_i(\xi_i^2 + \eta_i^2) + M(x_0^2 + y_0^2) + 2x_0 \Sigma m_i \xi_i + 2y_0 \Sigma m_i \eta_i. \end{aligned}$$

If p is the perpendicular distance between the two axes, then

$$p^2 = x_0^2 + y_0^2;$$

and the above expression reduces to

$$Mk^2 = Mk_0^2 + Mp^2,$$

or

$$k^2 = k_0^2 + p^2. \tag{1}$$

Since p^2 is always positive or zero, it follows that *a principal radius of gyration is smaller than the radius of gyration for any other parallel axis.*

If k is the radius of gyration with respect to a plane, k_0 the radius of gyration with respect to a parallel plane through the center of gravity, and p is the perpendicular distance between the two planes, Eq. (1) still holds, and the principal radius of gyration is a minimum.

Similarly, if k is the radius of gyration with respect to a point, k_0 is the radius of gyration with respect to the center of gravity, and r is the distance between these two points, it is found that

$$k^2 = k_0^2 + r^2,$$

and *the radius of gyration with respect to the center of gravity is smaller than the radius of gyration with respect to any other point.*

For the products of inertia it is easily shown that

$$\Sigma m_i x_i y_i = M x_0 y_0 + \Sigma m_i \xi_i \eta_i,$$

that is, the product of inertia with respect to any two perpendicular axes is equal to the product of inertia with respect to a parallel set of axes through the center of gravity plus the product of inertia with respect to the original axes of a particle of mass M situated at the center of gravity. Since the product $x_0 y_0$ may be either positive or negative, there is no minimum principle involved.

19. The Direction of the Axis Varies.—In the preceding section it was shown how the moment of inertia varies from any axis to any parallel axis, the constant element being the direction of the axes. In the present Section the constant element will be a fixed point O, and attention will be directed to the changes which occur in the moment of inertia as the direction of the line through O changes.

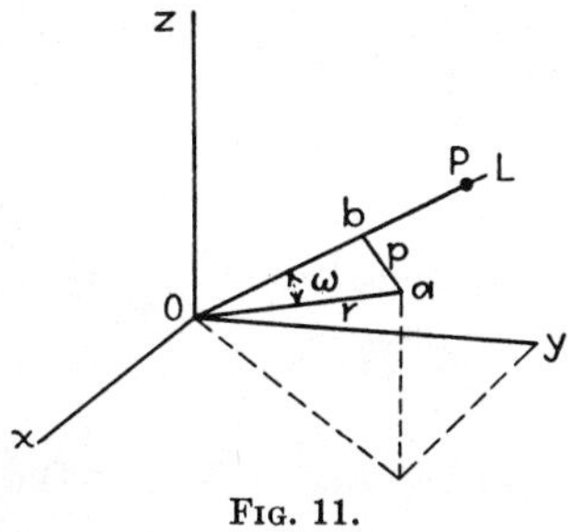

FIG. 11.

Let the point O be taken as the origin of a system of rectangular coordinates, Fig. 11; let OL be any line through O, and α, β, γ be its direction cosines. Let a be any point of the body with the coordinates x, y, z; $\overline{ab} = p$ the perpendicular from the point a to the line OL; and r the distance Oa. Then

$$p^2 = r^2 - \overline{Ob}^2. \tag{1}$$

The direction cosines of the lines r and OL are, respectively,

$$\frac{x}{r}, \quad \frac{y}{r}, \quad \frac{z}{r}; \qquad \alpha, \beta, \gamma.$$

If ω is the angle between these two lines, then

$$\cos \omega = \alpha\frac{x}{r} + \beta\frac{y}{r} + \gamma\frac{z}{r},$$

and

$$\overline{Ob} = r \cos \omega = \alpha x + \beta y + \gamma z.$$

Hence, from (1),

$$\begin{aligned} p^2 &= (x^2 + y^2 + z^2) - (\alpha x + \beta y + \gamma z)^2 \\ &= (x^2 + y^2 + z^2)(\alpha^2 + \beta^2 + \gamma^2) - (\alpha x + \beta y + \gamma z)^2, \end{aligned}$$

since

$$\alpha^2 + \beta^2 + \gamma^2 = 1.$$

On expanding, it is found that

$$\begin{aligned} p^2 = \alpha^2(y^2 + z^2) + \beta^2(z^2 + x^2) + \gamma^2(x^2 + y^2) \\ -2\beta\gamma yz - 2\gamma\alpha zx - 2\alpha\beta xy. \end{aligned}$$

If the mass of the particle at a is m, the moment of inertia of the system of particles, or the body, with respect to the line OL is

$$\begin{aligned} I_L = \Sigma mp^2 = \alpha^2\Sigma m(y^2 + z^2) + \beta^2\Sigma m(z^2 + x^2) + \gamma^2\Sigma m(x^2 + y^2) \\ -2\beta\gamma\Sigma myz - 2\gamma\alpha\Sigma mzx - 2\alpha\beta\Sigma mxy. \end{aligned}$$

Let

$$\left.\begin{aligned} A &= \Sigma m(y^2 + z^2), & B &= \Sigma m(z^2 + x^2), & C &= \Sigma m(x^2 + y^2), \\ D &= \Sigma myz, & E &= \Sigma mzx, & F &= \Sigma mxy. \end{aligned}\right\} \tag{2}$$

These quantities are the moments and products of inertia of the body with respect to the coordinate axes, and are therefore independent of the direction of the line L. With this notation then,

$$\Sigma mp^2 = I_L = A\alpha^2 + B\beta^2 + C\gamma^2 - 2D\beta\gamma - 2E\gamma\alpha - 2F\alpha\beta, \tag{3}$$

and the moment of inertia with respect to the line L is thereby expressed in terms of the direction cosines of L and the moments and products of inertia of the body, or system of particles, with respect to the coordinate axes.

20. Cauchy's Ellipsoid of Inertia.—The relation Eq. (19.3) can be represented in a simple manner to the intuition by taking a point P on L at such a distance from O that

$$I_L = \frac{M\lambda^4}{\overline{OP}^2}, \tag{1}$$

where M is the total mass and λ is an arbitrary length. Then, on setting,

$$\overline{OP} = \rho, \qquad \rho\alpha = \xi, \qquad \rho\beta = \eta, \qquad \rho\gamma = \zeta, \tag{2}$$

Eq. (3) becomes

$$A\xi^2 + B\eta^2 + C\zeta^2 - 2D\eta\zeta - 2E\zeta\xi - 2F\xi\eta = M\lambda^4. \tag{3}$$

This is a central conicoid which, evidently, is an ellipsoid, since the moment of inertia is essentially positive, and therefore ρ is always real and finite. There is but one possible exception and that is the moment of inertia of a straight line with respect to itself. In this case the ellipsoid of inertia is an infinitely long cylinder which has the given line as its axis.

This ellipsoid is called the *momental ellipsoid*, or the *ellipsoid of inertia*. It was introduced by Cauchy,[1] but owing to the skillful use made of it by Poinsot, it is sometimes called Poinsot's ellipsoid of inertia. Since the surface is an ellipsoid, there exists, in general, a direction for which the moment of inertia is a maximum and one for which it is a minimum, these directions corresponding to the minimum and maximum axes of the ellipsoid. In order to find the values of the moments of inertia which correspond to the axes of symmetry of the ellipsoid, consider the direction cosines of the normal at a point ξ, η, ζ of the ellipsoid. If the equation of the ellipsoid is $\varphi(\xi, \eta, \zeta) = 0$, the direction cosines of the normal are proportional to

$$\frac{\partial\varphi}{\partial\xi}, \qquad \frac{\partial\varphi}{\partial\eta}, \qquad \frac{\partial\varphi}{\partial\zeta},$$

and the direction cosines of the radius vector to the point under consideration are proportional to ξ, η, ζ. At the ends of the axes

[1] Cauchy, "Exercices de Mathématique," Vol. II, p. 93 (1827).

of symmetry the direction of the normal coincides with the direction of the radius vector. Hence, at these points,

$$\frac{A\xi - F\eta - E\zeta}{\xi} = \frac{B\eta - D\zeta - F\xi}{\eta} = \frac{C\zeta - E\xi - D\eta}{\zeta},$$

or, on account of Eq. (2),

$$\frac{A\alpha - F\beta - E\gamma}{\alpha} = \frac{B\beta - D\gamma - F\alpha}{\beta} = \frac{C\gamma - E\alpha - D\beta}{\gamma} = I.$$

If the numerator and denominator of the first of these ratios is multiplied by α, the second by β, and the third by γ, then, since

$$\frac{a_1}{b_1} = \frac{a_2}{b_2} = \frac{a_3}{b_3} = \frac{a_1 + a_2 + a_3}{b_1 + b_2 + b_3},$$

it is found that the common value of these ratios is I. The following three equations then follow easily:

$$\begin{aligned} (A - I)\alpha \qquad & -F\beta \qquad & -E\gamma &= 0, \\ -F\alpha + (B - I)\beta \qquad & & -D\gamma &= 0, \\ -E\alpha \qquad & -D\beta + (C - I)\gamma & &= 0. \end{aligned}$$

In order that these three linear equations may be compatible, it is necessary, since α, β, and γ cannot all be zero, that the determinant shall vanish. That is,

$$\begin{vmatrix} (A - I) & -F & -E \\ -F & (B - I) & -D \\ -E & -D & (C - I) \end{vmatrix} = 0. \tag{4}$$

The three values of I which are determined by this cubic equation are the moments of inertia of the body with respect to axes which coincide with the three axes of symmetry of the ellipsoid of inertia at the point O. If the direction of the axes of reference, which up to this point have been arbitrary, are chosen in such a way as to coincide with the axes of symmetry of the ellipsoid, Eq. (3) reduces to

$$A\xi^2 + B\eta^2 + C\zeta^2 = M\lambda^4, \tag{5}$$

and therefore the products of inertia, D, E, and F, referred to these axes, all vanish; it will be observed also that the roots of Eq. (4) become A, B, and C, as, of course, they should.

Lines which coincide with the axes of symmetry of the ellipsoid of inertia at the point O are called *the principal axes of inertia at the point* O, and the moments of inertia with respect to these lines are called *the principal moments of inertia at the point* O. If the point O is the center of gravity of the system, the ellipsoid is called the *central ellipsoid of inertia.* If the ellipsoid of inertia is a spheroid, every axis in the plane of its equator is a principal axis; and if it is a sphere, every axis through the point O is a principal axis.

It is evident that if a body has three planes of symmetry which are mutually perpendicular these three planes are the *principal planes* of the central ellipsoid of inertia.

Imagine that the ellipsoid of inertia at the point O has been drawn. The moment of inertia of any line OL which passes through O and intersects the surface of the ellipsoid in the point P is

$$I_L = \frac{M\lambda^4}{\overline{OP}^2} = \frac{M\lambda^4}{\rho^2}.$$

It is evident from this that I_L is a maximum when ρ is a minimum, and conversely. Furthermore, if a, b, and c are the semiaxes of the ellipsoid, with respect to which A, B, and C are the moments of inertia, and if

$$A < B < C, \qquad \text{then} \qquad a > b > c.$$

Example 1.—It is seen from I, **98**, that if the edges of a right parallelopiped are $2S_x$, $2S_y$, $2S_z$ and are parallel to the x-, y-, and z-axes respectively, the principal moments of inertia of the central ellipsoid are

$$\begin{aligned} A &= \frac{M\lambda^4}{a^2} = \frac{M}{3}(S_y^2 + S_z^2), \\ B &= \frac{M\lambda^4}{b^2} = \frac{M}{3}(S_z^2 + S_x^2), \\ C &= \frac{M\lambda^4}{c^2} = \frac{M}{3}(S_x^2 + S_y^2). \end{aligned}$$

For an ordinary brick the dimensions are 8, 4, and 2 inches. The axes of the central ellipsoid expressed in inches, $\lambda = 1$ inch, are

$$\begin{aligned} a &= \sqrt{\tfrac{3}{5}} = 0.775, \\ b &= \sqrt{\tfrac{3}{17}} = 0.420, \\ c &= \sqrt{\tfrac{3}{20}} = 0.388. \end{aligned}$$

Example 2.—For a homogeneous ellipsoid, the corresponding results are (II, **48**)

$$A = \frac{M\lambda^4}{a^2} = \frac{M}{5}(S_y^2 + S_z^2),$$
$$B = \frac{M\lambda^4}{b^2} = \frac{M}{5}(S_z^2 + S_x^2),$$
$$C = \frac{M\lambda^4}{c^2} = \frac{M}{5}(S_x^2 + S_y^2).$$

If S_x, S_y, and S_z are the same for the parallelopiped and the ellipsoid, the central ellipsoids for the two bodies are similar, since the axes are proportional. The long axis of the ellipsoid of inertia is the same as the long axis of the body, and the short axis of the ellipsoid of inertia coincides with the short axis of the body. For a cube, or a sphere, or any regular polyhedron, the central ellipsoid of inertia is a sphere.

21. Not All Ellipsoids Are Possible.—If a, b, and c are the axes of the ellipsoid of inertia, and if, for definiteness,

$$A \leqq B \leqq C,$$

then,

$$a \geqq b \geqq c.$$

From their definitions, Eq. (19.2), it is evident that the sum of any two of the three quantities A, B, C is greater than the third, equality not excluded; in particular

$$A + B \geqq C.$$

If e_z and e_y are the eccentricities of the ellipsoid in the planes $z = 0$ and $y = 0$ respectively, it is found that

$$e_z^2 = \frac{B - A}{B}, \qquad \text{and} \qquad e_y^2 = \frac{C - A}{C}. \tag{1}$$

Starting with the inequality

$$\frac{1}{B} \geqq \frac{1}{C} \geqq \frac{1}{A + B},$$

multiply through by $-A$ and add $+1$ to each member; there result the inequalities

$$\frac{B - A}{B} \leqq \frac{C - A}{C} \leqq \frac{B}{A + B}, \tag{2}$$

or, Eq. (1),

$$0 \leqq e_z^2 \leqq e_y^2 \leqq \frac{1}{2 - e_z^2}. \tag{3}$$

That is, for a given value of e_z, the values of e_y are restricted. This result is shown graphically in Fig. 12, the shaded area representing the possible positions of the point (e_z^2, e_y^2). The lower limit is attained, as is seen from Eq. (1), if $B = C$; and the upper limit is attained if

$$A + B = C.$$

In the first case, $B = C$, the ellipsoid of inertia

$$A\xi^2 + B\eta^2 + C\zeta^2 = M\lambda^4$$

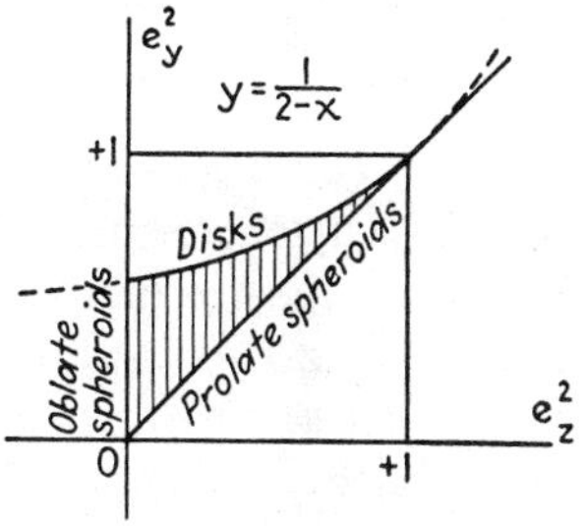

FIG. 12.

is a prolate spheroid about the ξ-axis, and its eccentricity may have any value from zero to one; that is, the prolate spheroid may be anything from a sphere to an infinitely long cylinder, the latter being attained if all of the particles lie on a straight line.

In the second case, $A + B = C$, it is necessary that, Eq. (19.2),

$$\Sigma mz^2 = 0,$$

which means that all of the particles lie in the xy-plane, or, in the case of a continuous body, is a disk of some sort.

The third limiting case is $e_z^2 = 0$, or $A = B$. In this case the ellipsoid is an oblate spheroid. It is evident from the diagram, Fig. 12, that the maximum value of e_y^2 is one-half. Hence, while there may be prolate spheroids with any degree of prolateness from a sphere to an infinitely long cylinder, the oblate spheroids range only from the sphere to the spheroid of maximum oblateness

$$(\sqrt{2} - 1)/\sqrt{2}.$$

22. A Property of the Central Ellipsoid.—In order that the z-axis, say, may be a principal axis of inertia at the origin, it is necessary that the products of inertia which are linear in z should vanish; that is

$$D = \Sigma myz = 0, \qquad E = \Sigma mxz = 0. \tag{1}$$

Suppose these conditions are satisfied at a certain point O, and that O_1 is any other point on the z-axis at a distance h from O. In order that the z-axis may be a principal axis at O_1 it is necessary that

$$\Sigma mx(z - h) = 0, \qquad \Sigma my(z - h) = 0,$$

and therefore

$$h\Sigma mx = 0, \qquad h\Sigma my = 0.$$

These conditions are satisfied if, and only if, the z-axis passes through the center of gravity of the system.

Theorem.—A principal axis of inertia of the central ellipsoid is a principal axis of inertia for all of its points. Conversely, if any axis is a principal axis of inertia for any two of its points, it is a principal axis of inertia for all of its points, and it passes through the center of gravity.

23. Envelope of Planes with Respect to Which the Moment of Inertia Is Constant.—Let the coordinate system be chosen so as to coincide with the principal axes of the central ellipsoid of inertia. Let the moments of inertia with respect to the coordinate planes be

$$Ma^2 = \Sigma mx^2, \qquad Mb^2 = \Sigma my^2, \qquad Mc^2 = \Sigma mz^2,$$

where M is the total mass of the system. The moment of inertia with respect to the plane

$$u\xi + v\eta + w\zeta = 1 \tag{1}$$

is

$$Mk^2 = \sum mp_i^2 = \sum m_i \frac{(ux_i + vy_i + wz_i - 1)^2}{u^2 + v^2 + w^2}.$$

On expanding the numerator of this expression and bearing in mind that by virtue of the choice of coordinate axes

$$\begin{aligned} \Sigma mx &= \Sigma my = \Sigma mz = 0, \\ \Sigma myz &= \Sigma mzx = \Sigma mxy = 0. \end{aligned}$$

there results

$$Mk^2 = \frac{Ma^2u^2 + Mb^2v^2 + Mc^2w^2 + M}{u^2 + v^2 + w^2}.$$

Cleared of fractions this becomes

$$u^2(k^2 - a^2) + v^2(k^2 - b^2) + w^2(k^2 - c^2) = 1, \tag{2}$$

a relation that must exist between the given constant k and the coefficients of Eq. (1). It is evident that k^2 must be greater than the smallest one of the three quantities a^2, b^2, c^2.

On account of this relationship, Eq. (2), the coefficients u, v, and w can be regarded as functions of two independent parameters, q_1 and q_2. On taking

$$\frac{1}{\alpha^2} = k^2 - a^2, \qquad \frac{1}{\beta^2} = k^2 - b^2, \qquad \frac{1}{\gamma^2} = k^2 - c^2,$$

Eq. (2) takes the familiar form

$$\frac{u^2}{\alpha^2} + \frac{v^2}{\beta^2} + \frac{w^2}{\gamma^2} = 1. \tag{3}$$

Since Eq. (3) represents a conicoid, I, **353** suggests the parametric representation

$$u^2 = \frac{\alpha^2(\alpha^2 - q_1)(\alpha^2 - q_2)}{(\alpha^2 - \beta^2)(\alpha^2 - \gamma^2)},$$
$$v^2 = \frac{\beta^2(\beta^2 - q_1)(\beta^2 - q_2)}{(\beta^2 - \alpha^2)(\beta^2 - \gamma^2)},$$
$$w^2 = \frac{\gamma^2(\gamma^2 - q_1)(\gamma^2 - q_2)}{(\gamma^2 - \alpha^2)(\gamma^2 - \beta^2)}.$$

The elimination of q_1 and q_2 between the three equations

$$f(q_1, q_2) = 1, \qquad \frac{\partial f}{\partial q_1} = 0, \qquad \frac{\partial f}{\partial q_2} = 0,$$

where $f(q_1, q_2)$ is the left member of Eq. (1), gives the envelope of the planes which satisfy Eq. (2). These three equations are

$$u\xi + v\eta + w\zeta = 1,$$
$$\frac{1}{\alpha^2 - q_1}u\xi + \frac{1}{\beta^2 - q_1}v\eta + \frac{1}{\gamma^2 - q_1}w\zeta = 0,$$
$$\frac{1}{\alpha^2 - q_2}u\xi + \frac{1}{\beta^2 - q_2}v\eta + \frac{1}{\gamma^2 - q_2}w\zeta = 0,$$

which are linear in $u\xi$, $v\eta$, and $w\zeta$. By subtracting the first column from each of the second and third, removing common factors, and then repeating the operation, it is found readily that the determinant is

$$D = \frac{(\alpha^2 - \beta^2)(\beta^2 - \gamma^2)(\alpha^2 - \gamma^2)(q_2 - q_1)}{(\alpha^2 - q_1)(\alpha^2 - q_2)(\beta^2 - q_1)(\beta^2 - q_2)(\gamma^2 - q_1)(\gamma^2 - q_2)}.$$

The solution follows easily

$$u\xi = \frac{u^2}{\alpha^2}, \qquad \alpha\xi = \frac{u}{\alpha},$$
$$v\eta = \frac{v^2}{\beta^2}, \quad \text{or} \quad \beta\eta = \frac{v}{\beta},$$
$$w\zeta = \frac{w^2}{\gamma^2}, \qquad \gamma\zeta = \frac{w}{\gamma},$$

and the substitution of these results in this last column in Eq. (3) gives the desired eliminant

$$\alpha^2\xi^2 + \beta^2\eta^2 + \gamma^2\zeta^2 = 1;$$

or, in terms of the original constants a^2, b^2, c^2, and k^2,

$$\frac{\xi^2}{k^2 - a^2} + \frac{\eta^2}{k^2 - b^2} + \frac{\zeta^2}{k^2 - c^2} = 1. \tag{4}$$

The envelope, therefore, is a surface of the second order, or a conicoid. Through any given point $O(\xi, \eta, \zeta)$ there pass three of these surfaces which are mutually perpendicular, and the values of the parameter k^2 for these three surfaces are the three values of k^2 which satisfy Eq. (4).

Let these three roots be denoted by k_1^2, k_2^2, k_3^2. For definiteness these quantities can be arranged in order of magnitude as follows:

$$0 < c^2 < k_3^2 < b^2 < k_2^2 < a^2 < k_1^2.$$

Then these surfaces are

$$\left.\begin{aligned}
&\frac{\xi^2}{k_1^2 - a^2} + \frac{\eta^2}{k_1^2 - b^2} + \frac{\zeta^2}{k_1^2 - c^2} = 1 \qquad \text{(ellipsoid)},\\
&\frac{\xi^2}{k_2^2 - a^2} + \frac{\eta^2}{k_2^2 - b^2} + \frac{\zeta^2}{k_2^2 - c^2} = 1 \qquad \text{(hyp. of one sheet)},\\
&\frac{\xi^2}{k_3^2 - a^2} + \frac{\eta^2}{k_3^2 - b^2} + \frac{\zeta^2}{k_3^2 - c^2} = 1 \qquad \text{(hyp. of two sheets)}.
\end{aligned}\right\} \tag{5}$$

The tangent planes at a point $P(\xi_0, \eta_0, \zeta_0)$ are respectively

$$\left.\begin{aligned} &\frac{\xi_0\xi}{k_1^2 - a^2} + \frac{\eta_0\eta}{k_1^2 - b^2} + \frac{\zeta_0\zeta}{k_1^2 - c^2} = 1 \qquad \text{(ellipsoid)},\\ &\frac{\xi_0\xi}{k_2^2 - a^2} + \frac{\eta_0\eta}{k_2^2 - b^2} + \frac{\zeta_0\zeta}{k_2^2 - c^2} = 1 \qquad \text{(hyp. of one sheet)},\\ &\frac{\xi_0\xi}{k_3^2 - a^2} + \frac{\eta_0\eta}{k_3^2 - b^2} + \frac{\zeta_0\zeta}{k_3^2 - c^2} = 1 \qquad \text{(hyp. of two sheets)}.\end{aligned}\right\} \quad (6)$$

24. Binet's Theorem.—It is possible now to prove the very beautiful theorem due originally to Binet.[1]

The three principal planes of inertia at the point $P(\xi_0, \eta_0, \zeta_0)$ are the three planes which are tangent to the three confocal conicoids which pass through the point $P(\xi_0, \eta_0, \zeta_0)$; and the moments of inertia with respect to these three planes are Mk_1^2, Mk_2^2, and Mk_3^2 respectively.

Since the ξ-, η-, ζ-axes coincide with the principal axes of inertia at the center of gravity, it will be recalled that

$$\begin{aligned} &\Sigma m\xi^2 = Ma^2, && \Sigma m\eta^2 = Mb^2, && \Sigma m\zeta^2 = Mc^2,\\ &\Sigma m\eta\zeta = 0, && \Sigma m\zeta\xi = 0, && \Sigma m\xi\eta = 0,\\ &\Sigma m\xi = 0, && \Sigma m\eta = 0, && \Sigma m\zeta = 0.\end{aligned}$$

Let a new system of axes be taken with its origin at the point ξ_0, η_0, ζ_0 with the x-axis normal to the ellipsoid, the y-axis normal to the hyperboloid of one sheet, and the z-axis normal to the hyperboloid of two sheets. The equations of transformation are

$$\left.\begin{aligned} \xi &= \xi_0 + \alpha_1 x + \alpha_2 y + \alpha_3 z,\\ \eta &= \eta_0 + \beta_1 x + \beta_2 y + \beta_3 z,\\ \zeta &= \zeta_0 + \gamma_1 x + \gamma_2 y + \gamma_3 z.\end{aligned}\right\} \quad (1)$$

Since the direction cosines $\alpha_1, \ldots, \gamma_3$ in this transformation are proportional to the coefficients in Eqs. (23.6), it is easily verified that

$$\left.\begin{aligned} &\alpha_1 = \rho_1\frac{\xi_0}{k_1^2 - a^2}, && \alpha_2 = \rho_2\frac{\xi_0}{k_2^2 - a^2}, && \alpha_3 = \rho_3\frac{\xi_0}{k_3^2 - a^2},\\ &\beta_1 = \rho_1\frac{\eta_0}{k_1^2 - b^2}, && \beta_2 = \rho_2\frac{\eta_0}{k_2^2 - b^2}, && \beta_3 = \rho_3\frac{\eta_0}{k_3^2 - b^2},\\ &\gamma_1 = \rho_1\frac{\zeta_0}{k_1^2 - c^2}, && \gamma_2 = \rho_2\frac{\zeta_0}{k_2^2 - c^2}, && \gamma_3 = \rho_3\frac{\zeta_0}{k_3^2 - c^2},\end{aligned}\right\} \quad (2)$$

[1] BINET, J., *Journal de l'École Polytechnique* (1813).

where

$$\frac{1}{\rho_i} = \sqrt{\left(\frac{\xi_0}{k_i^2 - a^2}\right)^2 + \left(\frac{\eta_0}{k_i^2 - b^2}\right)^2 + \left(\frac{\zeta_0}{k_i^2 - c^2}\right)^2}. \tag{3}$$

Since, from Eq. (2),

$$\alpha_i\xi_0 + \beta_i\eta_0 + \gamma_i\zeta_0 = \rho_i,$$

the inversion of Eqs. (1) gives

$$\begin{aligned} x &= \alpha_1\xi + \beta_1\eta + \gamma_1\zeta - \rho_1, \\ y &= \alpha_2\xi + \beta_2\eta + \gamma_2\zeta - \rho_2, \\ z &= \alpha_3\xi + \beta_3\eta + \gamma_3\zeta - \rho_3. \end{aligned}$$

The moment of inertia with respect to the yz-plane, that is, the plane tangent to the ellipsoid, is

$$\begin{aligned} \Sigma mx^2 &= \Sigma m(\alpha_1\xi + \beta_1\eta + \gamma_1\zeta - \rho_1)^2 \\ &= M(a^2\alpha_1^2 + b^2\beta_1^2 + c^2\gamma_1^2 + \rho_1^2) \\ &= M\rho_1^2\left(\frac{a^2\xi_0^2}{(k_1^2 - a^2)^2} + \frac{b^2\eta_0^2}{(k_1^2 - b^2)^2} + \frac{c^2\zeta_0^2}{(k_1^2 - c^2)^2} + 1\right). \end{aligned}$$

But since, by the first of Eqs. (23.5),

$$\frac{k_1^2\xi_0^2 - a^2\xi_0^2}{(k_1^2 - a^2)^2} + \frac{k_1^2\eta_0^2 - b^2\eta_0^2}{(k_1^2 - b^2)^2} + \frac{k_1^2\zeta_0^2 - c^2\zeta_0^2}{(k_1^2 - c^2)^2} - 1 = 0,$$

this reduces to

$$\Sigma mx^2 = Mk_1^2\rho_1^2\left(\frac{\xi_0^2}{(k_1^2 - a^2)^2} + \frac{\eta_0^2}{(k_1^2 - b^2)^2} + \frac{\zeta_0^2}{(k_1^2 - c^2)^2}\right),$$

or

$$\Sigma mx^2 = Mk_1^2, \text{ by Eqs. (3);}$$

and similarly,

$$\begin{aligned} \Sigma my^2 &= Mk_2^2, \\ \Sigma mz^2 &= Mk_3^2. \end{aligned}$$

The products of inertia vanish, as is readily verified. The ellipsoid of inertia at P is, then,

$$(k_2^2 + k_3^2)x^2 + (k_3^2 + k_1^2)y^2 + (k_1^2 + k_2^2)z^2 = \lambda^4;$$

its longest axis is normal to the ellipsoid which passes through P, and its shortest axis is normal to the hyperboloid of two sheets.

25. The Equimomental Cone.—The intersection of the ellipsoid of inertia at P with a sphere whose center is also at P defines a curve L upon the ellipsoid of inertia which has the property that all of its points are equidistant from P. Hence the cone which is described by a straight line through P which always touches the curve L is an equimomental cone, that is, the moment of inertia with respect to the straight line is constant.

In order to find the equation of this cone, let I be the given moment of inertia, and α, β, γ the direction cosines of a line through P with respect to the principal axes of inertia. Then for any line of the cone

$$\begin{aligned} A\alpha^2 + B\beta^2 + C\gamma^2 &= I \\ &= I(\alpha^2 + \beta^2 + \gamma^2). \end{aligned}$$

Hence

$$(A - I)\alpha^2 + (B - I)\beta^2 + (C - I)\gamma^2 = 0;$$

or, in rectangular coordinates

$$(A - I)\xi^2 + (B - I)\eta^2 + (C - I)\zeta^2 = 0, \qquad (1)$$

which is a cone of the second order.

If

$$A < B < C,$$

it is evident that

$$A < I < C,$$

since the terms of Eq. (1) cannot all have the same sign. If I is equal to A, the cone degenerates into a straight line which coincides with the ξ-axis. If I equals C, the cone degenerates into the ζ-axis. But if $I = B$, the cone opens out into two planes which are defined by the equation

$$\zeta = \pm\sqrt{\frac{I - A}{C - I}}\xi.$$

26. The Principal Point of a Line.—Given a body, or a system of particles, B, and any line L. Does there exist on L a point $P(x, y, z)$ at which L is a principal axis of inertia for the body B? Obviously, the point P must lie on the line L, if it exists at all.

Consider first the case in which the central ellipsoid of inertia is a sphere. In this case every line through the center of gravity is a principal axis for all of its points. If the line L does not pass through the center of gravity, drop a perpendicular Λ upon it from the center of gravity. At the point of intersection Λ is a principal axis, and the ellipsoid of inertia at that point is a spheroid about Λ as an axis. Since L lies in the equator of this ellipsoid and intersects Λ, it, too, is a principal axis of inertia, and the point of intersection is the point P which is required. The point P is called the *principal point on the line* L, and there always exists such a point if the central ellipsoid of inertia is a sphere and the line L does not pass through the center of gravity.

Suppose the central ellipsoid of inertia is not a sphere, and that the principal moments of inertia of the central ellipsoid are Ma^2, Mb^2, Mc^2, and that the coordinate axes are chosen so as to coincide with the principal axes of the central ellipsoid. If the direction cosines of L are α, β, γ, the parametric equations of L are

$$\left.\begin{aligned} x &= x_0 + \alpha t, \\ y &= y_0 + \beta t, \\ z &= z_0 + \gamma t. \end{aligned}\right\} \tag{1}$$

If the point $P(x, y, z)$ is a principal point of L, one of the three surfaces through P, which are defined by the equation, Eq. (9.4),

$$\frac{x^2}{k^2 - a^2} + \frac{y^2}{k^2 - b^2} + \frac{z^2}{k^2 - c^2} = 1, \tag{2}$$

must be normal to L. This condition gives the three equations

$$\left.\begin{aligned} \alpha &= \frac{1}{R}\frac{x_0 + \alpha t}{k^2 - a^2}, \\ \beta &= \frac{1}{R}\frac{y_0 + \beta t}{k^2 - b^2}, \\ \gamma &= \frac{1}{R}\frac{z_0 + \gamma t}{k^2 - c^2}, \end{aligned}\right\} \tag{3}$$

where

$$R^2 = \left(\frac{x_0 + \alpha t}{k^2 - a^2}\right)^2 + \left(\frac{y_0 + \beta t}{k^2 - b^2}\right)^2 + \left(\frac{z_0 + \gamma t}{k^2 - c^2}\right)^2.$$

If the line L passes through the center of gravity,

$$\frac{x_0}{\alpha} = \frac{y_0}{\beta} = \frac{z_0}{\gamma} = \lambda, \tag{4}$$

and the three equations, Eq. (3), can be satisfied only if two of the three quantities α, β, γ are zero and the third is unity, and this requires that L shall coincide with one of the coordinate axes. Hence if L passes through the center of gravity and does not coincide with a principal axis, a principal point on it does not exist.

If L does not pass through the center of gravity, Eqs. (3) become

$$R = \frac{x_0 + \alpha t}{\alpha(k^2 - a^2)} = \frac{y_0 + \beta t}{\beta(k^2 - b^2)} = \frac{z_0 + \gamma t}{\gamma(k^2 - c^2)}. \tag{5}$$

The second and third members of this equality give the equation

$$\frac{k^2 - b^2}{k^2 - a^2} = \frac{\alpha}{\beta} \frac{y_0 + \beta t}{x_0 + \alpha t}.$$

On subtracting unity from both members and then multiplying by suitable factors, it is found that

$$\frac{x_0 + \alpha t}{\alpha(k^2 - a^2)} = \frac{\dfrac{y_0}{\beta} - \dfrac{x_0}{\alpha}}{a^2 - b^2},$$

and similarly,

$$\frac{y_0 + \beta t}{\beta(k^2 - b^2)} = \frac{\dfrac{z_0}{\gamma} - \dfrac{y_0}{\beta}}{b^2 - c^2},$$

$$\frac{z_0 + \gamma t}{\gamma(k^2 - c^2)} = \frac{\dfrac{x_0}{\alpha} - \dfrac{z_0}{\gamma}}{c^2 - a^2}.$$

Hence, on account of Eqs. (5),

$$\frac{\dfrac{y_0}{\beta} - \dfrac{x_0}{\alpha}}{a^2 - b^2} = \frac{\dfrac{z_0}{\gamma} - \dfrac{y_0}{\beta}}{b^2 - c^2} = \frac{\dfrac{x_0}{\alpha} - \dfrac{z_0}{\gamma}}{c^2 - a^2} = R. \tag{6}$$

This condition on the given constants must certainly be satisfied if a principal point exists. The third member of Eq. (6) is merely a consequence of the equality of the first two and does not impose a second condition. It reduces to the single equation

$$\frac{b^2 - c^2}{\alpha} x_0 + \frac{c^2 - a^2}{\beta} y_0 + \frac{a^2 - b^2}{\gamma} z_0 = 0.$$

This is the equation of a plane through the origin, if the direction cosines α, β, γ are regarded as given; and the line L lies in it as is easily verified by means of Eq. (1). Lines parallel to this plane, but not lying in it, cannot have a principal point, even though the direction cosines are α, β, and γ.

From Eqs. (5) and Eq. (2), it is found that

$$R^2\alpha^2(k^2 - a^2) + R^2\beta^2(k^2 - b^2) + R^2\gamma^2(k^2 - c^2) = 1, \quad (7)$$

or

$$R^2k^2 - R^2(a^2\alpha^2 + b^2\beta^2 + c^2\gamma^2) = 1. \quad (8)$$

Hence

$$k^2 = \frac{1}{R^2} + (a^2\alpha^2 + b^2\beta^2 + c^2\gamma^2).$$

This equation determines k^2 uniquely, since R is given by Eq. (6). From the equations just preceding Eq. (6) are obtained

$$t = R(k^2 - a^2) - \frac{x_0}{\alpha},$$

$$t = R(k^2 - b^2) - \frac{y_0}{\beta},$$

$$t = R(k^2 - c^2) - \frac{z_0}{\gamma}.$$

If the first of these equations is multiplied by α^2, the second by β^2, and the third by γ^2, and are then added, there results

$$t = Rk^2 - R(a^2\alpha^2 + b^2\beta^2 + c^2\gamma^2) - (\alpha x_0 + \beta y_0 + \gamma z_0);$$

and by virtue of Eq. (8) this reduces to

$$t = \frac{1}{R} - (\alpha x_0 + \beta y_0 + \gamma z_0). \quad (9)$$

Thus t, which is the distance from the given point x_0, y_0, z_0, to the principal point, also is uniquely defined, and, in general, there is but one principal point on a line, if there is any at all. The three principal axes of the central ellipsoid are exceptions, and also, of course, if the ellipsoid is a spheroid, all lines in the plane of the equator which pass through the center of gravity.

27. The Ellipsoid of Gyration.—The ellipsoids

$$(E_1) \qquad \frac{x^2}{a^2} + \frac{y^2}{b^2} + \frac{z^2}{c^2} = 1$$

and

$$(E_2) \qquad a^2x^2 + b^2y^2 + c^2z^2 = g^4$$

are called reciprocal ellipsoids because the products of the corresponding axes, that is, the two x-axes, the two y-axes, and the two z-axes, are constant and equal to g^2.

If p is the perpendicular distance from the center of the ellipsoid E_1 to a tangent plane and α, β, γ are the direction cosines of this perpendicular, then

$$p^2 = a^2\alpha^2 + b^2\beta^2 + c^2\gamma^2. \tag{1}$$

Let the point Q on this perpendicular be at a distance q from the center of E_1, and let q be related to p in such a way that

$$pq = g^2.$$

Then the locus of the point Q is the ellipsoid E_2; for if Eq. (1) is multiplied by q^2, there results

$$p^2q^2 = g^4 = q^2(a^2\alpha^2 + b^2\beta^2 + c^2\gamma),$$

or in rectangular coordinates

$$(E_2) \qquad a^2x^2 + b^2y^2 + c^2z^2 = g^4.$$

If the same operations are carried out starting with E_2 and the product $pq = 1/g^2$, it is found that E_1 is the locus.

The ellipsoid of inertia at any point O, referred to axes which coincide with the principal axes of inertia, is

$$Ax^2 + By^2 + Cz^2 = M\lambda^4.$$

The reciprocal ellipsoid

$$\frac{x^2}{A} + \frac{y^2}{B} + \frac{z^2}{C} = \frac{1}{M},$$

where M is the mass of the body, is called the *ellipsoid of gyration*, since its x-axis is the radius of gyration for the x-axis, and similarly for the y-, and z-axes. That is

$$Mk_x^2 = A, \qquad Mk_y^2 = B, \qquad Mk_z^2 = C.$$

This relation holds only for the principal axes. It does not hold for directions in general, since the inversion of an ellipsoid by reciprocal radii gives a surface of the fourth order, and not another ellipsoid.

Problems

1. The moment of inertia of a rectangle, the sides of which are $2a$ and $2b$, about an axis in its plane and perpendicular to the side $2a$ at its center is $\frac{1}{3}a^2$; and about an axis through its center and perpendicular to its plane is $\frac{1}{3}(a^2 + b^2)$.

2. The moment of inertia of an ellipse whose axes are $2a$ and $2b$ about the axis $2a$ is $\frac{1}{4}b^2$; about the axis $2b$ is $\frac{1}{4}a^2$; and about an axis perpendicular to its plane through its center is $\frac{1}{4}(a^2 + b^2)$.

3. The moment of inertia of an ellipsoid whose semiaxes are a, b, and c, about the axes a, b, and c, is $\frac{1}{5}M(b^2 + c^2)$, $\frac{1}{5}M(c^2 + a^2)$, and $\frac{1}{5}M(a^2 + b^2)$ respectively.

4. Show that if $a > b > c$ are the semiaxes of an ellipsoid of inertia, the semiaxis c is always greater than the perpendicular dropped from the center of the ellipsoid to the straight line that joins the extremities of a and b.

5. The moment of inertia of a right parallelopiped whose edges are $2a$, $2b$, and $2c$ about an axis through its center and parallel to the edges $2a$ is $\frac{1}{3}M(b^2 + c^2)$.

6. Show by differentiation that the moment of inertia about the a-axis of an infinitely thin homogeneous ellipsoidal shell which is bounded by two similar and similarly placed ellipsoids is $\frac{1}{3}M(b^2 + c^2)$.

7. Show that the expressions

$$A + B + C,$$
$$AB + BC + CA - D^2 - E^2 - F^2,$$
$$ABC - 2DEF - AD^2 - BE^2 - CF^2,$$

are always positive, and at any fixed point are independent of the axes of reference.

8. If d is the length of a diameter of an elliptical disk whose semiaxes are a and b, show that the moment of inertia of the disk about this diameter is

$$\frac{M}{4}\frac{a^2b^2}{d^2}.$$

9. If k_1, k_2, and k_3 are the radii of gyration of a body B with respect to the principal planes of the central ellipsoid, and E is a homogeneous ellipsoid of the same mass as B and which, referred to the principal axes of the central ellipsoid is defined by the equation

$$\frac{\xi^2}{k_1^2} + \frac{\eta^2}{k_2^2} + \frac{\zeta^2}{k_3^2} = 5,$$

then the ellipsoid E (Legendre's ellipsoid) and the body B are equimomental; that is, they have the same moments of inertia with respect to any given line or plane.

10. Let a body B be transformed into the body A by the method of reciprocal radii with respect to a point O and a sphere S of radius a (see II, **106**). If r is the distance of a point in B from O, and ρ is the distance of the corresponding point in A from O, then $r\rho = a^2$. If the ratio of the density at the transformed point to the density at the original point is

$$\left(\frac{a}{\rho}\right)^{10}, \quad \left(\frac{a}{\rho}\right)^{8}, \quad \text{or} \quad \left(\frac{a}{\rho}\right)^{6},$$

according as the body B is a volume distribution of matter, a surface distribution, or a line distribution, the moment of inertia of the body B with respect to any line L which passes through O is the same as the moment of inertia of A with respect to the line L, and therefore the two ellipsoids of inertia at O for B and A are identical.

11. Continuing from the preceding problem: let O_1 be any point at a distance r_1 from O, and let O_2 be the corresponding transformed point. Let I_B be the moment of inertia of the body B relative to the point O_1, and I_A be the moment of inertia of the body A relative to the point O_2. Prove that

$$I_A = \left(\frac{a}{r_1}\right)^2 I_B,$$

if the ratio of the density at a point of A to the density at the corresponding point of B is

$$\left(\frac{a}{\rho}\right)^{8}, \quad \left(\frac{a}{\rho}\right)^{6}, \quad \text{or} \quad \left(\frac{a}{\rho}\right)^{4},$$

according as the body B is a volume, a surface, or a line distribution of matter.

12. Show that an edge of a tetrahedron will coincide with a principal axis of inertia at some point if, and only if, it is perpendicular to the opposite edge.

13. In order that there may exist a point at which the ellipsoid of inertia is a sphere, it is necessary that the central ellipsoid of inertia be an oblate spheroid. If this condition is satisfied, there exist two such points, both of which lie on the axis of revolution of the central ellipsoid of inertia.

14. Show that the plane

$$\frac{x}{a} + \frac{y}{b} + \frac{z}{c} = 1$$

is a principal plane at the point where it intersects the straight line

$$ax - A = by - B = cz - C.$$

15. Show that any straight line drawn on a lamina is a principal axis of inertia at some point.

16. A line L is drawn through a fixed point O. The radius of gyration of a given body with respect to L is k. At a distance k from O a plane is drawn perpendicular to L. Show that the envelope of these planes, as L varies in direction, is an ellipsoid.

17. Show that of all homogeneous bodies of a given mass the moment of inertia with respect to a fixed point O is least for a sphere which has O as its center.

18. If r_{ij} is the distance between the particles m_i and m_j, and $\mu_i = m_i/M$, where $M = m_1 + m_2 + \cdots + m_n$, show that the moment of inertia of n particles, distributed in any manner in space, with respect to the center of gravity of the particles can be written

$$I = \tfrac{1}{2}M\sum_{i=1}^{n}\sum_{j=1}^{n}\mu_i\mu_j r_{ij}^2.$$

19. Assuming the earth to be a sphere which is homogeneous in concentric layers, the law of its density as given by Laplace has the form

$$\sigma = \sigma_0 \frac{\sin m\rho}{\rho \sin m},$$

where σ_0 is the surface density, m is a constant which depends upon the earth's mass, and ρ is the relative distance of the point from the earth's center, so that if a is the radius of the earth, and r is the distance from the center

$$\rho = \frac{r}{a}.$$

Show that with this law of density the mass of the earth is

$$M = 4\pi\sigma_0 a^3 \frac{\sin m - m \cos m}{m^2 \sin m},$$

and its moment of inertia with respect to a diameter is

$$\begin{aligned} I &= \frac{8}{3}\pi\sigma_0 a^5 \frac{(3m^2 - 6)\sin m - (m^3 - 6m)\cos m}{m^4 \sin m} \\ &= \frac{2}{3}Ma^2\left[\frac{(3m^2 - 6)\sin m - (m^3 - 6m)\cos m}{m^2(\sin m - m\cos m)}\right]. \end{aligned}$$

Taking the radius of the earth at 3958 miles and the mean density at 5.5 show that

$$m = 141° \; 40.'5 = 2.4727$$

and

$$I = .335Ma^2.$$

20. Given a closed plane area, and a point O in the plane. Show that there exists an inertial ellipse for the plane area at the point O, similar to the ellipsoid of inertia for a volume, and that for properly chosen axes its equation is

$$\frac{x^2}{a^2} + \frac{y^2}{b^2} = \frac{k^6}{Ca^2b^2},$$

where k is a factor of proportionality that has the dimension of a length, C is the area, and b and a are the radii of gyration of the area with respect to the x- and y-axis respectively.

21. The moment of inertia of a homogeneous, solid, right circular cone about a generator of the surface is

$$\frac{3}{20}\frac{r^2 + 6h^2}{r^2 + h^2}Mr^2,$$

where h is the height of the cone and r is the radius of the base.

22. If D has the dimensions of a moment of inertia show that the three principal moments of inertia of any body can be written in the form

$$A = (1 + \eta)D, \qquad B = (1 + \xi\eta)D, \qquad C = (1 - \xi)D,$$

where ξ and η are pure numbers that lie between minus one and plus one.

CHAPTER III

SYSTEMS OF FREE PARTICLES

28. The Equations of Motion.—If $\mathbf{r}$ is the position vector of a free particle of mass m relative to a fixed point O, and if $\mathbf{F}$ is the resultant of all of the forces which are acting upon the particle, then in accordance with Newton's laws of motion,

$$m\mathbf{r}'' = \mathbf{F} \tag{1}$$

is the equation of motion of the particle in vector notation. It is a vector differential equation of the second order. If $\mathbf{i}$, $\mathbf{j}$, and $\mathbf{k}$ are three mutually perpendicular unit vectors, if

$$\left.\begin{aligned} \mathbf{r} &= x\mathbf{i} + y\mathbf{j} + z\mathbf{k}, \\ \mathbf{F} &= X\mathbf{i} + Y\mathbf{j} + Z\mathbf{k}, \end{aligned}\right\} \tag{2}$$

and if equation (1) is resolved into its three components, it yields the three ordinary differential equations,

$$\left.\begin{aligned} mx'' &= X, \\ my'' &= Y, \\ mz'' &= Z, \end{aligned}\right\} \tag{3}$$

which is a system of differential equations of the sixth order. Six integrals are required for a complete solution and therefore six independent constants of integration. These six constants can be regarded as the three coordinates of position and the three components of velocity at the time $t = 0$.

If a system of n free particles is given, a vector differential equation similar to Eq. (1) is required for each particle. If m_j is the mass of the jth particle, $\mathbf{r}_j$ its position vector, and $\mathbf{F}_j$ is the resultant of all of the forces which are acting upon it, these differential equations are

$$m_j\mathbf{r}_j'' = \mathbf{F}_j, \qquad j = 1, \cdots, n, \tag{4}$$

and these n vector differential equations can be transformed into $3n$ ordinary differential equations each of the second order similar to Eqs. (3). The problem is therefore of the order $6n$. If the initial coordinates of position and velocity are given, the subsequent motion is determined by Eqs. (4) for as long a period of time as Eqs. (4) remain valid.

29. The Nature of the Forces.—It will be assumed that the particles of the system attract or repel one another according to some law, and that the mutual action of any two particles is a pair of forces which lies in the line that joins them. In accordance with Newton's third law these two forces are equal and opposite. Forces of this kind will be called *interior forces*. Necessarily, they occur in pairs, the two members of which are collinear, equal in magnitude and oppositely directed.

A second class of forces is represented by the mutual action of the particles of the system under consideration with other particles which are exterior to the system. Forces of this kind will be called *exterior forces*. Exterior forces also occur in pairs, the two members of which are equal and opposite and have the same line of action; but only one of the two members acts upon the given system, the other member acting upon something else which is exterior to the system under consideration. It is this difference which gives rise to the classification of interior and exterior forces.

If $\mathbf{F}_j^{(i)}$ is the resultant of all of the interior forces that are acting upon the particle m_j, $\mathbf{F}_j^{(e)}$ is the resultant of all of the exterior forces that are acting, and $\mathbf{F}_j$ is the resultant of all of the forces of every kind that are acting, then

$$\mathbf{F}_j = \mathbf{F}_j^{(i)} + \mathbf{F}_j^{(e)},$$

and Eqs. (4) become

$$m_j\mathbf{r}_j'' = \mathbf{F}_j^{(i)} + \mathbf{F}_j^{(e)}, \qquad j = 1, \cdots, n. \tag{1}$$

30. The Equation of Motion of the Center of Gravity.—Let

$$M = \Sigma m_j, \qquad \text{and} \qquad M\mathbf{G} = \Sigma m_j\mathbf{r}_j; \tag{1}$$

then M is the total mass of the system and $\mathbf{G}$ is the position vector of the center of gravity of the system. By differentiation, it is seen that

$$M\mathbf{G}' = \Sigma m_j\mathbf{r}_j' \tag{2}$$

is the total momentum of the system. Stated in words this equation says that *the total momentum of the system is the same as the momentum of a particle of mass M that moves in such a way as to be always at the center of gravity.*

If the sum of all of the equations in Eqs. (29.1) is taken, there results

$$\Sigma m_j \mathbf{r}_j'' = \Sigma \mathbf{F}_j^{(i)} + \Sigma \mathbf{F}_j^{(e)}. \tag{3}$$

Since the interior forces occur in pairs, the members of which are equal and opposite, it follows that

$$\Sigma \mathbf{F}_j^{(i)} = 0;$$

and since m_j and M are constant,

$$\Sigma m_j \mathbf{r}_j'' = (\Sigma m_j \mathbf{r}_j')' = (M\mathbf{G}')';$$

so that Eq. (3) reduces to

$$(M\mathbf{G}')' = \Sigma \mathbf{F}_j^{(e)}. \tag{4}$$

This equation can be stated in words as follows: *The time rate of change of the total momentum of the system is equal to the vector sum of all of the exterior forces that are acting on the system.*

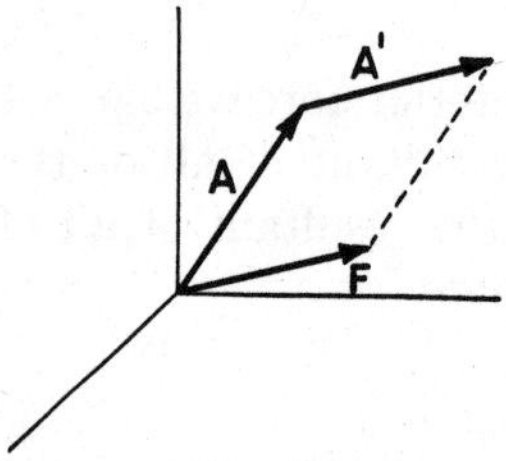

FIG. 13.

This theorem can be represented geometrically as follows: Let **F** be the vector sum of all of the exterior forces, and let **A** be the total momentum of the system; then

$$\mathbf{A} = M\mathbf{G}' \quad \text{and} \quad \mathbf{F} = \Sigma \mathbf{F}_j^{(e)}.$$

Equation (4) now becomes

$$\mathbf{A}' = \mathbf{F}. \tag{5}$$

Since **A**′ represents the velocity of the terminus of the vector **A**, it is seen that the velocity of the terminus of the vector **A** is equal and parallel to the vector **F**, Fig. 13.

If a single particle of mass M were at the center of gravity of the system and had the same velocity at the instant, say $t = 0$, and if forces, which are equal to the exterior forces that are acting upon the individual particles of the system, were acting upon it (that is, upon M) the particle M would move exactly like the center of gravity of the system.

Examples.—Suppose a handful of small pebbles is thrown into the air, that the resistance of the air can be neglected, and that gravity acts upon the pebbles in lines that are parallel. Since the mutual attraction of the pebbles upon one another is negligibly small it can be said that the only forces that are acting are the exterior forces $m_j\mathbf{g}$, where $\mathbf{g}$ is the acceleration of gravity; and since

$$\Sigma \mathbf{F}_j^{(e)} = \Sigma m_j \mathbf{g} = M\mathbf{g},$$

Eq. (4) becomes

$$M\mathbf{G}'' = M\mathbf{g}, \qquad \text{or} \qquad \mathbf{G}'' = \mathbf{g}.$$

The acceleration of the center of gravity is therefore constant, and the center of gravity describes a parabola relative to the surface of the earth, just as a single particle with the same velocity does.

On the other hand, if the moon in its motion around the earth should explode, the exterior forces which would act upon the fragments would be directed towards the center of the earth, and after the fragments had scattered somewhat the vector sum of the forces which were acting upon the fragments would not be the same as they would be if the fragments were united into a single unit, the original moon. Therefore the motion of the center of gravity of the system would be altered by the explosion. The mutual attraction of the fragments, however, would not affect the motion of this common center of gravity.

31. The Motion of the Center of Gravity of an Isolated System.—A system is isolated if there are no exterior forces acting, or if the exterior forces are so small as to be negligible. The sun with its attendant family of planets is such a system for an interval of time which is not too great. In this case the equation of motion of the center of gravity, Eq. (30.4), reduces to

$$M\mathbf{G}'' = 0, \tag{1}$$

an equation which is immediately integrable. The first integral is, after removing the mass factor,

$$\mathbf{G}' = \mathbf{V}, \tag{2}$$

where V is a constant of integration. Hence the velocity of the center of gravity, $\mathbf{G}'$, is constant. The second integral is

$$\mathbf{G} = t\mathbf{V} + \mathbf{G}_0, \tag{3}$$

in which $\mathbf{G}_0$ is the value of $\mathbf{G}$ at the time $t = 0$. This is the vector equation of a straight line, the parameter being t, in this case the time.

Hence the center of gravity of an isolated system moves on a straight line with constant speed. It will be observed therefore that Newton's first law of motion can be extended to the motion of the center of gravity of any isolated system.

The resultant attraction of all of the stars upon the solar system must be very small. Relative to the stars in its neighborhood the sun is moving in the general direction of the bright star Vega with a speed of about 12 miles per second. Millions of years must elapse before either its direction or its speed is sensibly altered by the attraction of other stars. It is only for such intervals of time that the system can be regarded as isolated, but in hundreds of millions of years its direction, and probably its speed also, will undergo sensible changes. In the strict sense of the term there are probably no isolated systems in existence.

32. The Moment of Momentum of a Free System.—The equations of motion of any system of free particles are Eqs. (29.1),

$$m_j\mathbf{r}_j'' = \mathbf{F}_j^{(i)} + \mathbf{F}_j^{(e)}, \qquad j = 1, \cdots, n. \tag{1}$$

Let the jth equation of this system be multiplied by $\mathbf{r}_j\times$ and then summed as to j. There results the single equation

$$\sum_j m_j(\mathbf{r}_j \times \mathbf{r}_j'') = \sum_j(\mathbf{r}_j \times \mathbf{F}_j^{(i)}) + \sum_j(\mathbf{r}_j \times \mathbf{F}_j^{(e)}). \tag{2}$$

The resultant force $\mathbf{F}_j^{(i)}$ which is acting upon the jth particle is the vector sum of the interior forces which are acting upon it. If $\mathbf{f}_{jk}$ is the force acting upon the jth particle which is due to the kth particle, then

$$\mathbf{F}_j^{(i)} = \sum_k \mathbf{f}_{jk}, \qquad k \neq j$$

and

$$\mathbf{r}_j \times \mathbf{F}_j^{(i)} = \sum_k \mathbf{r}_j \times \mathbf{f}_{jk},$$

is the moment of $\mathbf{F}_j^{(i)}$ with respect to the origin. Let $\mathbf{f}_{kj}$ be the action of the jth body on the kth body, then by Newton's third law

$$\mathbf{f}_{jk} = -\mathbf{f}_{kj},$$

and the two forces lie in the same straight line. Consequently

$$(\mathbf{r}_j \times \mathbf{f}_{jk}) = -(\mathbf{r}_k \times \mathbf{f}_{kj}),$$

or

$$(\mathbf{r}_j \times \mathbf{f}_{jk}) + (\mathbf{r}_k \times \mathbf{f}_{kj}) = 0.$$

That is the sum of the moments of these two equal and opposite forces which lie in the same straight line with respect to the origin is zero. Indeed, it is zero with respect to any point whatever. Therefore

$$\sum_j (\mathbf{r}_j \times \mathbf{F}_j^{(i)}) = \sum_j \sum_k (\mathbf{r}_j \times \mathbf{f}_{jk}),$$

which is merely the sum of the moments of all such pairs of forces with respect to the origin, is necessarily zero.

Since

$$\sum_j (\mathbf{r}_j \times \mathbf{F}_j^{(i)}) = 0,$$

Eq. (2) reduces to

$$\sum_j m_j(\mathbf{r}_j \times \mathbf{r}_j'') = \sum (\mathbf{r}_j \times \mathbf{F}_j^{(e)}), \tag{3}$$

the right member of which is the sum of the moments of all the exterior forces which are acting upon the system with respect to the origin. The left member can be written

$$\sum m_j(\mathbf{r}_j \times \mathbf{r}_j'') = \sum_j m_j[(\mathbf{r}_j \times \mathbf{r}_j'') + (\mathbf{r}_j' \times \mathbf{r}_j')] = \sum_j m_j(\mathbf{r}_j \times \mathbf{r}_j')',$$

since

$$\mathbf{r}_j' \times \mathbf{r}_j' \equiv 0.$$

Consequently Eq. (3) can be written

$$\frac{d}{dt}\sum_j m_j(\mathbf{r}_j \times \mathbf{r}_j') = \sum_j m_j(\mathbf{r}_j \times \mathbf{r}_j')' = \sum_j (\mathbf{r}_j \times \mathbf{F}_j^{(e)}).$$

Finally, since

$$\sum_j m_j(\mathbf{r}_j \times \mathbf{r}_j')$$

is the moment of momentum of the system with respect to the origin, Eq. (4) can be stated in words as follows:

The time rate of change of the total moment of momentum (or angular momentum) of any system of free particles with respect to any point O of fixed space is equal to the sum of the moments with respect to O, of the exterior forces which are acting upon the system.

This theorem, like the theorem on momentum, Sec. 30, can be represented geometrically as follows:

Let $\mathbf{L}$ be the total moment of momentum of the system, and let $\mathbf{N}$ be the sum of the moments of the forces; then

$$\mathbf{L} = \Sigma m_j(\mathbf{r}_j \times \mathbf{r}_j') \qquad \text{and} \qquad \mathbf{N} = \Sigma(\mathbf{r}_j \times \mathbf{F}_j^{(e)}).$$

Equation (3) now becomes

$$\mathbf{L}' = \mathbf{N}, \tag{5}$$

that is, the velocity of the terminus of the vector $\mathbf{L}$ is equal and parallel to $\mathbf{N}$, Fig. 14.

In this theorem the moment of momentum and the moment of the forces are taken with respect to any point in fixed space. But since, I, **134**, the moment of a vector with respect to any axis which passes through a given point is equal to the projection upon that axis of the moment with respect to the given point, it follows that:

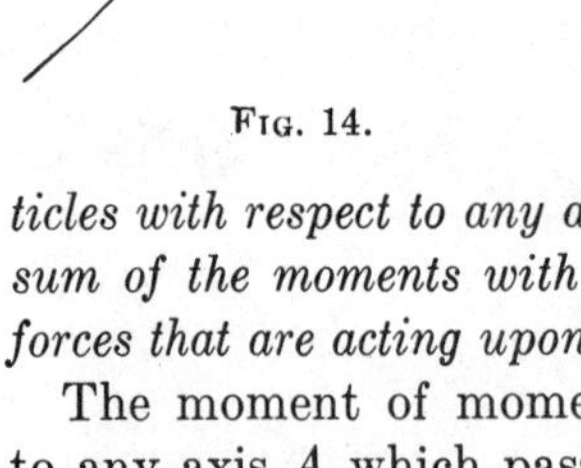

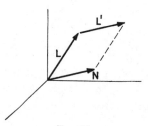

FIG. 14.

The time rate of change of the total moment of momentum (or angular momentum) of any system of free particles with respect to any axis which is fixed in space is equal to the sum of the moments with respect to that axis of all of the exterior forces that are acting upon the system.

The moment of momentum $\mathbf{M}_A$ of the system with respect to any axis A which passes through the origin and for which $\mathbf{a}$ is a unit vector is

$$\mathbf{M}_A = \mathbf{a} \cdot \Sigma m_j(\mathbf{r}_j \times \mathbf{r}_j')\ \mathbf{a} = \Sigma m_j[\mathbf{a}\mathbf{r}_j\mathbf{r}_j']\ \mathbf{a}.$$

If there are no exterior forces acting, the moment of the exterior forces is zero and the moment of momentum with respect to any fixed axis is constant. Even though the exterior forces are not all zero, there may exist fixed axes with respect to which the sum of the moments of the exterior forces is always zero. In this event the moment of momentum of the system with respect to such axes is constant. For example, if the system of exterior forces is a system of forces parallel to a given axis fixed in space then the sum of the moments of the forces with respect to such an axis is zero, for the moment of each force separately is zero.

33. Extension of the Theorem on Moment of Momentum.— The preceding theorem, which relates to an axis fixed in space, can be extended to an axis which passes through the center of gravity of the system, and therefore moving with it, but fixed as to direction, as follows:

Let $\mathbf{G}$ be the position vector of the center of gravity with respect to a point O of fixed space, and let $\boldsymbol{\rho}_j$ be the position vector of the particle m_j with respect to the center of gravity, so that

$$\Sigma m_j\boldsymbol{\rho}_j = 0, \qquad \Sigma m_j\boldsymbol{\rho}_j' = 0. \tag{1}$$

Then

$$\begin{aligned} \mathbf{r}_j &= \mathbf{G} + \boldsymbol{\rho}_j, \\ \mathbf{r}_j' &= \mathbf{G}' + \boldsymbol{\rho}_j'; \end{aligned}$$

and

$$\mathbf{r}_j \times \mathbf{r}_j' = \mathbf{G} \times \mathbf{G}' + \boldsymbol{\rho}_j \times \mathbf{G}' + \mathbf{G} \times \boldsymbol{\rho}_j' + \boldsymbol{\rho}_j \times \boldsymbol{\rho}_j'.$$

With this change of variables Eq. (32.4) becomes

$$\begin{aligned} \Sigma m_j(\mathbf{G} \times \mathbf{G}')' + \Sigma m_j(\boldsymbol{\rho}_j \times \mathbf{G}')' + \Sigma m_j(\mathbf{G} \times \boldsymbol{\rho}_j')' + \\ \Sigma m_j(\boldsymbol{\rho}_j \times \boldsymbol{\rho}_j')' = \Sigma(\mathbf{G} \times \mathbf{F}_j^{(e)}) + \Sigma(\boldsymbol{\rho}_j \times \mathbf{F}_j^{(e)}). \end{aligned} \tag{2}$$

But

$$\begin{aligned} \Sigma m_j(\mathbf{G} \times \mathbf{G}')' &= M(\mathbf{G} \times \mathbf{G}')' = M(\mathbf{G} \times \mathbf{G}''), \\ \Sigma m_j(\boldsymbol{\rho}_j \times \mathbf{G}') &= (\Sigma m_j\boldsymbol{\rho}_j) \times \mathbf{G}' \equiv 0, \qquad \text{by Eq. (1)}, \\ \Sigma m_j(\mathbf{G} \times \boldsymbol{\rho}_j') &= \mathbf{G} \times \Sigma m\boldsymbol{\rho}_j' \equiv 0, \qquad \text{by Eq. (1)}. \end{aligned}$$

Hence Eq. (2) reduces to

$$\begin{aligned} M(\mathbf{G} \times \mathbf{G}'') + \Sigma m_j(\boldsymbol{\rho}_j \times \boldsymbol{\rho}_j')' = \Sigma(\mathbf{G} \times \mathbf{F}_j^{(e)}) + \\ \Sigma(\boldsymbol{\rho}_j \times \mathbf{F}_j^{(e)}). \end{aligned} \tag{3}$$

From Eq. (30.4),

$$MG'' = \Sigma \mathbf{F}_j^{(e)},$$

and therefore

$$M(\mathbf{G} \times \mathbf{G}'') = \Sigma(\mathbf{G} \times \mathbf{F}_j^{(e)}). \tag{4}$$

On subtracting Eq. (4) from Eq. (3), there remains

$$\Sigma m_j(\boldsymbol{\rho}_j \times \boldsymbol{\rho}_j')' = \Sigma(\boldsymbol{\rho}_j \times \mathbf{F}_j^{(e)}), \tag{5}$$

which is the same in form as Eq. (32.4). The origin of the vectors $\boldsymbol{\rho}_j$, however, is the center of gravity of the system instead of a point in fixed space. The desired theorem follows at once, namely:

The time rate of change of the moment of momentum of the system with respect to any axis which passes through the center of gravity (and therefore moves with the system) and is fixed in direction is equal to the moment of the exterior forces with respect to that axis.

If the system is an isolated one the moment of momentum with respect to any axis which passes through the center of gravity is constant. In this case the plane which passes through the center of gravity and is perpendicular to the vector which represents the total moment of momentum is called the invariable plane.

Since the moment of momentum with respect to any axis is the projection of the total moment of momentum on that axis it follows that the tensor of the total moment of momentum is the maximum for all axes.

34. The Energy of the System.—The equations of motion of the system, Eqs. (29.1), are

$$m_j\mathbf{r}_j'' = \mathbf{F}_j^{(i)} + \mathbf{F}_j^{(e)}, \qquad j = 1, \cdots, n.$$

If the jth equation of this system of equations is multiplied by $\mathbf{r}_j'\cdot$, and then summed as to j, there results

$$\Sigma m_j\mathbf{r}_j'\cdot \mathbf{r}_j'' = \Sigma(\mathbf{r}_j'\cdot \mathbf{F}_j^{(i)} + \mathbf{r}_j'\cdot \mathbf{F}_j^{(e)}). \tag{1}$$

Since

$$\mathbf{r}_j'\cdot \mathbf{r}_j'' = \tfrac{1}{2}(\mathbf{r}_j'\cdot \mathbf{r}_j')',$$

it is seen that, if Eq. (1) is multiplied by dt and then integrated from t_0 to t,

$$\tfrac{1}{2}\Sigma m_j\mathbf{r}_j'\cdot \mathbf{r}_j' - \tfrac{1}{2}(\Sigma m_j\mathbf{r}_j'\cdot \mathbf{r}_j')_0 = \int \Sigma(\mathbf{F}_j^{(i)}\cdot d\mathbf{r}_j + \mathbf{F}_j^{(e)}\cdot d\mathbf{r}_j). \tag{2}$$

But

$$m_j \mathbf{r}_j' \cdot \mathbf{r}_j' = m_j v_j^2,$$

where v_j is the speed of the particle m_j. Hence the left side of Eq. (2) is the change in kinetic energy of the system in the interval of time specified.

The right member of Eq. (2) cannot be integrated formally without further information, but since $\mathbf{F}_j^{(i)}$ and $\mathbf{F}_j^{(e)}$ are forces and $d\mathbf{r}_j$ is the displacement of the jth particle, it is readily seen that right member represents the total amount of work done on the system by both the internal and the external forces. If the kinetic energy of the system is denoted by T, so that

$$T = \Sigma \tfrac{1}{2} m_j v_j^2 = \Sigma \tfrac{1}{2} m_j \mathbf{r}_j' \cdot \mathbf{r}_j',$$

and if $W^{(i)}$ is the total work done by the interior forces, and $W^{(e)}$ is the total work done by the exterior forces, Eq. (2) can be written

$$T - T_0 = W^{(i)} + W^{(e)};$$

or, expressed in words, *the change in the kinetic energy of the system in any interval of time is equal to the total work done on the system by both the interior and the exterior forces during that interval of time.*

The change in the momentum and in the moment of momentum of the system due to a pair of equal but oppositely directed interior forces is zero; but the work done by such a pair of forces would vanish only if the components of the displacements of the two particles, on which the forces were acting, in the line of the forces were the same in both magnitude and direction. Since, in general, this is not the case, the work done by the interior forces does not vanish in general.

35. Interior and Exterior Kinetic Energy.—The position vectors $\mathbf{r}_j$ of the particles are referred to a point O of fixed space. Let $\mathbf{G}$ be the position vector of the center of gravity of the system, and $\boldsymbol{\varrho}_j$ the position vectors of the particles referred to the center of gravity. Then

$$\mathbf{r}_j = \mathbf{G} + \boldsymbol{\varrho}_j, \qquad \mathbf{r}_j' = \mathbf{G}' + \boldsymbol{\varrho}_j',$$

and

$$\Sigma m_j \boldsymbol{\varrho}_j = 0, \qquad \Sigma m_j \boldsymbol{\varrho}_j' = 0.$$

Since

$$\mathbf{r}_j' \cdot \mathbf{r}_j' = \mathbf{G}' \cdot \mathbf{G}' + 2\mathbf{G}' \cdot \boldsymbol{\varrho}_j' + \boldsymbol{\varrho}_j' \cdot \boldsymbol{\varrho}_j',$$

and

$$\Sigma m_j \mathbf{G}' \cdot \boldsymbol{\varrho}_j' = \mathbf{G}' \cdot \Sigma m_j \boldsymbol{\varrho}_j' = 0,$$

it is easily seen that

$$\tfrac{1}{2}\Sigma m_j \mathbf{r}_j' \cdot \mathbf{r}_j' = \tfrac{1}{2}M\mathbf{G}' \cdot \mathbf{G}' + \tfrac{1}{2}\Sigma m_j \boldsymbol{\varrho}_j' \cdot \boldsymbol{\varrho}_j', \tag{1}$$

where $M = \Sigma m_j$ is the total mass of the system. The expression

$$\tfrac{1}{2}\Sigma m_j \boldsymbol{\varrho}_j' \cdot \boldsymbol{\varrho}_j'$$

is the kinetic energy of the system relative to the center of gravity, and, for the sake of a name, may be called the *interior kinetic energy*. The expression

$$\tfrac{1}{2}M\mathbf{G}' \cdot \mathbf{G}'$$

is the kinetic energy which the system would have, relative to fixed space, if it were a particle of mass M moving like the center of gravity, and may be called the *exterior kinetic energy*. Hence the total kinetic energy of the system relative to fixed space is the sum of the exterior and the interior kinetic energies.

It is seen from Sec. 31 that a change in the exterior kinetic energy is due to the exterior forces. Indeed, [Eq. (30.4)],

$$M\mathbf{G}'' = \Sigma \mathbf{F}_j^{(e)};$$

therefore

$$M\mathbf{G}' \cdot \mathbf{G}'' = \Sigma \mathbf{F}_j^{(e)} \cdot \mathbf{G}',$$

and on integrating,

$$\tfrac{1}{2}M\mathbf{G}' \cdot \mathbf{G}' - \tfrac{1}{2}M(\mathbf{G}' \cdot \mathbf{G}')_0 = \int \Sigma \mathbf{F}_j^{(e)} \cdot d\mathbf{G}. \tag{2}$$

That is, *the change in the exterior kinetic energy in any interval of time is equal to the work done on the system by the exterior forces in the displacement of the center of gravity that actually occurs.*

This does not, however, represent the total work done on the system by the exterior forces; for the total work done by all of the forces is, Eq. (34.2),

$$\int \Sigma(\mathbf{F}_j^{(i)} + \mathbf{F}_j^{(e)}) \cdot (d\mathbf{G} + d\boldsymbol{\varrho}_j) = \int \Sigma \mathbf{F}_j^{(i)} \cdot d\mathbf{G} + \int \Sigma \mathbf{F}_j^{(e)} \cdot d\mathbf{G} + \int \Sigma(\mathbf{F}_j^{(i)} + \mathbf{F}_j^{(e)}) \cdot d\boldsymbol{\varrho}_j.$$

The first of these integrals

$$\int \Sigma \mathbf{F}_j^{(i)} \cdot d\mathbf{G} = \int d\mathbf{G} \cdot \Sigma \mathbf{F}_j^{(i)}$$

vanishes, since the sum of the interior forces vanishes. Hence the interior forces have no effect upon the exterior kinetic energy. It is the second integral that affects the exterior kinetic energy, as is indicated in Eq. (2).

The third and fourth integrals

$$\int \Sigma (\mathbf{F}_j^{(i)} + \mathbf{F}_j^{(e)}) \cdot d\boldsymbol{\rho}_j$$

measure the change in the interior kinetic energy due to the interior and the exterior forces. The interior work done by the exterior forces is

$$\int \Sigma \mathbf{F}_j^{(e)} \cdot d\boldsymbol{\rho}_j.$$

This does not vanish in general, but it may do so; for example, if

$$\mathbf{F}_j^{(e)} = m_j \mathbf{F}$$

where $\mathbf{F}$ is independent of the letter j, the expression

$$\int \Sigma \mathbf{F}_j^{(e)} \cdot d\boldsymbol{\rho}_j \qquad \text{becomes} \qquad \int \mathbf{F} \cdot \Sigma m_j \, d\boldsymbol{\rho}_j,$$

which vanishes, since

$$\Sigma m_j \, d\boldsymbol{\rho}_j = 0.$$

The exterior forces that are acting upon the solar system are of this type, in so far as they are due to the attraction of the stars, on account of the remoteness of the stars; but if in the course of time the solar system should pass close by some star, then the exterior forces acting on the various members of the solar family, due to the attraction of this star, would not be parallel, and the internal energy of the solar system would be altered.

36. There Exists a Potential Function.—If a single particle is moving in a field of force for which there exists a potential function $U(x, y, z)$, the force acting upon the particle, by Eq. (11.6), is

$$\nabla U = \frac{\partial U}{\partial x}\mathbf{i} + \frac{\partial U}{\partial y}\mathbf{j} + \frac{\partial U}{\partial z}\mathbf{k},$$

and therefore the equation of motion of the particle is [Eq. (13.8)]

$$m\mathbf{r}'' = \nabla U.$$

For a system of many particles, m_s, an operator ∇_s can be defined, namely,

$$\nabla_s U = \frac{\partial U}{\partial x_s}\mathbf{i} + \frac{\partial U}{\partial y_s}\mathbf{j} + \frac{\partial U}{\partial z_s}\mathbf{k},$$

and the equations of motion are

$$m_s\mathbf{r}_s'' = \nabla_s U, \qquad s = 1, \cdots, n, \tag{1}$$

provided, of course, a potential function $U(x_s, y_s, z_s)$ exists.

Let Eq. (1) be multiplied by $\mathbf{r}_s' \cdot$, and the n equations so derived be added. It is found then that

$$\Sigma m_s\mathbf{r}_s' \cdot \mathbf{r}_s'' = \Sigma \mathbf{r}_s' \cdot \nabla_s U.$$

On multiplying this equation by dt and integrating, it is found that

$$\tfrac{1}{2}\Sigma m_s\mathbf{r}_s' \cdot \mathbf{r}_s' = \int \Sigma\, d\mathbf{r}_s \cdot \nabla_s U. \tag{2}$$

The left member, evidently, is the kinetic energy T. The right member can be written

$$\begin{aligned}\int \sum (dx_s\mathbf{i} + dy_s\mathbf{j} + dz_s\mathbf{k}) \cdot \left(\frac{\partial U}{\partial x_s}\mathbf{i} + \frac{\partial U}{\partial y_s}\mathbf{j} + \frac{\partial U}{\partial z_s}\mathbf{k}\right) \\ = \int \sum \left(\frac{\partial U}{\partial x_s}\,dx_s + \frac{\partial U}{\partial y_s}\,dy_s + \frac{\partial U}{\partial z_s}\,dz_s\right) \\ = \int dU = U + E,\end{aligned}$$

where E is a constant. Thus Eq. (2) becomes

$$T - U = E, \tag{3}$$

in which T is the kinetic energy, $-U$ is the potential energy, and E, the total energy, is a constant. Consequently, if there exists a potential function which depends only upon the positions of the particles, and not at all upon their velocities, or the time, the sum of the kinetic and potential energies is constant.

37. The Problem of N Bodies.—In the problem of n bodies it is assumed that the exterior forces are zero and that gravitation is the only interior force. The positions and the velocities of the bodies at some specified instant are supposed to be given, but they may be anything whatever. It is required to find the positions and velocities of the n bodies at any time whatever in the future. It is assumed further that in their mutual attractions they act like particles, and are therefore centrobaric (II, **110**). The most important class of centrobaric bodies, undoubtedly, are spheres which are homogeneous in concentric layers.

Since gravitation is a conservative force, there exists a potential function (II, **76**), namely,

$$U = \frac{k^2}{2}\sum_{v=1}^{n}\sum_{u=1}^{n}\frac{m_v m_u}{r_{uv}}, \qquad u \neq v, \tag{1}$$

where k^2 is the gravitational constant, m_u is the mass of the uth body, and

$$r_{uv} = r_{vu} = \sqrt{(x_u - x_v)^2 + (y_u - y_v)^2 + (z_u - z_v)^2}$$

is the distance between the centers of gravity of the two bodies m_u and m_v. In its expanded form

$$U = \frac{k^2}{2}\left\{\begin{array}{l} 0 + \frac{m_1m_2}{r_{12}} + \frac{m_1m_3}{r_{13}} + \cdots + \frac{m_1m_n}{r_{1n}} \\ + \frac{m_2m_1}{r_{21}} + 0 + \frac{m_2m_3}{r_{23}} + \cdots + \frac{m_2m_n}{r_{2n}} \\ + \frac{m_3m_1}{r_{31}} + \frac{m_3m_2}{r_{32}} + 0 + \cdots + \frac{m_3m_n}{r_{3n}} \\ + \cdots\cdots\cdots\cdots\cdots\cdots \\ + \frac{m_nm_1}{r_{n1}} + \frac{m_nm_2}{r_{n2}} + \frac{m_nm_3}{r_{n3}} + \cdots + 0, \end{array}\right\} \tag{2}$$

the duplication of terms accounting for the factor $\frac{1}{2}$.

The equations of motion are

$$m_s\mathbf{r}_s'' = \nabla_s U, \qquad s = 1, \cdots, n, \tag{3}$$

which resolved into their three rectangular components give rise to $3n$ differential equations, each of the second order. The entire problem therefore, from the point of view of differential equations, is of order $6n$.

On carrying out the operation $\nabla_s U$ in accordance with its definition in Sec. 36, it is seen that

$$\left.\begin{aligned}\nabla_s U &= -k^2 \sum_{\substack{t=1\\t\neq s.}}^{n} \frac{m_s m_t}{r_{st}^3}[(x_s - x_t)\mathbf{i} + (y_s - y_t)\mathbf{j} + (z_s - z_t)\mathbf{k}]\\ &= +k^2 \sum_{t=1}^{n} \frac{m_s m_t}{r_{st}^3}\mathbf{r}_{st} = k^2 \sum \frac{m_s m_t}{r_{st}^3}(\mathbf{r}_t - \mathbf{r}_s),\end{aligned}\right\} \quad (4)$$

where $\mathbf{r}_{st}$ is a vector with its origin at m_s and its terminus at m_t, so that

$$\mathbf{r}_{st} = \mathbf{r}_t - \mathbf{r}_s.$$

Hence the equations of motion can also be written

$$m_s \mathbf{r}_s'' = k^2 \sum_{\substack{t=1\\t\neq s.}}^{n} \frac{m_s m_t}{r_{st}^3}\mathbf{r}_{st} = k^2 \sum \frac{m_s m_t}{r_{st}^3}(\mathbf{r}_t - \mathbf{r}_s). \quad (5)$$

Since the only forces acting are the interior forces, and these are collinear in pairs, the members of which are equal and oppositely directed, the six integrals of the center of gravity (Sec. 31) and the three integrals of moment of momentum (Sec. 32) are immediately applicable. Therefore:

The center of gravity of the system moves uniformly in a straight line, and

The total moment of momentum of the system is constant; that is, the vector which represents the moment of momentum is fixed in magnitude and in direction.

Finally, since the potential function exists (Sec. 36), *the sum of the potential and kinetic energies of the system is constant.*

Thus ten of the $6n$ integrals which are necessary for a complete solution are known, and they are all algebraic when expressed in rectangular coordinates. In *Acta Mathematica* (1887) Vol. 11, there is a proof, given by Bruns, that no more such algebraic integrals exist. In Vol. 13 of the same journal a proof is given by Poincaré that, if $n > 2$, there do not exist any uniform transcendental integrals for values of the masses sufficiently small other than the above ten integrals, which are frequently called the ten classical integrals.

38. Permanent Configurations in the Problem of Two Bodies. On removing the mass factor m_s, Eq. (37.5) becomes

$$\mathbf{r}_s'' = k^2 \sum_{t=1}^{n} \frac{m_t}{r_{st}^3}\mathbf{r}_{st} \qquad t \neq s, \qquad s = 1, \cdots, n; \tag{1}$$

and if the origin of the vectors is at the center of gravity of the system, there exists also the relation,

$$\Sigma m_s \mathbf{r}_s = 0. \tag{2}$$

By a permanent configuration is meant a configuration in which the ratios of the distances between the bodies remain constant throughout the motion. In the problem of two bodies, the two masses always lie on a straight line, and the ratio of the distances from the center of gravity is

$$\frac{r_1}{r_2} = \frac{m_2}{m_1}$$

irrespective of the type of the orbit described. As this ratio is constant, the straight-line configuration of the two bodies is a permanent one, although the distance between the two bodies themselves may be constantly changing.

For the two-body problem the equations of motion are, from Eq. (1),

$$\mathbf{r}_1'' = \frac{k^2 m_2}{r_{12}^3}\mathbf{r}_{12}, \qquad \mathbf{r}_2'' = \frac{k^2 m_1}{r_{12}^3}\mathbf{r}_{21}, \tag{3}$$

and, if the motion is referred to the center of gravity,

$$m_1\mathbf{r}_1 + m_2\mathbf{r}_2 = 0.$$

Let M be the sum of the two masses, then since

$$\mathbf{r}_{12} = \mathbf{r}_2 - \mathbf{r}_1, \qquad \mathbf{r}_{21} = \mathbf{r}_1 - \mathbf{r}_2,$$

$$M\mathbf{r}_1 = m_2(\mathbf{r}_1 - \mathbf{r}_2) = -m_2\mathbf{r}_{12},$$

and

$$M\mathbf{r}_2 = m_1(\mathbf{r}_2 - \mathbf{r}_1) = -m_1\mathbf{r}_{21},$$

Eqs. (3) can also be written

$$\mathbf{r}_1'' = -\frac{k^2 M}{r_{12}^3}\mathbf{r}_1, \qquad \mathbf{r}_2'' = -\frac{k^2 M}{r_{12}^3}\mathbf{r}_2. \tag{4}$$

Thus the two vectors $\mathbf{r}_1$ and $\mathbf{r}_2$ satisfy the same differential equation, in which

$$r_{12} = r_1 + r_2.$$

The solutions of Eqs. (4), of course, are Keplerian conics. Let a_1 and a_2 be the major semiaxes of the conics which are described by m_1 and m_2 relative to their common center of gravity, and let a_{12} be the major semiaxis of the conic which m_2 describes relative to m_1. Then

$$a_{12} = a_1 + a_2,$$

and

$$\frac{a_{12}}{r_{12}} = \frac{a_1}{r_1} = \frac{a_2}{r_2} \tag{5}$$

for all values of the time. Again, let

$$k^2M = \omega^2 a_{12}^3,$$

then Eqs. (4) become

$$\mathbf{r}_1'' = -\omega^2\left(\frac{a_{12}}{r_{12}}\right)^3 \mathbf{r}_1, \qquad \mathbf{r}_2'' = -\omega^2\left(\frac{a_{12}}{r_{12}}\right)^3 \mathbf{r}_2,$$

and, by virtue of Eqs. (5), they can also be written,

$$\mathbf{r}_1'' = -\omega^2\left(\frac{a_1}{r_1}\right)^3 \mathbf{r}_1, \qquad \mathbf{r}_2'' = -\omega^2\left(\frac{a_2}{r_2}\right)^3 \mathbf{r}_2. \tag{6}$$

If the motion is circular, so that $r_1 = a_1$ and $r_2 = a_2$, Eqs. (6) become the equation of simple harmonic motion with the period

$$P = \frac{2\pi}{\omega} = \frac{2\pi a_{12}^{\frac{3}{2}}}{k\sqrt{M}}; \tag{7}$$

and since the period of Keplerian motion is independent of the eccentricity (I, **309**), Eq. (7) is the general expression for the period.

39. Permanent Configurations in the Problem of N Bodies.—The equations of motion of the n-body problem are, Eqs. (38.1),

$$\mathbf{r}_s'' = k^2 \sum_{\substack{t=1 \\ t\neq s}}^{n} \frac{m_t}{r_{st}^3}\mathbf{r}_{st}, \qquad s = 1, \cdots, n; \tag{1}$$

and, if the origin is at the center of gravity, as will be assumed,

$$m_1\mathbf{r}_1 + m_2\mathbf{r}_2 + \cdots + m_n\mathbf{r}_n = 0.$$

Suppose there exists a configuration of the n bodies such that

$$k^2 \sum \frac{m_t}{r_{st}^3}\mathbf{r}_{st} = -\omega^2\left(\frac{a_s}{r_s}\right)^3 \mathbf{r}_s, \qquad s = 1, \cdots, n, \tag{2}$$

where the a's are constants which can be regarded as the values of r's at some instant, and such that

$$\frac{a_{st}}{r_{st}} = \frac{a_1}{r_1} = \frac{a_2}{r_2} = \cdots = \frac{a_n}{r_n} = \frac{1}{\rho} \tag{3}$$

at every instant, that is, the ratios of the mutual distances are constants. Equations (1) then become

$$\mathbf{r}_s'' = -\omega^2\left(\frac{a_s}{r_s}\right)^3 \mathbf{r}_s, \qquad s = 1, \cdots, n, \tag{4}$$

which are satisfied by Keplerian motion in conics for which the major semiaxes are a_s [Eqs. (38.6)], with the common period

$$P = \frac{2\pi}{\omega}.$$

Suppose

$$\mathbf{r}_s = \mathbf{a}_s, \qquad \mathbf{r}_{st} = \mathbf{a}_{st}, \qquad s, t = 1, \cdots, n, \tag{5}$$

for which the tensors a_s and a_{st} are constants, is a solution of Eqs. (2), then whatever positive value ρ may have

$$\mathbf{r}_s = \rho\mathbf{a}_s, \qquad \mathbf{r}_{st} = \rho\mathbf{a}_{st} \tag{6}$$

also are solutions, since Eqs. (2) are homogeneous in the r's. This is equivalent to saying that the validity of Eqs. (2) does not depend upon the size of the configuration, and evidently it does not depend upon its orientation. It depends only on the nature of the configuration.

If the tensors of the vectors $\mathbf{r}_s$ and $\mathbf{r}_{st}$ are constant, Eqs. (5), the configuration is a rigid one, and the motion of each body is a circle with its center at the center of mass of the system. Equations (4) become simply

$$\mathbf{r}_s'' = -\omega^2\mathbf{r}_s,$$

and the period of the motion is

$$P = \frac{2\pi}{\omega}.$$

Since the accelerations are always directed toward the center of mass and the ratios of the mutual distances are constants, the n bodies must lie in the same plane.

If the tensors of the vectors $\mathbf{r}_s$ and $\mathbf{r}_{st}$ are not constants, the general solutions of Eqs. (4) are conics, Eq. (38.6), and by I, **294,**

$$r_s = a_s(1 - e_s \cos E_s),$$

if the orbits are ellipses, where e_s is the eccentricity and E_s is the eccentric anomaly (I, **297**) of the ellipse associated with the subscript s. Equations (3) then require that

$$1 - e_1 \cos E_1 = 1 - e_2 \cos E_2 = \cdots = 1 - e_n \cos E_n,$$

or

$$e_1 = e_2 = \cdots = e_n,$$
$$E_1 = E_2 = \cdots = E_n.$$

That is, the various conics described by the n bodies are all similar, and their positions in the conics all have the same eccentric angle, which is the same as saying that the bodies occupy corresponding positions in their orbits at any given instant. Evidently the ellipses must all lie in the same plane.

If the configuration which satisfies Eqs. (2) is a space configuration, as, for example, any four masses at the vertices of a regular tetrahedron, Eqs. (3) can be satisfied only if the motion is along straight lines through the center of mass. In this case the differential equations (4) become algebraic, and can be written

$$\left(\frac{r_s}{a_s}\right)'' = -\omega^2\left(\frac{a_s}{r_s}\right)^2,$$

which, on integrating, becomes

$$\left(\frac{r_s}{a_s}\right)'^2 = \omega^2\left(\frac{2a_s}{r_s} + c\right).$$

If the constant of integration, c, is the same for every s, it is readily seen that

$$\frac{r_s}{a_s} = \varphi(t, c),$$

where $\varphi(t, c)$ is a function of the time which is independent of the subscript s, and therefore Eqs. (3) are satisfied. That is, the configuration is preserved. If the motion is toward the center of mass, the n bodies arrive at that point at the same instant, and the configuration is permanent only in the sense that it lasts as long as the differential equations are valid. But if the motion is away from the center of mass and the constant c is positive, the configuration is permanent in a real sense; it is merely expanding, and this it can do without limit.

40. The Permanent Configurations of Three Bodies.—It remains to be shown that there exist configurations for which Eqs. (39.2) are satisfied, and this is essentially a matter of geometry. The first solutions of this kind, the equilateral triangle and the straight-line configurations of the problem of three bodies, were given by Lagrange[1] in his widely known memoir on the problem of three bodies. They were the only rigorous solutions of the problem that were known until the method of periodic solutions was developed by Poincaré.[2]

Written out in full, Eqs. (39.2) for three bodies are (on taking $k^2 = 1$)

$$\left.\begin{aligned}
\frac{m_2}{r_{12}^3}\mathbf{r}_{12} - \frac{m_3}{r_{31}^3}\mathbf{r}_{31} &= -\omega^2\mathbf{r}_1, \\
\frac{m_3}{r_{23}^3}\mathbf{r}_{23} - \frac{m_1}{r_{12}^3}\mathbf{r}_{12} &= -\omega^2\mathbf{r}_2, \\
\frac{m_1}{r_{31}^3}\mathbf{r}_{31} - \frac{m_2}{r_{23}^3}\mathbf{r}_{23} &= -\omega^2\mathbf{r}_3,
\end{aligned}\right\} \qquad (1)$$

to which must be added

$$m_1\mathbf{r}_1 + m_2\mathbf{r}_2 + m_3\mathbf{r}_3 = 0,$$

[1] LAGRANGE, "Collected Works," Vol. VI, p. 229 (1772).

[2] POINCARÉ, H., "Méthodes Nouvelles de la Mécanique Céleste," 3 Vols. (1892).

which expresses the fact that the center of mass is at the origin. Since

$$\begin{aligned} \mathbf{r}_{12} &= \mathbf{r}_2 - \mathbf{r}_1, \\ \mathbf{r}_{23} &= \mathbf{r}_3 - \mathbf{r}_2, \\ \mathbf{r}_{31} &= \mathbf{r}_1 - \mathbf{r}_3, \end{aligned}$$

all of these vectors can be expressed in terms of $\mathbf{r}_1$ and $\mathbf{r}_2$ alone, namely,

$$\left.\begin{aligned} \mathbf{r}_{12} &= -\mathbf{r}_1 + \mathbf{r}_2, \\ \mathbf{r}_{23} &= -\frac{m_1}{m_3}\mathbf{r}_1 - \frac{m_2 + m_3}{m_3}\mathbf{r}_2, \\ \mathbf{r}_{31} &= \frac{m_1 + m_3}{m_3}\mathbf{r}_1 + \frac{m_2}{m_3}\mathbf{r}_2, \\ \mathbf{r}_3 &= -\frac{m_1}{m_3}\mathbf{r}_1 - \frac{m_2}{m_3}\mathbf{r}_2. \end{aligned}\right\} \tag{2}$$

For simplicity of notation, let

$$\frac{1}{r_{ij}^3} = R_{ij};$$

Eqs. (1) become

$$\begin{aligned} -R_{31}[(m_1 + m_3)\mathbf{r}_1 + m_2\mathbf{r}_2] - R_{12}[m_2\mathbf{r}_1 - m_2\mathbf{r}_2] &= -\omega^2\mathbf{r}_1, \\ +R_{12}[m_1\mathbf{r}_1 - m_1\mathbf{r}_2] - R_{23}[m_1\mathbf{r}_1 + (m_2 + m_3)\mathbf{r}_2] &= -\omega^2\mathbf{r}_2, \\ +m_2R_{23}[m_1\mathbf{r}_1 + (m_2 + m_3)\mathbf{r}_2] + m_1R_{31}[(m_1 + m_3)\mathbf{r}_1 + m_2\mathbf{r}_2]& \\ &= +\omega^2[m_1\mathbf{r}_1 + m_2\mathbf{r}_2]; \end{aligned}$$

and finally

$$\left.\begin{aligned} &[-(m_1 + m_3)R_{31} - m_2R_{12} + \omega^2]\mathbf{r}_1 + [+R_{12} - R_{31}]m_2\mathbf{r}_2 = 0, \\ &[R_{12} - R_{23}]m_1\mathbf{r}_1 - [m_1R_{12} + (m_2 + m_3)R_{23} - \omega^2]\mathbf{r}_2 = 0, \\ &[m_2R_{23} + (m_1 + m_3)R_{31} - \omega^2]m_1\mathbf{r}_1 \\ &\qquad + [(m_2 + m_3)R_{23} + m_1R_{31} - \omega^2]m_2\mathbf{r}_2 = 0. \end{aligned}\right\} \tag{3}$$

Equilateral Triangular Configuration.—If $\mathbf{r}_1$ and $\mathbf{r}_2$ are not collinear, that is, the three bodies do not lie in a straight line, all the coefficients in Eqs. (3) must vanish. It is readily seen that this condition requires, and is satisfied by,

$$R_{12} = R_{23} = R_{31},$$

or

$$r_{12} = r_{23} = r_{31} = r,$$

and

$$\omega^2 = \frac{m_1 + m_2 + m_3}{r^3} = \frac{M}{r^3}.$$

Thus the triangle is equilateral whatever the masses may be, and there is no other triangular configuration.

Straight-line Configuration.—If $\mathbf{r}_1$ and $\mathbf{r}_2$ are collinear, Eqs. (1) become algebraic and r_i and r_{ij} may be positive or negative. In order to be precise, let the order of the masses on the line be m_1, m_2, m_3, so that r_1, measured from the center of gravity, is negative, and r_3 is positive. In order to simplify the notation, let (Fig. 15)

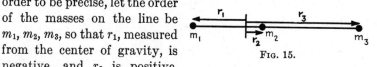

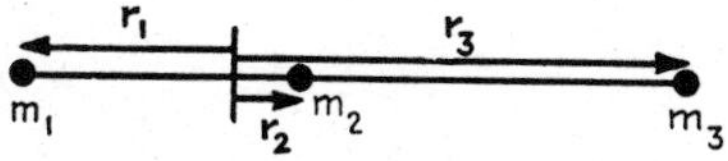

FIG. 15.

$$r_{12} = r, \qquad \text{and} \qquad r_{23} = xr,$$

so that

$$r_{13} = (1 + x)r.$$

Then

$$r_1 = -\frac{m_2 + (1 + x)m_3}{M}r, \qquad r_2 = \frac{+m_1 - m_3 x}{M}r,$$
$$r_3 = \frac{(1 + x)m_1 + xm_2}{M}r;$$

and Eqs. (1), neglecting the second which is superfluous, become

$$\left.\begin{aligned} \frac{m_2}{r^2} + \frac{m_3}{(1 + x)^2 r^2} &= \frac{\omega^2}{M}[m_2 + (1 + x)m_3]r, \\ \frac{m_1}{(1 + x)^2 r^2} + \frac{m_2}{x^2 r^2} &= \frac{\omega^2}{M}[(1 + x)m_1 + xm_2]r. \end{aligned}\right\} \qquad (4)$$

On eliminating ω^2 between these two equations and then clearing of fractions, the following equation, which determines x, results:

$$(m_1 + m_2)x^5 + (3m_1 + 2m_2)x^4 + (3m_1 + m_2)x^3 - (m_2 + 3m_3)x^2 - (2m_2 + 3m_3)x - (m_2 + m_3) = 0. \qquad (5)$$

This quintic equation was first obtained by Lagrange. Since there is but one change of sign in the coefficients, there is one, and only one, real positive root,[1] and therefore, for a given order

[1] By Descartes' rule of signs.

of the masses, one and only one distribution of the masses along the line which satisfies the conditions of the problem.

If x is the real positive root of Eq. (5), it is found from Eqs. (4) that

$$\omega^2 = \frac{M}{r^3}\frac{m_2(1+x)^2 + m_3}{m_2(1+x)^2 + m_3(1+x)^3}$$
$$= \frac{M}{r^3}\frac{m_1x^2 + m_2(1+x)^2}{m_1x^2(1+x)^3 + m_2x^3(1+x)^2} = \frac{M}{r^3}\frac{m_1x^2 - m_3}{m_1x^2 - m_3x^3}.$$

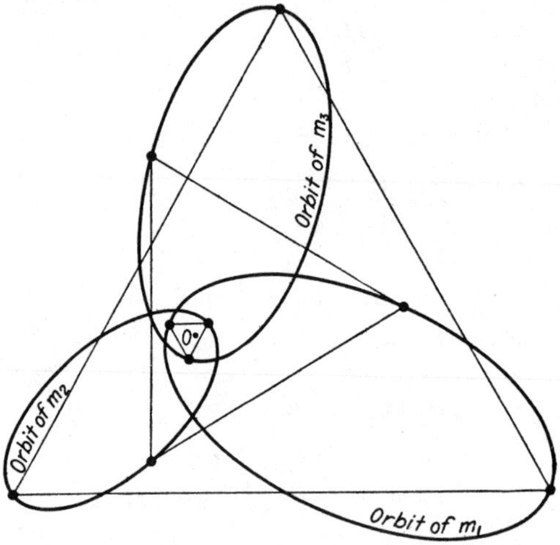

FIG. 16.

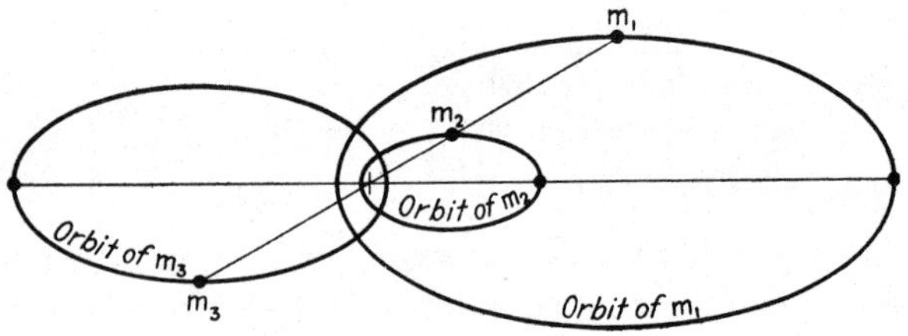

FIG. 17.

Orbits for the equilateral triangular configuration and for the straight-line configurations are shown in Figs. 16 and 17. In these examples

$$m_1 : m_2 : m_3 : : 1 : 2 : 3,$$

and the eccentricity of the orbits is $\frac{1}{2}\sqrt{3}$.

41. The Permanent Configurations of Four Bodies.—It was shown by F. R. Moulton[1] in 1900 that the straight-line configuration exists in the problem of n bodies. That is, given any n centrobaric masses and their order on a straight line, there exists one, and only one, configuration of the masses that can be preserved under Keplerian motion. Particular instances of other configurations have been given by Hoppe, Andoyer, and Longley. An exhaustive analysis of the permanent configurations of the problem of four bodies was given in 1932 by MacMillan and Bartky.[2] The character of the analysis is similar to that of Secs. 39 and 40, but is very much more complicated and too lengthy for reproduction here; although some of the principal results can be stated without proof.

If any four centrobaric masses are placed at the vertices of a regular tetrahedron, the resultant acceleration of each mass due to the attraction of the other three is directed toward the center of gravity of the system and in magnitude is proportional to the distance of that mass from the center of gravity. The bodies can therefore move along the lines which join them to the center of gravity in such a way that the tetrahedron remains regular. If the four masses are particles and they fall to the center of gravity, all four arrive at the center of gravity at the same instant and collision occurs; the configuration is not permanent in the proper sense of the term. But if the masses are moving away from the center of gravity with speeds sufficient to carry them to infinity, the configuration of the regular tetrahedron can be preserved permanently.

The regular tetrahedron whose orientation also is preserved is the only space configuration that is permanent. All of the others are plane or straight-line configurations. The plane configurations, excluding those that form a straight line, are quadrilaterals of two distinct types, *convex* quadrilaterals and *concave* quadrilaterals. A quadrilateral is convex if a string which is passed around it and drawn taut touches all four corners. If the string forms a triangle, one corner is in the interior of the triangle and the quadrilateral is concave. If there exists a set of four masses for which a given quadrilateral can form a per-

[1] "Periodic Orbits," Carnegie Institution of Washington, p. 285 (1920).

[2] "Permanent Configurations in the Problem of Four Bodies," *Transactions of the American Mathematical Society*, Vol. 34, p. 838 (1932).

manent configuration, the quadrilateral is said to be an *admissible* quadrilateral. If four equal masses are placed at the corners of a square and are given suitable velocities, the four masses will always form a square. Hence a square is an admissible quadrilateral. In the problem of three bodies there is but one admissible triangle, namely, the equilateral triangle. An isosceles triangle is not admissible unless it is equilateral; and a right triangle is never admissible.

In the problem of four bodies there is an infinite variety of admissible quadrilaterals, and yet not all quadrilaterals are admissible. The ratio of the diagonals of a convex quadrilateral, for example, must lie between $3^{\frac{1}{2}}$ and $3^{-\frac{1}{2}}$, if the quadrilateral is

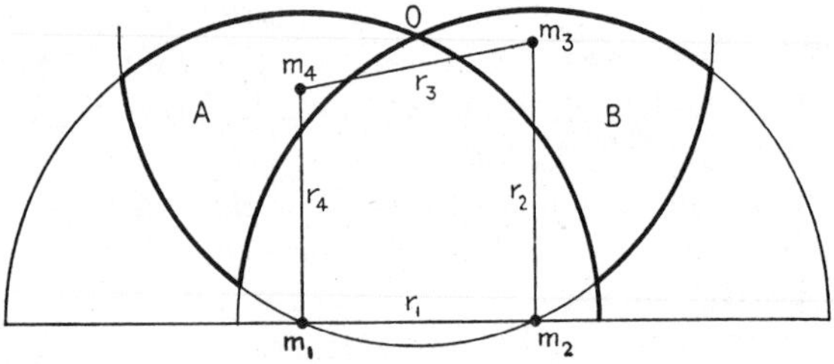

FIG. 18.

an admissible one; each of its interior angles must lie between 60° and 120°; and the interior angles must be divided by the diagonals into two angles, each of which is less than 60°.

There are two classes of admissible quadrilaterals that possess an axial symmetry. If r_1, r_2, r_3, and r_4 are the sides of the quadrilateral taken in order, one class of symmetrical admissible quadrilaterals is that in which adjacent sides are equal in pairs, for example $r_1 = r_2$, $r_3 = r_4$. In this case the two masses which do not lie on the diagonal of symmetry are always equal. Such quadrilaterals may be convex or concave. A second class is formed by isosceles trapezoids, that is, trapezoids in which the non-parallel sides are equal, whose interior angles lie between 60° and 120°. In this case the two masses on the base of the trapezoid are equal, and the remaining pair of masses also are equal.

For the general case let the masses be numbered in order m_1, m_2, m_3, m_4 and the sides likewise r_1, r_2, r_3, and r_4, as in Fig. 18. Let

P be the period of the motion, $\omega = 2\pi/\rho$, and let r without subscript, be defined by the relation

$$\omega^2 = \frac{M}{r^3},$$

just as in the problem of three bodies, where M is the sum of the four masses. In any admissible *convex* quadrilateral the inequalities

$$r_1, r_2, r_3, r_4 \leqq r \leqq r_5, r_6$$

are satisfied, where r_5 and r_6 are the diagonals, r_5 joining m_1 and m_3, and r_6 joining m_2 and m_4. Let the notation be chosen so that

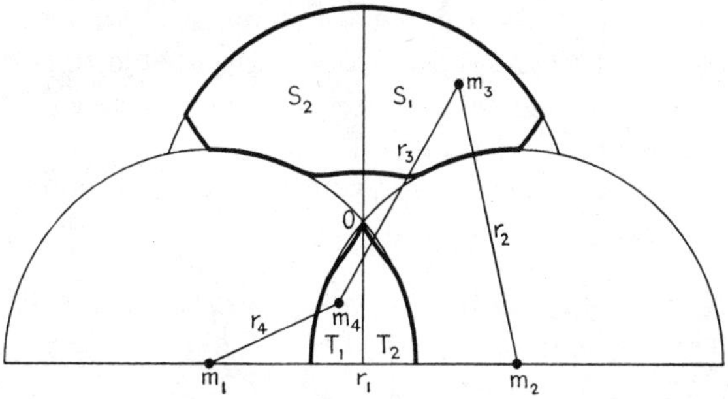

FIG. 19.

r_1 is the longest of the four sides. Then in any admissible *concave* quadrilateral the corresponding inequalities are

$$r_1, r_2, r_5 \geqq r \geqq r_3, r_4, r_6.$$

Let the line joining m_1 and m_2 be r_1. With m_1 and m_2 as centers and a radius equal to r, draw semicircles which intersect in the point O, Fig. 18. With O as a center and the same radius, draw the semicircle which passes through m_1 and m_2. These semicircles define two areas, A and B. If m_3 is any point in B, there exists one and only one point m_4 in A, and none at all outside of it, such that $m_1m_2m_3m_4$ forms an admissible, convex quadrilateral; and if any point m_4 in A is chosen, there exists one and only one point m_3 in B, and none outside of it, such that $m_1m_2m_3m_4$ forms an admissible convex quadrilateral.

A similar representation is possible for concave quadrilaterals, Fig. 19, but the areas so defined S_1, S_2; T_1, T_2, which correspond to the regions A and B of Fig. 18, are somewhat too large; but if they are properly restricted, as indicated in the figure, a theorem similar to the above can be stated, namely: For each point m_4 of the area $T_1 + T_2$ there exists one and only one point m_3 in the area $S_1 + S_2$ such that $m_1m_2m_3$ and m_4 forms an admissible concave quadrilateral; and for each point m_3 of $S_1 + S_2$ there exists one and only one point m_4 in $T_1 + T_2$ such that $m_1m_2m_3$ and m_4 forms an admissible concave quadrilateral. Furthermore if m_3 lies in S_1, m_4 lies in T_1, and if m_3 lies in S_2, m_4 lies in T_2.

If an admissible quadrilateral is given, the masses are uniquely determined, with the exception of the single case of three equal masses at the vertices of an equilateral triangle and a fourth mass at its center. In this case the masses can be anything whatever. If four masses are given it is possible to state that: *For every four given masses and assigned order, there exists at least one admissible convex quadrilateral.*

A corresponding theorem for concave quadrilaterals was not proved.

42. The Moment of Inertia with Respect to the Center of Mass.—The moment of inertia of a system of particles with respect to the center of mass is

$$I = \Sigma m_s r_s^2 = \Sigma m_s \mathbf{r}_s \cdot \mathbf{r}_s, \tag{1}$$

the origin of the vectors $\mathbf{r}_s$ being at the center of mass. If this expression is differentiated twice with respect to the time, it is found that

$$\tfrac{1}{2}I'' = \Sigma m_s \mathbf{r}_s \cdot \mathbf{r}_s'' + \Sigma m_s \mathbf{r}_s' \cdot \mathbf{r}_s'. \tag{2}$$

If the equations of motion are

$$m_s \mathbf{r}_s'' = \mathbf{F}_s,$$

this equation becomes

$$\tfrac{1}{2}I'' = \Sigma m_s \mathbf{r}_s' \cdot \mathbf{r}_s' + \Sigma \mathbf{r}_s \cdot \mathbf{F}_s \tag{2a}$$

If the system is a conservative one, there exists a potential function U, such that

$$m_s \mathbf{r}_s'' = \nabla_s U, \qquad s = 1, \cdots, n. \tag{3}$$

On multiplying Eq. (3) by $\mathbf{r}_s \cdot$ and then summing with respect to s, there results

$$\Sigma m_s \mathbf{r}_s \cdot \mathbf{r}_s'' = \Sigma \mathbf{r}_s \cdot \nabla_s U,$$

which is the value of the second term of Eq. (2). Now

$$\mathbf{r} \cdot \nabla = (x\mathbf{i} + y\mathbf{j} + z\mathbf{k}) \cdot \left(\frac{\partial}{\partial x}\mathbf{i} + \frac{\partial}{\partial y}\mathbf{j} + \frac{\partial}{\partial z}\mathbf{k}\right)$$
$$= x\frac{\partial}{\partial x} + y\frac{\partial}{\partial y} + z\frac{\partial}{\partial z}.$$

Hence

$$\sum m_s \mathbf{r}_s \cdot \mathbf{r}_s'' = \sum \mathbf{r}_s \cdot \nabla_s U = \sum \left(x_s\frac{\partial U}{\partial x_s} + y_s\frac{\partial U}{\partial y_s} + z_s\frac{\partial U}{\partial z_s}\right)$$
$$= \sum r_s \frac{\partial U}{dr_s}. \qquad (4)$$

A function $f(\xi_1, \ldots, \xi_m)$ is said to be homogeneous of degree n in the letters $\xi_1, \ldots, \xi_m$ if, on replacing each letter ξ_i by $\lambda\xi_i$, it is true that

$$f(\lambda\xi_1, \cdots, \lambda\xi_m) \equiv \lambda^n f(\xi_1, \cdots, \xi_m). \qquad (5)$$

On differentiating Eq. (5) with respect to λ, it is seen that

$$\sum_j \xi_j \frac{\partial}{\partial(\lambda\xi_j)} f(\lambda\xi_i) \equiv n\lambda^{n-1} f(\xi_i).$$

Since this is true for every value of λ, it is true in particular for $\lambda = 1$. Hence, if $f(\xi_i)$ is homogeneous of degree n in the letters ξ_i, $i = 1, \cdots, m$, it is true that

$$\sum_{j=1}^{m} \xi_i \frac{\partial f(\xi_j)}{\partial \xi_i} \equiv n f(\xi_j),$$

which is Euler's theorem on homogeneous functions.

If the only forces that are acting upon the particles arise from their mutual gravitational attractions, it is seen from Eq. (37.1) that U is a homogeneous function of degree -1 in the letters $x_s, y_s, z_s, s = 1, \cdots, n$. Hence, by Euler's theorem,

$$\sum \left(x_s\frac{\partial U}{\partial x_s} + y_s\frac{\partial U}{\partial y_s} + z_s\frac{\partial U}{\partial z_s}\right) = -U.$$

On substituting this expression in Eq. (2) and setting

$$\Sigma m_s \mathbf{r}_s' \cdot \mathbf{r}_s' = 2T,$$

where T is obviously the kinetic energy of the system, it is found that Eq. (2) becomes

$$\tfrac{1}{2}I'' = 2T - U, \tag{6}$$

a result which is due to Jacobi. Also, by Eq. (36.3),

$$E = T - U \tag{7}$$

where E, the total energy of the system, is a constant. If T is eliminated between Eqs. (6) and (7), there is obtained finally

$$\tfrac{1}{2}I'' = 2E + U. \tag{8}$$

If the system of particles is in a steady state, as seems to be the case with the globular star clusters, the moment of inertia I is a constant, and Eq. (6) reduces to

$$2T = U, \qquad T = -E, \qquad U = -2E, \tag{9}$$

and, since U is the negative of the potential energy of the system, this can be phrased in the theorem:

In a steady state of a system of particles which are acted upon only by their mutual gravitation, the kinetic energy is constant and is equal to one half of the negative of the potential energy.

A particular instance of an exact steady state is found in the permanent configurations when the orbits are circles about the center of mass. In the globular star clusters it is probable that the steady state is only approximate.

The moment of inertia with respect to the origin is a homogeneous function of degree $+2$, and the potential function for gravitation is a homogeneous function of degree -1. Therefore if the r_s in Eq. (1) are replaced by λr_s, the ratios of the mutual distances remain constant while the configuration expands or contracts according as $\lambda \gtrless 1$, and

$$I = \lambda^2 I_1,$$

where I_1 is the value of I for $\lambda = 1$. Similarly, since U is homogeneous of degree -1,

$$U = \lambda^{-1} U_1.$$

Consequently,

$$IU^2 = I_1U_1^2 = k_1^2, \tag{10}$$

where k_1 is a constant which may be called the configuration constant, since it depends upon the nature of the configuration but is independent of the size of the system.

If then the system expands or contracts in such a way that the ratio of the mutual distances is preserved, the relation

$$U = k_1 I^{-\frac{1}{2}}$$

holds, and Eq. (8) becomes

$$\tfrac{1}{2}I'' = 2E + k_1 I^{-\frac{1}{2}}, \tag{11}$$

an equation that can be integrated. On multiplying through by $4I'$ and integrating, it is found that

$$I'^2 = 8EI + 8k_1 I^{\frac{1}{2}} + C, \tag{12}$$

where C is the constant of integration.

Let a new constant k_2 be introduced by the relation

$$C = \frac{2(k_1^2 - k_2^2)}{E};$$

then Eq. (12) becomes

$$I'^2 = \frac{2}{E}[(2EI^{\frac{1}{2}} + k_1)^2 - k_2^2]. \tag{13}$$

The energy E may be either positive or negative, since the potential energy is always negative. If E is negative and a new variable φ is defined by the equation

$$k_2 \cos\varphi = 2EI^{\frac{1}{2}} + k_1,$$

and the ratio k_2/k_1 is replaced by the letter e, it is found that Eq. (13) reduces to

$$(1 - e\cos\varphi)\varphi' = \frac{(-2E)^{\frac{3}{2}}}{k_1},$$

which, by integration, becomes Kepler's equation (I, **297**),

$$\varphi - e\sin\varphi = \frac{(-2E)^{\frac{3}{2}}}{k_1}(t - t_0). \tag{14}$$

It follows from I, **300** that φ is a periodic function of t with the period

$$P = \frac{2\pi k_1}{(-2E)^{\frac{3}{2}}}.$$

Therefore the period is a function of the total energy and the configuration constant alone.

If the energy E is positive and the substitution

$$k_2 \cosh \varphi = 2EI^{\frac{1}{2}} + k_1$$

is made, Eq. (14) takes the form

$$e \sinh \varphi - \varphi = \frac{(2E)^{\frac{3}{2}}}{k_1}(t - t_0),$$

and the system, if it is expanding, continues to expand indefinitely. If it is contracting, the moment of inertia attains a minimum at $\varphi = 0$, namely

$$I_{\text{min.}} = \left(\frac{k_2 - k_1}{2E}\right)^2,$$

and thereafter the system expands indefinitely. It follows therefore that if the energy is positive the moment of inertia, and therefore the size of the system, eventually will increase beyond all limits.

Application to the Kinetic Theory.—According to the kinetic theory, the temperature of a solid, liquid or gaseous mass is proportional to the mean kinetic energy of its molecules. In a solid or liquid the motion of the molecules is one of oscillation about a mean position that is fixed in the case of a solid or slowly movable in the case of a liquid. In the case of a gas the molecules move about freely except for their mutual collisions. These collisions are assumed to be perfectly elastic, so that there is no loss of energy.

According to Eq. (2*a*) the kinetic energy is

$$T = \tfrac{1}{4}I'' - \tfrac{1}{2}\Sigma \mathbf{r}_s \cdot \mathbf{F}_s,$$

and for solid or liquid masses at rest and for homogeneous gases in an enclosed vessel, the moment of inertia with respect to the center of gravity is essentially constant, so that $I'' = 0$. Therefore

$$T = -\tfrac{1}{2}\Sigma \mathbf{r}_s \cdot \mathbf{F}_s.$$

The mean value of the expression

$$-\tfrac{1}{2}\Sigma \mathbf{r}_s \cdot \mathbf{F}_s = S$$

is the quantity which was called the *virial* by Clausius.[1] Hence his theorem: *The kinetic energy of the system of particles is equal to its virial.*

Imagine the mass to expand in such a way that the ratio of the distances between the particles remains constant, and therefore

$$r_s = (1 + d\lambda)r_{s0},$$

or

$$dr_s = r_s\, d\lambda.$$

The work done in the expansion is

$$\begin{aligned} dW &= \Sigma\, d\mathbf{r}_s \cdot \mathbf{F}_s \\ &= (\Sigma \mathbf{r}_s \cdot \mathbf{F}_s)\, d\lambda = -2S\, d\lambda. \end{aligned}$$

Similarly for the volume

$$V_0 = \int dx\, dy\, dz, \qquad V = (1 + d\lambda)^3 \int dx\, dy\, dz,$$

so that

$$V - V_0 = dV = 3V\, d\lambda.$$

The elimination of $d\lambda$ then gives

$$S = -\frac{3}{2} V \frac{dW}{dV}.$$

If the work done in expanding is due to interior forces, this expression represents the interior virial.

For exterior forces, consider the case of a mass subject to a pressure p which is everywhere normal to the surface. Let $\mathbf{n}_s$ be a unit vector to the surface where $\mathbf{r} = \mathbf{r}_s$. Then

$$\mathbf{F}_s = -p\mathbf{n}_s,$$

[1] *Philosophical Magazine*, August, 1870.

and the expression for the virial becomes

$$S = +\tfrac{1}{2}p\Sigma \mathbf{r}_s \cdot \mathbf{n}_s,$$

the sum being taken over the entire surface. In order to evaluate it let $d\omega$ be an element of the surface; then

$$S = \tfrac{1}{2}p\int \mathbf{r} \cdot \mathbf{n}\, d\omega.$$

By the formula II, **56**,

$$\int_V \left(\frac{\partial F}{\partial x} + \frac{\partial G}{\partial y} + \frac{\partial H}{\partial z}\right) d\tau = \int_S W_n\, d\omega,$$

where F, G, and H are the x-, y-, and z-components of a vector $\mathbf{W}$ and W_n is the component of $\mathbf{W}$ normal to the surface. In the present case,

$$\mathbf{W} = \mathbf{r}, \qquad F = x, \qquad G = y, \qquad \text{and} \qquad H = z.$$

Hence

$$3V = 3\int_V d\tau = \int_S \mathbf{r} \cdot \mathbf{n}\, d\omega$$

and

$$S = \tfrac{3}{2}pV.$$

For a small mass of gas enclosed in a vessel, the interior forces are vanishingly small and the interior virial vanishes, and there remains

$$T = \Sigma\tfrac{1}{2}mv^2 = \tfrac{3}{2}pV.$$

The fundamental law of perfect gases is

$$pV = nR\theta,$$

where $R = 82{,}600{,}000$ (in the c.g.s. system) is the gas constant, θ is the temperature, and n is the number of molecules present. From these two equations it follows that the kinetic energy of a chemically homogeneous perfect gas is

$$T = \tfrac{3}{2}Rn\theta,$$

where θ is the absolute temperature measured in centigrade degrees, and T is expressed in ergs. The energy is expressed in small calories by dividing the above result by 4.19×10^7.

Problems

1. The particle m_1 with the velocity $\mathbf{V}_1$ collides and unites with a particle m_2 with the velocity $\mathbf{V}_2$. If $\mathbf{V}$ is their common velocity after collision, write the vector equation which relates these three velocities.

2. A stone tied to the end of a string is describing a circle with the linear speed s. If the string is allowed to wind around a cylinder at the center of the circle what is the linear speed of the stone when the string is shortened by one half?

3. Two spheres are free to slide on a light rod. The two spheres are tied together with a weak string and the system is tossed into the air. The string breaks while the system is in motion and the spheres move out to the ends of the rod. What effect does the breaking of the string have on the rate of spin? What effect does it have on the motion of the center of gravity of the system?

4. In the equilateral triangular configuration let $m_1 = m_2 = m_3 = 1$ and let the length of the side of the triangle be the unit of length. Find the radius of the circle which a particle of negligible mass would describe around one of the bodies in the same period as that of the three equal masses about their center of gravity. *Ans.* $r = 1/\sqrt[3]{3}$.

5. If the masses are in the ratio

$$m_1 : m_2 : m_3 :: 1 : 2 : 3$$

and the side of the equilateral triangle is 1, what are the distances in the straight-line solution which has the same period?

$$\textit{Ans. } r_1 = .84923, \qquad r_2 = 1.51220, \qquad r_3 = .66297.$$

6. Show that the distances of the three masses from the center of gravity in the equilateral configuration are given by

$$\frac{r_1}{\sqrt{m_2^2 + m_2 m_3 + m_3^2}} = \frac{r_2}{\sqrt{m_3^2 + m_3 m_1 + m_1^2}} = \frac{r_3}{\sqrt{m_1^2 + m_1 m_2 + m_2^2}}.$$

7. Prove that if the particles are at rest in any configuration that admits a solution of the problem of n bodies in which the ratios of the distances are constant they will all fall to the center of gravity in the same time.

8. Show that, if three masses each equal to the sun are at the vertices of an equilateral triangle the sides of which are one astronomical unit, the period of revolution about the center of gravity which is necessary to maintain that configuration with circular orbits is 210.9 days, and that if they are in the straight-line configuration with one astronomical unit between them the period is 326.7 days.

9. If the two masses at the ends of each diagonal of a rhomb are equal, there exists a solution of the problem of four bodies for which the rhomb configuration is maintained, provided the ratio of the diagonals, δ, satisfies the inequalities

$$\frac{1}{\sqrt{3}} < \delta < \sqrt{3}.$$

The ratio of the two masses at the end of a side is

$$\frac{m_1}{m_2} = \frac{8 - (1 + \delta^2)^{\frac{3}{2}}}{8\delta - (1 + \delta^2)^{\frac{3}{2}}}, \quad \text{(Longley)}.$$

10. If two equal finite masses move in circles in the xy-plane with the center of gravity at the origin, the motion of an infinitesimal particle which moves along the z-axis can be determined by an elliptic integral.

11. Two equal particles are constrained to move one along the x-axis and the other along the y-axis, without friction, subject only to their mutual attraction. Show that their center of gravity moves just as though it were a particle which is attracted toward the origin by a force which varies inversely as the square of the distance. Generalize to a force that varies inversely as the nth power of the distance.

CHAPTER IV

GENERAL THEOREMS ON THE MOTION OF A RIGID BODY

43. Definition of a Rigid Body.—A rigid body is a system of particles bound together by interior forces which lie in the lines that join the particles, and are of such a nature that the mutual distances between the particles are constant, whatever the exterior forces may be. It is a mechanical ideal that is useful because many natural objects are close approximations for many purposes.

An alternative view is that the particles are subject to the constraints

$$r_{ij} = \sqrt{(x_i - x_j)^2 + (y_i - y_j)^2 + (z_i - z_j)^2} = \text{constant}, \qquad i, j = 1, \cdots, n,$$

where x_i, y_i, z_i are rectangular coordinates of the ith particle and n is the number of particles in the body. There are, of course, $n(n - 1)/2$ such constraints, but they are not all independent. It is readily seen that if four particles are at the vertices of a tetrahedron, the six constraints are independent, since any one of the six distances can be altered without changing the other five. A fifth particle can be added, and its position is uniquely defined if its distances to any three non-collinear particles of the tetrahedron are given. The distance to the fourth particle is then determined. Of the ten constraints, nine are independent and one is dependent. If a sixth particle is added, three of the additional constraints are independent and two are dependent, and so on. For each particle added after the third three of the new constraints are independent and the remainder are dependent. But for the first four particles the number of independent constraints is six instead of twelve. Hence, for a system of n particles which form a rigid body, there are $3n - 6$ independent constraints. Since $3n$ parameters x, y, z are necessary to define the positions of the n particles and there are $3n - 6$ independent constraints, it follows that there are only six parameters that are free. That is, a rigid body has six degrees of freedom (I, **313**).

The number of degrees of freedom, of course, can be reduced by outside constraints, but for a single body the number cannot be increased.

Since a rigid body is a system of free particles in which all of the interior forces lie in lines which join the individual particles, all of the theorems of Chapter III for which these forces were not specialized are applicable to the motion of rigid bodies. They are the principle of momentum, the principle of the moment of momentum, and the principle of energy.

44. The Principle of Momentum.—*The time rate of change of the momentum of a body is equal to the vector sum of all of the applied (or exterior) forces that are acting upon it.* If M is the mass of a body and $\mathbf{G}$ the position vector of its center of gravity relative to a point of fixed space, the momentum of the body in fixed space is $M\mathbf{G}'$, and if $\mathbf{F}$ is the vector sum of all of the applied forces, the principle of momentum is expressed in the formula

$$M\mathbf{G}'' = \mathbf{F}. \tag{1}$$

It must be carefully noted that $\mathbf{F}$ is the vector sum of all of the forces that are actually acting upon the body, that is, what the force at the center of gravity would be if each particle, together with the force which is actually acting upon it in its initial position, were moved to the center of gravity, and the sum of the forces were then taken. This may be, and in general is, very different from what the force would be if each of the particles were moved to the center of gravity and then the force which would act upon it at the center of gravity were taken.

It is worthy of note that, since the vector sum of a couple is zero, *a couple that is acting on a rigid body, irrespective of the points of application of the forces of the couple, has no effect upon the motion of the center of gravity of the body.*

First Example.—Suppose two iron balls each of mass 2 are connected rigidly by a glass rod of mass 1, and that O is a center of magnetic force (Fig. 20). The iron balls are attracted toward O just as though they were particles of mass 2 located at the centers of the spheres, while the glass is not attracted at all. Suppose the centers of the balls are at distances of 2 and 3 respectively from the point O. Since the magnetic force varies inversely as the square of the distance, the forces $\mathbf{F}_1$ and $\mathbf{F}_2$ which are acting upon the balls are directed toward O and are in the ratio of 9 to 4. The total mass M of the rigid body is 5, and

$$\mathbf{F} = \mathbf{F}_1 + \mathbf{F}_2$$

acts at the center of mass. It will be observed that, in general, **F** is not directed toward the point O as would be the case if the entire mass were concentrated at the center of mass and then acted upon by the magnetic force. Obviously, **F** depends not only upon the distance of the center of mass from O but also upon the orientation of the body with respect to O. The equation of motion of the center of mass is

$$5\mathbf{G}'' = -2k^2\left(\frac{\mathbf{R}_1}{R_1^{\,3}} + \frac{\mathbf{R}_2}{R_2^{\,3}}\right),$$

and the constraint

$$\mathbf{R}_1 - \mathbf{R}_2 = \mathbf{L},$$

where L is constant, must be satisfied.

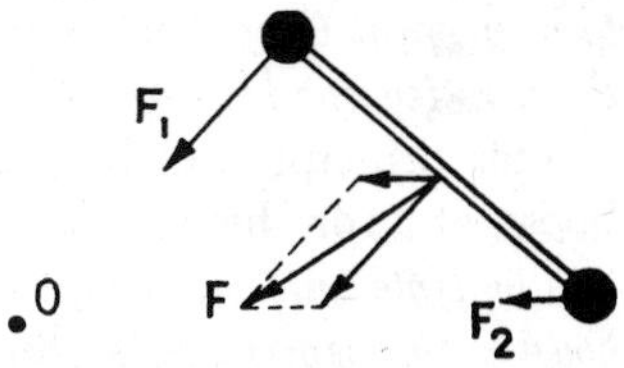

Fig. 20.

Second Example.—Suppose the same rigid body as in the previous example were thrown into the air and that the resistance of the air could be neglected. A force equal to $m\mathbf{g}$ acts upon each particle of the body, **g** being the same for each particle. In this case,

$$\mathbf{F} = \Sigma m\mathbf{g} = M\mathbf{g},$$

which is independent of the orientation of the body with respect to the earth.

The equation of motion of the center of gravity is therefore

$$M\mathbf{G}'' = M\mathbf{g}, \qquad \text{or} \qquad \mathbf{G}'' = \mathbf{g},$$

where **g** is a constant vector. Doubtless, the body is spinning in some fashion. But whatever the spin may be the center of gravity describes a parabola, just as a single particle would do (Sec. 13).

Third Example.—Suppose every particle of a rigid body is attracted toward a fixed point O by a force which is proportional to the mass of the particle and directly proportional to its distance from O. Required the motion of its center of mass.

In this case

$$\mathbf{F} = -k^2\Sigma m\mathbf{R} \equiv -k^2 M\mathbf{G},$$

and the equation of motion is

$$M\mathbf{G}'' = -k^2 M\mathbf{G}, \qquad \text{or simply} \qquad \mathbf{G}'' = -k^2\mathbf{G},$$

which is the equation of simple harmonic motion (Sec. 13). In this case also the force acting upon the center of mass is independent of the orientation of the body and the motion of translation is entirely independent of the motion of rotation.

45. The Principle of Moment of Momentum.—*The time rate of change of the moment of momentum of a rigid body with respect to any point O of fixed space is equal to the sum of the moments of the applied (or exterior) forces with respect to that point* (Sec. 32).

This principle can be extended to the center of gravity of the body, and for this case the statement is:

The time rate of change of the moment of momentum of a rigid body with respect to its center of gravity is equal to the sum of the moments of the applied (or exterior) forces with respect to the center of gravity (Sec. 33).

This theorem is true whatever the motion of the center of gravity may be, but the directions of the vectors are to be interpreted as the directions of fixed space, and not one that is in rotation with respect to a fixed space. By a fixed space is meant space referred to a coordinate system that is at rest relative to the center of mass of the galaxy (the system of the fixed stars) or in uniform translation with respect to it. If the time and space scale under consideration is so great that this definition is inadequate, an extension to the system of visible spirals would, perhaps, serve. At any rate, as the time and space scale under consideration increases, larger and larger material systems are necessary to which fixed directions can be referred. At the present time the system of spirals is the largest system that can be recognized.

It will be observed that the moment with respect to the center of gravity of a force which acts at the center of gravity is zero. Consequently, *a force which acts at the center of gravity of a rigid body has no effect whatever upon the rotation of the body.*

This theorem and the analogous theorem on the motion of the center of gravity, in Sec. 44, together constitute the principle of the independence of the motions of rotation and translation of a rigid body.

If **L** is the moment of momentum of the body and **N** is the moment of applied forces, the formulation of either of the above principles gives

$$\mathbf{L}' = \mathbf{N}, \tag{1}$$

(See Fig. 14). It is evident from the discussion in Sec. 33 that *the moment of momentum of any system of particles of total mass M, rigid or otherwise, with respect to any point O of fixed space is equal to the moment of momentum with respect to the point O of a single particle of mass M moving with the center of gravity plus the moment of momentum of the system of particles with respect to its center of gravity.*

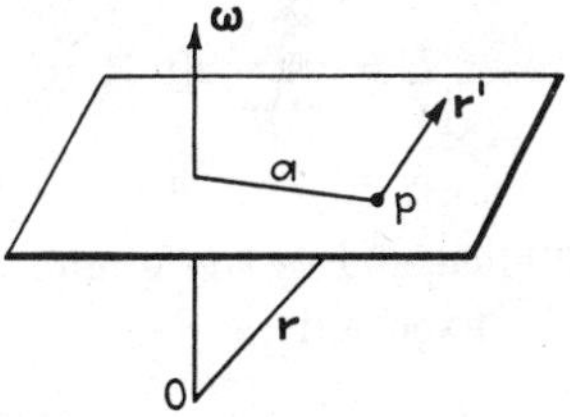

Fig. 21.

If the field of force in which the body is moving is of such a nature that the force **F** acting on the center of gravity is independent of the orientation of the body and depends only upon its position, the path described by the body is independent of the manner in which the body rotates; and if the moment of the forces **N** is independent of the position of the center of gravity, the rotation of the body is independent of its translation. It rotates just as it would if its center of gravity were fixed and the same forces were acting. Both of these conditions are satisfied in a limited field of the earth's gravity. But in general, rotation and translation are not independent of each other because the forces acting depend upon both position and orientation.

46. The Moment of Momentum of a Rigid Body with Respect to a Fixed Axis about Which It Is Turning.—In Fig. 21, let the line in which $\boldsymbol{\omega}$ lies be the axis about which the body is rotating, and $\boldsymbol{\omega}$ the angular velocity; let O be any point on the axis, $\mathbf{r}$ the position vector of any particle p of the body, and m the mass of the particle. In its motion of rotation about $\boldsymbol{\omega}$ the particle p describes a circle in a plane perpendicular to $\boldsymbol{\omega}$. If a is the radius of the circle, the speed of p is

$$v = a\omega = r\omega \sin \widehat{\mathbf{r}\boldsymbol{\omega}},$$

and the direction of its motion is perpendicular to a plane which passes through $\boldsymbol{\omega}$ and $\mathbf{r}$. Hence

$$\mathbf{r}' = \boldsymbol{\omega} \times \mathbf{r}. \tag{1}$$

The moment of momentum of the body with respect to the point O is therefore

$$\begin{aligned} \mathbf{L}_o &= \Sigma m\, \mathbf{r} \times \mathbf{r}' = \Sigma m\, \mathbf{r} \times (\boldsymbol{\omega} \times \mathbf{r}), \\ &= \Sigma m[r^2\boldsymbol{\omega} - (\mathbf{r} \cdot \boldsymbol{\omega})\mathbf{r}] \text{ by Eq. (5.7).} \end{aligned} \tag{2}$$

The moment of momentum with respect to an axis through O is the projection upon that axis of the moment of momentum with respect to the point O. That is, if $\mathbf{L}$ is the moment of momentum with respect to the axis, its scalar value is

$$\begin{aligned} L &= \sum m[\mathbf{r} \times (\boldsymbol{\omega} \times \mathbf{r})] \cdot \frac{\boldsymbol{\omega}}{\omega} = \sum m\left[r^2\omega - \frac{(\mathbf{r} \cdot \boldsymbol{\omega})^2}{\omega}\right] \\ &= \Sigma m[r^2\omega - r^2\omega \cos^2 \widehat{\mathbf{r}\boldsymbol{\omega}}] = \Sigma m a^2 \omega. \end{aligned}$$

Hence, if I is the moment of inertia of the body with respect to the fixed axis

$$\mathbf{L} = I\boldsymbol{\omega}. \tag{3}$$

From Fig. 21, it is seen the $\mathbf{r}$ can be written

$$\mathbf{r} = \zeta\frac{\boldsymbol{\omega}}{\omega} + \mathbf{a},$$

where ζ is the perpendicular distance from O to the plane and $\mathbf{a}$ is a vector that coincides with the arm a in the diagram. If this expression for $\mathbf{r}$ is substituted in the formula

$$L_o = \Sigma m\, \mathbf{r} \times (\boldsymbol{\omega} \times \mathbf{r}),$$

it is found, after reduction, that

$$\mathbf{L}_o = I\boldsymbol{\omega} - \omega\Sigma m\zeta\mathbf{a}. \tag{4}$$

Since the scalars ζ depend upon the position of the point O, the moment of momentum with respect to the point O depends upon the position of O on the axis, while the moment with respect to the axis, which is the $\boldsymbol{\omega}$ component of $\mathbf{L}_o$, does not depend upon the position of O.

If $\mathbf{i}_0$ and $\mathbf{j}_0$ are mutually perpendicular unit vectors each of which is perpendicular to the axis of rotation and fixed in the body, the vector $\mathbf{a}$ can be written

$$\mathbf{a} = \xi\mathbf{i}_0 + \eta\mathbf{j}_0,$$

and

$$\begin{aligned}\Sigma m\zeta\mathbf{a} &= \Sigma m\xi\zeta\mathbf{i}_0 + \Sigma m\eta\zeta\mathbf{j}_0\\ &= P_1\mathbf{i}_0 + P_2\mathbf{j}_0,\end{aligned}$$

where P_1 and P_2 are products of inertia at the point O. Consequently

$$\Sigma m\zeta\mathbf{a} = P_1\mathbf{i}_0 + P_2\mathbf{j}_0 = \mathbf{P}$$

is a certain vector which is fixed in the body and which depends upon the products of inertia of the body at the point O. It is obviously perpendicular to the axis of rotation.

The moment of momentum of the body with respect to the point O, Eq. (4), can therefore be written

$$L_o = I\omega - \omega\mathbf{P}. \qquad (5)$$

47. Example.—The two ends of a straight uniform bar AB (Fig. 22) of length $2a$ and mass m are constrained to move without friction on the circumference of a fixed horizontal circle of radius r. A bug of the same mass m is placed on one end A of the bar, and the entire system is at rest. Eventually, the bug begins to crawl along the bar with a constant speed with respect to the bar. Determine the motion with respect to a fixed horizontal plane.

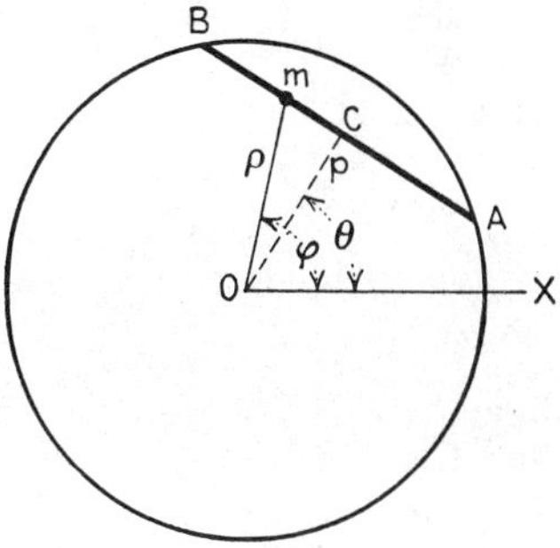

FIG. 22.

Let p be the perpendicular OC from the center of the circle to the center of the bar, OX a fixed line in the plane, ρ the radius vector Om of the bug, φ the angle between the fixed line and ρ, and θ the angle between the fixed line and p. If t is measured from the time the bug is at the center of the bar, s is his speed with respect to the bar, and d is his distance from the center of the bar, then

$$Cm = d = st.$$

Just before the bug started to move, the entire system was at rest. Therefore the exterior forces, the weight of system, and the reaction of the plane have a zero resultant and a zero moment resultant, which is equivalent to saying that there are no exterior forces acting. When the bar is in motion the reactions of the circle on the bar pass through the axis of the circle and their moment with respect to the axis is zero. The upward reaction of the plane is parallel to the axis. Hence the exterior forces which act on the system have a zero moment, and therefore the moment of momentum with respect to the axis is a constant. Inasmuch as it was zero at the start it remains zero throughout the motion.

If k^2 is the moment of inertia of the bar with respect to the axis of the circle, the moment of momentum of the bar is $mk^2\theta'$. The moment of momentum of the bug is $m\rho^2\varphi'$, since φ' is the angular velocity of the bug. Hence

$$mk^2\theta' + m\rho^2\varphi' = 0,$$

or

$$k^2\theta' + \rho^2\varphi' = 0. \tag{1}$$

Since p is constant and d is equal to st, it is evident that

$$\rho = \sqrt{p^2 + s^2t^2},$$

and that

$$\varphi = \theta + \tan^{-1}\frac{st}{p}.$$

These values, substituted in Eq. (1), reduce the problem to a quadrature, namely,

$$\theta' = -\frac{sp}{k^2 + p^2 + s^2t^2},$$

for which the solution is

$$\theta = \theta_0 - \frac{p}{\sqrt{k^2 + p^2}}\tan^{-1}\frac{st}{\sqrt{k^2 + p^2}}.$$

The radius of gyration k_1 of the bar with respect to its own center is $a/\sqrt{3}$ (I, **97**), and the square of the radius of gyration of the bar with respect to the center of the circle is (I, **95**)

$$\begin{aligned} k^2 &= k_1^2 + p^2, \\ &= \frac{a^2}{3} + r^2 - a^2 = r^2 - \tfrac{2}{3}a^2, \end{aligned}$$

and

$$k^2 + p^2 = 2r^2 - \tfrac{5}{3}a^2.$$

When the bug started to move at A the value of t was $-a/s$, and when it arrived at B the value of t was $+a/s$. Hence the angle through which the bar turned during the entire motion was

$$-2\sqrt{\frac{r^2 - a^2}{2r^2 - \frac{5}{3}a^2}} \tan^{-1} \frac{a}{\sqrt{2r^2 - \frac{5}{3}a^2}}.$$

It was turning most rapidly when the bug was at the center of the bar.

48. The Principle of Energy.—If M is the mass of a rigid body, and $\mathbf{G}$ is the position vector of its center of gravity relative to fixed space, the theorem of Sec. 35 becomes:

The change in the exterior kinetic energy of a rigid body in any interval of time is equal to the exterior work done on the body by the exterior forces in the displacement of the center of gravity that actually occurs.

Expressed as a formula, this statement is [Eq. (35.2)]

$$\tfrac{1}{2}M\mathbf{G}' \cdot \mathbf{G}' - \tfrac{1}{2}M(\mathbf{G}' \cdot \mathbf{G}')_0 = \int \mathbf{F} \cdot d\mathbf{G}, \qquad (1)$$

where

$$\mathbf{F} = \Sigma \mathbf{F},^{(e)}.$$

and $d\mathbf{G}$ is the displacement of the center of gravity that actually occurs.

Example.—A rigid body falls freely under the action of gravity. What is the change in its exterior kinetic energy?

Let v be the speed of the center of gravity relative to the surface of the earth, and h its height above the surface. Equation (1) gives

$$\tfrac{1}{2}M(v^2 - v_0^2) = \int M\mathbf{g} \cdot d\mathbf{G} = Mg\int dh = Mgh.$$

Since $\mathbf{g}$ is a constant vertical vector, $\mathbf{g} \cdot d\mathbf{G}$ is the scalar g multiplied by the vertical component of $d\mathbf{G}$, or $g\,dh$. Therefore the change in the exterior energy is its weight multiplied by the vertical distance through which its center of gravity has fallen, whatever the horizontal displacement may be, and whatever the state of its rotation may be.

The work done by the interior forces of a rigid body vanishes. The expression used in Sec. 35 for the work done by the interior forces was $\Sigma \mathbf{F}_j^{(i)} \cdot d\boldsymbol{\rho}_j$. In this expression $\mathbf{F}_j^{(i)}$ is the sum of all of the individual forces, due to the other particles, on the particle m_j. Therefore

$$\mathbf{F}_j^{(i)} = \sum_k \mathbf{F}_{jk},$$

where $\mathbf{F}_{jk}$ is the force on m_j due to the particle m_k. The force $\mathbf{F}_{kj}$, due to the action of m_j on m_k is equal and opposite. Hence the work done by this pair of forces is

$$dW_{jk} = \mathbf{F}_{jk} \cdot d\boldsymbol{\rho}_j + \mathbf{F}_{kj} \cdot d\boldsymbol{\rho}_k = \mathbf{F}_{jk} \cdot (d\boldsymbol{\rho}_j - d\boldsymbol{\rho}_k).$$

But,

$$\boldsymbol{\rho}_j = \boldsymbol{\rho}_k + \boldsymbol{\rho}_{jk},$$

so that

$$d\boldsymbol{\rho}_j - d\boldsymbol{\rho}_k = d\boldsymbol{\rho}_{jk},$$

and since the tensor of $\boldsymbol{\rho}_{jk}$ is constant,

$$\boldsymbol{\rho}_{jk} \cdot \boldsymbol{\rho}_{jk} = \rho_{jk}^2, \qquad \boldsymbol{\rho}_{jk} \cdot d\boldsymbol{\rho}_{jk} = 0;$$

therefore $d\boldsymbol{\rho}_{jk}$ is perpendicular to $\boldsymbol{\rho}_{jk}$ and likewise to $\mathbf{F}_{jk}$. Hence

$$dW_{jk} = \mathbf{F}_{jk} \cdot d\boldsymbol{\rho}_{jk} = 0,$$

and the interior forces of a rigid body, whatever they may be, do no work. *The change in the interior kinetic energy is equal to the interior work done by the exterior forces;* and the equations of Sec. 35 give

$$\tfrac{1}{2}\Sigma m\boldsymbol{\rho}' \cdot \boldsymbol{\rho}' - \tfrac{1}{2}(\Sigma m\boldsymbol{\rho}' \cdot \boldsymbol{\rho}')_0 = \Sigma \mathbf{F}_j^{(e)} \cdot d\boldsymbol{\rho}_j,$$

the vectors $\boldsymbol{\rho}$ having their origin at the center of gravity.

These two statements can be combined into the single statement: *The change in the kinetic energy of a rigid body in any interval of time is equal to the work done upon it (both interior and exterior) by the applied (exterior) forces in that interval of time.*

49. The Kinetic Energy of a Rigid Body Which Is Rotating about a Fixed Axis.—Let the angular velocity of rotation be $\boldsymbol{\omega}$; then the direction of $\boldsymbol{\omega}$ coincides with the axis of rotation. Let O

be any point on the axis, $\mathbf{r}$ the position vector of any particle of the body relative to O, $\mathbf{G}$ the position vector of the center of gravity of the body, and $\boldsymbol{\rho}$ the position of the particle relative to the center of gravity. Then

$$\mathbf{r} = \mathbf{G} + \boldsymbol{\rho}.$$

Since the particle is in rotation about a fixed axis,

$$\mathbf{r}' = \boldsymbol{\omega} \times \mathbf{r} = (\boldsymbol{\omega} \times \mathbf{G}) + (\boldsymbol{\omega} \times \boldsymbol{\rho}),$$

by Eq. (46.1). The kinetic energy of the body is therefore

$$\begin{aligned} \tfrac{1}{2}\Sigma m\mathbf{r}' \cdot \mathbf{r}' &= \tfrac{1}{2}\Sigma m[(\boldsymbol{\omega} \times \mathbf{G}) + (\boldsymbol{\omega} \times \boldsymbol{\rho})] \cdot [(\boldsymbol{\omega} \times \mathbf{G}) + (\boldsymbol{\omega} \times \boldsymbol{\rho})] \\ &= \tfrac{1}{2}M(\boldsymbol{\omega} \times \mathbf{G}) \cdot (\boldsymbol{\omega} \times \mathbf{G}) + \tfrac{1}{2}\Sigma m(\boldsymbol{\omega} \times \boldsymbol{\rho}) \cdot (\boldsymbol{\omega} \times \boldsymbol{\rho}), \end{aligned}$$

since the cross product term $(\boldsymbol{\omega} \times \mathbf{G}) \cdot \Sigma m(\boldsymbol{\omega} \times \boldsymbol{\rho})$ vanishes by virtue of the fact that $\Sigma m\boldsymbol{\rho}$ vanishes. But

$$\tfrac{1}{2}M(\boldsymbol{\omega} \times \mathbf{G}) \cdot (\boldsymbol{\omega} \times \mathbf{G})$$

is the kinetic energy of a particle of mass M moving with the center of gravity about the axis (the exterior kinetic energy), and the term

$$\tfrac{1}{2}\Sigma m(\boldsymbol{\omega} \times \boldsymbol{\rho}) \cdot (\boldsymbol{\omega} \times \boldsymbol{\rho})$$

is the kinetic energy of body rotating with the angular velocity $\boldsymbol{\omega}$ about an axis through the center of gravity and fixed in the body (the interior kinetic energy).

If a is the distance from the center of gravity to the axis, the exterior kinetic energy T_e is obviously

$$T_e = \tfrac{1}{2}Ma^2\omega^2.$$

As for the interior kinetic energy T_i let p be the distance of the particle from the parallel axis through the center of gravity. Then

$$(\boldsymbol{\omega} \times \boldsymbol{\rho}) \cdot (\boldsymbol{\omega} \times \boldsymbol{\rho}) = p^2\omega^2,$$

and

$$T_i = \tfrac{1}{2}\omega^2\Sigma mp^2 = \tfrac{1}{2}I\omega^2,$$

if I is the moment of inertia of the body with respect to the axis through the center of gravity. If k is the radius of gyration with respect to this axis,

$$I = Mk^2,$$

and the interior kinetic energy is

$$T_i = \tfrac{1}{2}Mk^2\omega^2. \tag{1}$$

Hence the total kinetic energy T of the body with respect to the original fixed axis through O is

$$T = \tfrac{1}{2}M(a^2 + k^2)\omega^2.$$

The square of the radius of gyration with respect to this axis is [Eq. (18.1)]

$$k_1^2 = a^2 + k^2,$$

and the expression for the total kinetic energy can be written

$$T = \tfrac{1}{2}Mk_1^2\omega^2.$$

50. The Kinetic Energy of the Earth.—The two conspicuous motions of the earth are its revolution about the sun and its daily rotation about an axis approximately fixed in the earth. With respect to the sun its kinetic energy of translation is

$$T_e = \tfrac{1}{2}Mr^2\omega_1^2,$$

where r is its distance from the sun and ω_1 is its angular speed about the sun.

Its kinetic energy of rotation is

$$T_i = \tfrac{1}{2}I\omega^2 = .335Ma^2\omega^2, \qquad \text{by Chapter II, problem 18,}$$

where M is the mass of the earth, a is its radius, and ω is its angular speed of rotation.

The ratio of these two kinetic energies is

$$\frac{T_i}{T_e} = .67\left(\frac{a}{r}\right)^2\left(\frac{\omega}{\omega_1}\right)^2 = 1.63 \times 10^{-4} = \frac{1}{6{,}130},$$

since

$$\frac{a}{r} = 4.26 \times 10^{-5} \qquad \text{and} \qquad \frac{\omega}{\omega_1} = 366.25.$$

The kinetic energy of translation is therefore 6,130 times the kinetic energy of rotation.

The mass of the earth is 5.994×10^{27} grams, its radius is 6.374×10^{8} cm., and

$$\omega = \frac{2\pi}{86{,}164} = 0.00007292 = 7.292 \times 10^{-5}.$$

Consequently

$$\begin{aligned} T_i &= 4.334 \times 10^{36} \text{ ergs}, \\ &= 7.232 \times 10^{8} \text{ ergs per gram.} \end{aligned}$$

Since there are 4.186×10^{7} ergs in one calorie of heat, the kinetic energy of the earth's rotation expressed in heat units is 17.28 calories per gram. If Q is the number of calories of heat per gram of mass that is applied to a body, and η is the specific heat of the body, the temperature of the body is raised Q/η degrees centigrade. Assuming that the specific heat of the earth is $\frac{1}{7}$, and this is merely a guess, the interior kinetic energy of the earth is sufficient, if converted into heat, to raise the temperature of the entire earth 121° centigrade.

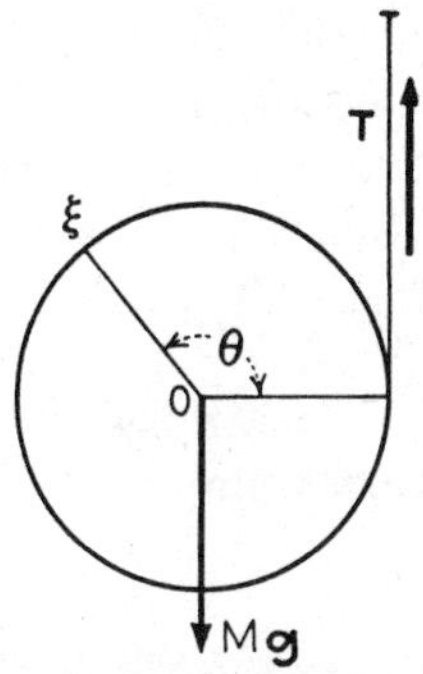

Fig. 23.

The temperature of a mathematically rigid body is necessarily zero, if temperature is defined as the mean kinetic energy of the molecules; for the particles of a rigid body have no independent motions. The concept of rigidity is a very useful one for many mechanical purposes, since many bodies act as a rigid body would do. A definition of rigidity that would satisfy mechanical requirements and also satisfy the requirements of thermal changes would, perhaps, be difficult.

51. Example.—A tape of negligible weight and thickness is wound tightly around a heavy cylinder of radius a, the length of the cylinder being equal to the width of the tape. The cylinder is held in a horizontal position with the tape taut and the free end of the tape in a vertical position is fastened to a rigid support. The cylinder is then allowed to fall freely. Describe the motion that ensues.

There are two forces acting on the cylinder, namely, its weight and the tension of the tape (Fig. 23). Both of these forces are vertical. If M is the mass of the cylinder and $\mathbf{T}$ is the tension of the tape, the equation of motion of the center of gravity of the cylinder is

$$M\mathbf{G}'' = M\mathbf{g} + \mathbf{T}. \tag{1}$$

Let z be a vertical axis, taken positively upward; then Eq. (1) becomes

$$Mz'' = -Mg + T. \tag{2}$$

The motion of the cylinder about its center of gravity is evidently a rotation about the axis of the cylinder. The moment of inertia of the cylinder with respect to its axis is $\frac{1}{2}Ma^2$. If θ represents the angle through which the cylinder has turned at the instant t, the angular speed ω is θ', and the principle of moment of momentum then gives

$$(\tfrac{1}{2}Ma^2\theta')' = aT,$$

or

$$Ma\theta'' = 2T. \tag{3}$$

On eliminating T between Eqs. (2) and (3) and removing the factor M, there is obtained

$$z'' - \tfrac{1}{2}a\theta'' = -g. \tag{4}$$

Now from the nature of the constraints,

$$z = z_0 - a\theta, \tag{5}$$

where z_0 is the initial height of the center of gravity. Hence

$$z'' = -a\theta'',$$

and Eq. (4) becomes

$$\theta'' = \frac{2}{3}\frac{g}{a},$$

and then from Eqs. (3) and (2)

$$T = \tfrac{1}{3}Mg, \qquad z'' = -\tfrac{2}{3}g,$$

and the center of gravity falls with exactly two thirds of the acceleration of a body that is entirely free, whatever the radius of the cylinder may be.

That the cylinder falls vertically is evident from the fact that at every instant the forces acting upon it are resolvable into a force $M\mathbf{g} + \mathbf{T}$ which acts vertically at the center of gravity, and a couple whose moment is aT. The couple has no effect upon the motion of the center of gravity, and inasmuch as the center of gravity had no horizontal motion initially, it cannot acquire one.

The kinetic energy of rotation absorbs one third and the kinetic energy of translation absorbs two thirds of the potential energy lost in falling.

52. The Three Angles of Euler.—The six parameters that are used to define the position of a rigid body to a large extent are a subject of choice. Three parameters, for example, are necessary to define the position of some fixed point O of the body with respect to a given coordinate system. Two more are necessary to define the direction of a line through O which is fixed in the body; and one is necessary to define a rotation of the body about this line.

The last three of these parameters are angles which define the orientation of the body. Imagine a trihedron, ξ, η, ζ, rigidly attached to the body, and a second trihedron, x, y, z, in fixed space. The position of the body in fixed space is determined if the origin of the ξ, η, ζ trihedron, x_0, y_0, z_0, relative to the x, y, z trihedron, together with the nine direction cosines of the ξ-, η-, and ζ-axes are given. If then ξ, η, ζ is a point fixed in the body, its coordinates in fixed space are

$$\left.\begin{aligned} x &= x_0 + \alpha_1\xi + \alpha_2\eta + \alpha_3\zeta, \\ y &= y_0 + \beta_1\xi + \beta_2\eta + \beta_3\zeta, \\ z &= z_0 + \gamma_1\xi + \gamma_2\eta + \gamma_3\zeta. \end{aligned}\right\}, \tag{1}$$

The nine direction cosines $\alpha_1, \ldots, \gamma_3$, however, are not independent, for there exist six independent relations among them, namely,

$$\left.\begin{aligned} \alpha_1^2 + \beta_1^2 + \gamma_1^2 &= 1, & \alpha_1\alpha_2 + \beta_1\beta_2 + \gamma_1\gamma_2 &= 0, \\ \alpha_2^2 + \beta_2^2 + \gamma_2^2 &= 1, & \alpha_2\alpha_3 + \beta_2\beta_3 + \gamma_2\gamma_3 &= 0, \\ \alpha_3^2 + \beta_3^2 + \gamma_3^2 &= 1, & \alpha_3\alpha_1 + \beta_3\beta_1 + \gamma_3\gamma_1 &= 0. \end{aligned}\right\} \tag{2}$$

The equations in the first column hold because α_i, β_i, and γ_i are the direction cosines of the ξ-, η-, and ζ-axes, and the sum of the squares of the direction cosines of any straight line is unity; the equations in the second column hold because ξ-, η-, and ζ-axes are mutually perpendicular.

The nine direction cosines, therefore, can be regarded as functions of three independent parameters. These parameters will be chosen as follows: Let θ be the angle between the z- and ζ-axes, Fig. 24, and therefore also the angle between the xy- and the $\xi\eta$-planes; ψ the longitude of the ascending node of the $\xi\eta$-plane, $K\xi S$, on the xy-plane; and φ the angle between the line of nodes, OK, and the ξ-axis, $O\xi$. These three angles θ, ψ, and φ are known as Euler's angles. It will be observed that θ and ψ determine the direction of the ζ-axis, while φ defines a rotation about the ζ-axis. It is desirable to have the nine direction cosines explicitly as functions of θ, ψ, and φ.

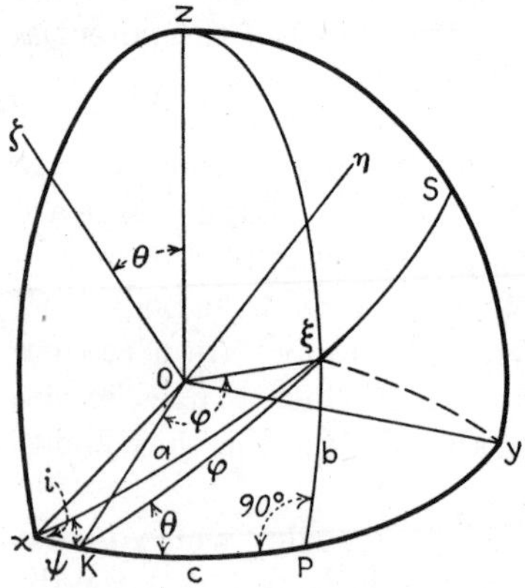

FIG. 24.

In any spherical triangle in which a, b, and c are the sides and A, B, and C are the angles opposite these sides the three equations

$$\begin{aligned} \cos a &= \cos b \cos c + \sin b \sin c \cos A, \\ \cos B \sin a &= \cos b \sin c - \sin b \cos c \cos A, \\ \sin B \sin a &= \sin b \sin A, \end{aligned} \tag{3}$$

hold. In the triangle $\xi x P$, Fig. 24, the sides are lettered a, b, and c; the angle B is denoted by i, and $A = 90°$. Hence

$$\begin{aligned} \cos a &= \cos b \cos c, &&= \cos \widehat{\xi x}, \\ \cos i \sin a &= \cos b \sin c, &&= \cos \widehat{\xi y}, \\ \sin i \sin a &= \sin b, &&= \cos \widehat{\xi z}. \end{aligned}$$

By applying the first of Eqs. (3) to the triangle $\xi P y$ it is found that

$$\cos \widehat{\xi y} = \cos (90° - c) \cos b = \cos b \sin c.$$

Since

$$\widehat{\xi z} = 90° - b,$$
$$\cos \widehat{\xi z} = \sin b,$$

and obviously

$$\cos \widehat{\xi x} = \cos a.$$

On applying Eqs. (3) to the triangle $x\xi K$ it is seen that

$$\begin{aligned}
\alpha_1 &= \cos \widehat{\xi x} = \cos a = \cos \psi \cos \varphi - \sin \varphi \sin \psi \cos \theta, \\
\beta_1 &= \cos \widehat{\xi y} = \cos i \sin a = \sin \psi \cos \varphi + \sin \varphi \cos \psi \cos \theta, \\
\gamma_1 &= \cos \widehat{\xi z} = \sin i \sin a = + \sin \varphi \sin \theta.
\end{aligned}$$

The formulas for α_2, β_2, and γ_2 are derived from the above merely by changing φ into $90° + \varphi$, since a rotation of 90° about the ζ-axis brings the ξ-axis to the original position of the η-axis.

In order to get α_3, β_3, and γ_3, it is necessary merely to draw the triangles $x\zeta z$, in which $\zeta z = \theta$, $xz = 90°$ and the angle at $z = 90° - \psi$, and $y\zeta z$, in which the angle at z is equal to $180° - \psi$, and then apply the first of Eqs. (3). There results the following table of values of the nine direction cosines as functions of the three Euler angles:

$$\left.\begin{aligned}
\alpha_1 &= - \sin \varphi \cos \theta \sin \psi + \cos \varphi \cos \psi, \\
\beta_1 &= + \sin \varphi \cos \theta \cos \psi + \cos \varphi \sin \psi, \\
\gamma_1 &= + \sin \varphi \sin \theta,
\end{aligned}\right\} \tag{4}$$

$$\left.\begin{aligned}
\alpha_2 &= - \cos \varphi \cos \theta \sin \psi - \sin \varphi \cos \psi, \\
\beta_2 &= + \cos \varphi \cos \theta \cos \psi - \sin \varphi \sin \psi, \\
\gamma_2 &= + \cos \varphi \sin \theta,
\end{aligned}\right\} \tag{5}$$

$$\left.\begin{aligned}
\alpha_3 &= + \sin \theta \sin \psi, \\
\beta_3 &= - \sin \theta \cos \psi, \\
\gamma_3 &= + \cos \theta.
\end{aligned}\right\} \tag{6}$$

The position of a body is uniquely defined by the six obviously independent parameters, x_0, y_0, z_0; ψ, φ, θ. If a body moves in such a way that ψ, φ, and θ remain constant, the motion is a pure translation; and if it moves in such a way that x_0, y_0, and z_0 remain constant the motion is a pure rotation about the origin of the trihedron which is fixed in the body. A rigid body has therefore three degrees of freedom of translation and three degrees of freedom of rotation. The freedom of a rigid body can be reduced by various kinds of constraint, but under no circumstances can the number of degrees of freedom exceed six.

53. The Laws of Friction.—It was first pointed out by Coulomb (1781), and later confirmed by Morin (1834), that within very wide limits, sliding friction is governed by two laws, namely,

1. Friction is proportional to the normal pressure between the surfaces in contact, and therefore is independent of the areas of the surfaces.

2. Friction is independent of the speed with which one surface slides over the other.

Nevertheless these laws are not mathematical laws in the sense that they hold under all circumstances. If the normal pressures are very high and have been long continued, the friction between the surfaces is notably increased. The friction between two surfaces relatively at rest (static friction) is greater than when the two surfaces are in motion (kinetic friction), and the friction is again diminished when the relative speeds are very high. However, for ordinary pressures and speeds, these laws represent the action of friction in a satisfactory manner.

If N is the normal force between the two surfaces in contact and F is the tangential force that is just necessary to produce slippage, the ratio

$$\frac{F}{N} = \mu$$

is called the coefficient of friction, and its value depends only on the nature of substances in contact (I, **113**).

If one body rolls upon another, both bodies are deformed and instead of a point of contact there is a small area in contact. In addition to the normal force and the force of sliding friction, there enters a frictional couple **C**, whose axis lies in the tangent plane perpendicular to the direction of motion. It was found by Osborne Reynolds[1] that this couple is very small and can usually be neglected. Of course, if the body has an angular velocity about the normal at the point of contact, there is also a frictional couple **T** which is called the couple of twisting friction.

[1] *Philosophical Transactions*, 1876.

This also is usually very small, but if the frictional force also is very small, both of these couples may be important.

Problems

1. A cannon resting on a rough horizontal plane is fired and the muzzle velocity of the projectile with respect to the cannon is v. If m_1 is the mass of the cannon, m_2 the mass of the projectile, the mass of the powder being negligible, and μ is the coefficient of friction, show that the distance of recoil of the cannon is

$$\left(\frac{m_2 v}{m_1 + m_2}\right)^2 \frac{1}{2\mu g}.$$

2. Two men each of mass m_2 are standing at the center of a uniform horizontal beam of mass m_1 which is rotating with uniform angular speed ω about a vertical axis through its center. If the two men walk out to the ends of the beam and ω_1 is then the angular speed, show that

$$\omega_1 = \frac{m_1}{m_1 + 6m_2}\omega.$$

3. If a shell at rest explodes and breaks into two fragments, show that the two fragments move in opposite directions along the same straight line with speeds that are inversely proportional to their masses.

4. A sheet of paper on which is drawn the circumference of a circle of radius a rests on a smooth table. A pin is pushed through the circumference into the table, so that the paper is free to turn about the pin. A bug of mass m is placed at rest at the end of the diameter through the pin and crawls with uniform speed along the circumference to the pin. If I is the moment of inertia of the paper with respect to the pin and

$$\mu = \frac{4ma^2}{I},$$

prove that the angle θ through which the paper has turned when the bug arrives at the pin is

$$\theta = \left(1 - \frac{1}{\sqrt{1+\mu}}\right)\frac{\pi}{2},$$

5. A circular hoop of mass m_1 and radius a lies on a smooth table, and a bug of mass m_2 is placed at rest on the hoop. The bug starts to crawl along the hoop with constant speed with respect to the hoop. If i and j are two relatively prime integers such that

$$i > (3 + 2\sqrt{2})j,$$

and if

$$\frac{m_1}{m_2} = \frac{(i - 3j) \pm \sqrt{i^2 - 6ij + j^2}}{2j},$$

show that when the bug has traveled around the hoop i times both the bug and the hoop are in their initial positions relative to the smooth plane.

6. Show that in the two-body problem for circular orbits

$$r^3\omega^2 = k^2(m_1 + m_2),$$

where k^2 is the gravitational constant, r is the distance between the two bodies, and ω is the angular speed in the orbits.

7. Tidal action of the moon on the earth is slowing down the rotation of the earth and lengthening the month. Neglecting the action of the sun and planets on the earth-moon system, and assuming that the orbits of the earth and moon are circles about their common center of gravity, show that the earth and moon will revolve just as though they were a single rigid body rotating about an axis through the center of gravity when the day and the month have a common period of approximately 48 days. The kinetic energy in the final state is approximately 10 per cent of the present kinetic energy of the system.

8. If μ is the coefficient of friction, the couple necessary to start into rotation a right circular cylinder of radius a and weight w that is standing on its base on a rough horizontal plane is $\frac{2}{3}wa\mu$. For a square cylinder of side a, it is $.743wa\mu$.

9. A uniform plank of thickness $2h$ rests in equilibrium on the top of a rough, horizontal cylinder of radius a. Show that, if $a > h$ the equilibrium is stable, and that if the plank is started to oscillating, the energy equation is

$$\frac{1}{2}(k^2 + h^2 + a^2\theta^2)\theta'^2 + g[a\theta \sin \theta - (a + h)][1 - \cos \theta] = \text{const.},$$

as long as the motion is a pure rolling.

10. A rod of length $2a$ and mass m slides without friction on a horizontal plane. A bead of the same mass m slides freely on the rod. Find the motion of the system and the constraint between the rod and the bead.

Let θ be the angle which the rod makes with a fixed line in the plane and $2r$ the distance of the bead from the center of the rod. In the particular case in which the center of gravity of the system is at rest and $r' = 0$, the path of the bead is given by the equations

$$(r^2 + \tfrac{1}{2}k^2)\theta' = c,$$
$$r'^2 + (r^2 + \tfrac{1}{2}k^2)\theta'^2 = h,$$

and therefore r can be expressed as an elliptic function of θ. (Greenhill, "Elliptic Functions," page 74.)

11. A uniform rod of mass m bent into the form of a plane curve slides without friction on a horizontal plane. Referred to its center of gravity G and a polar axis GA associated with the rod the equation of the curve is $\theta = f(r)$. A bead also of mass m slides freely on the rod. Let α be the angle at G which the bead makes with a fixed direction in the plane, and β the angle which GA makes with the same direction.

The principle of energy gives the equation

$$r'^2 + r^2\alpha'^2 + 2k^2\beta'^2 = h,$$

and the principle of angular momentum gives

$$r^2\alpha' + 2k^2\beta' = C;$$

and finally

$$\alpha - \beta = \theta = f(r).$$

These three equations determine α, β, and r as functions of the time.

12. Given a circle of radius a in a vertical plane and a vertical line L through its center. A heavy bar of length $2l$ has one extremity constrained to move without friction on L and slides without friction on the circle. The bar is placed initially at rest in a horizontal position and then released. Examine the motion. Show that, if $2a = \sqrt{3}l$, the angle θ which the bar makes with the horizontal oscillates between 0 and $\pi/3$.

13. A horizontal windlass of two heavy coaxial cylinders of different radii, r_1 and r_2, rigidly connected has two ropes wound in such a manner that when the windlass turns, one rope winds up and the other unwinds. Two weights w_1 and w_2 are attached to the ends of the ropes. If equilibrium does not exist under the action of the two weights, one weight will ascend while the other descends. Show that the motion is uniformly accelerated, and that the tension in the descending rope is less, and in the ascending rope greater, than it would be if the windlass were clamped and the entire system were in equilibrium.

14. Find the motion of a system composed of two uniform bars AB and CD, of the same length and mass, if the extremities of the bars A and C, also B and D, are connected by light strings of length l. The upper bar pivots at its mid-point and the motion is confined to a vertical plane.

15. A heavy body is rigidly attached to an axle of radius r in such a way that its center of gravity is on the axle. The axle is supported in a horizontal position by two bearings in which the axle is free to turn. It is acted upon by a vertical force F through the axle and a couple of moment C. Show that the equation of motion of the body is

$$Mk^2\omega' = C - Fr \sin \epsilon,$$

where ϵ is the angle of friction.

16. Given a horizontal wheel with hollow spokes, and in each spoke a ball which can be regarded as a particle of mass m. Initially the balls are all at the same distance from the center. An angular velocity ω is given to the system and it is then left to itself. Show that if there is no friction the equation of the path of each ball has the form

$$r \operatorname{cn} \theta = c.$$

(Greenhill, "Elliptic Functions," p. 75.)

17. A horizontal cylinder rolls down the side of a wedge that rests on a horizontal plane. Determine the motion under the assumption that there is no friction between the wedge and the plane on which it rests.

18. A solid triangle ABC of weight w_1 pivots at the corner C on a smooth horizontal plane. A particle of weight w_2 is constrained to move without friction along the side AB by an elastic string, of length h equal in length to the perpendicular from O to AB, attached to the point O. Determine the motion of the system.

CHAPTER V

MOTION PARALLEL TO A FIXED PLANE

ONE DEGREE OF FREEDOM

54. Introduction.—Since a perfectly free rigid body has six degrees of freedom, three of translation and three of rotation, a body that has but one degree of freedom may have one degree of freedom of translation without rotation, or it may rotate about a fixed axis without translation, or it may have both translation and rotation, the translation and rotation being related in some definite manner. The problem of translation does not differ essentially from the problem of motion of a single particle, since the center of gravity moves just as though all of the mass and all of the forces that are acting upon the body were concentrated at that point. It is only the forces of constraint that require additional attention.

55. Motion of Translation.—A uniform bar is free to slide along a straight line which it touches in two points (the end points), Fig. 25. An elastic string of negligible mass passes

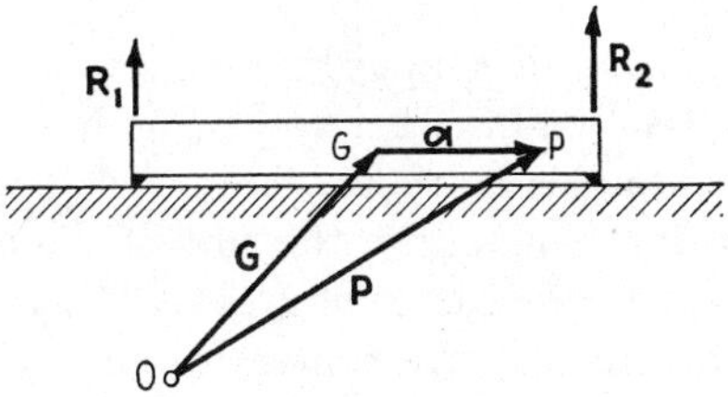

FIG. 25.

through a small hole at O and is attached to a point P of the bar, so that OP represents the stretch of the string. Determine the motion under the assumption that all of the constraints are smooth.

Taking O as an origin, let $\mathbf{P}$ be the point at which the string is attached, and $\mathbf{G}$ the center of gravity. Then

$$\mathbf{P} = \mathbf{G} + \mathbf{a}, \tag{1}$$

where **a** is a constant vector which will be assumed parallel to the line of motion. The force acting on the bar due to the stretched string is

$$\mathbf{T} = -k^2\mathbf{P},$$

where k^2 is a constant factor of proportionality, and the forces of constraint, $\mathbf{R}_1$ and $\mathbf{R}_2$, are perpendicular to the line along which the bar slides. The principle of momentum (Sec. 44) gives

$$M\mathbf{G}'' = -k^2\mathbf{P} + \mathbf{R}_1 + \mathbf{R}_2. \tag{2}$$

Let **i** be a unit vector parallel to the line of motion, and let Eq. (2) be multiplied by $\mathbf{i}\cdot$. There results

$$M\mathbf{i}\cdot\mathbf{G}'' = -k^2\mathbf{i}\cdot\mathbf{P}, \tag{3}$$

since

$$\mathbf{i}\cdot\mathbf{R}_1 = \mathbf{i}\cdot\mathbf{R}_2 = 0.$$

By Eq. (1),

$$\mathbf{P}'' = \mathbf{G}'',$$

and

$$\mathbf{i}\cdot\mathbf{G}'' = \mathbf{i}\cdot\mathbf{P}'' = (\mathbf{i}\cdot\mathbf{P})''.$$

Let $\mathbf{i}\cdot\mathbf{P}$, the component of **P** in the line of motion, be denoted by $\mathbf{P}_1$. Then Eq. (3) becomes

$$M\mathbf{P}_1'' = -k^2\mathbf{P}_1,$$

which is the equation of simple harmonic motion. Therefore, whatever the initial conditions may be, the bar slides back and forth in simple harmonic motion.

Since the bar does not rotate, the sum of the moments of the forces with respect to the center of gravity is zero. Let $\mathbf{l}_1$ and $\mathbf{l}_2$ be vectors, with origin at the center of gravity, perpendicular to $\mathbf{R}_1$ and $\mathbf{R}_2$ respectively and terminating in them. Then the equation of moments is

$$(\mathbf{l}_1 \times \mathbf{R}_1) + (\mathbf{l}_2 \times \mathbf{R}_2) + k^2(\mathbf{a} \times \mathbf{P}) = 0, \tag{4}$$

with

$$l_1 = l_2 = l.$$

If $\mathbf{P}_2$ is the component of $\mathbf{P}$ which is perpendicular to the line of motion, Eq. (4) gives the scalar equation

$$-lR_1 + lR_2 - k^2aP_2 = 0. \tag{5}$$

The sum of the forces perpendicular to the line of motion also vanishes, and this gives

$$R_1 + R_2 - k^2P_2 = 0, \tag{6}$$

and from Eqs. (5) and (6) it is found that

$$R_1 = k^2\frac{l - a}{2l}P_2, \qquad \text{and} \qquad R_2 = k^2\frac{l + a}{2l}P_2.$$

Since $\mathbf{P}_2$ is constant, the constraints $\mathbf{R}_1$ and $\mathbf{R}_2$ likewise are constant. The magnitudes of the constraints depend upon the point of attachment of the elastic string, **a**, but the period of the motion, $2\pi/k$, does not.

56. A Rough Cylinder Slides Down an Inclined Plane.—A right circular cylinder resting on its base slides down a plane which makes an angle α with a horizontal plane, the coefficient of sliding friction being $\mu = \tan \epsilon$. Determine the motion (Fig. 26).

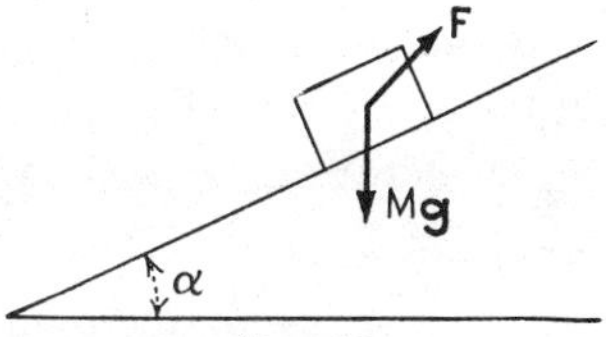

FIG. 26.

Let **i**, **j**, **k** be a system of unit vectors in fixed space, the **k**-axis being parallel to the intersection of the inclined and horizontal planes, the **j**-axis horizontal, and the **i**-axis vertical downward. Let $\mathbf{i}_0$, $\mathbf{j}_0$, $\mathbf{k}_0$ be a system which is fixed with respect to the cylinder, the $\mathbf{k}_0$-axis parallel to the **k**-axis, the $\mathbf{j}_0$-axis directed up the plane and the $\mathbf{i}_0$-axis normal to the inclined plane. Then

$$\mathbf{i} = \mathbf{i}_0 \cos \alpha - \mathbf{j}_0 \sin \alpha,$$
$$\mathbf{j} = \mathbf{i}_0 \sin \alpha + \mathbf{j}_0 \cos \alpha.$$

The forces acting on the cylinder are its weight, $Mg\,\mathbf{i}$, and the constraint, or reaction, of the plane. The constraint of the plane is equivalent to a single force **F** acting at the center of gravity and a couple (I, **150**). Since the cylinder does not rotate in any manner, the couple is obviously zero, and the principle of momentum gives the equation of motion

$$\begin{aligned} M\mathbf{G}'' &= Mg\,\mathbf{i} + \mathbf{F} \\ &= Mg(\cos\alpha\,\mathbf{i}_0 - \sin\alpha\,\mathbf{j}_0) + \mathbf{F}, \end{aligned}$$

the origin of $\mathbf{G}$ being arbitary.

On taking

$$\mathbf{F} = F_1\mathbf{i}_0 + F_2\mathbf{j}_0 + F_3\mathbf{k}_0,$$

it is evident that

$$F_3 = 0, \qquad \text{and} \qquad F_1 = -Mg\cos\alpha,$$

since there is no motion normal to the plane. The frictional component F_2 in magnitude is μ times the normal component F_1 and is directed up the plane. Hence

$$\mathbf{F} = -Mg\cos\alpha\,\mathbf{i}_0 + Mg\mu\cos\alpha\,\mathbf{j}_0,$$

and

$$\begin{aligned} M\mathbf{G}'' &= Mg(\mu\cos\alpha - \sin\alpha)\mathbf{j}_0 \\ &= -Mg\frac{\sin(\alpha - \epsilon)}{\cos\epsilon}\mathbf{j}_0. \end{aligned}$$

The angle α must be equal to or greater than the angle ϵ, since friction certainly will not make the cylinder slide up the plane. The acceleration is zero or down the plane and is constant in magnitude.

57. Rotation about a Fixed Axis.—If a rigid body moves about an axis which is fixed in the body and fixed also in space, the axis must be supported by outside forces; that is, the axis is constrained to remain in a fixed straight line, and it will be assumed that the axis cannot slip along this line. Two supports acting at Q_1 and Q_2 (Fig. 27) are sufficient for this purpose, and the constraints which are acting at these points will be denoted by $\mathbf{R}_1$ and $\mathbf{R}_2$.

The applied forces that are acting on the body, whatever they may be, are equivalent to a single force $\mathbf{F}$, which is acting at the center of gravity, and a couple $\mathbf{C}$ (I, **150**). Let a plane be passed through the center of gravity perpendicular to the axis, and let the intersection of the axis and the plane be the point O. With O as the point of reference, let $\mathbf{G}$ be the position vector of the center of gravity, and therefore perpendicular to the axis.

If M is the mass of the body, the principle of momentum (Sec. 44) gives the equation

$$M\mathbf{G}'' = \mathbf{F} + \mathbf{R}_1 + \mathbf{R}_2. \tag{1}$$

Let the axis of rotation be the **k**-axis of an **i**, **j**, **k** system of mutually orthogonal unit vectors in fixed space. The moment of **F** with respect to the point O is $\mathbf{G} \times \mathbf{F}$; and if

$$OQ_1 = z_1, \qquad \text{and} \qquad OQ_2 = z_2,$$

(z_1 is negative in the diagram), the moments of $\mathbf{R}_1$ and $\mathbf{R}_2$ with respect to the point O are

$$z_1(\mathbf{k} \times \mathbf{R}_1) \qquad \text{and} \qquad z_2(\mathbf{k} \times \mathbf{R}_2).$$

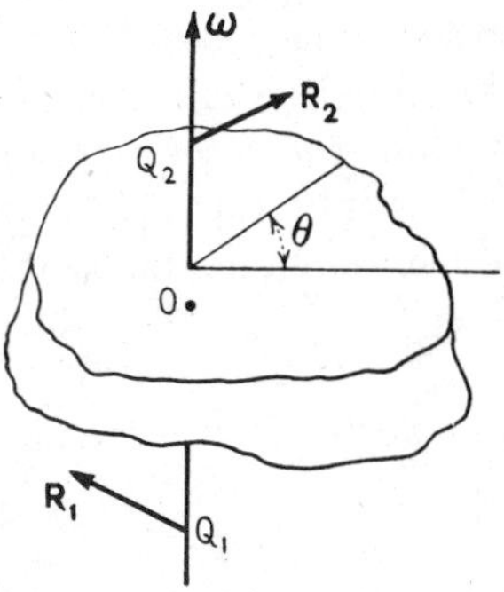

FIG. 27.

The moment of all of the forces with respect to the point O is therefore

$$\mathbf{N}_o = \mathbf{C} + (\mathbf{G} \times \mathbf{F}) + z_1(\mathbf{k} \times \mathbf{R}_1) + z_2(\mathbf{k} \times \mathbf{R}_2). \tag{2}$$

The moment of momentum of the body with respect to the point O is, by Eq. (46.5),

$$\mathbf{L}_o = I\boldsymbol{\omega} - \omega\mathbf{P},$$

where I is the moment of inertia with respect to the axis of rotation; $\boldsymbol{\omega}$, which coincides in direction with the axis, represents the angular velocity about the axis; and **P** is a vector, perpendicular to the axis and fixed in the body, which depends upon the products of inertia of the body at the point O. Since **P** is fixed in the body,

$$\mathbf{P}' = \boldsymbol{\omega} \times \mathbf{P},$$

and

$$\mathbf{L}_o' = I\boldsymbol{\omega}' - \omega'\mathbf{P} - \omega(\boldsymbol{\omega} \times \mathbf{P}).$$

The principle of moment of momentum [Eq. (45.1)] now gives the equation

$$\mathbf{L}_o' = \mathbf{N}_o,$$

or

$$I\boldsymbol{\omega}' - \omega'\mathbf{P} - \omega(\boldsymbol{\omega} \times \mathbf{P}) = [\mathbf{C} + (\mathbf{G} \times \mathbf{F})] + \mathbf{k} \times [z_1\mathbf{R}_1 + z_2\mathbf{R}_2]. \tag{3}$$

If Eq. (3) is multiplied by $\mathbf{k}\,\cdot$, there results the scalar equation

$$I\omega' = \mathbf{k} \cdot [\mathbf{C} + (\mathbf{G} \times \mathbf{F})], \tag{4}$$

which determines the motion about the axis.

58. Determination of the Constraints.—Since Eq. (57.4) contains only quantities that are given in the problem, it is reducible to an ordinary differential equation of the second order. Suppose this equation has been solved and therefore ω is known. There remains the determination of the constraints $\mathbf{R}_1$ and $\mathbf{R}_2$.

Multiply Eq. (57.3) by $\mathbf{k}\,\times$. Since $\boldsymbol{\omega}$ is fixed in direction, $\boldsymbol{\omega}'$ has the same direction as $\boldsymbol{\omega}$. Therefore

$$I\mathbf{k} \times \boldsymbol{\omega}' = 0.$$

The vector $\mathbf{P}$ is perpendicular to $\boldsymbol{\omega}$, so that

$$\mathbf{k} \times \mathbf{P} = \mathbf{P}_{90},$$

where $\mathbf{P}_{90}$ is the vector obtained by rotating $\mathbf{P}$ forward through 90°, keeping it perpendicular to $\boldsymbol{\omega}$. By Eq. (5.4)

$$\mathbf{k} \times (\boldsymbol{\omega} \times \mathbf{P}) = -\omega\mathbf{P},$$
$$\mathbf{k} \times [\mathbf{k} \times (z_1\mathbf{R}_1 + z_2\mathbf{R}_2)] = [\mathbf{k} \cdot (z_1\mathbf{R}_1 + z_2\mathbf{R}_2)]\mathbf{k} - (z_1\mathbf{R}_1 + z_2\mathbf{R}_2).$$

The vector $[\mathbf{k} \cdot (z_1\mathbf{R}_1 + z_2\mathbf{R}_2)]\mathbf{k}$ is the $\mathbf{k}$-component of

$$(z_1\mathbf{R}_1 + z_2\mathbf{R}_2);$$

let it be denoted by the letter $\mathbf{K}$. The result of multiplying Eq. (57.3) by $\mathbf{k}\,\times$ is therefore

$$z_1\mathbf{R}_1 + z_2\mathbf{R}_2 = \mathbf{A} = \boldsymbol{\omega}'\mathbf{P}_{90} - \omega^2\mathbf{P} + \mathbf{k} \times [\mathbf{C} + (\mathbf{G} \times \mathbf{F})] - \mathbf{K}. \tag{1}$$

Since

$$\mathbf{G}' = \boldsymbol{\omega} \times \mathbf{G}, \qquad \text{and} \qquad \mathbf{G}'' = (\boldsymbol{\omega}' \times \mathbf{G}) - \omega^2\mathbf{G},$$

Eq. (57.1) gives the relation

$$\mathbf{R}_1 + \mathbf{R}_2 = \mathbf{B} = M(\boldsymbol{\omega}' \times \mathbf{G}) - M\omega^2\mathbf{G} - \mathbf{F}. \tag{2}$$

If $z_2 - z_1$, which is the distance between Q_1 and Q_2 in Fig. 27, is denoted by the letter h, the solution of Eqs. (1) and (2) gives the expressions for the forces of constraint

$$\left.\begin{aligned} h\mathbf{R}_1 &= -\mathbf{A} + z_2\mathbf{B}, \\ h\mathbf{R}_2 &= +\mathbf{A} - z_1\mathbf{B}. \end{aligned}\right\} \tag{3}$$

The vector **A** contains an unknown vector **K**, which is parallel to the axis. The **k**-components of $\mathbf{R}_1$ and $\mathbf{R}_2$ are therefore undetermined, and it is obvious from Fig. 27 that this must be so; for if any force parallel to the axis is introduced at Q_1, and the same force reversed is applied at Q_2, the operation would have no effect upon the motion of the body and no effect upon the components of the constraints perpendicular to the axis. Hence, although the sum,

$$\mathbf{R}_1 + \mathbf{R}_2 = \mathbf{B},$$

is uniquely determined, the difference

$$h(\mathbf{R}_2 - \mathbf{R}_1) = 2\mathbf{A} - (z_1 + z_2)\mathbf{B},$$

contains an arbitrary vector which is parallel to the axis. The components perpendicular to the axis are completely determined by Eq. (3).

59. The Nature of the Constraints.—It will be observed that the vector **A** contains the term $\omega^2\mathbf{P}$ and that **B** contains the term $\omega^2\mathbf{G}$. In rapidly rotating machinery these terms may rise to very high values, since ω itself is large, unless **P** and **G** vanish, and they may be large even though **P** and **G** are merely small. As is seen from Eqs. (58.3), **B** occurs in $\mathbf{R}_1$ and $\mathbf{R}_2$ with the same sign, if the body is rotating between the two points of support.

The term $M\omega^2\mathbf{G}$ corresponds to centrifugal force. It acts in the same direction, perpendicular to the axis, on both bearings. The term $\omega^2\mathbf{P}$, which occurs in **A**, enters $\mathbf{R}_1$ and $\mathbf{R}_2$ with opposite signs, forming a couple whose axis is perpendicular to the axis of rotation. Since **P** and **G** are fixed in the body the constraints are reversed at each half revolution. It is not difficult to see that a very rapid rotation will soon tear a machine to pieces unless **P** and **G** are extremely small or zero.

The condition $\mathbf{G} = 0$ means that the center of gravity of the body lies on the axis of rotation, and the condition $\mathbf{P} = 0$ means that the axis of rotation is a principal axis of inertia at the point O. If both of these conditions are satisfied, the axis of rotation coincides with a principal axis of inertia at the center of gravity; the component of **A** which is perpendicular to the axis of rotation vanishes, and **B** is reduced to $-\mathbf{F}$. The constraints and the force **F** are a system of forces in equilibrium and produce no effect upon the rotation. Equation (57.4) reduces to

$$I\omega' = \mathbf{k} \cdot \mathbf{C}. \tag{1}$$

60. The System of Forces Has a Unique Resultant Which Passes Through the Axis.—Let two forces **F** and $-\mathbf{F}$ be introduced at any point Q on the axis, and let the distance from O to Q (Fig. 28) be z, taken positively if Q is above O and negatively if below. These two forces form a system in equilibrium, and have no effect upon the body or upon the constraints. The force $-\mathbf{F}$ at Q and the force $+\mathbf{F}$ at G form a couple, namely,

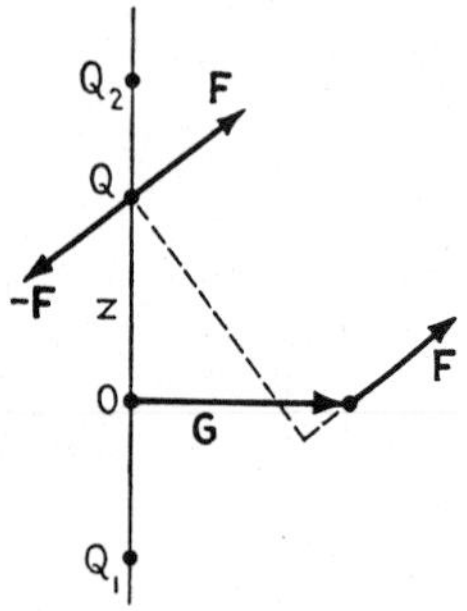

FIG. 28.

$$(\mathbf{G} - z\mathbf{k}) \times \mathbf{F}.$$

Consequently the two forces at Q and the single force at the center of gravity are equivalent to a single force **F** which passes through the axis and a couple. If this couple neutralizes the couple **C**, then the couple **C** and the single force acting at the center of gravity are equivalent to a single force **F** which passes through the axis at Q. Hence, the condition that the forces acting upon the body should have a unique resultant which passes through the axis is

$$(\mathbf{G} - z\mathbf{k}) \times \mathbf{F} = -\mathbf{C},$$

or

$$\mathbf{C} + (\mathbf{G} \times \mathbf{F}) = z(\mathbf{k} \times \mathbf{F}),$$

where z is some scalar.

Now

$$\mathbf{k} \cdot \mathbf{k} \times \mathbf{F} = \mathbf{k} \times \mathbf{k} \cdot \mathbf{F} = 0,$$

and Eq. (57.4) becomes

$$I\omega' = 0, \tag{1}$$

from which it follows that ω is a constant, and the body spins about the axis with a constant angular speed.

Also

$$-\mathbf{k} \times (\mathbf{k} \times \mathbf{F}) = \mathbf{F} - (\mathbf{k} \cdot \mathbf{F})\mathbf{k}$$

is the component of **F** which is perpendicular to the axis. Let it be denoted by $\mathbf{F}_P$. The expressions for **A** and **B** become, neglecting the **k**-components,

$$\mathbf{A} = -\omega^2\mathbf{P} - z\mathbf{F}_P,$$
$$\mathbf{B} = -\omega^2 M\mathbf{G} - \mathbf{F}_P;$$

and the constraints are

$$h\mathbf{R}_1 = +\omega^2(\mathbf{P} - z_2 M\mathbf{G}) - (z_2 - z)\mathbf{F}_P,$$
$$h\mathbf{R}_2 = -\omega^2(\mathbf{P} - z_1 M\mathbf{G}) + (z_1 - z)\mathbf{F}_P.$$

The vector **P** in these expressions is the vector defined in Sec. 46 and is associated with the point O. If $\mathbf{P}_{Q_1}$ and $\mathbf{P}_{Q_2}$ are the corresponding vectors associated with the points Q_1 and Q_2, it is a simple matter to show that

$$\mathbf{P}_{Q_1} = \mathbf{P} - z_1 M\mathbf{G}, \qquad \mathbf{P}_{Q_2} = \mathbf{P} - z_2 M\mathbf{G},$$

so that

$$\left.\begin{aligned} h\mathbf{R}_1 &= +\omega^2\mathbf{P}_{Q_2} - (z_2 - z)\mathbf{F}_P, \\ h\mathbf{R}_2 &= -\omega^2\mathbf{P}_{Q_1} + (z_1 - z)\mathbf{F}_P. \end{aligned}\right\} \qquad (2)$$

If the axis of rotation is a principal axis of inertia at the point Q_1, $\mathbf{P}_{Q_1}$ vanishes, and if $z = z_1$, that is if **F** passes through Q_1, the constraint at Q_2 disappears altogether. Hence the theorem:

Theorem.—If a solid body, rotating about a fixed point, is acted upon by forces which have a unique resultant which passes through that point, and if the axis of rotation is a principal axis of inertia at the fixed point, then the body will continue to turn indefinitely about this axis with constant angular velocity.

For this reason the principal axes of inertia at any point are sometimes called *the permanent axes of rotation.*

Under what conditions can the constraint at Q_1 also vanish? Equation (2) gives the condition

$$\omega^2\mathbf{P}_{Q_2} = h\mathbf{F}_P.$$

Since the vector $\mathbf{P}_{Q_2}$ is fixed in the body, it is necessary that $\mathbf{F}_P$ should be constant in magnitude and rotate about the axis with the same speed as the body; or, that

$$\mathbf{F}_P = 0, \qquad \mathbf{P}_{Q_2} = 0.$$

These last conditions will be satisfied if there are no exterior forces, and if the axis of rotation is a principal axis not only at Q_1 but also at Q_2. By the theorem of Sec. 22, if any line is a principal axis of inertia for two of its points it is a principal axis for all of its points, and the line passes through the center of gravity. Consequently:

Theorem.—A rigid body that is turning about a principal axis of inertia of the central ellipsoid and is not acted on by any exterior force will continue to turn about that axis with constant speed, without any constraints.

This fact has given to the principal axes of the central ellipsoid of inertia the name *the spontaneous axes of rotation.*

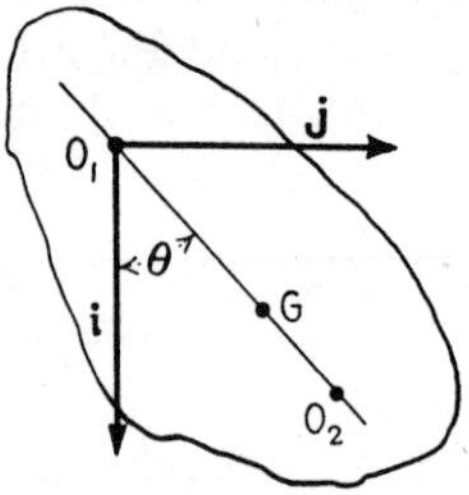

FIG. 29.

61. The Compound Pendulum.—Any heavy rigid body that turns freely about a horizontal axis and is acted upon by no exterior force except gravity is a compound pendulum.

In accordance with the previous notation, the horizontal axis of rotation will be taken as the **k**-direction of an **i**, **j**, **k** system, the **j**-direction being horizontal, and the **i**-direction vertical downward (Fig. 29). The only forces acting upon the body are its weight,

$$\mathbf{F} = Mg\,\mathbf{i},$$

acting at the center of gravity, and the constraints acting on the horizontal axis.

Inasmuch as there is no applied couple, Eq. (57.4) gives the equation of motion, namely,

$$I\omega' = \mathbf{k} \cdot \mathbf{G} \times \mathbf{F}. \tag{1}$$

In Fig. 29 the line O_1GO_2 passes through the center of gravity G and is perpendicular to the horizontal axis of rotation, so that

$$\mathbf{G} = \overrightarrow{O_1G},$$

and

$$\theta = \widehat{\mathbf{iG}}.$$

Now

$$\mathbf{k} \cdot \mathbf{G} \times \mathbf{F} = Mg\,\mathbf{k} \cdot \mathbf{G} \times \mathbf{i} = -Mg\,\mathbf{j} \cdot \mathbf{G} = -Mgl_1 \sin \theta.$$

It is convenient here to depart from the customary notation and let

$$\text{tensor of } \mathbf{G} = O_1G = l_1.$$

As usual,

$$I = Mk_1^2,$$

where k_1 is the radius of gyration of the body with respect to the axis.

Since

$$\omega = \theta',$$

Eq. (1) becomes, after removing the mass factor M,

$$k_1^2\theta'' = -gl_1 \sin \theta. \tag{2}$$

On comparing this equation with the equation of motion of a simple pendulum of length $l_1 + l_2$, namely,

$$(l_1 + l_2)\theta'' = -g \sin \theta,$$

it is plain that the motion of a compound pendulum is the same as that of a simple pendulum whose length is

$$l_1 + l_2 = \frac{k_1^2}{l_1}, \qquad \text{or} \qquad l_1(l_1 + l_2) = k_1^2. \tag{3}$$

On the straight line O_1G measure a length O_1O_2 equal to $l_1 + l_2$. The particle at O_2 of the solid body moves just as though it were tied to the axis by a thread without weight and were not acted upon by the rest of the body.

Let k_0 be the radius of gyration about an axis through the center of mass parallel to the axis of rotation, and let k_2 be the radius of gyration relative to a parallel axis at O_2. Then

$$k_1^2 = k_0^2 + l_1^2 \qquad \text{and} \qquad k_2^2 = k_0^2 + l_2^2. \tag{4}$$

On eliminating k_1^2 between Eq. (3) and the first of Eqs. (4), it is seen that

$$l_1l_2 = k_0^2. \tag{5}$$

Since l_1 and k_0^2 are positive, the same is true of l_2, and the center of gravity lies between the points O_1 and O_2.

On the line O_1O_2 erect a perpendicular at G equal to k_0 (Fig. 30). Join the extremity of this perpendicular to the points O_1 and O_2.

By Eqs. (4), these lines represent k_1 and k_2 in magnitude and they are mutually perpendicular, by Eq. (5). If ψ is the angle between k_0 and k_1, then

$$k_1 = k_0 \sec \psi, \qquad l_1 = k_0 \tan \psi,$$
$$k_2 = k_0 \operatorname{cosec} \psi, \qquad l_2 = k_0 \cot \psi.$$

It is evident from Fig. 30, and also from Eq. (5), that if the point O_1 recedes from G the point O_2 approaches G, and vice versa. Since

$$l_1 + l_2 = 2k_0 \operatorname{cosec} 2\psi,$$

the distance between the two points has a minimum when

$$l_1 = l_2 = k_0.$$

For small oscillations the period of the pendulum is

$$P = 2\pi\sqrt{\frac{l_1 + l_2}{g}} = 2\pi\sqrt{\frac{2k_0}{g \sin 2\psi}}.$$

Therefore for a given direction of the axis with respect to the body there exists a minimum of period. The period of oscillation cannot be less than

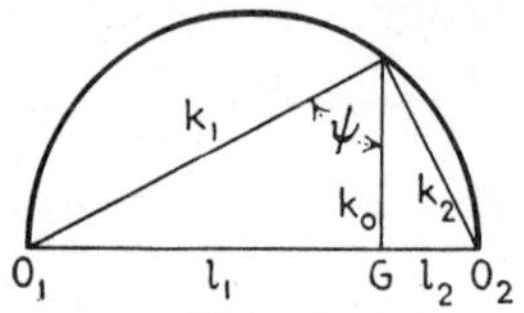

FIG. 30.

$$P_{min} = 2\pi\sqrt{\frac{2k_0}{g}},$$

no matter where the axis may be in the body.

The axis through O_1 is called *the axis of suspension*, and the parallel axis through O_2 was given the name *the axis of oscillation* by Huygens, who first analyzed this problem correctly. From the symmetrical manner in which the lengths l_1 and l_2 enter the formulas, it is evident that if the axis through O_2 be taken as the axis of suspension, the axis through O_1 becomes the axis of oscillation, and that the period of oscillation is unaltered. The point O_2 is called the *center of oscillation.*

62. The Reversible Pendulum.—The fact that the axes of suspension and oscillation are interchangeable without alteration of period was utilized very cleverly by Captain Henry Kater[1] in 1818 for the construction of what is equivalent to a simple pendulum. Kater's reversible pendulum was a bar of rec-

[1] *Philosophical Transactions*, 1818, 1819.

tangular cross section with two steel knife-edges perpendicular to the plane of the bar and fixed in position, their distances from the center of mass being unequal. A heavy ring, movable micrometrically along the bar, permitted a slight change in the position of the center of mass. The bar was allowed to oscillate first on one knife-edge and then on the other and the heavy ring was adjusted until the times of oscillation on the two knife-edges were equal. When equality was attained, the distance between the two knife-edges was the length of the equivalent simple pendulum.

In order to obtain the time of oscillation accurately, the pendulum is placed before the pendulum of an astronomical clock whose rate is accurately known. On the clock pendulum is fastened a white surface on which is ruled a black line such that when the two pendulums are at rest the experimental pendulum coincides in position with the black line. The pendulums are then set into motion. Assuming that the periods of the two pendulums are approximately, but not exactly, the same, the instant of a coincidence, with the two pendulums moving in the same direction, is noted. At the end of the first complete oscillation after this instant one of the pendulums will have gained on the other and coincidence will have ceased. After a sufficient interval of time there will be a second coincidence with the two pendulums moving in the same direction. If the clock pendulum has made n swings (n half periods) the experimental pendulum will have made $n + 2$ or $n - 2$ swings, according as it swings more rapidly or more slowly than the clock pendulum. Assuming that the clock pendulum swings in exactly one second, the time of swing of the experimental pendulum (the half period) is

$$T = \frac{n}{n \pm 2} \text{ seconds.}$$

In an experiment of this kind, it was observed by Biot and Mathieu that a pendulum oscillated 7015.5 in 7017.5 seconds. Consequently the time of a single swing of the pendulum was 1.00026251, and if an error of 5 seconds was made in the observed value of n, the time of oscillation was 1.00026253 seconds, a difference of only two hundred-millionths of a second. The distance between the two knife-edges, the equivalent simple pendulum, is, of course, obtained by a very careful measurement.

Routh has listed the following points to which careful attention should be paid in the construction of a reversible pendulum.[1]

1. The axes of suspension, or knife-edges, must not be at the same distance from the center of mass. They should be parallel to each other.

2. The times of oscillation about the knife-edges should be nearly equal.

3. The external form of the body must be symmetrical, and the same about the two axes of suspension.

4. The pendulum must be of such regular shape that the dimensions of all of the parts can be readily calculated.

These conditions are satisfied if the pendulum be of rectangular shape with two cylinders placed one at each end. The external forms of these cylinders should be equal and similar, but one solid and the other hollow, and such that the distance between the knife-edges is as nearly as possible equal to the length of the simple equivalent pendulum found by *calculation*.

5. The pendulum should be made, as far as possible, of one metal, so that as the temperature changes it may always be similar to itself. In this case since the times of oscillations of similar bodies vary as the square root of their linear dimensions, it is easy to reduce the observed time of oscillation to a standard temperature. The knife-edges however must be made of some strong substance not likely to be easily injured.

63. Determination of the Constraints.—The vectors which determine the constraints are [Eqs. (58.1) and (58.2)]

$$\mathbf{A} = \omega'\mathbf{P}_{90} - \omega^2\mathbf{P} + \mathbf{k} \times (\mathbf{G} \times \mathbf{F}),$$
$$\mathbf{B} = M(\boldsymbol{\omega}' \times \mathbf{G}) - M\omega^2\mathbf{G} - \mathbf{F}.$$

For definiteness it will be assumed that the body is symmetrical with respect to a plane which passes through the center of gravity perpendicular to the axis of rotation. With this assumption

$$\mathbf{P} = \mathbf{P}_{90} = 0,$$

since the axis of rotation is a principal axis of inertia at the point O_1. Both of the vectors **F** and **G** are perpendicular to the axis of rotation, and therefore $\mathbf{G} \times \mathbf{F}$ is parallel to the axis. From this it follows that

[1] Routh, E. J., "Elementary Rigid Dynamics," 5th ed., p. 84 (1891).

$$\mathbf{k} \times (\mathbf{G} \times \mathbf{F}) = 0,$$

and the vector **A** is always zero.

Suppose the axis has two supports equidistant from O_1, and that the distance is a. Then

$$-z_1 = z_2 = a,$$

and the constraints are [Eq. (58.3)]

$$\mathbf{R}_1 = \mathbf{R}_2 = \tfrac{1}{2}\mathbf{B} = \tfrac{1}{2}M(\boldsymbol{\omega}' \times \mathbf{G}) - \tfrac{1}{2}M\omega^2\mathbf{G} - \tfrac{1}{2}\mathbf{F}.$$

From Eq. (61.2) it is seen that

$$\boldsymbol{\omega}' = -\frac{l_1}{k_1^2}g \sin\theta\, \mathbf{k}.$$

Let $\mathbf{i}_0$ and $\mathbf{j}_0$ be mutually orthogonal unit vectors rigidly attached to the body perpendicular to the axis of rotation, and let $\mathbf{i}_0$ coincide in direction with **G**. Then

$$\mathbf{i} = \mathbf{i}_0 \cos\theta - \mathbf{j}_0 \sin\theta,$$

and

$$\boldsymbol{\omega}' \times \mathbf{G} = -\frac{l_1^2}{k_1^2}g \sin\theta (\mathbf{k} \times \mathbf{i}_0) = -\frac{l_1^2}{k_1^2}g \sin\theta\, \mathbf{j}_0.$$

Since

$$\mathbf{F} = Mg\, \mathbf{i},$$

the expression for **B** becomes

$$\mathbf{B} = -M\left[\frac{l_1^2}{k_1^2}g \sin\theta\, \mathbf{j}_0 + \{l_1 w^2\, \mathbf{i}_0 + g(\mathbf{i}_0 \cos\theta - \mathbf{j}_0 \sin\theta)\}\right].$$

On multiplying Eq. (61.2) by 2ω and then integrating, it is found that

$$\omega^2 = C + 2\frac{l_1}{k_1^2}g \cos\theta,$$

and with this value of ω^2, the expression for **B** becomes

$$\mathbf{B} = \left[-\frac{k_0^2 + 3l_1^2}{k_0^2 + l_1^2}Mg \cos\theta - MCl_1\right]\mathbf{i}_0 + \frac{k_0^2}{k_0^2 + l_1^2}Mg \sin\theta\, \mathbf{j}_0.$$

If ω vanishes for $\theta = \theta_0$,

$$C = -2\frac{l_1}{k_1^2}g \cos \theta_0,$$

and the expression for **B** can be written

$$\mathbf{B} = \left[-\frac{k_0^2 + 3l_1^2}{k_0^2 + l_1^2}Mg(\cos \theta - \cos \theta_0) - Mg \cos \theta_0 \right]\mathbf{i}_0 + \frac{k_0^2}{k_0^2 + l_1^2}Mg \sin \theta \, \mathbf{j}_0.$$

If θ_0 is real and $\cos \theta_0 > 0$, the $\mathbf{i}_0$ component of **B** is always negative, but if $\cos \theta_0 < 0$, this component changes sign at the point where

$$\frac{\cos \theta}{\cos \theta_0} = \frac{2l_1^2}{k_0^2 + 3l_1^2} < \frac{2}{3}.$$

The $\mathbf{j}_0$ component changes sign with $\sin \theta$ always. If the center of gravity is on the right side of a vertical plane through the axis, the $\mathbf{j}_0$ component is directed toward the right of this plane; and if the center of gravity is on the left side, the $\mathbf{j}_0$ component of the constraint is also directed toward the left of this plane.

64. A Cylinder Rolls Down an Inclined Plane.—A cylinder of radius a rolls down an inclined plane, the inclination being α, from a position of rest. Determine the motion under the assumptions that there is no slipping and that the rolling couple of friction can be neglected.

Since the constraints do no work and the kinetic energy initially was zero, the kinetic energy at any instant is equal to the work done upon the cylinder by gravity.

In Fig. 31, let the **i**-direction be downward normal to the plane, the **j**-direction up the plane, and the **k**-direction parallel to the horizontal axis of the cylinder. Let **G**, the center of gravity, be measured from its initial position and the angle θ regarded as a vector be measured along the **k**-axis. The principle of energy (Sec. 48) gives the equation, after removing the factor $M/2$,

$$\mathbf{G}' \cdot \mathbf{G}' + k^2 \, \boldsymbol{\omega} \cdot \boldsymbol{\omega} = -2g \sin \alpha \, \mathbf{G} \cdot \mathbf{j}, \tag{1}$$

where k is the radius of gyration of the cylinder with respect to its axis, and not the tensor of **k** which is unity. Now

$$\mathbf{G} = a(\mathbf{i} \times \boldsymbol{\theta}) = a(\mathbf{i} \times \theta\,\mathbf{k}) = -a\theta\,\mathbf{j}$$
$$\mathbf{G}' = -a\omega\,\mathbf{j},$$

so that

$$\mathbf{G}' \cdot \mathbf{G}' = a^2\boldsymbol{\omega} \cdot \boldsymbol{\omega}, \qquad \text{or} \qquad \boldsymbol{\omega} \cdot \boldsymbol{\omega} = \frac{1}{a^2}\mathbf{G}' \cdot \mathbf{G}',$$

and Eq. (1), by the elimination of $\boldsymbol{\omega} \cdot \boldsymbol{\omega}$, becomes

$$\frac{a^2 + k^2}{a^2}\mathbf{G}' \cdot \mathbf{G}' = -2g \sin \alpha \, \mathbf{G} \cdot \mathbf{j}, \tag{2}$$

which by differentiation gives

$$\mathbf{G}' \cdot \left[\frac{a^2 + k^2}{a^2}\mathbf{G}'' + g \sin \alpha \, \mathbf{j}\right] = 0.$$

Since these two vectors are not perpendicular and $\mathbf{G}' \not\equiv 0$, it follows that

$$\mathbf{G}'' = -\frac{a^2}{a^2 + k^2} g \sin \alpha \, \mathbf{j}. \tag{3}$$

If the cylinder were sliding down the plane without friction, and not rolling, the corresponding equation would be

$$\mathbf{G}'' = -g \sin \alpha \, \mathbf{j}, \tag{4}$$

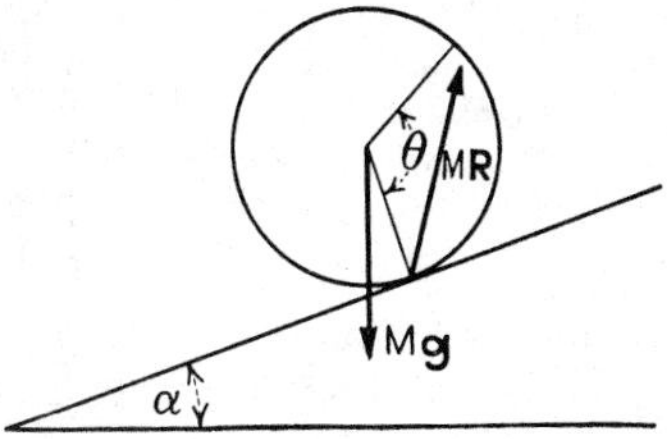

FIG. 31.

which is what Eq. (3) becomes for $k^2 = 0$. The rolling acceleration is constant, but the cylinder rolls down more slowly than it would slide down without friction.

This analysis assumes that the center of gravity lies on the axis of the cylinder, but it does not assume that the cylinder is homogeneous. If it is homogeneous,

$$k^2 = \frac{1}{2}a^2, \qquad \text{and} \qquad \frac{a^2}{a^2 + k^2} = \frac{2}{3}.$$

Let the constraint of the plane be denoted by $M\mathbf{R}$. The principle of momentum furnishes the equation

$$\mathbf{G}'' = g \cos \alpha \, \mathbf{i} - g \sin \alpha \, \mathbf{j} + \mathbf{R}.$$

Using the value of $\mathbf{G}''$ from Eq. (3), this equation gives

$$\mathbf{R} = -g \cos \alpha \, \mathbf{i} + \frac{k^2}{a^2 + k^2} g \sin \alpha \, \mathbf{j}. \tag{5}$$

The ratio of the interior kinetic energy to the exterior kinetic energy is

$$\frac{k^2\omega^2}{G'^2} = \frac{k^2}{a^2}.$$

This also is constant, and since k^2 is never greater than a^2 the kinetic energy of rotation never exceeds the kinetic energy of translation.

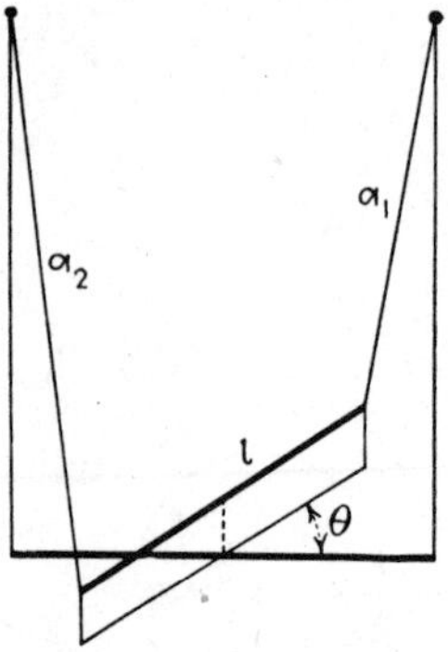

FIG. 32.

65. A Bifilar Pendulum.—A straight rod of length l is suspended by two light strings each of length a from two points in the ceiling. The distance between the two points of suspension also is l, so that when the rod is at rest in its position of equilibrium, it is horizontal and the two strings are parallel (Fig. 32). It is assumed that the center of mass is at the center of the rod, but otherwise the loading of the rod may be anything whatever. The rod is turned through a certain angle and released from a position of rest in which the rod is horizontal and the center of mass lies in the same vertical line as it did in the position of equilibrium. It is required to determine the motion and the tensions in the strings.

Let **i, j, k** be a system of unit vectors fixed with respect to the bar, **i** being directed along the bar, **j** directed 90° ahead and **k** directed vertical upward; and let $\mathbf{i}_0$, $\mathbf{j}_0$, $\mathbf{k}_0$ be a corresponding system in fixed space, the two systems coinciding when the rod is in its position of equilibrium. For any other position, in which the bar is turned through an angle θ,

$$\left.\begin{aligned} \mathbf{i}_0 &= \cos\theta\,\mathbf{i} - \sin\theta\,\mathbf{j}, \\ \mathbf{j}_0 &= \sin\theta\,\mathbf{i} + \cos\theta\,\mathbf{j}, \\ \mathbf{k}_0 &= \mathbf{k}. \end{aligned}\right\} \tag{1}$$

Let $M\mathbf{T}_1$ be the tension directed along a_1, and $M\mathbf{T}_2$ the tension in a_2. From symmetry

$$T_1 = T_2 = T.$$

Let **G** be the position of the center of gravity with respect to the equilibrium position. Then, from I, **149,**

$$G = a - \sqrt{a^2 - l^2 \sin^2 \tfrac{1}{2}\theta}. \tag{2}$$

From the principles of momentum and moment of momentum,

$$\mathbf{G}'' = -g\mathbf{k} + \mathbf{T}_1 + \mathbf{T}_2, \tag{3}$$

$$k^2\boldsymbol{\omega}' = \tfrac{1}{2}l[\mathbf{i} \times (\mathbf{T}_1 - \mathbf{T}_2)] \cdot \mathbf{k}\ \mathbf{k}; \tag{4}$$

and from the principle of energy

$$\mathbf{G}' \cdot \mathbf{G}' + k^2\boldsymbol{\omega} \cdot \boldsymbol{\omega} = 2g(\mathbf{G}_0 - \mathbf{G}) \cdot \mathbf{k}. \tag{5}$$

By differentiation of Eq. (2), it is found that

$$G' = \frac{l^2 \sin \theta}{4(a - G)}\omega,$$

and then from Eq. (5)

$$\left(\frac{l^4 \sin^2 \theta}{16(a - G)^2} + k^2\right)\theta'^2 = 2g(G_0 - G). \tag{6}$$

Let $\mathbf{a}_1$ and $\mathbf{a}_2$ be unit vectors which have the directions of $\mathbf{T}_1$ and $\mathbf{T}_2$. It follows from the geometry of Fig. 32 that, if $\lambda = l/a$,

$$\mathbf{a}_1 = +\frac{\lambda}{2}(1 - \cos\theta)\,\mathbf{i}_0 - \frac{\lambda}{2}\sin\theta\,\mathbf{j}_0 + \sqrt{1 - \lambda^2 \sin^2 \frac{1}{2}\theta}\,\mathbf{k}_0,$$

$$\mathbf{a}_2 = -\frac{\lambda}{2}(1 - \cos\theta)\,\mathbf{i}_0 + \frac{\lambda}{2}\sin\theta\,\mathbf{j}_0 + \sqrt{1 - \lambda^2 \sin^2 \frac{1}{2}\theta}\,\mathbf{k}_0;$$

or, by virtue of Eqs. (1),

$$\mathbf{a}_1 = -\lambda \sin^2 \tfrac{1}{2}\theta\,\mathbf{i} - \lambda \sin \tfrac{1}{2}\theta \cos \tfrac{1}{2}\theta\,\mathbf{j} + \sqrt{1 - \lambda^2 \sin^2 \tfrac{1}{2}\theta}\,\mathbf{k},$$
$$\mathbf{a}_2 = +\lambda \sin^2 \tfrac{1}{2}\theta\,\mathbf{i} + \lambda \sin \tfrac{1}{2}\theta \cos \tfrac{1}{2}\theta\,\mathbf{j} + \sqrt{1 - \lambda^2 \sin^2 \tfrac{1}{2}\theta}\,\mathbf{k}.$$

Therefore

$$\mathbf{T}_1 + \mathbf{T}_2 = 2T\sqrt{1 - \lambda^2 \sin^2 \tfrac{1}{2}\theta}\,\mathbf{k},$$
$$\mathbf{T}_1 - \mathbf{T}_2 = 2T\lambda(-\sin^2 \tfrac{1}{2}\theta\,\mathbf{i} - \sin \tfrac{1}{2}\theta \cos \tfrac{1}{2}\theta\,\mathbf{j}),$$

and

$$[\mathbf{i} \times (\mathbf{T}_1 - \mathbf{T}_2)] \cdot \mathbf{k} = -T\lambda \sin\theta.$$

Hence, from Eqs. (3) and (4),

$$\left.\begin{aligned} G'' &= -g + 2T\sqrt{1 - \lambda^2 \sin^2 \tfrac{1}{2}\theta}, \\ k^2\omega' &= -\tfrac{1}{2}lT\lambda \sin\theta. \end{aligned}\right\} \tag{7}$$

If Eq. (6) is differentiated, the value of $\theta'' = \omega'$ replaced by the second of Eq. (7), and the resulting equation then solved for T, it is found that

$$T = 8gak^2\left[\frac{a - G}{[16k^2(a - G)^2 + l^4 \sin^2 \theta]} + \frac{8(G_0 - G)[a^2(l^2 - a^2) + (a - G)^4]}{[16k^2(a - G)^2 + l^4 \sin^2 \theta]^2}\right],$$

which, by virtue of Eq. (2), can be expressed wholly in terms of θ or of G.

If $\theta/2$ is replaced by φ, Eq. (6) can be written

$$\sqrt{\frac{4k^2(a^2 - l^2 \sin^2 \varphi) + l^4 \sin^2 \varphi \cos^2 \varphi}{4(a^2 - l^2 \sin^2 \varphi)(G_0 - a + \sqrt{a^2 - l^2 \sin^2 \varphi})}}\, d\varphi = \sqrt{2g}\, dt.$$

The relation between the angle θ and the time t is a quadrature, which, unfortunately, cannot be effected. But if the oscillations are very small (infinitesimal), the terms of lowest order in Eq. (6) give

$$k^2\theta'^2 = g\frac{l^2}{4a}(\theta_0^2 - \theta^2),$$

and, by differentiation, the harmonic equation

$$\theta'' + \frac{l^2 g}{4ak^2}\theta = 0.$$

Hence the period of a small oscillation is

$$P = 2\pi\frac{2k}{l}\sqrt{\frac{a}{g}}.$$

For a uniform rod $2k = l/\sqrt{3}$ (I, **97**), and the period of a small oscillation is

$$P_1 = 2\pi\sqrt{\frac{a}{3g}}.$$

If the rod swings without rotation, it is essentially a simple pendulum with the period $P_2 = 2\pi\sqrt{a/g}$. The ratio of these periods gives the equation

$$P_2 = P_1\sqrt{3}.$$

The rod oscillates more rapidly when rotating than when it is merely swinging, provided both oscillations are small.

TWO DEGREES OF FREEDOM

66. The Cylinder Rolls and Slides.—Returning to the problem of Sec. 64, it is seen from Eq. (64.5) and Fig. 31, that the tangent of the angle which the reaction of the plane **R** upon the cylinder makes with the normal to the plane is

$$\frac{k^2}{(a^2 + k^2)} \tan \alpha,$$

which, for a given cylinder, is a constant. In order that the cylinder may roll only, it is necessary that the angle between **R** and the normal to the plane shall be less than the angle of friction ϵ, and therefore

$$\frac{k^2}{a^2 + k^2} \tan \alpha < \mu, \tag{1}$$

where μ is the tangent of ϵ and therefore the coefficient of friction.

If the inclination of the plane, α, is so large that Eq. (1) is not satisfied, the reaction of the plane makes the constant angle ϵ with the normal; for by the nature of friction this is the largest angle which the reaction can make. Slipping begins at once, and the cylinder both rolls and slides.

Using the notation of Sec. 64, the principles of momentum and moment of momentum give the equations

$$\left.\begin{aligned} \mathbf{G}'' &= \mathbf{g} + \mathbf{R}, \\ k^2\boldsymbol{\omega}' &= a(\mathbf{i} \times \mathbf{R}). \end{aligned}\right\} \tag{2}$$

The energy equation, Eq. (64.1), no longer holds, since part of the work done in falling is dissipated by friction. Since

$$\begin{aligned} \mathbf{G} &= -G\,\mathbf{j}, \\ \mathbf{g} &= g \cos \alpha\,\mathbf{i} - g \sin \alpha\,\mathbf{j}, \\ \mathbf{R} &= -R \cos \epsilon\,\mathbf{i} + R \sin \epsilon\,\mathbf{j}, \end{aligned}$$

Eqs. (2) lead at once to the scalar equations

$$\left.\begin{aligned} G'' &= g \sin \alpha - R \sin \epsilon, \\ k^2\omega' &= aR \sin \epsilon, \\ 0 &= R \cos \epsilon - g \cos \alpha. \end{aligned}\right\} \tag{3}$$

The last of Eqs. (3) gives

$$R \sin \epsilon = \mu g \cos \alpha,$$

and then the first two become

$$\left.\begin{aligned} G'' &= g(\sin \alpha - \mu \cos \alpha) = g\frac{\sin (\alpha - \epsilon)}{\cos \epsilon}, \\ k^2\theta'' &= ag\mu \cos \alpha. \end{aligned}\right\} \tag{4}$$

Let

$$s = G - a\theta, \tag{5}$$

represent the distance through which the cylinder has slipped. Then from Eqs. (4),

$$\begin{aligned} s'' &= \frac{g}{\cos \epsilon}\left(\sin (\alpha - \epsilon) - \frac{a^2}{k^2} \cos \alpha \sin \epsilon\right) \\ &= \frac{g}{\cos \epsilon}\left(\sin \alpha \cos \epsilon - \frac{a^2 + k^2}{k^2} \cos \alpha \sin \epsilon\right), \end{aligned}$$

which is positive, since, by hypothesis,

$$\mu < \frac{k^2}{a^2 + k^2} \tan \alpha.$$

If the first of Eqs. (4) is multiplied by G' and integrated, and the second is multiplied by θ' and integrated, and the two equations are then added, it is found that the kinetic energy is

$$\begin{aligned} \frac{1}{2}M(G'^2 + k^2\theta'^2) &= Mg\left[\frac{\sin (\alpha - \epsilon)}{\cos \epsilon}G + a\mu\theta \cos \alpha\right] \\ &= Mg[G \sin \alpha - s\mu \cos \alpha]. \end{aligned}$$

A comparison of this equation with Eq. (64.1) shows that the loss of energy due to slip is

$$Mgs\mu \cos \alpha,$$

an expression that could have been anticipated.

When the cylinder rolls without slipping the position of the center of gravity depends upon the radius of gyration, Eq. (64.3), but if it rolls and slides, it is independent of the radius of gyration, Eq. (4).

67. A Rocking Pendulum.—If a rigid body rolls upon a cylindrical axis instead of pivoting upon a linear axis, it is a rocking pendulum. The motion may be a pure rolling, a roll and a slip, or there may be no friction of any kind.

It will be assumed that the rolling axis is a right circular cylinder of radius r, that the distance of the center of gravity from the axis of the cylinder is l, that k is the principal radius of gyration, and that the pendulum is symmetrical with respect to a plane through the center of gravity and perpendicular to the axis. Let O be the position of the axis, Fig. 33, when the pendulum hangs at rest and let **G** be the position of the center of gravity referred to the point O. Finally, take an **i, j, k** system of unit

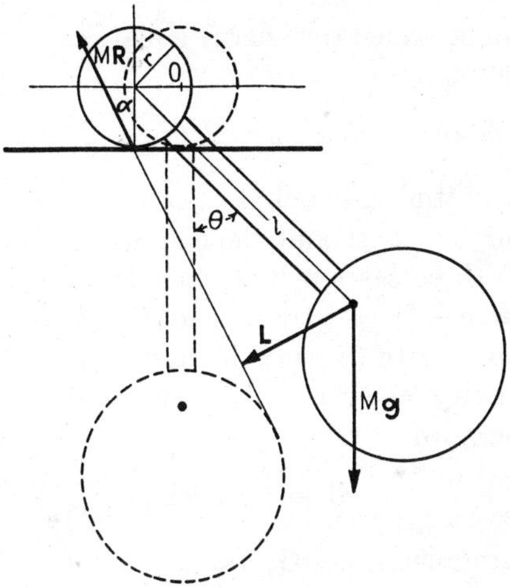

FIG. 33.

vectors with **i** directed vertically downward, **j** horizontal and perpendicular to the axis of the cylinder, and **k** parallel to this axis. By virtue of symmetry the reaction $M\mathbf{R}$ of the horizontal surface on which the cylinder rolls can be regarded as lying in the plane through the center of gravity perpendicular to the axis of the cylinder. Let α be the angle which **R** makes with the normal. The vector **R** lies on the left side of the normal in Fig. 33, and therefore α is positive, if the pendulum is descending, that is ω, or θ', is negative, and to the right, if θ' is positive.

With the symbolism thus established, the principles of momentum and moment of momentum give the two equations

$$\left.\begin{aligned} \mathbf{G}'' &= \mathbf{g} + \mathbf{R}, \\ k^2\omega' &= \mathbf{L} \times \mathbf{R}, \end{aligned}\right\} \tag{1}$$

where **L** is a vector from the center of gravity, perpendicular to the line of **R**. It is seen from the geometry that

$$L = l \sin(\theta - \alpha) + r \sin \alpha,$$

so that

$$\mathbf{L} \times \mathbf{R} = -R[l \sin(\theta - \alpha) + r \sin \alpha]\,\mathbf{k}.$$

Equations (1), therefore, can be written

$$\left.\begin{aligned} \mathbf{G}'' &= (g - R\cos\alpha)\,\mathbf{i} - R\sin\alpha\,\mathbf{j}, \\ k^2\boldsymbol{\omega}' &= -R[l\sin(\theta-\alpha) + r\sin\alpha]\,\mathbf{k}, \end{aligned}\right\} \tag{2}$$

and to these can be added the energy equation, except in the case of rolling and slipping,

$$\mathbf{G}' \cdot \mathbf{G}' + k^2\boldsymbol{\omega} \cdot \boldsymbol{\omega} = 2g(\mathbf{G} - \mathbf{G}_0) \cdot \mathbf{i}, \tag{3}$$

where $\mathbf{G}_0$ is the initial value of **G**.

The equations of constraint depend upon the nature of the motion and the three cases will be considered separately.

(*A*) *No Friction.*—In case there is no friction and the pendulum is released from a state of rest, the first of Eqs. (2) shows that the center of gravity falls vertically from its initial value $\mathbf{G}_0$, since α is zero. Therefore

$$\mathbf{G} = l \cos\theta\,\mathbf{i}. \tag{4}$$

With this expression for **G**, the energy equation [Eq. (3)] becomes

$$(k^2 + l^2 \sin^2\theta)\theta'^2 = 2gl(\cos\theta - \cos\theta_0), \tag{5}$$

and, by differentiation and simplification,

$$\theta'' = -\frac{gl\sin\theta}{k^2 + l^2\sin^2\theta}\left[1 + \frac{2l^2\cos\theta(\cos\theta - \cos\theta_0)}{k^2 + l^2\sin^2\theta}\right], \tag{6}$$

which for infinitesimal oscillations reduces to that of the compound pendulum [Eq. (61.2)].

The second equation of Eqs. (2) then gives the reaction

$$R = -\frac{k^2\theta''}{l\sin\theta} = \frac{gk^2}{k^2 + l^2\sin^2\theta}\left[1 + \frac{2l^2\cos\theta(\cos\theta - \cos\theta_0)}{k^2 + l^2\sin^2\theta}\right]. \tag{7}$$

(*B*) *Pure Rolling.*—In case friction exists the motion is one of pure rolling as long as the angle of the reaction α with the normal is less than the angle of friction, ϵ. It will be shown that α is not a constant and that the pendulum may roll for a while and then slip. As long as the motion is one of pure rolling, the equation of constraint is

$$\mathbf{G} = l \cos \theta \, \mathbf{i} + (l \sin \theta - r\theta) \, \mathbf{j}. \tag{8}$$

If the couple of rolling friction be neglected, no work is done by friction and the energy equation holds. By the use of Eq. (8), and the substitution $h = l \cos \theta_0$, Eq. (3) becomes

$$\theta'^2 = \frac{2g(l \cos \theta - h)}{l^2 + r^2 + k^2 - 2rl \cos \theta}, \tag{9}$$

and again, by differentiation and simplification,

$$\theta'' = -\frac{l^2 + r^2 + k^2 - 2rh}{[l^2 + r^2 + k^2 - 2rl \cos \theta]^2} gl \sin \theta. \tag{10}$$

For small oscillations, this equation becomes

$$\theta'' = \frac{-gl\theta}{(l - r)^2 + k^2},$$

and the period of the oscillation is

$$P = 2\pi \sqrt{\frac{(l - r)^2 + k^2}{gl}}.$$

On differentiating Eq. (8) twice, it is found that

$$\mathbf{G}'' = -[l\theta'' \sin \theta + l\theta'^2 \cos \theta] \, \mathbf{i} + [l\theta'' \cos \theta - l\theta'^2 \sin \theta] \, \mathbf{j};$$

and if this result is substituted in Eq. (2), there results

$$\left.\begin{aligned} R \sin \alpha &= -(l \cos \theta - r)\theta'' + l\theta'^2 \sin \theta, \\ R \cos \alpha &= g + l \sin \theta \theta'' + l\theta'^2 \cos \theta. \end{aligned}\right\} \tag{11}$$

Since θ'' [Eq. (10)] carries $\sin \theta$ as a factor and $R > 0$, the first equation of Eq. (11) shows that α has the same sign as θ, and vanishes with θ. If therefore the angle of friction ϵ is not zero, for small values of θ, $\alpha < \epsilon$, and the pendulum begins to roll and it will continue to roll as long as $\tan \alpha < \mu$. In order to abbreviate the expression as much as possible let

$$n^2 = l^2 + r^2 + k^2, \qquad x = l \cos \theta.$$

The expression for tan α in terms of θ is then

$$\tan \alpha = \frac{\{[-n^2(r + 2h) + 2r^2h] + [3n^2 + 2rh]x - 4rx^2\}l \sin \theta}{[n^2(r^2 + k^2) + 2rhl^2] - 2n^2[2r + h]x + [3n^2 + 4r^2 + 2rh]x^2 - 4rx^4}. \tag{12}$$

This expression is too complicated to solve for θ in terms of α, and therefore of μ. Suppose however a series of increasingly large oscillations are made. For what value of h will the pendulum be on the point of slipping at the end of its swing? Under these conditions $l \cos \theta$ is equal to h, by Eq. (9). Then from Eqs. (10) and (11) it is found that

$$\mu = \frac{(h - r)\sqrt{l^2 - h^2}}{k^2 + (h - r)^2}, \tag{13}$$

an equation that determines h in terms of μ, r, k and l.

(*C*) *Rolling and Slipping.*—The angle α cannot exceed ϵ in magnitude. When $\alpha = \epsilon$ sliding begins. Let s represent the amount of the slide. Then

$$\mathbf{G} = [l \cos \theta]\,\mathbf{i} + [l \sin \theta - r\theta - s]\,\mathbf{j}$$

and Eqs. (2) become

$$\begin{aligned} \mathbf{G}'' &= [g - R \cos \epsilon]\,\mathbf{i} - [R \sin \epsilon]\,\mathbf{j}, \\ k^2\boldsymbol{\omega}' &= -R[l \sin (\theta - \epsilon) + r \sin \epsilon]\mathbf{k}. \end{aligned}$$

The angle ϵ is now a constant, and s is a new variable. These equations are equivalent to the scalar equations

$$\begin{aligned} l \sin \theta\theta'' + l \cos \theta\theta'^2 &= -g + R \cos \epsilon, \\ (l \cos \theta - r)\theta'' - l \sin \theta\theta'^2 &= s'' - R \sin \epsilon, \\ k^2\theta'' &= -Rl \sin (\theta - \epsilon) + Rr \sin \epsilon. \end{aligned}$$

The result of eliminating R from the first two equations is

$$[l \sin (\theta - \epsilon) - r\theta \cos \epsilon]'' = -g \sin \epsilon + s'' \cos \epsilon.$$

If R is eliminated from the third equation by means of the first, there results a differential equation which contains only θ and its derivatives. If this equation

$$k^2\theta'' - [l \sec \epsilon \sin (\theta - \epsilon) + r\mu](l \cos \theta)'' = gr\mu$$

could be integrated, the other functions would be obtained by quadratures and the problem would be solved completely.

The loss of energy due to the sliding is

$$M\int R \sin \epsilon ds.$$

68. A Billiard Ball.—If the stroke of a billiard cue on the ball is like the one indicated in Fig. 34 and the line of the force lies outside the cone of friction of the ball with the table and inside the cone of friction of the cue with the ball, the ball moves forward on the table and at the same time spins on a horizontal axis that is perpendicular to the line of motion of the ball. It is desired to follow the subsequent motion of the ball, neglecting the couple of rolling friction.

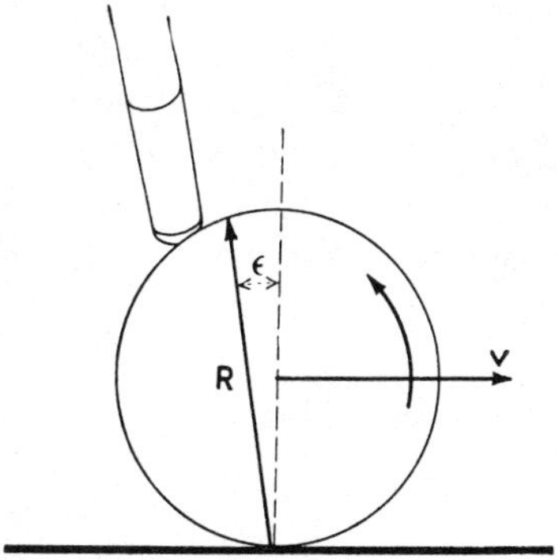

FIG. 34.

Let **G** be the position of the center of gravity of the ball, relative to its initial position. The ball is assumed to be uniform in density and therefore the center of gravity is at the center of the ball. Let ω be the angular velocity about the horizontal axis which is perpendicular to the plane of the paper in Fig. 34. The principles of momentum and moment of momentum give at once the two scalar equations

$$MG'' = -MR \sin \epsilon,$$
$$Mk^2\omega' = -MaR \sin \epsilon,$$

where $\boldsymbol{MR}$ is the reaction of the table. Since the ball has no motion in a vertical direction

$$MR \cos \epsilon = Mg.$$

Therefore R is constant and, since $k^2 = \frac{2}{5}a^2$, the equations of motion become

$$\left.\begin{aligned} G'' &= -g\mu, \\ \omega' &= -\frac{5}{2}\frac{g\mu}{a}, \end{aligned}\right\} \qquad (1)$$

with the initial conditions

$$G = 0, \qquad \theta = 0,$$
$$G' = v, \qquad \theta' = \omega_0.$$

Then, by integration,

$$\left.\begin{aligned} G' &= -g\mu t + v, & \theta' &= -\frac{5}{2}\frac{g\mu}{a}t + \omega_0, \\ G &= -\frac{1}{2}g\mu t^2 + vt, & \theta &= -\frac{5}{4}\frac{g\mu}{a}t^2 + \omega_0 t. \end{aligned}\right\} \tag{2}$$

The differential equations, Eq. (1), are valid as long as the ball slips on the table, and the solutions, Eq. (2), also. The speed of the lowest point of the ball is $G' + a\theta'$. Therefore Eqs. (1) and (2) are valid until

$$G' + a\theta' = 0,$$

when the sliding stops; and since, from Eqs. (2),

$$G' + a\theta' = -\tfrac{7}{2}g\mu t + a\omega_0 + v,$$

this happens for

$$t = \frac{2}{7}\frac{a\omega_0 + v}{g\mu}.$$

At this instant

$$G' = +\tfrac{5}{7}v - \tfrac{2}{7}a\omega_0,$$

and

$$a\theta' = -\tfrac{5}{7}v + \tfrac{2}{7}a\omega_0.$$

If the condition

$$v = \tfrac{2}{5}a\omega_0 \tag{3}$$

is satisfied, translation and rotation cease at the same instant, and the ball stops. The reaction $M\mathbf{R}$ changes abruptly and becomes normal to the table, and in magnitude is equal to Mg. The forces which are acting upon the ball form a system that is in equilibrium, and since the ball is at rest, it continues at rest.

If the condition Eq. (3) is not satisfied, let

$$v = \tfrac{2}{5}a\omega_0 + \tfrac{7}{5}u,$$

where u is a new constant. Then at the instant sliding ceases

$$G' = u, \qquad a\theta' = -u. \tag{4}$$

Since the point of contact with the table is at rest, while the center of the ball is moving, the ball begins to roll, in a forward direction if u is positive, and backward if u is negative.

Suppose that at this instant the table became perfectly smooth. The reaction $M\mathbf{R}$ would be normal to the table, passing through the center of the sphere. The equations of motion would be

$$G'' = 0, \qquad k^2\theta'' = 0.$$

With the initial conditions [Eq. (4)] the geometrical relation,

$$G + a\theta = \text{constant} = \frac{7}{25}\frac{(a\omega_0 + u)^2}{g\mu}, \tag{5}$$

would be satisfied, and the ball would roll with constant speed. Continued friction, therefore, is not necessary to make the ball roll. It will roll without friction. It is here that the couple of rolling friction becomes important for the ball certainly will not continue to roll with constant speed.

The force which has been represented by $M\mathbf{R}$ now makes an unknown angle α with the normal and it does not represent the entire reaction of the table. There must be added the frictional couple, which can be denoted by $MCag$, the axis of which is parallel to the table and perpendicular to the line of motion. The equations of motion are

$$\left.\begin{aligned} G'' &= -R \sin \alpha, \\ k^2\theta'' &= -aR \sin \alpha + Cag. \end{aligned}\right\} \tag{6}$$

The geometrical relation,

$$G + a\theta = \frac{7}{25}\frac{(a\omega_0 + u)^2}{g\mu},$$

still holds, and of course

$$R \cos \alpha = g.$$

On differentiating the geometrical relation twice and then substituting from the other relations, it is found that

$$\tan \alpha = +\tfrac{5}{7}C.$$

Eqs. (6) now become

$$G'' = -\tfrac{5}{7}Cg, \qquad k^2\theta'' = +\tfrac{2}{7}Cag, \qquad a\theta'' = \tfrac{5}{7}Cg. \tag{7}$$

The sign of the constant C depends upon θ'; in fact, it is opposite in sign, since the friction opposes rolling. If $u > 0$, it is readily seen from Eqs. (4) that

$$G' > 0, \qquad \theta' < 0, \qquad C > 0, \qquad G'' < 0 \quad \text{and} \quad \theta'' > 0;$$

and if $u < 0$, the inequalities are all reversed.

The integration of Eqs. (7) shows that the rolling ceases when

$$t = \frac{7}{5}\frac{u}{Cg},$$

t being counted from the instant when rolling began. The total

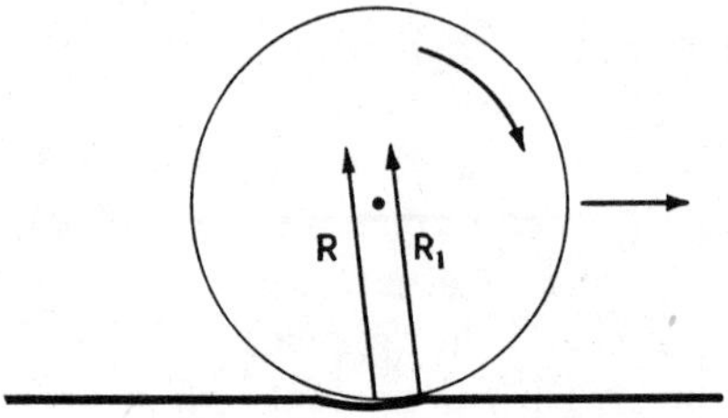

FIG. 35.

amount of time elapsed from the beginning of the motion to the end is therefore

$$T = \frac{2}{7}\frac{a\omega_0 + v}{g\mu} + \frac{7}{5}\frac{u}{Cg} = \frac{2}{5}\frac{a\omega_0 + u}{g\mu} + \frac{7}{5}\frac{u}{Cg}.$$

The reaction of the table and the frictional couple can be combined into a single reaction $\mathbf{R}_1$, Fig. 35, but the point of application is displaced forward. Since Eqs. (7) must be satisfied it is evident that

$$\mathbf{R}_1 = \mathbf{R}.$$

Let δ be the distance from the center of the sphere to the line of $\mathbf{R}_1$. The moment of $\mathbf{R}_1$ with respect to the center of the sphere is then $R\delta$, and therefore

$$R\delta = \frac{2}{7}Cag, \qquad \text{or} \qquad \delta = \frac{2}{7}\frac{C}{R}ag.$$

The vector $\mathbf{R}$ must therefore be displaced parallel to itself by an amount

$$a \sin \alpha + \delta = \frac{5}{7}\frac{C}{R}ag + \frac{2}{7}\frac{C}{R}ag = \frac{C}{R}ag = Ca \cos \alpha,$$

and the horizontal displacement is Ca.

The couple of rolling friction is due to a slight deformation of the table, or of the ball, or of both.

69. The Instantaneous Axis of Rotation—Centrodes.—Since any displacement of a rigid body parallel to a fixed plane can be effected by a rotation about a suitable axis perpendicular to the plane (I, **124**) any continuous motion of a body parallel to a fixed plane can be resolved into a series of infinitesimal rotations about an axis which, in general, is itself in continuous motion both with respect to the body and with respect to the plane. If the motion of the axis were discontinuous, the motion of the body also would be regarded as discontinuous.

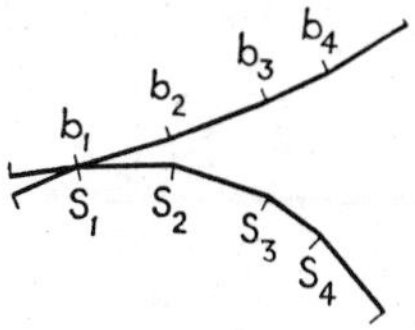

FIG. 36.

The axis about which the body is rotating at any instant in this resolution of the motion is called the *instantaneous axis of rotation.* The locus of the instantaneous axis in the body is called the *body centrode,* and the locus of the axis with respect to the fixed plane is called the *space centrode.* It is fairly evident that the motion of the body is just the same as though the body-centrode, rigidly attached to the body, were rolling without slipping upon the space centrode. In order to make this clear, however, imagine a series of small but finite rotations. In Fig. 36 let s_1, s_2, s_3, s_4 be four consecutive positions of the instantaneous axis on the fixed plane at the instants t_1, t_2, t_3, t_4, and b_1, b_2, b_3, b_4 be the positions in the body at the same instants. In the interval $t_2 - t_1$ the body pivots on b_1 which coincides with s_1. This rotation brings b_2 into coincidence with s_2. In the interval $(t_3 - t_2)$ the body pivots on s_2 and b_2 until b_3 is brought into coincidence with s_3, etc. The motion is the same as the rolling of one polygon on another. The motion is discontinuous at each corner, and the axis jumps by finite amounts. The rate of rolling may vary in any manner whatever, but the displacement at each pivot is definite. If the sides of the polygons are diminished indefinitely, the centrodes become smooth curves, and if the motion of the body is continuous, the body centrode rolls without slipping upon the space centrode. The instantaneous axis is at the point of contact of the two centrodes and the motion is always one of pivoting on the instantaneous axis.

70. The Centrodes for the Billiard Ball.—In the case of a sphere rolling on a plane, the body centrode is a great circle of the sphere, and the space centrode is the straight line along which the sphere rolls. It is otherwise, however, if the ball both rolls and slides.

Consider again the motion of the billiard ball described in Sec. 68. Let O_1 and O_2 be the center of the ball at any two instants (Fig. 37), and let O_1A_1 and O_1B_1 be two radii which include the angle θ. Let O_1O_2 be denoted by G. If the ball has turned through the angle θ in the interval of time in which the center of the ball has advanced from O_1 to O_2, and if O_1B_1 was vertical at the first instant, O_2A_2 was vertical at the second instant. The chord A_1B_1 in the first position has become the chord A_2B_2 in the second position. The point of intersection, O, of the perpendicular bisectors of A_1B_1 and A_2B_2 is the center of a pure rotation which will bring the ball from the first position to the second. The point O is at a distance

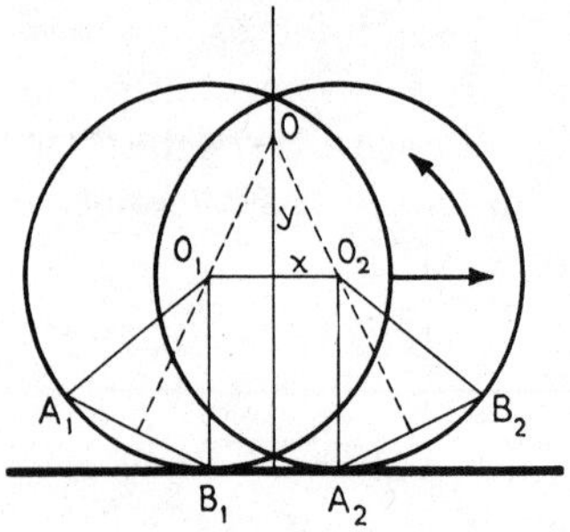

FIG. 37.

$$y = \frac{\frac{1}{2}G}{\tan \frac{1}{2}\theta}$$

above the line of centers; and the limit of this expression as the two instants of time approach coincidence is

$$y = \frac{dG}{d\theta},$$

and this is the distance of the instantaneous axis above the center of the ball at any instant.

Let $g\mu t$ be denoted by τ. Then Eqs. (68.2) become

$$\left.\begin{aligned} G' &= v - \tau, & 2g\mu G &= -\tau^2 + 2v\tau, \\ \theta' &= \omega_0 - \frac{5\tau}{2a}, & 5g\mu\theta &= -\frac{25}{4a}\tau^2 + 5\omega_0\tau. \end{aligned}\right\} \qquad (1)$$

The solutions of the two equations in the second column give two expressions for τ; one in G, and one in θ, namely,

and

$$\left.\begin{aligned}\tau &= v - \sqrt{v^2 - 2g\mu G},\\ 5\tau &= 2a\omega_0 - 2\sqrt{a^2\omega_0{}^2 - 5ag\mu\theta}.\end{aligned}\right\}\qquad(2)$$

Since

$$y = \frac{dG}{d\theta} = \frac{G'}{\theta'} = \frac{2a(v - \tau)}{2a\omega_0 - 5\tau}$$

is the ordinate of the instantaneous axis above the line of centers and $G = x$ is the abscissa, the equation of the space centrode in rectangular coordinates is

$$y = \frac{2a\sqrt{v^2 - 2g\mu x}}{(2a\omega_0 - 5v) + 5\sqrt{v^2 - 2g\mu x}}.$$

The equation of the body centrode in polar coordinates is

$$y = \rho = \frac{10av - 4a^2\omega_0 + 4a\sqrt{a^2\omega_0{}^2 - 5ag\mu\theta}}{10\sqrt{a^2\omega_0{}^2 - 5ag\mu\theta}},$$

which, evidently, is a spiral.

As a particular example, suppose the ball is $2\frac{1}{4}$ inches in diameter, or $\frac{3}{32}$ of a foot, $g = 32$, $\mu = \frac{1}{3}$; that the ball advances 9″ before it begins to retreat, and that it begins to roll when it reaches its initial position.

It is found from the first of Eqs. (1) and (2) that

$$v = \tau_1 = 4,$$

when G' vanishes, and

$$2v = \tau_2 = 8,$$

when the ball begins to roll. The ball reaches its most advanced position in $\frac{3}{8}$ of a second, and it begins to roll in $\frac{3}{4}$ of a second. Since

$$G' = a\theta' = 0 = v + a\omega_0 - \tfrac{7}{2}\tau_2,$$

when the ball begins to roll, it is found that

$$a\omega_0 = 24, \qquad \text{and} \qquad \omega_0 = 256.$$

The equations for the space and body centrodes become

$$y = \frac{3}{16}\frac{\sqrt{9 - 12x}}{21 + 5\sqrt{9 - 12x}},$$

$$\rho = \frac{3}{80}\frac{\sqrt{576 - 5\theta} - 14}{\sqrt{576 - 5\theta}}.$$

The space centrode is shown in Fig. 38. It is not practical to draw the entire body centrode, as there are too many coils and they are too close together; that part of it which lies between

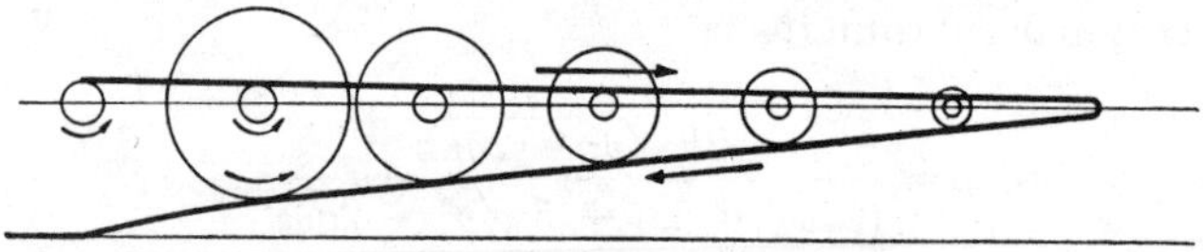

FIG. 38.

$\theta = 112 - 2\pi$ and $\theta = 112 + 2\pi$ is shown in Fig. 39. The value of θ when the ball begins to roll is 112, and for values of θ larger than this the body centrode is a circle. For values of θ smaller than 112 it is a spiral, as indicated. The body centrode rolls on the under side of the upper branch of the space centrode when the ball is advancing, and on the upper side of the lower branch when it is retreating.

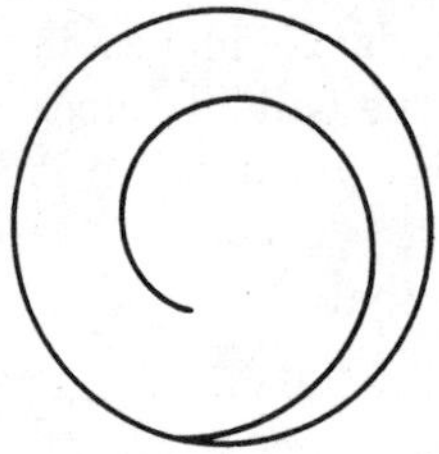

FIG. 39.

71. The Friction on a Sliding Base.—If any object is sliding on a rough plane, its motion at any instant is one of rotation about some axis which is perpendicular to the plane. It is desired to find the single force, and its line of action, which is equivalent to the friction that is acting on its base. For perfectly rigid bodies this problem is indeterminate, since three points are sufficient to support the object and by hypothesis the base and the plane are in contact in infinitely many points. The concept of perfect rigidity must be laid aside. It will be assumed that plane yields slightly to the pressure that is applied to it and that the amount it yields is proportional to the pressure, the surface of contact still remaining a plane.

Consider first the normal pressures when the object is at rest upon a horizontal plane. Let the undistorted rough plane be taken as a reference plane and the center of area of the base be taken as the origin of a rectangular coordinate system, the axes coinciding with the axes of the inertial ellipse at the center of area. Then, if $d\omega$ is an element of area at the point x, y,

$$\int x\,d\omega = 0, \qquad \int y\,d\omega = 0, \qquad \int xy\,d\omega = 0. \tag{1}$$

Let A and B be the moments of inertia of the area of the base with respect to the x- and y-axes, so that

$$\left.\begin{aligned} A &= \int y^2\,d\omega, & B &= \int x^2\,d\omega,\\ &= C\beta^2, & &= C\alpha^2, \end{aligned}\right\} \tag{2}$$

where β and α are the radii of gyration of the area of the base with respect to the x- and y-axes, respectively, and C is the area of the base.

Let the equation of the plane of contact be

$$z = ax + by + c. \tag{3}$$

By Hooke's law the pressure of the plane on any element $d\omega$ of the base is $kz\,d\omega$, where k is the factor of proportionality. Since the total pressure on the plane is the weight W of the object, it follows that

$$k\int z\,d\omega = W, \tag{4}$$

or

$$W = k\int (ax + by + c)\,d\omega = ka\int x\,d\omega + kb\int y\,d\omega + kc\int d\omega.$$

By virtue of Eqs. (1), this reduces to

$$W = kcC, \qquad \text{and} \qquad c = \frac{W}{kC}.$$

If x_0, y_0 is the projection of the center of gravity of the body on the xy-plane, the principle of moments gives the two equations

$$k\int zx\,d\omega = Wx_0, \qquad k\int zy\,d\omega = Wy_0, \tag{5}$$

which, in view of Eqs. (3), (1), and (2), give

$$a = \frac{Wx_0}{kC\alpha^2}, \qquad b = \frac{Wy_0}{kC\beta^2}.$$

Hence the equation of the surface of contact is

$$kz = \frac{W}{C}\left[\frac{x_0 x}{\alpha^2} + \frac{y_0 y}{\beta^2} + 1\right]. \tag{6}$$

Since the pressure on any element of the base is $kz\,d\omega$, it follows at once that, if

$$x_0 = y_0 = 0,$$

the pressure is everywhere the same. Hence the theorem:

Theorem.—If the projection of the center of gravity of a body upon its base coincides with the center of area of the base, then when the body is resting upon a horizontal plane, the pressure of the body upon the plane, due to its weight, is uniformly distributed over the base.

The equation of the inertial ellipse of the base is

$$\frac{x^2}{\alpha^2} + \frac{y^2}{\beta^2} = \frac{1}{C\alpha^2\beta^2}; \tag{7}$$

and the equation of the line through the center of area and the projection of the center of gravity upon the base is

$$y_0x - x_0y = 0.$$

The lines of equal pressure on the base, Eq. (6),

$$\frac{x_0x}{\alpha^2} + \frac{y_0y}{\beta^2} = \text{constant},$$

are therefore parallel to the conjugate of the diameter of the inertial ellipse which passes through the point x_0, y_0. If the inertial ellipse is a circle the lines of equal pressure are perpendicular to the line which joins the center of area to the projection of the center of gravity.

Since negative pressures are not admissible, it is necessary for this analysis that the line of zero pressure,

$$\frac{x_0x}{\alpha^2} + \frac{y_0y}{\beta^2} + 1 = 0,$$

shall lie outside of the base, so that the pressures on the base are everywhere positive. This will be the case if the point x_0, y_0 is not too far from the center of area.

Translation.—If the body is sliding without rotation, and the coefficient of friction is μ, the frictional force acting on the element $d\omega$ is

$$dF = k\mu z\,d\omega,$$

and since these elements of force have all the same direction the total force of friction is

$$F = k\mu\int z\, d\omega = W\mu.$$

The system of forces dF is a system of parallel forces and the magnitude of each force is independent of the direction. For a pure translation therefore the friction acting on the plane base of a sliding body is quite similar to the force of gravity acting on the particles of a rigid body, and the equivalent single force passes through a fixed point of the base whatever the direction of the friction may be. This point will be called *the center of friction.* Let ξ and η be its coordinates. The moment of **F** with respect to the origin is (I, **132**)

$$M = (\xi F \sin\theta - \eta F \cos\theta) = W\mu\xi \sin\theta - W\mu\eta \cos\theta, \quad (8)$$

where θ is the angle that **F** makes with the x-axis.

The moment of dF acting at the point x, y with respect to the origin is

$$x\, dF \sin\theta - y\, dF \cos\theta.$$

Since

$$dF = k\mu z\, d\omega,$$

the moment of the entire system of frictional forces is

$$k\mu \sin\theta \int zx\, d\omega - k\mu \cos\theta \int zy\, d\omega,$$

which, by Eqs. (5), becomes

$$W\mu x_0 \sin\theta - W\mu y_0 \sin\theta;$$

and a comparison of this expression with Eq. (8) shows that

$$\xi = x_0, \qquad \eta = y_0.$$

The center of friction, therefore, coincides with the projection of the center of gravity on the base.

Rotation.—The pressure P per unit area at any point x, y is kz. If the body is rotating about some point O, the friction per unit area is $P\mu$, and its direction is perpendicular to the radius from the point O. The element of friction at the point x, y is then, by Eq. (6),

$$dF = \frac{W\mu}{C}\left[\frac{x_0 x}{\alpha^2} + \frac{y_0 y}{\beta^2} + 1\right] d\omega. \quad (9)$$

The magnitude, but not the direction, of the friction is constant along the lines of equal pressure. If the diameter of the inertial ellipse at the center of area which is parallel to these lines is taken as the ξ-axis of a rectangular coordinate system (Fig. 40), and the angle between the ξ-axis and the x-axis is γ, the equations of transformation are

$$\begin{aligned} x &= \xi \cos \gamma + \eta \sin \gamma, \\ y &= -\xi \sin \gamma + \eta \cos \gamma, \end{aligned}$$

where

$$\sin \gamma = \frac{\beta^2 x_0}{\sqrt{\beta^4 x_0^2 + \alpha^4 y_0^2}}, \qquad \cos \gamma = \frac{\alpha^2 y_0}{\sqrt{\beta^4 x_0^2 + \alpha^4 y_0^2}}. \tag{10}$$

The element of friction dF then takes the form

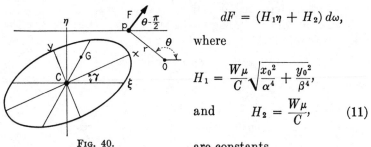

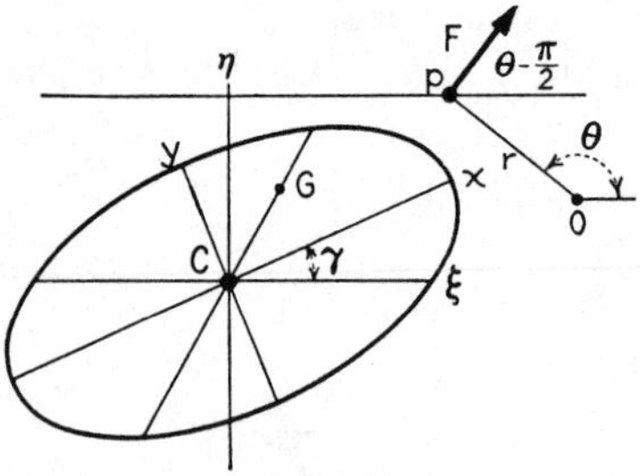

FIG. 40.

$$dF = (H_1 \eta + H_2)\, d\omega,$$

where

$$H_1 = \frac{W\mu}{C}\sqrt{\frac{x_0^2}{\alpha^4} + \frac{y_0^2}{\beta^4}},$$

and

$$H_2 = \frac{W\mu}{C}, \tag{11}$$

are constants.

Let θ be the angle which the line r from the axis of rotation O to the element $d\omega$ makes with the ξ-axis. If ξ_1, η_1 are the coordinates of the point O, and ξ, η are the coordinates of the element $d\omega$,

$$r = \sqrt{(\xi - \xi_1)^2 + (\eta - \eta_1)^2},$$

and

$$\cos \theta = \frac{\xi - \xi_1}{r} = \frac{\partial r}{\partial \xi},$$

$$\sin \theta = \frac{\eta - \eta_1}{r} = \frac{\partial r}{\partial \eta}.$$

The components F_ξ and F_η of the single force F, which is equivalent to the friction acting on the base, are

$$F_\xi = +\int (H_1 \eta + H_2) \sin \theta \, d\omega = +\iint (H_1 \eta + H_2) \frac{\partial r}{\partial \eta} d\eta \, d\xi,$$

$$F_\eta = -\int (H_1\eta + H_2)\cos\theta\, d\omega = -\iint (H_1\eta + H_2)\frac{\partial r}{\partial \xi} d\xi\, d\eta.$$

In order to locate the line of action of the equivalent single force, it is necessary to have the sum of the moments, M, of the elements of friction, and this must be the moment of F. It is evident that

$$M = \iint (H_1\eta + H_2) r\, d\xi\, d\eta.$$

If p is the perpendicular distance from O to the line of F, the equation

$$pF = M$$

determines the length of p, and therefore the line of action of F. The direction of F is determined by its components F_ξ and F_η.

By taking

$$Q_1 = \frac{1}{2}H_1\left[(\eta - \eta_1)r - (\xi - \xi_1)^2 \sinh^{-1}\frac{\eta - \eta_1}{\xi - \xi_1}\right] + (H_1\eta_1 + H_2)r$$

and

$$Q_2 = (H_1\eta + H_2)r,$$

it is easily verified that

$$F_\xi = +\iint \frac{\partial Q_1}{\partial \eta} d\eta\, d\xi, \qquad \text{and} \qquad F_\eta = -\iint \frac{\partial Q_2}{\partial \xi} d\xi\, d\eta.$$

Consequently[1]

$$F_\xi = -\int_B Q_1\, d\xi, \qquad \text{and} \qquad F_\eta = -\int_B Q_2\, d\eta,$$

the integrals being taken around the boundary of the base in the counterclockwise direction.

Using the method of integration by parts, it is found that

$$\int (\xi - \xi_1)^2 \sinh^{-1}\frac{\eta - \eta_1}{\xi - \xi_1} d\xi = \left[\frac{1}{3}(\xi - \xi_1)^3 \sinh^{-1}\frac{\eta - \eta_1}{\xi - \xi_1}\right]$$
$$- \frac{1}{3}\int\left[\frac{(\xi - \xi_1)^3}{r}\frac{d\eta}{d\xi} - \frac{(\eta - \eta_1)(\xi - \xi_1)^2}{r}\right] d\xi.$$

[1] GOURSAT-HEDRICK, "Mathematical Analysis," Vol. 1, p. 263.

When restricted to real values, the inverse of the hyperbolic sine is a single valued function. Consequently when the integral is taken around the boundary the integrated term returns to its initial value and contributes nothing to the integral. That is,

$$\int_B (\xi - \xi_1)^2 \sinh^{-1} \frac{\eta - \eta_1}{\xi - \xi_1} d\xi = -\frac{1}{3}\int_B \frac{(\xi - \xi_1)^2}{r}[(\xi - \xi_1)\, d\eta - (\eta - \eta_1)\, d\xi].$$

For convenience of notation let

$$\begin{aligned} \mathfrak{A} &= \int_B r\, d\xi, & \mathfrak{E} &= \int_B r\, d\eta, \\ \mathfrak{B} &= \int_B (\eta - \eta_1) r\, d\xi, & \mathfrak{F} &= \int_B (\eta - \eta_1) r\, d\eta, \quad (12) \\ \mathfrak{C} &= \int_B r^3\, d\xi, & \mathfrak{G} &= \int_B \frac{(\xi - \xi_1)^3}{r} d\eta. \\ \mathfrak{D} &= \int_B \frac{(\xi - \xi_1)^2(\eta - \eta_1)}{r} d\xi, \end{aligned}$$

It is then found without further difficulty that

$$\begin{aligned} F_\xi &= -\tfrac{1}{2}H_1\mathfrak{B} - (H_1\eta_1 + H_2)\mathfrak{A} - \tfrac{1}{6}H_1(\mathfrak{G} - \mathfrak{D}), \\ F_\eta &= -\; H_1\mathfrak{F} - (H_1\eta_1 + H_2)\mathfrak{E}, \qquad (13) \\ M &= -\tfrac{1}{3}H_1\mathfrak{C} - \tfrac{1}{2}(H_1\eta_1 + H_2)\mathfrak{B} + \tfrac{1}{6}(H_1\eta_1 + H_2)(\mathfrak{G} - \mathfrak{D}). \end{aligned}$$

Thus in the general case seven line integrals are required for a complete description of the friction; of course, these integrals can be evaluated only when the size and shape of the base are given. If the projection of the center of gravity coincides with the center of area, $x_0 = y_0 = 0$, and, as is seen from Eq. (11), H_1 vanishes. The integrals $\mathfrak{C}$ and $\mathfrak{F}$ are not required, and to this extent the computation is simplified by a uniform distribution of the pressure.

72. The Sliding Base Is a Circle.—For a circle the center of area is at the center of the circular base. The inertial ellipse also is a circle, for, if the radius of the base is a [Eq. (71.2)]

$$\alpha^2 = \beta^2 = \frac{a^2}{4}.$$

The lines of constant pressure are perpendicular to that diameter which passes through the projection of the center of gravity upon the base. Let this diameter be the η-axis, the perpendicular diameter the ξ-axis, and the coordinates of the projection of the center of gravity be 0, η_0. The lines of constant pressure are

$$\eta = \text{constant},$$

and the line of zero pressure is

$$\eta = -\frac{a^2}{4\eta_0}.$$

The Base Is Entirely in Contact.—The line of zero pressure lies outside of the base, or is tangent to it, if

$$|\eta_0| \leqq \tfrac{1}{4}a,$$

and in what follows it will be assumed that this condition is satisfied, and the entire base, therefore, is in contact with the plane on which it slides.

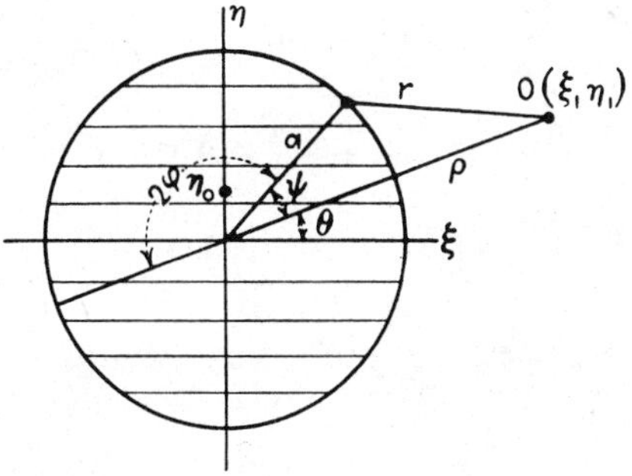

FIG. 41.

Let $O(\xi_1, \eta_1)$ be the point in the plane about which the base is turning, and ρ, θ its polar coordinates; let the distance from O to any point on the circumference whose polar angle is $\psi + \theta$ be r; and, finally, let the supplement of ψ be 2φ (Fig. 41). Then

$$\begin{aligned} r^2 &= a^2 + \rho^2 + 2a\rho \cos 2\varphi, \\ &= (a + \rho)^2 - 4a\rho \sin^2 \varphi. \\ \xi - \xi_1 &= -a \cos (2\varphi - \theta) - \rho \cos \theta, \\ d\xi &= +2a \sin (2\varphi - \theta)\, d\varphi, \\ \eta - \eta_1 &= +a \sin (2\varphi - \theta) - \rho \sin \theta, \\ d\eta &= +2a \cos (2\varphi - \theta)\, d\varphi. \end{aligned}$$

Now if a and ρ are positive, whatever their values may be

$$(a + \rho)^2 \geqq 4a\rho.$$

Let

$$k^2 = \frac{4a\rho}{(a+\rho)^2} \leqq 1 \quad \text{and} \quad \Delta\varphi = \sqrt{1 - k^2 \sin^2 \varphi}.$$

Then

$$r = (a + \rho)\Delta\varphi.$$

In tracing the circumference in the counterclockwise direction, ψ increases from 0 to 2π, and φ decreases from $+\pi/2$ to $-\pi/2$. Bearing this fact in mind, it is then found that

$$\mathfrak{A} = 4a(a+\rho)\sin\theta \int_0^{\frac{\pi}{2}} (1 - 2\sin^2\varphi)\Delta\varphi\, d\varphi,$$

$$\mathfrak{B} = -4a(a+\rho)^2 \sin^2\theta \int_0^{\frac{\pi}{2}} \Delta\varphi\, d\varphi - 16a^2(a+\rho)\cos 2\theta \times$$
$$\int_0^{\frac{\pi}{2}} \sin^2\varphi \cos^2\varphi \Delta\varphi\, d\varphi + 8a\rho(a+\rho)\sin^2\theta \int_0^{\frac{\pi}{2}} \sin^2\varphi \Delta\varphi\, d\varphi,$$

$$\mathfrak{C} = 4a(a+\rho)^3 \sin\theta \int_0^{\frac{\pi}{2}} (1 - 2\sin^2\varphi)\Delta^3\varphi\, d\varphi,$$

$$\mathfrak{E} = -4a(a+\rho)\cos\theta \int_0^{\frac{\pi}{2}} (1 - 2\sin^2\varphi)\Delta\varphi\, d\varphi,$$

$$\mathfrak{F} = -16a^2(a+\rho)\sin 2\theta \int_0^{\frac{\pi}{2}} \sin^2\varphi\cos^2\varphi\Delta\varphi\, d\varphi - 4a\rho(a+\rho) \times$$
$$\sin 2\theta \int_0^{\frac{\pi}{2}} \sin^2\varphi\Delta\varphi\, d\varphi + 2a(a+\rho)^2 \sin 2\theta \int_0^{\frac{\pi}{2}} \Delta\varphi\, d\varphi,$$

$$\mathfrak{G} - \mathfrak{D} = 4a(a+\rho)^2\cos^2\theta \int_0^{\frac{\pi}{2}} \frac{d\varphi}{\Delta\varphi} - \frac{32a^3\rho}{a+\rho}\cos 2\theta \int_0^{\frac{\pi}{2}} \frac{\sin^6\varphi}{\Delta\varphi}\, d\varphi$$
$$+ [-8a(a+\rho)(2a+\rho)\cos^2\theta + 16a^3\sin^2\theta] \int_0^{\frac{\pi}{2}} \frac{\sin^2\varphi}{\Delta\varphi}\, d\varphi +$$
$$\left[16a^2(a+2\rho)\cos^2\theta - 16a^3\frac{a+3\rho}{a+\rho}\sin^2\theta\right] \int_0^{\frac{\pi}{2}} \frac{\sin^4\varphi}{\Delta\varphi}\, d\varphi.$$

Now

$$\int_0^{\frac{\pi}{2}} \frac{d\varphi}{\Delta\varphi} \quad \text{and} \quad \int_0^{\frac{\pi}{2}} \Delta\varphi\, d\varphi$$

are Legendre's complete elliptic integrals of the first and second kinds for the modulus k, and are represented by the letters K and E respectively. The other integrals are reducible to these, for

$$\int_0^{\frac{\pi}{2}} \sin^2\varphi\Delta\varphi\,d\varphi = \frac{1-k^2}{3k^2}K - \frac{1-2k^2}{3k^2}E,$$

$$\int_0^{\frac{\pi}{2}} \sin^2\varphi\cos^2\varphi\Delta\varphi\,d\varphi = -\frac{2-3k^2+k^4}{15k^4}K + \frac{2-2k^2+2k^4}{15k^4}E,$$

$$\int_0^{\frac{\pi}{2}} \Delta^3\varphi\,d\varphi = -\frac{1-k^2}{3}K + \frac{4-2k^2}{3}E,$$

$$\int \sin^2\varphi\Delta^3\varphi\,d\varphi = \frac{3-7k^2+4k^4}{15k^2}K - \frac{3-13k^2+8k^4}{15k^2}E,$$

$$\int^{\frac{\pi}{2}} \frac{\sin^2\varphi}{\Delta\varphi}\,d\varphi = \frac{1}{k^2}K - \frac{1}{k^2}E,$$

$$\int_0^{\frac{\pi}{2}} \frac{\sin^4\varphi}{\Delta\varphi}\,d\varphi = \frac{2+k^2}{3k^4}K - \frac{2+2k^2}{3k^4}E,$$

$$\int_0^{\frac{\pi}{2}} \frac{\sin^6\varphi}{\Delta\varphi}\,d\varphi = \frac{8+3k^2+4k^4}{15k^6}K - \frac{8+7k^2+8k^4}{15k^6}E.$$

The complementary modulus is k_1, where

$$k_1^2 = 1 - k^2 = \left(\frac{a-\rho}{a+\rho}\right)^2;$$

consequently

$$k_1 = \frac{a-\rho}{a+\rho}.$$

If ρ is zero, $k_1 = +1$, and as ρ tends toward infinity k_1 tends toward -1. Hence the correspondence

$$\begin{array}{lcccc} \rho = 0 & \cdots & a & \cdots & \infty, \\ k_1 = +1 & \cdots & 0 & \cdots & -1; \end{array}$$

and

$$\rho = \frac{1-k_1}{1+k_1}a.$$

On replacing ρ by its value in terms of k_1 and taking

$$\left.\begin{aligned}
f_1(\rho) &= \frac{8a^2(1-k_1)}{3k^4}\{-2(1-k^2)K + (2-k^2)E\},\\
f_2(\rho) &= \frac{8a^3}{45k^6}\{[(-20+35k^2-15k^4) + k_1(+20-25k^2+5k^4)]K\\
&\qquad + [(+20-25k^2+15k^4) + k_1(-20+15k^2-10k^4)]E\},\\
f_3(\rho) &= \frac{8a^3}{15k^6}\{[(-12+23k^2-11k^4) + k_1(12-13k^2+k^4)]K\\
&\qquad + [(12-17k^2+7k^4) + k_1(-12+7k^2-2k^4)]E\},\\
f_4(\rho) &= \frac{32a^4(1-k_1)^3}{15k^8}\{[-2+3k^2-k^4]K + [2-2k^2+2k^4]E\},
\end{aligned}\right\} \quad (1)$$

it is found that

$$\begin{aligned}
\mathfrak{A} &= f_1 \sin\theta, & \mathfrak{E} &= -f_1\cos\theta,\\
\mathfrak{B} &= f_3\cos 2\theta - 3f_2, & \mathfrak{F} &= +f_3\sin 2\theta,\\
\mathfrak{C} &= 3f_4\sin\theta, & \mathfrak{G} - \mathfrak{D} &= 3f_3\cos 2\theta + 3f_2;
\end{aligned}$$

then, by substitution in Eq. (71.13),

$$\left.\begin{aligned}
F_\xi &= +H_1f_2 - H_1f_3\cos 2\theta - (H_1\eta_1 + H_2)f_1\sin\theta,\\
F_\eta &= \qquad\quad - H_1f_3\sin 2\theta + (H_1\eta_1 + H_2)f_1\cos\theta,\\
M &= \qquad\quad - H_1f_4\sin\theta + 2(H_1\eta_1 + H_2)f_2.
\end{aligned}\right\} \quad (2)$$

TABLE OF VALUES OF THE f FUNCTIONS

$k = \sin\beta$	$\frac{f_1}{a^2}$	$\frac{f_2}{a^3}$	$\frac{f_3}{a^3}$	$\frac{f_4}{a^4}$
$\beta =$ 0°	+ .0000	+ 1.0472	+ .0000	+ .00000
10°	+ .0240	+ 1.0472	+ .0007	+ .00601
20°	+ .0977	+ 1.0480	+ .0013	+ .02443
30°	+ .2254	+ 1.0512	+ .0061	+ .05650
40°	+ .4153	+ 1.0610	+ .0207	+ .10473
50°	+ .6791	+ 1.0842	+ .0555	+ .17380
60°	+1.0325	+ 1.1339	+ .1297	+ .27266
70°	+1.4925	+ 1.2331	+ .2774	+ .41943
80°	+2.0647	+ 1.4531	+ .5586	+ .65263
90°	+2.6667	+ 1.7778	+ 1.0667	+ 1.06667
100°	+2.9324	+ 2.4211	+ 1.8434	+ 1.8698
110°	+3.0441	+ 3.3011	+ 2.9239	+ 3.5588
120°	+3.0974	+ 4.7782	+ 4.5189	+ 7.3618
130°	+3.1229	+ 7.2668	+ 7.0968	+ 16.905
140°	+3.1347	+ 11.884	+ 11.7795	+ 45.048
150°	+3.1395	+ 21.893	+ 21.836	+ 152.66
160°	+3.1412	+ 50.528	+ 50.505	+ 812.76
170°	+3.1416	+204.94	+2,052.05	+13,417.
180°	+3.1416	+ ∞	+ ∞	+ ∞

Let F_ρ and F_θ be the components of F in the direction of ρ and perpendicular to it; and let η_1 be replaced by its value $\rho \sin \theta$. There result the somewhat simpler expressions

$$\left.\begin{aligned} F_\rho &= +H_1(f_2 - f_3)\cos\theta, \\ F_\theta &= -H_1(f_2 + f_3 - \rho f_1)\sin\theta + H_2 f_1, \\ M &= +H_1(-f_4 + 2\rho f_2)\sin\theta + 2H_2 f_2. \end{aligned}\right\} \qquad (3)$$

If the projection of the center of gravity coincides with the center of the base, H_1 vanishes, and these expressions become simply

$$F_\rho = 0, \qquad F_\theta = H_2 f_1, \qquad M = 2H_2 f_2. \qquad (4)$$

The Base Is Not in Contact.—If the distance from the projection of the center of gravity to the center of the circle is greater than $a/4$, the entire base is not in contact with the plane upon which it slides. The line of zero pressure cuts across the base, and it is desired to find the position of this line.

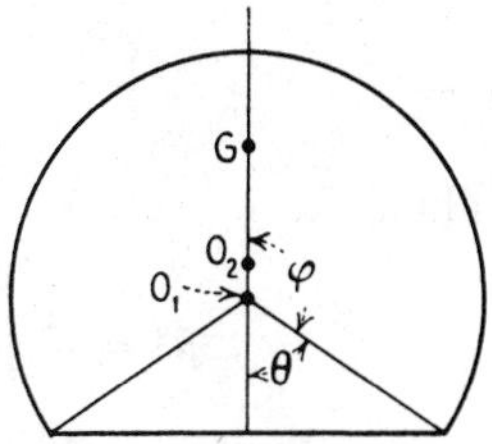

FIG. 42.

The center of area, O_2 (Fig. 42) is no longer at the center of the circular base, O_1; and the inertial ellipse is no longer a circle. The portion of the base which is still in contact, however, is symmetrical with respect to the diameter which is perpendicular to the line of zero pressure. By virtue of this symmetry, the center of area lies on this line, and this line is an axis of the inertial ellipse. The projection of the center of gravity upon the base, G, lies on the diameter of the ellipse that is conjugate to the diameter which is parallel to the line of zero pressure; that is, it lies upon the line of symmetry just mentioned.

Let the line of symmetry be the η-axis and the line through the center of area O_2, parallel to the line of zero pressure, be the ξ-axis. The coordinates of the projection of the center of gravity are then $0, \eta_0$. Let the distance O_1O_2 be g. Then, if y is measured from an x-axis through the center of the circle,

$$y = g + \eta, \qquad y_0 = g + \eta_0.$$

The equation of the line of zero pressure is

$$\eta\eta_0 = -\beta^2,$$

where [Eq. (71.2)]

$$\beta^2 = \frac{1}{C}\int \eta^2\, d\omega = \frac{1}{C}\int (y - g)^2\, d\omega,$$

$$C = \int d\omega.$$

and

$$g = \frac{1}{C}\int y\, d\omega,$$

It is not difficult to evaluate these expressions, and it is found that

$$C = [\varphi - \tfrac{1}{2}\sin 2\varphi]a^2,$$

where φ is the supplement of θ, and 2θ is the angle subtended by that portion of the line of zero pressure that lies within the base; and

$$g = \frac{4a \sin^3 \varphi}{3(2\varphi - \sin 2\varphi)}.$$

Then

$$\begin{aligned}\beta^2 &= \frac{1}{C}\int y^2\, d\omega - g^2 \\ &= \frac{(4\varphi - \sin 4\varphi)a^2}{8(2\varphi - \sin 2\varphi)} - g^2 = \beta_1{}^2 - g^2.\end{aligned}$$

Now on the line of zero pressure

$$\eta\eta_0 = -\beta^2,$$

or

$$(y - g)(y_0 - g) = -\beta_1{}^2 + g^2;$$

whence

$$yy_0 - g(y + y_0) = -\beta_1{}^2.$$

For the line of zero pressure, y is equal to $a \cos \varphi$. Therefore

$$y_0 = \frac{-\beta_1{}^2 + ag\cos\varphi}{a\cos\varphi - g},$$

and

$$\frac{y_0}{a} = \frac{-12\varphi + 8\sin 2\varphi - \sin 4\varphi}{48\varphi\cos\varphi - 36\sin\varphi - 4\sin 3\varphi}.$$

This equation determines φ if the ratio y_0/a is given, and therefore the position of the line of zero pressure.

Problems

1. A heavy beam of length l and mass m_1 turns about a hinge at O at one end of the beam. The other end A rests upon a wedge of mass m_2 and angle α. The wedge rests on a horizontal plane which passes through O, and the beam lies in a vertical plane that passes through the center of the wedge and is perpendicular to the edge. All contacts are smooth. If θ_0 is the angle which the beam makes with a horizontal plane when the system is at rest, show that when the beam has fallen to the horizontal position the speed of the wedge is given by the formula

$$v^2 = \frac{3m_1 gl \sin \theta_0}{3m_2 + m_1 \tan \alpha}.$$

2. A door is hung by two hinges in a fixed axis that makes an angle α with the vertical. Set up the equations of motion of the door and determine the constraints on the hinges.

3. If a compound pendulum swings in a complete circle, show that the $\mathbf{i}_0$-component of the constraint is always negative if

$$\sqrt{\frac{k_0^2 + l_1^2}{k_0^2 + 5l_1^2}} < \frac{\text{angular speed at top}}{\text{angular speed at bottom}} < 1.$$

4. A solid homogeneous hemisphere rests on a smooth horizontal plane with its base parallel to a smooth vertical wall with which the spherical surface is in contact. Initially at rest, it slips down under its own weight. Show that, when the base is horizontal,

$$\omega^2 = \frac{15}{8}\frac{g}{a}, \qquad v = \frac{3}{8}a\omega,$$

where v is the horizontal speed of its center of gravity, and the remaining letters have their usual significance. Show also that while it is sliding on the horizontal plane the angle between the base of the hemisphere and the plane of the horizon never exceeds

$$\cos^{-1} \tfrac{45}{128}.$$

5. Show that the tensions in the strings of the bifilar pendulum, Sec. 65, is a maximum at the lowest point, where

$$T = (2ak^2 + G_0 l^2)\frac{g}{4ak^2}.$$

6. A homogeneous spherical shell, for which the outer and inner radii are a and b respectively, rolls down a plane for which the angle of inclination to the horizontal is α. Show that the acceleration is constant and in magnitude is equal to

$$\frac{5a^2(a^3 - b^3)}{7a^5 - 5a^2b^3 - 2b^5} g \sin \alpha.$$

For a cylindrical shell the acceleration is

$$\frac{2a^2}{3a^2 + b^2} g \sin \alpha.$$

Hence for the same values of a and b the sphere rolls faster than the cylinder.

7. If the rod of the bifilar pendulum is uniform and of negligible diameter, but not negligible mass, let two spheres of the same size with small holes bored through their centers be placed symmetrically on the rod. Let l be the length of the rod, αl the radius of the spheres, βl the distance of the spheres from the center of the rod, M_r the mass of the rod, and M_s the mass of each sphere. In order that the periods of swing and rotation for infinitesimal oscillations may be equal, it is necessary that

$$5M_r = (24\alpha^2 + 60\beta^2 - 15)M_s.$$

8. A uniform disk of radius a which is spinning with the angular speed ω about a vertical axis is placed upon a horizontal table. If the disk presses uniformly upon the table and the coefficient of friction is μ, show that the disk will come to rest in

$$\frac{3}{4}\frac{a\omega}{g\mu} \text{ seconds.}$$

9. A circular steel hoop of radius a and mass m per unit length spins with an angular speed ω about a vertical axis through the center of the hoop, the plane of the hoop being horizontal. Show that the tension in the hoop is

$$T = ma^2\omega^2.$$

If the breaking tension of the steel is 10^5 pounds per sq. in. and its density is 7.85, show that the angular speed of the hoop cannot exceed

$$\omega = \frac{973}{a},$$

where a is expressed in feet.

10. A cylinder slips and rolls down an inclined plane in the time T_1. The friction is then increased until the motion is a pure rolling, and the time required to roll down the plane is T_2. Show that $T_2 > T_1$.

11. A heavy bar is constrained to move in a vertical plane with one point of it, A, in contact with a fixed horizontal line and another point, B, in contact with a fixed vertical line. Thus the mid-point of A and B describes a vertical circle. Find the equation of motion and show that it leads to a hyperelliptic integral.

12. Show that the angle θ at which the rocking pendulum, Sec. 67, begins to slide is determined by the formula

$$\sin(\epsilon - \theta) = \left[r + \frac{k^2(n^2 - 2rh)}{[n^2r + 2h(k^2 + l^2)] - [3n^2 + 2hr]x + 4rx^2}\right]\frac{\sin \epsilon}{l},$$

provided, of course, that $x > h$.

13. A pair of uniform wheels of radius a and mass m_1 are rigidly attached to a solid axle of radius b and mass m_2. One end of a string of length l is attached to a point at the center of the axle and is wound about the axle; to the free end is attached a weight w. The wheels run on a track under the motive power of the weight w. Initially the weight is on a level with the axle and the entire system is at rest. Under the assumption that the weight cannot swing and that there is no friction other than rolling friction, show that the motion is one of uniform acceleration except when the weight w is within a distance b of its lowest point.

14. A uniform rod leans against a smooth wall and rests upon a smooth floor. If it is released from a given position in a vertical plane, it will slip downward. Show that contact with the wall ceases when the upper end has fallen through one third of its original height.

15. A rocking pendulum is constructed of two cylinders joined together by a bar 12″ long and 1″ square, as in Fig. 31. The rolling cylinder has a length of 2″ and a radius 1″. The second cylinder is 4″ long and has a radius of 2″. Show that if $h > 11.92$ inches the pendulum will rock without sliding; but if $h = l/2$, the pendulum will begin to slide when $\theta = 11°43'$, assuming that $\sin \epsilon = \frac{1}{5}$.

16. A right circular cylinder rests on a rough horizontal plane. The plane is moved horizontally in any manner in a direction perpendicular to the axis of the cylinder. Prove that the cylinder will come to rest as soon as the plane does.

17. A uniform solid hemisphere of radius a rests upon a rough horizontal plane. It is rolled through a small angle and then allowed to rock freely. Show that the period of oscillation is the same as that of a simple pendulum of length

$$l = \tfrac{26}{15}a.$$

18. A homogeneous right circular cylinder of radius a rolls without slipping on the inside of a fixed cylinder of radius a_0, the axes of the two cylinders being parallel. Show that the axis of the moving cylinder oscillates exactly like a simple pendulum of length

$$l = \left(1 + \frac{k^2}{a^2}\right)(a_0 - a) = \frac{3}{2}(a_0 - a).$$

19. By using power series expansions for K and E in Eqs. (72.1) show that F_ρ in Eqs. (72.3) vanishes for $k_1 = -1$, and is equal to

$$\frac{4}{3}W\mu\frac{\eta_0}{a}\cos\theta$$

for $k_1 = +1$; that F_θ is equal to $W\mu$ for $k_1 = -1$, and equal to

$$-\frac{4}{3}W\mu\frac{\eta_0}{a}\sin\theta$$

for $k_1 = +1$, and finally that M is infinite for $k_1 = -1$, and equal to

$$-\tfrac{1}{3}W\mu a$$

for $k_1 = +1$.

20. Let the knife-edges in a reversible pendulum be replaced by cylinders of equal radii. Show that when the periods of oscillation are equal the length of the equivalent simple pendulum is equal to the shortest distance between the cylinders.

21. A triangular prism of mass m_1 rests on one of its sides on a smooth horizontal plane. A uniform sphere of mass m_2, starting from a position of rest, rolls, without slipping, down the central line of greatest slope of one of the sides of the prism which makes an angle α with the horizontal plane. If y is the distance along the inclined plane through which the sphere has rolled, and x is the horizontal distance through which the prism has slipped, show that

$$(m_1 + m_2)x = m_2 y \cos \alpha,$$

and that

$$\tfrac{7}{5}y - x \cos \alpha = \tfrac{1}{2}gt^2 \sin \alpha.$$

22. A uniform rod of length a has one extremity in contact with a horizontal plane. Released from rest with an inclination α to the plane, the rod falls freely. Show that when the rod has reached a horizontal position, its angular velocity is given by the equation

$$\omega^2 = \frac{3}{8}\frac{g}{a} \cos \alpha$$

whether the plane is smooth or rough, and that the end of the rod which is in contact with the plane will remain in contact.

23. A homogeneous sphere S of radius a is placed at rest on top of a fixed sphere S_0 of radius a_0. The equilibrium being unstable, S rolls down S_0 without slipping. If θ is the angle which the line of centers makes with the vertical, show that

$$\theta'^2 = \frac{10}{7}\frac{g}{a + a_0}(1 - \cos \theta),$$

and that S leaves S_0 at the point where

$$\cos \theta = \tfrac{10}{17}.$$

24. If, instead of being fixed as in the previous problem, S_0 rests upon a smooth horizontal plane, and if the masses and radii of the two spheres are equal, the two spheres move in such a way that the same two points of the two spheres remain in contact. Show, also, that

$$(7 + 5 \sin^2 \theta)a\theta'^2 = 10g(1 - \cos \theta),$$

and that when the two spheres separate

$$\cos^3 \theta - 6 \cos \theta + 4 = 0.$$

25. Let G be the center of gravity of a rigid body and O any point of the body. Any line through O in the plane that is perpendicular to GO can be regarded as an axis of suspension for the rigid body considered as a compound pendulum. Investigate the relation that exists between the direction of an axis of suspension through O and the period of oscillation of the equivalent simple pendulum. What are the restrictions on the position of the point O if the period of the equivalent simple pendulum is given (Bröklen, *Journal für Mathematik*, Vol. 93)?

26. If the latus rectum through one of the foci of a uniform elliptical disk is an axis of suspension and the latus rectum through the other focus is the axis of oscillation, show that the eccentricity of the ellipse is $\frac{1}{2}$.

27. A heavy circular arc, convex upward, pivots in a vertical plane about its mid-point. Prove that the length of the equivalent simple pendulum is independent of the length of the arc, and its length is twice the radius of the circular arc.

28. A heavy uniform rod of length $2l$ pivots freely in a vertical plane about one of its end points, the other end being just out of contact with the ground when the rod is in its equilibrium position. An angular velocity ω is imparted to the rod when it is at rest in this position, and when the rod arrives at a horizontal position the constraint at the pivot breaks. If the rod strikes the ground in a vertical position, show that

$$\omega^2 = \frac{g}{2l}\left(3 + \frac{p^2}{1+p}\right),$$

where p is any odd multiple of $\pi/2$.

29. A heavy ladder of length $2l$ rests against a vertical wall making an angle θ with the wall. If the coefficient of friction with the wall and with the floor is unity, the ladder is in equilibrium in all positions. The ladder is given a push that starts it sliding downward. Show that the equation of motion is

$$k^2\theta'' = l^2\theta'^2 - gl\cos\theta.$$

If

$$\frac{l^2}{k^2} = \frac{\lambda}{2}, \qquad \frac{gl}{k^2} = \frac{\mu}{2},$$

this equation has the integral

$$\theta'^2 = ce^{\lambda\theta} - \frac{\mu}{1+\lambda^2}(\sin\theta - \lambda\cos\theta).$$

The ladder will slide with increasing angular speed, or with decreasing angular speed, according as the initial value of θ' is greater or less than

$$\sqrt{\frac{\mu\cos\theta_0}{\lambda}}.$$

If it comes to rest before reaching the ground, it remains at rest in a position of equilibrium. (Appell.)

30. A homogeneous solid cylinder of given mass oscillates about an axis that is parallel to one of its generators. What are the shape of the cross-section and position of the axis of suspension if the period of the equivalent simple pendulum is a minimum? *Ans.* The cross section is a circle and the axis of suspension passes through the mid-point of a side of an inscribed square. (De Saint Germain, *Bulletin de la Soc. Math. de France*, 2, p. 54.)

31. A rod of mass M is bent into the form of a circle, and pivots freely about one of its points O in a horizontal plane. A bead of mass m slides freely on the rod and is repelled from the point O by a force that is proportional to the distance from O. Find the motion under the assumption that initially the system is at rest.

32. A uniform heavy bar is tied to a fixed point O by a light inextensible string attached to its center point. Initially the string is taut and the bar is horizontal at rest. Find the motion.

33. A rod OA of mass m and length l pivots freely at O in a horizontal plane. A second rod AB of mass m and length $2l$ is smoothly jointed to the first rod at A. The mid-point C of AB is attracted toward O by a force that varies inversely as the cube of the distance from O. Let θ be the angle that OA makes with a fixed line OX in the plane, and let φ be the angle COA. Initially the system is at rest with $\theta = 0$ and $\varphi = \pi/4$. Discuss the motion of the system.

34. A heavy rigid body turns about a fixed horizontal axis. The axis about which it turns is subject to the condition that it passes through a fixed point of the body and that the equivalent simple pendulum has a given length. Show that the axes which satisfy this condition are the generators of a quartic cone.

CHAPTER VI

MOTION OF A RIGID BODY IN SPACE

73. Historical.—The differential equations of motion of a system of free particles and the ten classical integrals which are associated with them were first published by Clairaut, but the first discussion of the motion of rotation of a free rigid body was made by d'Alembert in his work on the "Precession of the Equinoxes" published in 1749. According to Appell, d'Alembert was familiar with three of the six conditions necessary for the equilibrium of a rigid body, namely, that the vector sum of all of the forces that are acting upon the body must vanish, but he was not familiar with the other three conditions, namely, that the sum of the moments of the forces also must vanish. His work was based upon the principle now known as d'Alembert's principle (I, **383**) and the principle of moments was derived by him.

The equations of motion of a rigid body, one point of which is fixed, in the form in which they are used at the present time, are due to Euler, 1758. Euler also found the integrals that exist when the applied forces have a resultant that passes through the fixed point; for example, a rigid body which is supported at its center of gravity alone, and Jacobi completed the solution of this problem by expressing the nine direction cosines in terms of elliptic functions of the time.

Further contributions to the analysis of this problem were made by Lagrange, Laplace, and Poisson. Lagrange found in 1815 that if the ellipsoid of inertia at the fixed point is a spheroid, the axis of which passes through the center of gravity, the equations of motion are integrable; and Poisson made the same discovery somewhat later. A very beautiful discussion of Euler's problem by Poinsot from a geometrical point of view appeared in 1851; and finally, Mme Kowaleski in 1889 found that if the ellipsoid of inertia at the fixed point is a spheroid the equator of which passes through the center of gravity, and if the principal moments of inertia satisfy the relation

$$A = B = 2C,$$

then, again, the equations of motion can be integrated.

The theory of screws was developed largely by Sir Robert S. Ball during the latter half of the nineteenth century.

THE THEORY OF SCREWS

74. Displacement of a Point by a Rotation about a Fixed Axis. In Fig. 43 let $\mathbf{a}$ be a unit vector having the direction of the axis of rotation, and let $\mathbf{r}_0$ be the position vector of a point R_0 of the body referred to a point O on the axis of rotation, and therefore fixed relative to the rigid body. As the body rotates the point R_0 describes a circle in a plane perpendicular to the axis. Let P be the center of this circle, and let $\overrightarrow{PQ}$ be directed 90° ahead of the vector $\overrightarrow{PR_0}$. Then $\overrightarrow{PR_0}$, $\overrightarrow{PQ}$, and $\mathbf{a}$ form a right-handed system of mutually orthogonal vectors, so that

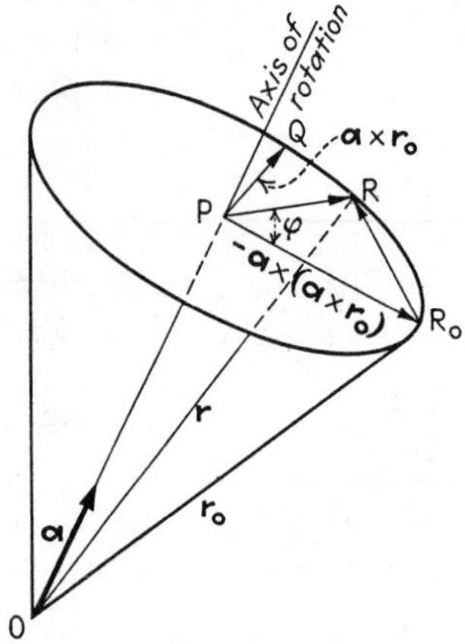

FIG. 43.

$$\overrightarrow{PQ} = \mathbf{a} \times \mathbf{r}_0,$$
$$\overrightarrow{PR_0} = -\mathbf{a} \times (\mathbf{a} \times \mathbf{r}_0).$$

These two vectors have the same length a, namely,

$$a = r_0 \sin \widehat{\mathbf{a}\mathbf{r}_0};$$

where a is the perpendicular distance from R_0 to the axis.

If the body is rotated through an angle φ, the vector $\mathbf{r}_0$ is transformed into the vector $\mathbf{r}$ $(=\overrightarrow{OR})$, and

$$\begin{aligned} \mathbf{r} &= \overrightarrow{OP} + \overrightarrow{PR} \\ &= [\mathbf{r}_0 + \mathbf{a} \times (\mathbf{a} \times \mathbf{r}_0)] + [-\mathbf{a} \times (\mathbf{a} \times \mathbf{r}_0) \cos \varphi + (\mathbf{a} \times \mathbf{r}_0) \sin \varphi], \end{aligned}$$

so that the displacement $\overrightarrow{R_0R}$ is

$$\left.\begin{aligned} \mathbf{r} - \mathbf{r}_0 &= (\mathbf{a} \times \mathbf{r}_0) \sin \varphi + \mathbf{a} \times (\mathbf{a} \times \mathbf{r}_0)(1 - \cos \varphi), \\ &= (\mathbf{a} \times \mathbf{r}_0) \sin \varphi + \mathbf{a} \times (\mathbf{a} \times \mathbf{r}_0) \operatorname{vers} \varphi. \end{aligned}\right\} \quad (1)$$

If the angle φ is very small, say $\Delta\varphi$, and the equation is divided through by Δt, it becomes

$$\frac{\Delta \mathbf{r}_0}{\Delta t} = (\mathbf{a} \times \mathbf{r}_0)\frac{\sin \Delta\varphi}{\Delta\varphi}\frac{\Delta\varphi}{\Delta t} + \mathbf{a} \times (\mathbf{a} \times \mathbf{r}_0)\frac{\text{vers } \Delta\varphi}{\Delta\varphi}\frac{\Delta\varphi}{\Delta t};$$

then, on passing to the limit, in which $\mathbf{r} = \mathbf{r}_0$,

$$\mathbf{r}' = (\mathbf{a} \times \mathbf{r})\varphi',$$

since

$$\lim \frac{\sin \varphi}{\Delta\varphi} = 1, \qquad \text{and} \qquad \lim \frac{\text{vers } \Delta\varphi}{\Delta\varphi} = 0.$$

Now

$$\varphi'\mathbf{a} = \boldsymbol{\omega}$$

is the angular velocity of the body about the axis of rotation. Consequently, the equation,

$$\mathbf{r}' = \boldsymbol{\omega} \times \mathbf{r}, \tag{2}$$

represents the velocity with respect to fixed space of any particle of a rigid body which is rotating about an axis which is fixed both in the body and in space [Eq. (46.1)].

75. The Most General Displacement of a Rigid Body.—It was shown at I, **123** that the most general displacement of a rigid body can be effected in infinitely many ways by a translation and a rotation about an axis which is fixed in the body. The most general rotation is represented by Eq. (74.1) which depends upon $\mathbf{r}_0$, since the displacements of the various points of the body are different; and $\mathbf{r}_0$ has its origin at a point O which lies on the axis and is therefore fixed in the body. In the translation $\mathbf{T}$, all points of the body have the same displacement which is therefore independent of $\mathbf{r}_0$. Hence the most general displacement of a rigid body is represented by the equation

$$\mathbf{D} = \mathbf{T} + (\mathbf{a} \times \mathbf{r}_0) \sin \varphi + \mathbf{a} \times (\mathbf{a} \times \mathbf{r}_0) \text{ vers } \varphi. \tag{1}$$

Since the displacement which is due to rotation is in a plane which is perpendicular to the axis of rotation, the projections of the rotational displacements upon the axis are all zero. Since the translational displacements are all equal it follows that for any displacement of a rigid body the projections of the displacements of the individual particles upon the axis of rotation are all equal. This can be verified by multiplying Eq. (1) by $\mathbf{a}\,\cdot$, and then evaluating the right member.

It was also shown at I, **123** that the choice of the point of reference O was entirely arbitrary, but that after this point is chosen then, for a given displacement, the straight-line translation and the rotation are uniquely determined. It will be of interest to compare the same displacement referred to two different points. Let O_1 be any point different from O, and let

$$\overrightarrow{OO_1} = \boldsymbol{\varrho}.$$

The position of the point R_0 (Fig. 43) with respect to O is $\mathbf{r}_0$, and with respect to O_1 is $\mathbf{r}_1$. Similarly let the two translations be $\mathbf{T}$ and $\mathbf{T}_1$. When referred to the point O, the displacement of O_1 is a translation $\mathbf{T}$ and a rotation $\mathbf{a} \times \boldsymbol{\varrho} \sin \varphi + \mathbf{a} \times (\mathbf{a} \times \boldsymbol{\varrho}) \operatorname{vers} \varphi$, but when referred to O_1 the displacement is merely the translation $\mathbf{T}_1$. Hence

$$\mathbf{T}_1 = \mathbf{T} + \mathbf{a} \times \boldsymbol{\varrho} \sin \varphi + \mathbf{a} \times (\mathbf{a} \times \boldsymbol{\varrho}) \operatorname{vers} \varphi. \tag{2}$$

Let $\mathbf{b}$ be a unit vector for the rotation about an axis through O_1, and let θ be the angle of rotation. Then, for any point of the body,

$$\mathbf{D}_1 = \mathbf{T}_1 + \mathbf{b} \times \mathbf{r}_1 \sin \theta + \mathbf{b} \times (\mathbf{b} \times \mathbf{r}_1) \operatorname{vers} \theta, \tag{3}$$

and

$$\mathbf{D}_0 = \mathbf{T} + \mathbf{a} \times \mathbf{r}_0 \sin \varphi + \mathbf{a} \times (\mathbf{a} \times \mathbf{r}_0) \operatorname{vers} \varphi.$$

Now

$$\mathbf{r}_0 = \mathbf{r}_1 + \boldsymbol{\varrho},$$

and therefore

$$\begin{aligned}\mathbf{D}_0 = \mathbf{T} &+ \mathbf{a} \times \boldsymbol{\varrho} \sin \varphi + \mathbf{a} \times (\mathbf{a} \times \boldsymbol{\varrho}) \operatorname{vers} \varphi \\ &+ \mathbf{a} \times \mathbf{r}_1 \sin \varphi + \mathbf{a} \times (\mathbf{a} \times \mathbf{r}_1) \operatorname{vers} \varphi;\end{aligned}$$

or, by Eq. (2),

$$\mathbf{D}_0 = \mathbf{T}_1 + \mathbf{a} \times \mathbf{r}_1 \sin \varphi + \mathbf{a} \times (\mathbf{a} \times \mathbf{r}_1) \operatorname{vers} \varphi. \tag{4}$$

Since

$$\mathbf{D}_0 = \mathbf{D}_1$$

for every $\mathbf{r}_1$, it follows from Eqs. (3) and (4) that

$$\mathbf{b} \times \mathbf{r}_1 \sin \theta + \mathbf{b} \times (\mathbf{b} \times \mathbf{r}_1) \text{ vers } \theta = \mathbf{a} \times \mathbf{r}_1 \sin \varphi + \mathbf{a} \times (\mathbf{a} \times \mathbf{r}_1) \text{ vers } \varphi.$$

By Eq. (74.1) the left member represents a rotation of the point $\mathbf{r}_1$ through an angle θ in a plane perpendicular to $\mathbf{b}$, while the right member is a rotation of the same point through an angle φ in a

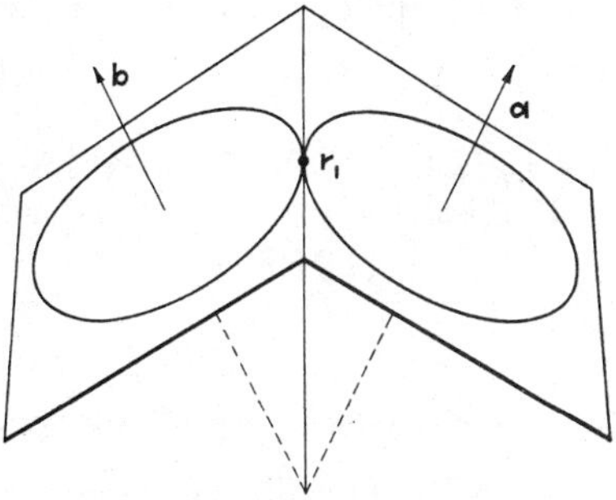

FIG. 44.

plane perpendicular to $\mathbf{a}$ (Fig. 44). In order that these two displacements be the same, it is necessary and sufficient that

$$\mathbf{a} = \mathbf{b} \quad \text{and} \quad \varphi = \theta;$$

and, if these conditions are satisfied, Eq. (2) is satisfied for every $\mathbf{r}_0$.

It follows therefore that in the two modes of representing the displacement, the two axes of rotation are parallel and the two angles of rotation are equal. Since O and O_1 are any pair of reference points, it follows that *the direction of the axis and magnitude of the angle of rotation are independent of the reference point which is chosen.*

76. Rotation about Parallel Axes without Translation.—Consider two equal rotations, without translation, about parallel axes which are fixed in the body. Let O_1 and O_2 be the two points of intersection of the axes with a plane P which is perpendicular to both axes. Let the position of a particle with respect to O_1 be $\mathbf{r}_1$, and with respect to O_2 be $\mathbf{r}_2$; and let the position of O_1 with respect to O_2 be $\boldsymbol{\rho}$. Then

$$\mathbf{r}_2 = \mathbf{r}_1 + \boldsymbol{\rho}. \tag{1}$$

If $\mathbf{D}_1$ is the displacement due to a rotation through an angle φ about the axis through O_1, $\mathbf{D}_2$ the displacement due to an equal rotation about the axis through O_2, and $\mathbf{a}$ is a unit vector which has the direction of the axes of rotation, then

$$\mathbf{D}_1 = (\mathbf{a} \times \mathbf{r}_1) \sin \varphi + \mathbf{a} \times (\mathbf{a} \times \mathbf{r}_1) \operatorname{vers} \varphi,$$

and

$$\mathbf{D}_2 = (\mathbf{a} \times \mathbf{r}_2) \sin \varphi + \mathbf{a} \times (\mathbf{a} \times \mathbf{r}_2) \operatorname{vers} \varphi,$$

or, on account of Eq. (1),

$$\begin{aligned} D_2 &= [\mathbf{a} \times (\mathbf{r}_1 + \boldsymbol{\varrho})] \sin \varphi + [\mathbf{a} \times \{\mathbf{a} \times (\mathbf{r}_1 + \boldsymbol{\varrho})\}] \operatorname{vers} \varphi \\ &= (\mathbf{a} \times \mathbf{r}_1) \sin \varphi + \mathbf{a} \times (\mathbf{a} \times \mathbf{r}_1) \operatorname{vers} \varphi \\ &\qquad + (\mathbf{a} \times \boldsymbol{\varrho}) \sin \varphi + \mathbf{a} \times (\mathbf{a} \times \boldsymbol{\varrho}) \operatorname{vers} \varphi; \end{aligned}$$

and therefore

$$\mathbf{D}_2 - \mathbf{D}_1 = (\mathbf{a} \times \boldsymbol{\varrho}) \sin \varphi + \mathbf{a} \times (\mathbf{a} \times \boldsymbol{\varrho}) \operatorname{vers} \varphi. \qquad (2)$$

The difference between the two displacements is independent of $\mathbf{r}_1$. It is the same for all points of the body, and is therefore a translation. This translation is the displacement of the point O_1 in the rotation about O_2, and is therefore perpendicular to the axes of rotation.

77. A Particular Representation of a Displacement.—The general expression for a displacement of a rigid body,

$$\mathbf{D} = \mathbf{T} + (\mathbf{a} \times \mathbf{r}) \sin \varphi + \mathbf{a} \times (\mathbf{a} \times \mathbf{r}) \operatorname{vers} \varphi,$$

contains an arbitrary element, namely the position of the axis of rotation with respect to the body. For a given displacement the direction of the axis and the angle of rotation are determined. It will be shown that for any given displacement the position of the axis can be chosen in such a way that the translation is parallel to the axis of rotation.

Suppose a given displacement is represented by the expression

$$\mathbf{D} = \mathbf{T} + (\mathbf{a} \times \mathbf{r}_1) \sin \varphi + \mathbf{a} \times (\mathbf{a} \times \mathbf{r}_1) \operatorname{vers} \varphi, \qquad (1)$$

the origin of the vectors $\mathbf{r}_1$ being at a point O_1 on the axis of rotation. Through O_1 pass a plane P perpendicular to the axis of rotation. Let $\mathbf{b}$ be a unit vector in the plane. Then $\mathbf{b}$, $\mathbf{a} \times \mathbf{b}$, and $\mathbf{a}$ form an $\mathbf{i}$, $\mathbf{j}$, $\mathbf{k}$ system of unit vectors.

In the direction **b** from O_1 choose a second reference point O_2 with respect to which the vectors are $\mathbf{r}_2$. If the distance between O_1 and O_2 is ρ, then

$$\overrightarrow{O_1O_2} = \rho\mathbf{b},$$

and

$$\mathbf{r}_1 = \rho\mathbf{b} + \mathbf{r}_2.$$

This expression for $\mathbf{r}_1$ substituted in Eq. (1) gives

$$\left.\begin{aligned}\mathbf{D} = \mathbf{T} + (\mathbf{a}\times\mathbf{b})\rho\sin\varphi + \mathbf{a}\times(\mathbf{a}\times\mathbf{b})\rho\operatorname{vers}\varphi\\ + (\mathbf{a}\times\mathbf{r}_2)\sin\varphi + \mathbf{a}\times(\mathbf{a}\times\mathbf{r}_2)\operatorname{vers}\varphi.\end{aligned}\right\} \quad (2)$$

The translation **T**, which is a definite one, can be represented by

$$\mathbf{T} = T_1\mathbf{a} + T_2\mathbf{c},$$

where **c** is some unit vector in the plane P. If ρ and the vector **b** are chosen in such a way that

$$T_2\mathbf{c} + (\mathbf{a}\times\mathbf{b})\rho\sin\varphi + \mathbf{a}\times(\mathbf{a}\times\mathbf{b})\rho\operatorname{vers}\varphi = 0, \quad (3)$$

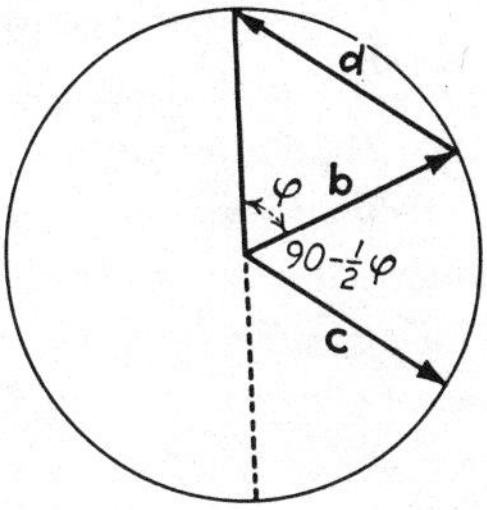

FIG. 45.

the expression for **D** becomes

$$\mathbf{D} = T_1\mathbf{a} + (\mathbf{a}\times\mathbf{r}_2)\sin\varphi + \mathbf{a}\times(\mathbf{a}\times\mathbf{r}_2)\operatorname{vers}\varphi, \quad (4)$$

an expression for the displacement in which the translation has the same direction as the axis of rotation. It remains to be shown that Eq. (3) can always be satisfied.

The vector

$$(\mathbf{a}\times\mathbf{b})\sin\varphi + \mathbf{a}\times(\mathbf{a}\times\mathbf{b})\operatorname{vers}\varphi = \mathbf{d}$$

represents the displacement of the terminus of the vector **b** when it is rotated through the angle φ (Fig. 45). Equation (3) becomes

$$T_2\mathbf{c} + \rho\mathbf{d} = 0, \quad (5)$$

that is, **d** is parallel to **c**, but oppositely directed. Evidently

$$\widehat{\mathbf{cb}} = 90° - \tfrac{1}{2}\varphi.$$

The tensor of **d** is $2\sin\frac{1}{2}\varphi$, as is seen from the diagram. Consequently Eq. (5) gives

$$\rho = \frac{T_2}{2 \sin \frac{1}{2}\varphi}.$$

The distance ρ and the vector **b** are therefore uniquely determined provided φ is not zero or a multiple of 2π, and in this exceptional case the rotational element of the displacement **D** vanishes, and **D** is a pure translation.

78. Screws and Twists.—The theorem that has just been proved, namely, that any displacement of a rigid body can be effected in one and only one way by a rotation about a certain axis and a translation parallel to that axis, is due to Chasles. This type of displacement is similar to the displacement of a nut on a threaded bolt. Hence the following definitions:

Definition.—A screw is a straight line with which a definite magnitude called the pitch is associated.

Definition.—A rigid body is said to receive a twist about a screw when it is rotated uniformly about the screw and at the same time is translated uniformly in a direction parallel to the screw through a distance which is equal to the product of the pitch and the circular measure of the angle of rotation.

If in Eq. (77.4)

$$T_1 = p\varphi,$$

the expression for the displacement becomes

$$\mathbf{D} = p\varphi\mathbf{a} + \mathbf{a} \times \mathbf{r} \sin \varphi + \mathbf{a} \times (\mathbf{a} \times \mathbf{r}) \text{ vers } \varphi, \qquad (1)$$

and if φ is proportional to the time, so that

$$\varphi' = \text{constant},$$

the displacement, which is a continuous function of the time, is a twist about a screw. The screw is the straight line which passes through the origin of **r** and has the direction of **a**, and its pitch is p. The angle φ is called the *amplitude of the twist*, and φ' is called the *twist velocity.*

The kinetic energy of the twist due to the translation of the body is $\frac{1}{2}Mp^2\varphi'^2$, and the kinetic energy due to the rotation about the axis is $\frac{1}{2}Mk^2\varphi'^2$ (Sec. 49); since these two motions are perpendicular to each other, the total kinetic energy of the twist is the sum of the two, or

$$\tfrac{1}{2}M(p^2 + k^2)\varphi'^2, \tag{2}$$

k being the radius of gyration of the body with respect to the screw.

At I, **151** it was shown that any system of forces that is acting at any instant upon a rigid body can be replaced by an equivalent wrench, that is, by a single force and a couple, the axis of the couple being parallel to the single force—a theorem due to Poinsot. From the point of view of dimensions (I, **71**) the moment of a couple divided by a force is a length. If M is the moment of a couple, F is the force, and p is the quotient,

$$M = pF.$$

If the force is directed along a screw whose pitch is p, the system of forces is called a *wrench on a screw.* The moment of the couple is then the product of the force and the pitch of the screw.

Six algebraic quantities are necessary for a complete specification of a twist about a screw, namely, four for a complete specification of a line, one for the pitch, and one for the amplitude of the twist. Likewise six magnitudes are necessary for a complete specification of a wrench on a screw, namely five for the screw itself and one for the *intensity of the wrench,* or the magnitude of the force which, associated with the couple, constitutes the entire wrench.

The application of the theory of screws is limited to states of equilibrium, impulsive forces, and small oscillations, and will not be pursued farther here. The theory has been developed largely by Sir Robert S. Ball, and any one who is interested in it should consult his "Theory of Screws" (1900).

THE MOTION OF A RIGID BODY THAT HAS ONE POINT FIXED

79. The Moving Trihedron.—Imagine a rigid body one point of which is fixed relative to fixed space. Let the fixed point O be taken as the origin of a rectangular trihedron, x, y, z, which is stationary relative to fixed space, and also let O be taken as the origin of a rectangular trihedron, ξ, η, ζ, which is fixed relative to the body. Then as the body moves relative to the fixed point, the ξ, η, ζ trihedron moves with it, and in order to describe the motion of the body it is sufficient to describe the motion of the ξ, η, ζ-trihedron relative to the x, y, z-trihedron, the two trihedrons having always the same origin O.

Let $\mathbf{r}$ be the position vector of a particle m of the body, and let $\mathbf{i}$, $\mathbf{j}$, $\mathbf{k}$ be unit vectors which have the directions of the ξ-, η-, and ζ-axes respectively. Then

$$\mathbf{r} = \xi\,\mathbf{i} + \eta\,\mathbf{j} + \zeta\,\mathbf{k}. \tag{1}$$

Since the particle is fixed in the body, its coordinates ξ, η, and ζ are constants, and it is only the unit vectors $\mathbf{i}$, $\mathbf{j}$, and $\mathbf{k}$ that vary as the body moves; that is, relative to fixed space,

$$d\mathbf{r} = \xi\,d\mathbf{i} + \eta\,d\mathbf{j} + \zeta\,d\mathbf{k}. \tag{2}$$

Inasmuch as $d\mathbf{r}$ is a vector, it is expressible in terms of $\mathbf{i}$, $\mathbf{j}$, and $\mathbf{k}$. By Eq. (6.5),

$$d\mathbf{r} = (d\mathbf{r}\cdot\mathbf{i})\mathbf{i} + (d\mathbf{r}\cdot\mathbf{j})\mathbf{j} + (d\mathbf{r}\cdot\mathbf{k})\mathbf{k}. \tag{3}$$

On substituting the expression for $d\mathbf{r}$ from Eq. (2) in the right member of Eq. (3), there results

$$\begin{aligned} d\mathbf{r} = {} & [\xi\,\mathbf{i}\cdot d\mathbf{i} + \eta\,\mathbf{i}\cdot d\mathbf{j} + \zeta\,\mathbf{i}\cdot d\mathbf{k}]\,\mathbf{i} \\ & + [\xi\,\mathbf{j}\cdot d\mathbf{i} + \eta\,\mathbf{j}\cdot d\mathbf{j} + \zeta\,\mathbf{j}\cdot d\mathbf{k}]\,\mathbf{j} \\ & + [\xi\,\mathbf{k}\cdot d\mathbf{i} + \eta\,\mathbf{k}\cdot d\mathbf{j} + \zeta\,\mathbf{k}\cdot d\mathbf{k}]\,\mathbf{k}. \end{aligned}$$

But

$$\begin{aligned} \mathbf{j}\cdot d\mathbf{i} &= -\mathbf{i}\cdot d\mathbf{j}, & \mathbf{i}\cdot d\mathbf{i} &= \mathbf{j}\cdot d\mathbf{j} = \mathbf{k}\cdot d\mathbf{k} = 0, \\ \mathbf{k}\cdot d\mathbf{j} &= -\mathbf{j}\cdot d\mathbf{k}, & \mathbf{i}\cdot\mathbf{j} &= \mathbf{j}\cdot\mathbf{k} = \mathbf{k}\cdot\mathbf{i} = 0, \\ \mathbf{i}\cdot d\mathbf{k} &= -\mathbf{k}\cdot d\mathbf{i}, & \mathbf{i}\cdot\mathbf{i} &= \mathbf{j}\cdot\mathbf{j} = \mathbf{k}\cdot\mathbf{k} = 1. \end{aligned}$$

The above expression for $d\mathbf{r}$ therefore reduces to

$$d\mathbf{r} = (\zeta\mathbf{i}\cdot d\mathbf{k} - \eta\mathbf{j}\cdot d\mathbf{i})\mathbf{i} + (\xi\mathbf{j}\cdot d\mathbf{i} - \zeta\mathbf{k}\cdot d\mathbf{j})\mathbf{j} + (\eta\mathbf{k}\cdot d\mathbf{j} - \xi\mathbf{i}\cdot d\mathbf{k})\mathbf{k};$$

and by Eq. (3.3) the right member of this equation is expressible as a vector product, namely,

$$d\mathbf{r} = (\mathbf{k}\cdot d\mathbf{j}\,\mathbf{i} + \mathbf{i}\cdot d\mathbf{k}\,\mathbf{j} + \mathbf{j}\cdot d\mathbf{i}\,\mathbf{k}) \times (\xi\,\mathbf{i} + \eta\,\mathbf{j} + \zeta\,\mathbf{k}),$$

or

$$d\mathbf{r} = \boldsymbol{\omega} \times \mathbf{r}\,dt, \tag{4}$$

if the infinitesimal vector

$$\mathbf{k}\cdot d\mathbf{j}\,\mathbf{i} + \mathbf{i}\cdot d\mathbf{k}\,\mathbf{j} + \mathbf{j}\cdot d\mathbf{i}\,\mathbf{k} \tag{5}$$

is denoted by $\boldsymbol{\omega}\, dt$. Thus the displacement of the point ξ, η, ζ is perpendicular to a plane that passes through $\mathbf{r}$, which depends upon the point ξ, η, ζ, and through a vector $\boldsymbol{\omega}$ which is independent of the point ξ, η, ζ. The line through O that has the direction of $\boldsymbol{\omega}$ is therefore an axis of rotation, and $\boldsymbol{\omega}$ is the angular velocity. From this it is evident that at any instant the state of motion of a rigid body, one point of which is fixed, is a rotation about some axis through the point O, and the motion is just the same as though the axis were fixed in space [Eq. (74.2)] although at a succeeding instant the position of the axis may be different. It is possible therefore to speak of the *instantaneous axis of rotation*, and this is the common practice. If Eq. (5) is divided by dt, there results

$$\mathbf{r}' = \boldsymbol{\omega} \times \mathbf{r}, \tag{6}$$

just as though the axis were fixed [Eq. (46.1)].

In particular, it follows that for a moving trihedron with a fixed origin

$$\mathbf{i}' = \boldsymbol{\omega} \times \mathbf{i}, \qquad \mathbf{j}' = \boldsymbol{\omega} \times \mathbf{j}, \qquad \mathbf{k}' = \boldsymbol{\omega} \times \mathbf{k}. \tag{7}$$

Acceleration.—Equation (6) is the velocity with respect to fixed space of a particle m that is fixed in the body. This particle also has an acceleration with respect to fixed space. If ξ, η, and ζ are constants,

$$\mathbf{r} = \xi\,\mathbf{i} + \eta\,\mathbf{j} + \zeta\,\mathbf{k},$$

and

$$\mathbf{r}' = \xi\,\mathbf{i}' + \eta\,\mathbf{j}' + \zeta\,\mathbf{k}' = \boldsymbol{\omega} \times \mathbf{r}, \tag{8}$$

$$\mathbf{r}'' = \xi\,\mathbf{i}'' + \eta\,\mathbf{j}'' + \zeta\,\mathbf{k}'' = \boldsymbol{\omega}' \times \mathbf{r} + \boldsymbol{\omega} \times \mathbf{r}'. \tag{9}$$

Thus the acceleration of a particle, whose position is $\mathbf{r}$ in a rigid body, one point of which is fixed, whose angular velocity is $\boldsymbol{\omega}$, is, by virtue of Eq. (6),

$$\mathbf{r}'' = \boldsymbol{\omega}' \times \mathbf{r} + \boldsymbol{\omega} \times (\boldsymbol{\omega} \times \mathbf{r}). \tag{10}$$

80. Extension to an Arbitrary Vector.—In the preceding section, $\mathbf{r}$ was a vector fixed in the body. If the restriction that the coordinates of its terminus, ξ, η, and ζ, be constants is removed, then, in the expression

$$\mathbf{r} = \zeta\,\mathbf{i} + \eta\,\mathbf{j} + \xi\mathbf{k},\text{l} \tag{1}$$

all the letters are variable, and

$$\mathbf{r}' = (\xi'\mathbf{i} + \eta'\mathbf{j} + \zeta'\mathbf{k}) + (\xi\,\mathbf{i}' + \eta\,\mathbf{j}' + \zeta\,\mathbf{k}'), \tag{2}$$

$$\mathbf{r}'' = (\xi''\mathbf{i} + \eta''\mathbf{j} + \zeta''\mathbf{k}) + 2(\xi'\mathbf{i}' + \eta'\mathbf{j}' + \zeta'\mathbf{k}') + (\xi\,\mathbf{i}'' + \eta\,\mathbf{j}'' + \zeta\,\mathbf{k}''). \tag{3}$$

Now let

$$\boldsymbol{\varrho} = \xi\mathbf{i} + \eta\,\mathbf{j} + \zeta\,\mathbf{k}, \tag{4}$$

$$\boldsymbol{\varrho}' = \xi'\mathbf{i} + \eta'\mathbf{j} + \zeta'\mathbf{k}, \tag{5}$$

$$\boldsymbol{\varrho}'' = \xi''\mathbf{i} + \eta''\mathbf{j} + \zeta''\mathbf{k}. \tag{6}$$

Then $\boldsymbol{\varrho}$ and $\mathbf{r}$ are identical, but $\boldsymbol{\varrho}'$ is the velocity of the terminus of $\boldsymbol{\varrho}$ relative to the moving trihedron, and $\boldsymbol{\varrho}''$ is the acceleration relative to the moving trihedron. They are termed the *relative velocity* and the *relative acceleration* respectively. The vectors $\mathbf{r}'$ and $\mathbf{r}''$ are called the *absolute velocity* and *absolute acceleration* of the terminus of $\mathbf{r}$, or $\boldsymbol{\varrho}$; that is, the velocity and acceleration relative to fixed space.

From Eqs. (2), (5), and (79.8),

$$\mathbf{r}' = \boldsymbol{\varrho}' + (\boldsymbol{\omega} \times \boldsymbol{\varrho}). \tag{7}$$

The vector $\boldsymbol{\omega} \times \boldsymbol{\varrho}$ is the absolute velocity which the terminus of $\boldsymbol{\varrho}$ must have in order to maintain its position in the body. It is therefore called the *velocity of following*. Expressed in words, Eq. (7) states that:

The absolute velocity of the terminus of any vector is equal to its relative velocity plus the velocity of following.

As is seen from Eq. (79.9),

$$\xi\,\mathbf{i}'' + \eta\,\mathbf{j}'' + \zeta\,\mathbf{k}'' = \boldsymbol{\omega}' \times \boldsymbol{\varrho} + \boldsymbol{\omega} \times (\boldsymbol{\omega} \times \boldsymbol{\varrho}) \tag{8}$$

is the acceleration of a point which is fixed in the body. It is therefore the *acceleration of following*. By Eqs. (79.7), the vector

$$2(\xi'\mathbf{i}' + \eta'\mathbf{j}' + \zeta'\mathbf{k}') = 2\,\boldsymbol{\omega} \times \boldsymbol{\varrho}', \tag{9}$$

and is called the *compound centrifugal acceleration*. It is perpendicular to the plane that passes through the axis of rotation and through the vector of relative velocity. It is twice the velocity which the terminus of the relative velocity vector would have if it remained fixed in the body. Its magnitude vanishes if the rotation vanishes, if the relative velocity vanishes, or if $\boldsymbol{\varrho}'$ and $\boldsymbol{\omega}$ are collinear. The vector $\xi''\mathbf{i} + \eta''\mathbf{j} + \zeta''\mathbf{k}$ is simply the *relative acceleration* $\boldsymbol{\rho}''$. Hence Eq. (3) becomes

$$\mathbf{r}'' = \boldsymbol{\rho}'' + 2\boldsymbol{\omega} \times \boldsymbol{\rho}' + [\boldsymbol{\omega}' \times \boldsymbol{\rho} + \boldsymbol{\omega} \times (\boldsymbol{\omega} \times \boldsymbol{\rho})], \tag{10}$$

which, expressed in words, gives the theorem:

The absolute acceleration is equal to the relative acceleration plus the acceleration of following, plus the compound centrifugal acceleration, which is the theorem of Coriolis.

Equation (10) can be derived directly from Eq. (7) by differentiation if it is kept in mind that the vectors $\boldsymbol{\rho}$ and $\boldsymbol{\rho}'$ are not fixed in the body; that is, the derivative of $\boldsymbol{\rho}$ is $\boldsymbol{\rho}' + \boldsymbol{\omega} \times \boldsymbol{\rho}$ and the derivative of $\boldsymbol{\rho}'$ is $\boldsymbol{\rho}'' + \boldsymbol{\omega} \times \boldsymbol{\rho}'$.

81. Infinitesimal Rotations Are Vectors.—That finite rotations are not vectors is readily shown by an example. Take a book in a horizontal plane; rotate it through an angle of 90° in a forward direction about a horizontal, east and west axis; then rotate it in a forward direction through an angle of 90° about a vertical axis. Note the final position of the book, and then return it to its initial position. Repeat the operations in a reverse order, rotating first about a vertical axis, and then about an east and west axis. It will be observed that the final position of the book is not the same as it was in the first trial. Since the final result depends upon the order of the operations, it is evident that the operations are not vectors, notwithstanding the fact that a finite rotation can be represented by a directed magnitude, namely a length, equal to the angle of rotation, along the axis of rotation.

Infinitesimal rotations, however, are vectors, and it is desirable, perhaps, to emphasize this fact. Let a rigid body be rotated about an axis L_1 that passes through a fixed point O, through an angle $\omega_1\,dt$, and then about an axis L_2, that also passes through O, through an angle $\omega_2\,dt$. The first rotation can be denoted by $\boldsymbol{\omega}_1\,dt$ and the second by $\boldsymbol{\omega}_2\,dt$. By the first rotation a vector $\mathbf{r}$ becomes

$$\mathbf{r}_1 = \mathbf{r} + d\mathbf{r} = \mathbf{r} + \boldsymbol{\omega}_1 \times \mathbf{r}\,dt.$$

By the second rotation the vector $\mathbf{r}_1$ becomes

$$\begin{aligned}\mathbf{r}_2 &= \mathbf{r}_1 + d\mathbf{r}_1 = \mathbf{r}_1 + \boldsymbol{\omega}_2 \times \mathbf{r}_1\,dt,\\ &= \mathbf{r} + \boldsymbol{\omega}_1 \times \mathbf{r}\,dt + \boldsymbol{\omega}_2 \times \{\mathbf{r} + \boldsymbol{\omega}_1 \times \mathbf{r}\,dt\}\,dt,\\ &= \mathbf{r} + \boldsymbol{\omega}_1 \times \mathbf{r}\,dt + \boldsymbol{\omega}_2 \times \mathbf{r}\,dt + \boldsymbol{\omega}_2 \times (\boldsymbol{\omega}_1 \times \mathbf{r})\,(dt)^2.\end{aligned}$$

Hence

$$\lim \frac{\mathbf{r}_2 - \mathbf{r}}{dt} = \mathbf{r}' = \boldsymbol{\omega}_1 \times \mathbf{r} + \boldsymbol{\omega}_2 \times \mathbf{r}, \tag{1}$$

since the last term $\boldsymbol{\omega}_2 \times (\boldsymbol{\omega}_1 \times \mathbf{r})\, dt$ vanishes.

Now let $\boldsymbol{\omega}$ be the vector sum of $\boldsymbol{\omega}_1$ and $\boldsymbol{\omega}_2$, or the resultant according to the parallelogram law, and let the rigid body be rotated through the angle $\omega\, dt$ about an axis that coincides with $\boldsymbol{\omega}$. Then

$$\mathbf{r}' = \boldsymbol{\omega} \times \mathbf{r} = (\boldsymbol{\omega}_1 + \boldsymbol{\omega}_2) \times \mathbf{r} = \boldsymbol{\omega}_1 \times \mathbf{r} + \boldsymbol{\omega}_2 \times \mathbf{r}. \tag{2}$$

That is, the single displacement about the axis $\boldsymbol{\omega}$ is the vector sum of the two displacements about $\boldsymbol{\omega}_1$ and $\boldsymbol{\omega}_2$, and infinitesimal rotations are vectors, since the directed magnitudes which represent them obey the parallelogram law. Angular velocities differ from infinitesimal rotations, only by the scalar factor dt, so that angular velocities also are vectors.

If $\boldsymbol{\omega}$ is the angular velocity of a rigid body about an instantaneous axis through the fixed point O, it can be resolved into components, $\boldsymbol{\omega}_i$, $\boldsymbol{\omega}_j$, $\boldsymbol{\omega}_k$ along the **i**-, **j**-, and **k**-axes, so that

$$\boldsymbol{\omega} = \boldsymbol{\omega}_i + \boldsymbol{\omega}_j + \boldsymbol{\omega}_k,$$

and $\boldsymbol{\omega}_i$, $\boldsymbol{\omega}_j$, $\boldsymbol{\omega}_k$ are angular velocities of the body about the **i**-, **j**-, and **k**-axes in the sense that an infinitesimal rotation $\omega_i\, dt$ about the **i**-axis, plus an infinitesimal rotation $\omega_j\, dt$ about the **j**-axis, plus an infinitesimal rotation $\omega_k\, dt$ about the **k**-axis, the rotations being taken successively in any order, or even simultaneously, give precisely the same displacement of the body as a single rotation through the angle $\omega\, dt$ about the axis of $\boldsymbol{\omega}$.

In Sec. 79 it was found that

$$(\mathbf{k} \cdot d\mathbf{j})\mathbf{i} + (\mathbf{i} \cdot d\mathbf{k})\mathbf{j} + (\mathbf{j} \cdot d\mathbf{i})\mathbf{k} = \boldsymbol{\omega}\, dt.$$

Hence

$$\boldsymbol{\omega} = (\mathbf{k} \cdot \mathbf{j}')\mathbf{i} + (\mathbf{i} \cdot \mathbf{k}')\mathbf{j} + (\mathbf{j} \cdot \mathbf{i}')\mathbf{k}, \tag{3}$$

and

$$\omega_i = \mathbf{k} \cdot \mathbf{j}', \qquad \omega_j = \mathbf{i} \cdot \mathbf{k}', \qquad \omega_k = \mathbf{j} \cdot \mathbf{i}'. \tag{4}$$

82. The Moment of Momentum Expressed in Terms of the Angular Velocities.—Since the motion of a rigid body about a fixed point at any instant is a rotation about some axis that passes through the fixed point, the moment of momentum and the kinetic energy of the body are expressible in terms of the angular velocities. It was found in Secs. 32 and 45 that the moment of momentum L of the rigid body with respect to the fixed point O is

$$\mathbf{L} = \Sigma m\, \mathbf{r} \times \mathbf{r}', \tag{1}$$

where m is the mass of a particle of the body, $\mathbf{r}$ is its position relative to the point O, and $\mathbf{r}'$ is its linear velocity in fixed space, or its absolute velocity. For a rigid body one point of which is fixed, Eq. (79.6) gives

$$\mathbf{r}' = \boldsymbol{\omega} \times \mathbf{r}.$$

Hence for such a rigid body the moment of momentum relative to the fixed point is

$$\begin{aligned} \mathbf{L} &= \Sigma m[\mathbf{r} \times (\boldsymbol{\omega} \times \mathbf{r})] \\ &= \Sigma m r^2 \boldsymbol{\omega} - \Sigma m \mathbf{r} \cdot \boldsymbol{\omega}\, \mathbf{r}, \qquad \text{by Eq. (5.4).} \end{aligned} \tag{2}$$

Since the unit vectors $\mathbf{i}$, $\mathbf{j}$, and $\mathbf{k}$ are mutually orthogonal,

$$\mathbf{L} = (\mathbf{L} \cdot \mathbf{i})\mathbf{i} + (\mathbf{L} \cdot \mathbf{j})\mathbf{j} + (\mathbf{L} \cdot \mathbf{k})\mathbf{k}; \tag{3}$$

and from Eq. (2)

$$\begin{aligned} \mathbf{L} \cdot \mathbf{i} &= \Sigma m r^2\, \boldsymbol{\omega} \cdot \mathbf{i} - \Sigma m\, (\mathbf{r} \cdot \boldsymbol{\omega})(\mathbf{r} \cdot \mathbf{i}), \\ \mathbf{L} \cdot \mathbf{j} &= \Sigma m r^2\, \boldsymbol{\omega} \cdot \mathbf{j} - \Sigma m\, (\mathbf{r} \cdot \boldsymbol{\omega})(\mathbf{r} \cdot \mathbf{j}), \\ \mathbf{L} \cdot \mathbf{k} &= \Sigma m r^2\, \boldsymbol{\omega} \cdot \mathbf{k} - \Sigma m\, (\mathbf{r} \cdot \boldsymbol{\omega})(\mathbf{r} \cdot \mathbf{k}). \end{aligned}$$

Since

$$\mathbf{r} = \xi \mathbf{i} + \eta \mathbf{j} + \zeta \mathbf{k},$$

and

$$\boldsymbol{\omega} = \omega_i \mathbf{i} + \omega_j \mathbf{j} + \omega_k \mathbf{k},$$

it follows that

$$\mathbf{r} \cdot \boldsymbol{\omega} = \xi \omega_i + \eta \omega_j + \zeta \omega_k.$$

On using the notation of Sec. 19,

$$\left.\begin{aligned} A &= \Sigma m(\eta^2 + \zeta^2), & D &= \Sigma m \eta \zeta, \\ B &= \Sigma m(\zeta^2 + \xi^2), & E &= \Sigma m \zeta \xi, \\ C &= \Sigma m(\xi^2 + \eta^2), & F &= \Sigma m \xi \eta, \end{aligned}\right\} \tag{4}$$

for the moments and products of inertia, it is found that Eq. (3) becomes

$$\mathbf{L} = (A\omega_i - F\omega_j - E\omega_k)\mathbf{i} + (B\omega_j - D\omega_k - F\omega_i)\mathbf{j} + (C\omega_k - E\omega_i - D\omega_j)\mathbf{k}. \quad (5)$$

If the vectors **i, j, k** coincide in direction with the principal axes of inertia at the fixed point O, the products of inertia vanish; that is

$$D = E = F = 0,$$

and the expression for the moment of momentum is much simplified, namely

$$\mathbf{L} = A\omega_i\mathbf{i} + B\omega_j\mathbf{j} + C\omega_k\mathbf{k}. \quad (6)$$

By comparing this expression for the moment of momentum with that of the instantaneous axis of rotation,

$$\boldsymbol{\omega} = \omega_i\mathbf{i} + \omega_j\mathbf{j} + \omega_k\mathbf{k}, \quad (7)$$

it is evident that the direction of the two axes does not coincide, in general. They will do so if

$$A = B = C,$$

that is, if the ellipsoid of inertia is a sphere; and also in case two of the angular velocities are zero, in which event both the instantaneous axis of rotation and the moment of momentum coincide with one of the principal axes of inertia of the body at the point O.

83. The Kinetic Energy in Terms of the Angular Velocities.—The kinetic energy of the body relative to the system of fixed axes, or the x-, y-, z-system, is

$$\begin{aligned} T &= \tfrac{1}{2}\Sigma mv^2 = \tfrac{1}{2}\Sigma m\mathbf{r}' \cdot \mathbf{r}' = \tfrac{1}{2}\Sigma m\mathbf{r}' \cdot (\boldsymbol{\omega} \times \mathbf{r}), \\ &= \tfrac{1}{2}\Sigma m[\mathbf{r}'\boldsymbol{\omega}\mathbf{r}] = \tfrac{1}{2}\Sigma m[\boldsymbol{\omega}\mathbf{r}\mathbf{r}'], \quad \text{by Eq. (4.2)}, \\ &= \tfrac{1}{2}\Sigma m\boldsymbol{\omega} \cdot \mathbf{r} \times \mathbf{r}' = \tfrac{1}{2}\boldsymbol{\omega} \cdot \Sigma m\mathbf{r} \times \mathbf{r}', \\ &= \tfrac{1}{2}\boldsymbol{\omega} \cdot \mathbf{L}, \quad \text{by Eq. (82.1).} \end{aligned} \quad (1)$$

The kinetic energy, therefore, is equal to one half the scalar product of the angular velocity and the moment of momentum.

If the scalar product of Eqs. (82.5) and (82.7) is taken, the expression for the kinetic energy in terms of the angular velocities and the moments and products of inertia is found to be

$$2T = A\omega_i^2 + B\omega_j^2 + C\omega_k^2 - 2D\omega_j\omega_k - 2E\omega_k\omega_i - 2F\omega_i\omega_j. \quad (2)$$

Of course, if the **i**-, **j**-, and **k**-, axes coincide with the principal axes of inertia at the fixed point O, the above expression reduces to

$$2T = A\omega_i^2 + B\omega_j^2 + C\omega_k^2, \tag{3}$$

since D, E, and F vanish.

If α, β, and γ are the direction cosines of $\boldsymbol{\omega}$ with respect to the ξ-, η-, ζ-axes, it is evident that

$$\omega_i = \alpha\omega, \qquad \omega_j = \beta\omega, \qquad \omega_k = \gamma\omega;$$

and these values, substituted in Eq. (2), give

$$2T = (A\alpha^2 + B\beta^2 + C\gamma^2 - 2D\beta\gamma - 2E\gamma\alpha - 2F\alpha\beta)\omega^2,$$

or

$$2T = I\omega^2, \tag{4}$$

where I is the moment of inertia of the body with respect to the instantaneous axis of rotation.

Equation (4) can be derived directly from the definition of the kinetic energy, as follows:

$$\begin{aligned} 2T &= \Sigma m\mathbf{r}' \cdot \mathbf{r}' = \Sigma m\, \boldsymbol{\omega} \times \mathbf{r} \cdot \boldsymbol{\omega} \times \mathbf{r} \\ &= \omega^2 \Sigma m r^2 \sin^2 \widehat{\mathbf{r}\boldsymbol{\omega}} \text{ by Chapter I, Problem 5.} \\ &= I\omega^2. \end{aligned}$$

By comparing Eq. (2) with Eq. (48.2) it will be observed that the moment of momentum can be written

$$\mathbf{L} = \frac{\partial T}{\partial \omega_i}\mathbf{i} + \frac{\partial T}{\partial \omega_j}\mathbf{j} + \frac{\partial T}{\partial \omega_k}\mathbf{k}. \tag{5}$$

84. The Rate of Change of Moment of Momentum.—If the ξ-, η-, and ζ-axes, which are rigidly attached to the body, coincide with the principal axes of inertia at the fixed point O, the moment of momentum of the body with respect to the origin is

$$\mathbf{L} = A\omega_i\mathbf{i} + B\omega_j\mathbf{j} + C\omega_k\mathbf{k}. \tag{1}$$

The time rate of change of L with respect to a set of axes that is fixed in space, the x-, y-, z-system, is

$$\mathbf{L}' = (A\omega_i'\mathbf{i} + B\omega_j'\mathbf{j} + C\omega_k'\mathbf{k}) + (A\omega_i\mathbf{i}' + B\omega_j\mathbf{j}' + C\omega_k\mathbf{k}').$$

Now, by Eq. (79.7),

$$\left.\begin{aligned} \mathbf{i}' &= \boldsymbol{\omega} \times \mathbf{i} = \omega_k\mathbf{j} - \omega_j\mathbf{k}, \\ \mathbf{j}' &= \boldsymbol{\omega} \times \mathbf{j} = \omega_i\mathbf{k} - \omega_k\mathbf{i}, \\ \mathbf{k}' &= \boldsymbol{\omega} \times \mathbf{k} = \omega_j\mathbf{i} - \omega_i\mathbf{j}, \end{aligned}\right\} \tag{2}$$

since

$$\boldsymbol{\omega} = \omega_i\mathbf{i} + \omega_j\mathbf{j} + \omega_k\mathbf{k}.$$

The substitution of these values of $\mathbf{i}'$, $\mathbf{j}'$ and $\mathbf{k}'$ in Eq. (2) gives

$$\mathbf{L}' = [A\omega_i' + (C - B)\omega_j\omega_k]\mathbf{i} + [B\omega_j' + (A - C)\omega_k\omega_i]\mathbf{j} \\ + [C\omega_k' + (B - A)\omega_i\omega_j]\mathbf{k}. \tag{3}$$

This equation can be derived by the method used in Sec. 80. Let the moment of momentum when referred to axes which are fixed in space, the x-, y-, z-system, be $\mathbf{L}$, and when referred to axes which are fixed in the body be $\boldsymbol{\Lambda}$. Then

$$\mathbf{L}' = \boldsymbol{\Lambda}' + \boldsymbol{\omega} \times \boldsymbol{\Lambda}. \tag{4}$$

The rate of change of the total moment of momentum is therefore equal the rate of change relative to the system of axes which are fixed in the body plus a vector $\boldsymbol{\omega} \times \boldsymbol{\Lambda}$, which is perpendicular to the plane which contains $\boldsymbol{\omega}$ and $\boldsymbol{\Lambda}$ and represents the velocity of the terminus of $\boldsymbol{\Lambda}$ as it is carried forward by the rotation $\boldsymbol{\omega}$.

Since, Eq. (1),

$$\boldsymbol{\Lambda} = A\omega_i\mathbf{i} + B\omega_j\mathbf{j} + C\omega_k\mathbf{k},$$

the expression for $\boldsymbol{\Lambda}'$ is

$$\boldsymbol{\Lambda}' = A\omega_i'\mathbf{i} + B\omega_j'\mathbf{j} + C\omega_k'\mathbf{k};$$

and

$$\boldsymbol{\omega} \times \boldsymbol{\Lambda} = \begin{vmatrix} \mathbf{i} & \mathbf{j} & \mathbf{k} \\ \omega_i & \omega_j & \omega_k \\ A\omega_i & B\omega_j & C\omega_k \end{vmatrix}, \text{ by Eq. (3.4),} \tag{5}$$

$$= (C - B)\omega_j\omega_k\mathbf{i} + (A - C)\omega_k\omega_i\mathbf{j} + (B - A)\omega_i\omega_j\mathbf{k},$$

The vector $\boldsymbol{\omega} \times \boldsymbol{\Lambda}$ is called the *centrifugal couple*. It represents the sum of the moments of the centrifugal forces with respect to the fixed point, the centrifugal forces being due to the rotation about the instantaneous axis, as will be shown.

Imagine a particle of mass m at the terminus of the vector $\mathbf{r}$, Fig. 43. The centrifugal force $\mathbf{f}$ at m due to the rotation about the instantaneous axis is equal to $mp\omega^2$ in magnitude, where p is the length of the perpendicular from m to the instantaneous axis, Since $\mathbf{f}$ is perpendicular to the axis and is directed away from it

$$\begin{aligned} \mathbf{f} &= -m\omega^2\mathbf{a} \times (\mathbf{a} \times \mathbf{r}) \\ &= -m\boldsymbol{\omega} \times (\boldsymbol{\omega} \times \mathbf{r}) = m\omega^2\mathbf{r} - m\boldsymbol{\omega} \cdot \mathbf{r}\, \boldsymbol{\omega}. \end{aligned}$$

The moment of $\mathbf{f}$ with respect to O is (I, **133**),

$$\mathbf{r} \times \mathbf{f} = m\, \boldsymbol{\omega} \cdot \mathbf{r}\, \boldsymbol{\omega} \times \mathbf{r},$$

and the resultant $\mathbf{Q}$ of the moments for all of the particles is

$$\mathbf{Q} = \Sigma m\boldsymbol{\omega} \cdot \mathbf{r}\, \boldsymbol{\omega} \times \mathbf{r}.$$

Now

$$\boldsymbol{\omega} \times \mathbf{r} = \begin{vmatrix} \mathbf{i} & \mathbf{j} & \mathbf{k} \\ \omega_i & \omega_j & \omega_k \\ \xi & \eta & \zeta \end{vmatrix},$$

and

$$\boldsymbol{\omega} \cdot \mathbf{r} = \xi\omega_i + \eta\omega_j + \zeta\omega_k;$$

therefore the product $\boldsymbol{\omega} \cdot \mathbf{r}\, \boldsymbol{\omega} \times \mathbf{r}$ gives

$$\mathbf{Q} = (C - B)\omega_j\omega_k\, \mathbf{i} + (A - C)\omega_k\omega_i\, \mathbf{j} + (B - A)\omega_i\omega_j\, \mathbf{k}, \quad (6).$$

since the products of inertia are all zero.

A comparison of this expression with Eq. (5) shows that

$$\mathbf{Q} = \boldsymbol{\omega} \times \boldsymbol{\Lambda},$$

as was to be proved.

85. Euler's Equations.—Let $\mathbf{N}$ be the moment of the exterior forces that are acting on the body. Then, in accordance with the principle of moment of momentum, Sec. 45,

$$\mathbf{L}' = \mathbf{N}. \tag{1}$$

If $\mathbf{N}$ is expressed in terms of the unit vectors $\mathbf{i}$, $\mathbf{j}$, $\mathbf{k}$,

$$\mathbf{N} = N_i\mathbf{i} + N_j\mathbf{j} + N_k\mathbf{k}, \tag{2}$$

where N_i, N_j, and N_k are the moments of the exterior forces with respect to axes that are fixed in direction, but which instantaneously coincide with the **i**-, **j**-, and **k**-axes of the moving body.

In view of Eq. (1), a comparison of Eqs. (2) and (84.3) gives the three scalar equations

$$\left.\begin{aligned} A\omega_i' + (C - B)\omega_j\omega_k &= N_i,\\ B\omega_j' + (A - C)\omega_k\omega_i &= N_j,\\ C\omega_k' + (B - A)\omega_i\omega_j &= N_k,\end{aligned}\right\} \tag{3}$$

which are the equations of motion of the body that were given by Euler in 1765. The rate of change of the angular velocities, since they are referred to axes that are moving with the body, depends not only upon the moments of the applied forces **N**, but also upon the inertial, or centrifugal, couple $\boldsymbol{\omega} \times \mathbf{\Lambda}$. The advantage of

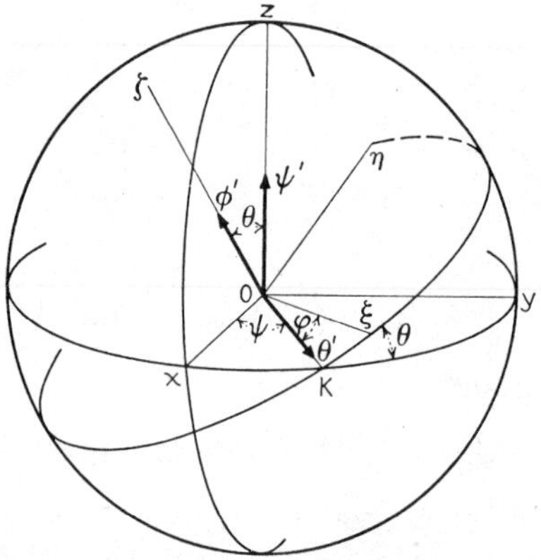

FIG. 46.

using axes that are fixed in the body is, obviously, that the moments and products of inertia with respect to such axes are constants.

In Eq. (3) the variables ω_i, ω_j, and ω_k are the angular velocities about the ξ-, η-, and ζ-axes which are fixed in the body and coincide with the principal axes of inertia at the origin O. In order to define the motion, the angular velocities must be related to some set of geometrical coordinates, and for this purpose Euler's angles will be chosen (Sec. 52).

In Fig. 46 the fixed point of the body is at O; the x-, y-, z-axes have their origin at O and are stationary relative to fixed space. The ξ-, η-, ζ-axes also have their origin at O. They are fixed in the body but are movable relative to fixed space; in other words they are free to turn about the fixed point. At any instant the $\xi\eta$-plane intersects the xy-plane in a straight line OK. Let the angle between the positive end of the x-axis and the positive end of the line OK be denoted by ψ. Let the dihedral angle which the $\xi\eta$-plane makes with the xy-plane be denoted by θ, and finally let the angle which the ξ-axis makes with the line OK be denoted by φ. The line OK is called the line of nodes, ψ is the longitude of the ascending node K, θ is the inclination, and φ is the angle of rotation. That these names are appropriate will be seen by imagining the body merely spinning about the ζ-axis in the positive direction.

The table of direction cosines is

	ξ	η	ζ
x	α_1	α_2	α_3
y	β_1	β_2	β_3
z	γ_1	γ_2	γ_3

The values of these direction cosines in terms of Euler's angles are given in Sec. 52.

The angular velocities ψ', φ', and θ' can be represented by vectors along the z-axis, the ζ-axis, and the line OK, respectively, for these lines are perpendicular to the planes in which ψ, φ, and θ lie. The angular velocities ω_i, ω_j, and ω_k are then the sum of the projections of ψ', φ', and θ' upon the ξ-axis, the η-axis, and the ζ-axis, respectively. These projections are easily read from the diagram, Fig. 46, and give

$$\begin{aligned} \omega_i &= \psi'\gamma_1 + \theta' \cos \varphi, \\ \omega_j &= \psi'\gamma_2 - \theta' \sin \varphi, \\ \omega_k &= \psi'\gamma_3 + \varphi', \end{aligned}$$

and, by inserting the values of γ_1, γ_2, and γ_3 from Sec. 52,

$$\left.\begin{aligned} \omega_i &= \psi' \sin \theta \sin \varphi + \theta' \cos \varphi, \\ \omega_j &= \psi' \sin \theta \cos \varphi - \theta' \sin \varphi, \\ \omega_k &= \psi' \cos \theta + \varphi'. \end{aligned}\right\} \cdot \tag{4}$$

Equations (3) and (4) taken together form a complete set of differential equations of the motion. If ω_i, ω_j, and ω_k were eliminated between them there would result three differential equations in ψ, φ, and θ, each of the second order. From the point of view of differential equations, therefore, the problem of the motion is of the sixth order.

If ψ, φ, and θ are known functions of the time ω_i, ω_j, and ω_k are given directly by Eq. (4). But if ω_i, ω_j, and ω_k are known functions of the time ψ, φ, and θ are defined by the differential equations

$$\left.\begin{aligned} \theta' &= \omega_i \cos\varphi - \omega_j \sin\varphi, \\ \sin\theta\psi' &= \omega_i \sin\varphi + \omega_j \cos\varphi, \\ \varphi' &= -(\omega_i \sin\varphi + \omega_j \cos\varphi)\cot\theta + \omega_k, \end{aligned}\right\} \tag{5}$$

which are obtained by solving Eqs. (4) for ψ', θ', and φ'. It has been shown that the solution of these equations can be made to depend upon the solution of a Riccati equation with complex coefficients.[1]

86. The Only Applied Force Is the Weight.—If the only force acting upon the body is its weight $M\mathbf{g}$, and if the body pivots upon the fixed point O without friction, the forces acting form a conservative system, and there exists, evidently, an energy integral.

The weight acts at the center of gravity **G**, and the moment of the weight with respect to O is (I, **133**)

$$\mathbf{N} = M\mathbf{G} \times \mathbf{g}.$$

Hence Eq (85.1) becomes

$$\mathbf{L}' = M\mathbf{G} \times \mathbf{g}, \tag{1}$$

and by multiplication by $\boldsymbol{\omega}\,\cdot$,

$$\boldsymbol{\omega} \cdot \mathbf{L}' = M\boldsymbol{\omega} \cdot \mathbf{G} \times \mathbf{g}. \tag{2}$$

The expression for the kinetic energy in terms of **L** and $\boldsymbol{\omega}$ is, Eq. (83.1),

$$T = \tfrac{1}{2}\boldsymbol{\omega} \cdot \mathbf{L},$$

so that

$$T' = \tfrac{1}{2}(\boldsymbol{\omega}' \cdot \mathbf{L} + \boldsymbol{\omega} \cdot \mathbf{L}').$$

Now, by Eq. (84.4),

$$\begin{aligned} \boldsymbol{\omega} \cdot \mathbf{L}' &= \boldsymbol{\omega} \cdot \boldsymbol{\Lambda} + \boldsymbol{\omega} \cdot \boldsymbol{\omega} \times \boldsymbol{\Lambda} = \boldsymbol{\omega} \cdot \boldsymbol{\Lambda}' \\ &= A\omega_i\omega_i' + B\omega_j\omega_j' + C\omega_k\omega_k'; \end{aligned}$$

[1] Darboux, "Leçons sur la théorie générale des surfaces," Vol. 1, chap. 2.

and if $\boldsymbol{\omega}$ and $\boldsymbol{\Omega}$ have the same relative significance as $\mathbf{L}$ and $\mathbf{\Lambda}$

$$\begin{aligned}\mathbf{L}\cdot\boldsymbol{\omega}' &= \mathbf{L}\cdot\boldsymbol{\Omega}' + \mathbf{L}\cdot\boldsymbol{\omega}\times\boldsymbol{\Omega} = \mathbf{L}\cdot\boldsymbol{\Omega}' \\ &= A\omega_i\omega_i' + B\omega_j\omega_j' + C\omega_k\omega_k'.\end{aligned}$$

Hence

$$\boldsymbol{\omega}\cdot\mathbf{L}' = \boldsymbol{\omega}'\cdot\mathbf{L},$$

and therefore

$$\mathbf{T}' = \boldsymbol{\omega}\cdot\mathbf{L}'. \tag{3}$$

Also

$$\boldsymbol{\omega}\cdot\mathbf{G}\times\mathbf{g} = \boldsymbol{\omega}\times\mathbf{G}\cdot\mathbf{g},$$

and since $\mathbf{G}$ is a vector that is fixed in the body

$$\boldsymbol{\omega}\times\mathbf{G} = \mathbf{G}'.$$

Equation (3) can therefore be written

$$T' = M\mathbf{G}'\cdot\mathbf{g},$$

and, by integration

$$T - T_0 = M\mathbf{G}\cdot\mathbf{g}, \tag{4}$$

which is the energy integral. It holds whatever may be the position of O relative to the center of gravity. If the fixed z-axis is vertical with the positive end upward,

$$\mathbf{G}\cdot\mathbf{g} = -gh,$$

where h is the distance of the center of gravity above the xy-plane, and Eqs. (4) and (83.3) express the energy integral in the form

$$A\omega_i^2 + B\omega_j^2 + C\omega_k^2 = 2T_0 - 2Mgh. \tag{5}$$

Since the weight is parallel to the z-axis, its moment with respect to the z-axis is always zero. Let $\mathbf{k}_0$ be a unit vector in the direction of the z-axis; then

$$\mathbf{g} = -g\mathbf{k}_0.$$

If Eq. (1) is multiplied by $\cdot\,\mathbf{k}_0$, there results

$$\mathbf{L}'\cdot\mathbf{k}_0 = 0,$$

since

$$M\mathbf{G}\times\mathbf{g}\cdot\mathbf{k}_0 = M\mathbf{G}\cdot\mathbf{g}\times\mathbf{k}_0 = 0.$$

Consequently

$$\mathbf{L} \cdot \mathbf{k}_0 = \text{constant}; \tag{6}$$

that is, the moment of momentum with respect to the z-axis is constant. Since the cosines of the angles which the **i-**, **j-**, and **k-**directions make with the z-axis are γ_1, γ_2, and γ_3, Eq. (6) can be written also

$$\mathbf{L} \cdot \mathbf{k}_0 = A\omega_i\gamma_1 + B\omega_j\gamma_2 + C\omega_k\gamma_3 = \text{constant}. \tag{7}$$

Equations (5) and (7) are the only integrals known that hold without further restrictions on the nature of the body or the position of the fixed point O in the body. There are several integrable cases when such restrictions are made, namely, Euler's case, in which the point O is at the center of gravity; Lagrange's case, in which the central ellipsoid of inertia is a spheroid and the point O is located on the axis of the spheroid; and Mme Kowaleski's case, in which also the central ellipsoid of inertia is a spheroid, but the point O is located in the plane of the equator of the spheroid. Before taking up these cases, however, it is desirable to determine the constraint that is acting at the fixed point O.

87. Determination of the Constraint.—If **F** is the vector sum of the applied forces and **R** is the constraint at O, the equation of momentum is

$$M\mathbf{G}'' = \mathbf{F} + \mathbf{R}.$$

Since **G** is a vector that is fixed in the body, by Eq. (79.10)

$$\mathbf{G}'' = \boldsymbol{\omega}' \times \mathbf{G} + \boldsymbol{\omega} \times (\boldsymbol{\omega} \times \mathbf{G}).$$

Hence

$$\mathbf{R} = M\boldsymbol{\omega}' \times \mathbf{G} + M\boldsymbol{\omega} \times (\boldsymbol{\omega} \times \mathbf{G}) - \mathbf{F}. \tag{1}$$

Since

$$\omega_i\mathbf{i}' + \omega_j\mathbf{j}' + \omega_k\mathbf{k}' \equiv 0,$$

as is seen from Eqs. (84.2), it follows that

$$\boldsymbol{\omega}' = \omega_i'\mathbf{i} + \omega_j'\mathbf{j} + \omega_k'\mathbf{k}. \tag{2}$$

By substituting the values of ω_i', ω_j', and ω_k' from Euler's equations [Eq. (85.3)] in Eq. (2), there results

$$\boldsymbol{\omega}' = \sum\left[\frac{B - C}{A}\omega_j\omega_k + \frac{N_i}{A}\right]\mathbf{i}, \tag{3}$$

where the symbol Σ means that the letters following it are to be permuted circularly, and the sum of the three expressions so derived is to be taken. If the coordinates of the center of gravity are $\bar{\xi}$, $\bar{\eta}$, $\bar{\zeta}$,

$$\mathbf{G} = \bar{\xi}\mathbf{i} + \bar{\eta}\mathbf{j} + \bar{\zeta}\mathbf{k},$$

and then

$$\boldsymbol{\omega}' \times \mathbf{G} = \sum\left[\left(\frac{C - A}{B}\bar{\xi}\omega_k - \frac{A - B}{C}\bar{\eta}\omega_j\right)\omega_i + \frac{1}{BC}(\bar{\zeta}CN_j - \bar{\eta}BN_k)\right]\mathbf{i}.$$

Also,

$$\boldsymbol{\omega} \times (\boldsymbol{\omega} \times \mathbf{G}) = \Sigma[\omega_i(\bar{\eta}\omega_j + \bar{\zeta}\omega_k) - \bar{\xi}(\omega_j^2 + \omega_k^2)]\mathbf{i}.$$

Hence

$$\mathbf{R} = -\mathbf{F} + M\sum\frac{1}{BC}(\bar{\zeta}CN_j - \bar{\eta}BN_k)\mathbf{i} + M\sum\left[-\bar{\xi}(\omega_j^2 + \omega_k^2) + \frac{B + C - A}{BC}(B\bar{\eta}\omega_j + C\bar{\zeta}\omega_k)\omega_i\right]\mathbf{i}. \quad (4)$$

It will be observed that **R** reduces to $-\mathbf{F}$, if the fixed point O is at the center of gravity.

If the only force acting is the weight, then

$$\mathbf{F} = M\mathbf{g};$$

the moment of **F** with respect to O is [Eq. (86.1)]

$$\mathbf{N} = M(\mathbf{G} \times \mathbf{g});$$

and

$$\left.\begin{aligned} N_i &= M\mathbf{G} \times \mathbf{g} \cdot \mathbf{i} = Mg(\gamma_2\bar{\zeta} - \gamma_3\bar{\eta}), \\ N_j &= M\mathbf{G} \times \mathbf{g} \cdot \mathbf{j} = Mg(\gamma_3\bar{\xi} - \gamma_1\bar{\zeta}), \\ N_k &= M\mathbf{G} \times \mathbf{g} \cdot \mathbf{k} = Mg(\gamma_1\bar{\eta} - \gamma_2\bar{\xi}). \end{aligned}\right\} \quad (5)$$

The first line in the expression for **R** becomes

$$-M\mathbf{g} + M^2g\sum\frac{1}{BC}[\bar{\xi}(B\gamma_2\bar{\eta} + C\gamma_3\bar{\zeta}) - \gamma_1(B\bar{\eta}^2 + C\bar{\zeta}^2)]\mathbf{i}; \quad (6)$$

the second line are inertial effects which are due to the state of rotation, and are independent of the applied forces.

Problems

1. Using the formulas of Sec. 80 prove the following statements: If the origin of a set of rectangular axes O is fixed but the axes themselves are moving about O, the components of the absolute velocity of a moving particle in the ξ-, η-, ζ-directions are

$$\begin{aligned} v_i &= \xi' + \zeta\omega_j - \eta\omega_k, \\ v_j &= \eta' + \xi\omega_k - \zeta\omega_i, \\ v_k &= \zeta' + \eta\omega_i - \xi\omega_j. \end{aligned}$$

The components of the absolute acceleration of the particle in the ξ-, η-, ζ-directions are

$$\begin{aligned} \alpha_i &= \xi'' + 2(\zeta'\omega_j - \eta'\omega_k) + (\zeta\omega_j' - \eta\omega_k') + (\xi\omega_i + \eta\omega_j + \zeta\omega_k)\omega_i - \xi\omega^2, \\ \alpha_j &= \eta'' + 2(\xi'\omega_k - \zeta'\omega_i) + (\xi\omega_k' - \zeta\omega_i') + (\xi\omega_i + \eta\omega_j + \zeta\omega_k)\omega_j - \eta\omega^2, \\ \alpha_k &= \zeta'' + 2(\eta'\omega_i - \xi'\omega_j) + (\eta\omega_i' - \xi\omega_j') + (\xi\omega_i + \eta\omega_j + \zeta\omega_k)\omega_k - \zeta\omega^2. \end{aligned}$$

If $\mathbf{s}$ is the absolute velocity of a particle and $\boldsymbol{\sigma} = \sigma_i\mathbf{i} + \sigma_j\mathbf{j} + \sigma_k\mathbf{k}$ is the same vector referred to the moving trihedron, then

$$\mathbf{s}' = \boldsymbol{\sigma}' + \boldsymbol{\omega} \times \boldsymbol{\sigma},$$

and the components of the absolute acceleration in the **i**-, **j**-, **k**-directions are

$$\begin{aligned} \alpha_i &= \sigma_i' + \sigma_k\omega_j - \sigma_j\omega_k, \\ \alpha_j &= \sigma_j' + \sigma_i\omega_k - \sigma_k\omega_i, \\ \alpha_k &= \sigma_k' + \sigma_j\omega_i - \sigma_i\omega_j. \end{aligned}$$

If $\boldsymbol{\Omega}$ is the angular velocity referred to fixed space and $\boldsymbol{\omega} = \omega_i\mathbf{i} + \omega_j\mathbf{j} + \omega_k\mathbf{k}$ is the angular velocity referred to the moving trihedron, then

$$\boldsymbol{\Omega}' = \boldsymbol{\omega}'.$$

If the angular momentum referred to fixed space is $\mathbf{l}$ and referred to moving space is $\boldsymbol{\lambda} = \lambda_i\mathbf{i} + \lambda_j\mathbf{j} + \lambda_k\mathbf{k}$, then $\mathbf{l}' = \boldsymbol{\lambda}' + \boldsymbol{\omega} \times \boldsymbol{\lambda}$, the components of which are

$$\begin{aligned} l_i' &= \lambda_i' + \lambda_k\omega_j - \lambda_j\omega_k, \\ l_j' &= \lambda_j' + \lambda_i\omega_k - \lambda_k\omega_i, \\ l_k' &= \lambda_k' + \lambda_j\omega_i - \lambda_i\omega_j. \end{aligned}$$

2. The particles of a rigid body, one point of which is fixed, that have the same speed with respect to a set of fixed axes lie on a right circular cylinder.

3. The origin of a rectangular set of axes is at some point on the axis of a screw. If x', y', z' are the components of velocity of a particle of a body that is twisting about the screw with the angular velocity ω, prove that the expression $x'\omega_x + y'\omega_y + z'\omega_z$ has the same value for all particles of the screw and that

$$\frac{x'\omega_x + y'\omega_y + z'\omega_z}{\omega_x^2 + \omega_y^2 + \omega_z^2} = p$$

is the pitch of the screw.

4. If at any instant vectors which represent the velocities of the particles of a rigid body that is moving in any manner are drawn with the same origin, the termini will all lie in the same plane.

5. The envelope at any instant of the tangents to the trajectories of all of the particles of a moving body that lie on a straight line is a hyperbolic paraboloid.

6. A rigid body is moved from one position to any other. Straight lines are drawn connecting the initial and terminal position of each particle. If the mid-points of these lines be regarded as forming a rigid body, this rigid body will permit an infinitesimal displacement in which each point moves along its own line. Also, all of the lines that pass through the same point lie on a cone of the second order. (Caley, *Report to the British Association* 1862.)

7. Show that the components of the instantaneous rotation along the axes that are fixed in space are

$$\begin{aligned} \omega_x &= +\varphi' \sin\theta \sin\psi + \theta' \cos\psi, \\ \omega_y &= -\varphi' \sin\theta \cos\psi + \theta' \sin\psi, \\ \omega_z &= +\varphi' \cos\theta + \psi'. \end{aligned}$$

8. *Parameters of Rodrigues.* The nine direction cosines $\alpha_1, \alpha_2, \ldots, \gamma_3$ were expressed in Sec. 52 as functions of the three Eulerian angles φ, ψ, and θ. By making the substitutions

$$\begin{aligned} \lambda &= \tau \sin \tfrac{1}{2}\theta \cos \tfrac{1}{2}(\psi - \varphi), & \nu &= \tau \cos \tfrac{1}{2}\theta \sin \tfrac{1}{2}(\psi + \varphi), \\ \mu &= \tau \sin \tfrac{1}{2}\theta \sin \tfrac{1}{2}(\psi - \varphi), & \rho &= -\tau \cos \tfrac{1}{2}\theta \cos \tfrac{1}{2}(\psi + \varphi), \end{aligned}$$

the nine direction cosines can be expressed very simply in terms of the four ratios λ/τ, μ/τ, ν/τ and ρ/τ. The result is

$$\begin{aligned} \tau^2\alpha_1 &= \lambda^2 - \mu^2 - \nu^2 + \rho^2, & \tau^2\alpha_2 &= 2(\lambda\mu + \nu\rho), \\ \tau^2\beta_1 &= 2(\lambda\mu - \nu\rho), & \tau^2\beta_2 &= -\lambda^2 + \mu^2 - \nu^2 + \rho^2, \\ \tau^2\gamma_1 &= 2(\lambda\nu + \mu\rho), & \tau^2\gamma_2 &= 2(\mu\nu - \lambda\rho), \end{aligned}$$

$$\begin{aligned} \tau^2\alpha_3 &= 2(\lambda\nu - \mu\rho), \\ \tau^2\beta_3 &= -2(\mu\nu + \lambda\rho), \\ \tau^2\gamma_3 &= -\lambda^2 - \mu^2 + \nu^2 + \rho^2, \end{aligned}$$

and the relation

$$\tau^2 = \lambda^2 + \mu^2 + \nu^2 + \rho^2.$$

If τ is eliminated it is seen that the nine direction cosines are expressed rationally in the ratios of any three of the other letters to the fourth.

For a discussion of these parameters see G. König, "Leçons de Cinématique," pp. 197, 340, 343; Klein and Sommerfeld, "Über die Theorie des Kreisels," chap. I.

9. In Sec. 85, show that

$$\begin{aligned} \gamma_1' &= \gamma_2\omega_3 - \gamma_3\omega_2, \\ \gamma_2' &= \gamma_3\omega_1 - \gamma_1\omega_3, \\ \gamma_3' &= \gamma_1\omega_2 - \gamma_2\omega_1. \end{aligned}$$

CHAPTER VII

INTEGRABLE CASES OF MOTION OF A RIGID BODY ABOUT A FIXED POINT

I. EULER'S CASE. THE SUM OF THE MOMENTS OF THE APPLIED FORCES VANISHES

88. The Differential Equations and Their Integrals.—If the sum of the moments of the applied forces is zero,

$$\mathbf{N} = 0,$$

and therefore Eq. (85.1) for the moment of momentum gives

$$\mathbf{L}' = 0; \tag{1}$$

and Euler's equations become

$$\left.\begin{aligned} A\omega_i' + (C - B)\omega_j\omega_k &= 0,\\ B\omega_j' + (A - C)\omega_k\omega_i &= 0,\\ C\omega_k' + (B - A)\omega_i\omega_j &= 0. \end{aligned}\right\} \tag{2}$$

From Eq. (1) it follows that

$$\mathbf{L} = \mathbf{l}, \tag{3}$$

where $\mathbf{l}$ is a constant vector, that is, constant with respect to fixed space. Likewise, Eqs. (86.3) and (1),

$$T' = \boldsymbol{\omega} \cdot \mathbf{L}' = 0,$$

and the kinetic energy also is constant. That is,

$$2T = A\omega_i^2 + B\omega_j^2 + C\omega_k^2 = h, \tag{4}$$

where h is a positive constant. Furthermore, since by Eq. (83.1)

$$2T = \boldsymbol{\omega} \cdot \mathbf{L},$$

it follows that the component of the instantaneous angular velocity, ω_l, in the fixed direction $\mathbf{l}$ is constant and equal to

$$\omega_l = \frac{h}{l}.$$

If the equation

$$\mathbf{L}\cdot\mathbf{L} = A^2\omega_i^2 + B^2\omega_j^2 + C^2\omega_k^2 = l^2 \tag{5}$$

is multiplied by h, Eq. (4) is multiplied by l^2 and then subtracted from Eq. (5), it is found that

$$(Ah - l^2)A\omega_i^2 + (Bh - l^2)B\omega_j^2 + (Ch - l^2)C\omega_k^2 = 0.$$

Let ξ, η, ζ be a point on the instantaneous axis. Then

$$\frac{\omega_i}{\xi} = \frac{\omega_j}{\eta} = \frac{\omega_k}{\zeta},$$

and for points on the instantaneous axis,

$$A(Ah - l^2)\xi^2 + B(Bh - l^2)\eta^2 + C(Ch - l^2)\zeta^2 = 0,$$

which shows that the instantaneous axis always lies on a cone of the second order.

Now let a new quantity D be defined by the relation

$$l = D\omega_l, \qquad \text{and therefore} \qquad h = D\omega_l^2.$$

The equation of the cone becomes

$$A(A - D)\xi^2 + B(B - D)\eta^2 + C(C - D)\zeta^2 = 0. \tag{6}$$

Suppose the axes of the moving trihedron, which coincide with the principal axes of inertia at the fixed point, are so lettered that the ξ-, or **i**-, axis coincides with the longest axis of the ellipsoid of inertia and the ζ-, or **k**-, axis coincides with the shortest axis. Then in magnitude the moments of inertia A, B, and C have the order

$$A < B < C.$$

It will be observed from Eq. (6) that if D, which has the dimensions of a moment of inertia, is equal to A, the coordinates ξ and η must both be zero and the cone reduces to the ξ-axis.

If D is equal to B, the cone degenerates into the two planes

$$\zeta = \pm\sqrt{\frac{A(B - A)}{C(C - B)}}\,\xi, \tag{7}$$

and if D is equal to C, the cone reduces again to a straight line which is this time the ζ-axis. In order that the cone be real, it is necessary, evidently, that

$$A \leqq D \leqq C.$$

89. The Angular Velocities Are Elliptic Functions of the Time.—If the first and third of Euler's set of equations [Eq. (88.2)] are replaced by the integrals of energy [Eq. (88.4)] and moment of momentum [Eq. (88.5)], the angular velocities are determined by the three equations

$$\left.\begin{aligned} B\omega_j' + (A - C)\omega_k\omega_i &= 0, \\ A\omega_i^2 + B\omega_j^2 + C\omega_k^2 &= D\omega_l^2, \\ A^2\omega_i^2 + B^2\omega_j^2 + C^2\omega_k^2 &= D^2\omega_l^2. \end{aligned}\right\} \tag{1}$$

The solution of last two of these equations for ω_i^2 and ω_k^2 gives

$$\left.\begin{aligned} \omega_i^2 &= \frac{B(C - B)}{A(C - A)}(f^2 - \omega_j^2), \quad \text{where} \quad f^2 = \frac{D(C - D)}{B(C - B)}\omega_l^2, \\ \omega_k^2 &= \frac{B(B - A)}{C(C - A)}(g^2 - \omega_j^2), \quad \text{where} \quad g^2 = \frac{D(D - A)}{B(B - A)}\omega_l^2. \end{aligned}\right\} \tag{2}$$

Since

$$f^2 - g^2 = \frac{D(C - A)(B - D)}{B(C - B)(B - A)}\omega_l^2,$$

f^2 is greater than g^2, if D lies between A and B, and f^2 is less than g^2 if D lies between B and C. In either case ω_j^2 must be less than the smaller of the two.

For definiteness, it will be assumed that

$$A < B < D < C,$$

so that

$$g^2 > f^2.$$

Then

$$-f < \omega_j < +f,$$

and the smallest value of ω_k^2 is

$$\omega_k^2 = \frac{B(B - A)}{C(C - A)}(g^2 - f^2) = \frac{D(D - B)}{C(C - B)}\omega_l^2. \tag{3}$$

As ω_k never vanishes, and therefore never changes sign, it can be regarded as always positive; but ω_i vanishes whenever

$$\omega_j = \pm f.$$

From the first equation of Eqs. (1), namely,

$$\omega_j' = \frac{C - A}{B}\omega_k\omega_i,$$

and the substitution of the values of ω_i and ω_k from Eq. (2), it is found that

$$\omega_j' = \pm\sqrt{\frac{(C - B)(B - A)}{AC}}\sqrt{(f^2 - \omega_j^2)(g^2 - \omega_j^2)}. \qquad (4)$$

If ω_k is regarded as being always positive, ω_j' has always the same sign as ω_i. Consequently ω_j is increasing, algebraically, as long as ω_i is positive; and decreasing as long as ω_i is negative.

It is evident that t is expressed in terms of ω_j by Eq. (4) as an elliptic integral. This integral is reduced to the first normal form of Legendre by taking

$$\omega_j = fs \qquad \text{and} \qquad k^2 = \frac{f^2}{g^2} = \frac{(B - A)(C - D)}{(D - A)(C - B)},$$

where s is a new variable. Obviously, k^2 is less than one. It is convenient also to introduce a new independent variable τ, which is related to the time by the equation

$$\tau = \sqrt{\frac{D(C - B)(D - A)}{ABC}}\omega_l(t - t_0),$$

so that Eq. (4) becomes

$$\tau = \int_0^s \frac{ds}{\sqrt{(1 - s^2)(1 - k^2s^2)}}.$$

The inversion of this integral gives

$$s = \operatorname{sn} \tau,$$

and then

$$\begin{aligned} \omega_i &= f\sqrt{\frac{B(C - B)}{A(C - A)}}\sqrt{1 - s^2} &&= +\omega_l\sqrt{\frac{D(C - D)}{A(C - A)}}\operatorname{cn} \tau, \\ \omega_j &= fs &&= +\omega_l\sqrt{\frac{D(C - D)}{B(C - B)}}\operatorname{sn} \tau, \qquad (5) \\ \omega_k &= g\sqrt{\frac{B(B - A)}{C(C - A)}}\sqrt{1 - k^2s^2} &&= +\omega_l\sqrt{\frac{D(D - A)}{C(C - A)}}\operatorname{dn} \tau. \end{aligned}$$

By adding ω_j^2 to Eqs. (2) it is found that

$$\omega^2 = \omega_i^2 + \omega_j^2 + \omega_k^2 = \frac{D(A - D + C)}{AC}\omega_l^2 - \frac{(B - A)(C - B)}{AC}\omega_j^2,$$

and then, on replacing ω_j by its value from Eq. (5),

$$\omega^2 = \omega_l^2 \frac{D}{C}\left[\frac{B - D + C}{B}\,\text{sn}^2\,\tau + \frac{A - D + C}{A}\,\text{cn}^2\,\tau\right],$$

$$= \omega_l^2 \frac{D}{C}\left[1 + (C - D)\left(\frac{\text{sn}^2\,\tau}{B} + \frac{\text{cn}^2\,\tau}{A}\right)\right],$$

which never vanishes since $C - D$ is positive.

The period in τ of these functions is

$$4K = 4\int_0^1 \frac{ds}{\sqrt{(1 - s^2)(1 - k^2s^2)}};$$

and the period in t is

$$P = \sqrt{\frac{ABC}{D(C - B)(D - A)}}\,\frac{4K}{\omega_l}.$$

At the expiration of this time, that is when $t = P$, the angular velocities, ω_i, ω_j, and ω_k retake their initial values. The instantaneous axis has completed its journey around the cone and retaken its initial position in the body, but, in general, is not in its initial position in fixed space, as will be demonstrated in Sec. 96.

90. The Angles of Euler as Functions of the Time.—In order to know the position of the body at any instant it is necessary to know the values of Euler's angles at that instant. It has been found that the moment of momentum of the body with respect to fixed space is constant. That is, the vector **l** is constant in magnitude and in direction. The orientation of the fixed x, y, z system is so far arbitrary. Let the orientation be chosen so that the z-axis coincides in direction with **l**.

The magnitude of the moment of momentum is l, and its components in the **i**-, **j**-, and **k**-directions are $A\omega_i$, $B\omega_j$, and $C\omega_k$. The cosines of the angles between the z-axis and the **i**-, **j**-, and **k**-axes are γ_1, γ_2, and γ_3, respectively. Hence

$$\left.\begin{aligned} l\gamma_1 &= l \sin\varphi \sin\theta = A\omega_i, \\ l\gamma_2 &= l \cos\varphi \sin\theta = B\omega_j, \\ l\gamma_3 &= l \cos\theta \qquad\;\; = C\omega_k. \end{aligned}\right\} \tag{1}$$

These equations do not contain ψ, and their solutions, therefore, give directly φ and θ as functions of ω_i, ω_j, and ω_k, and consequently as functions of t, without further integration. Indeed, the quotient of the second equation by the first gives

$$\cot \varphi = \frac{B\omega_j}{A\omega_i} = \sqrt{\frac{B}{A}\frac{C - A}{C - B}} \operatorname{tn} \tau, \tag{2}$$

while the third equation gives

$$\cos \theta = \frac{C\omega_k}{l} = \sqrt{\frac{C}{D}\frac{D - A}{C - A}} \operatorname{dn} \tau. \tag{3}$$

For the calculation of ψ, Eqs. (85.4) give

$$\omega_i = \psi' \sin \theta \sin \varphi + \theta' \cos \varphi,$$
$$\omega_j = \psi' \sin \theta \cos \varphi - \theta' \sin \varphi.$$

The elimination of θ' between these two equations shows that

$$\psi' = \frac{\omega_i \sin \varphi + \omega_j \cos \varphi}{\sin \theta};$$

and if the first of Eqs. (1) is multiplied by ω_i, the second by ω_j, and the two equations are then added, there results

$$\omega_i \sin \varphi + \omega_j \cos \varphi = \frac{A\omega_i^2 + B\omega_j^2}{l \sin \theta}.$$

Consequently

$$\psi' = l\frac{A\omega_i^2 + B\omega_j^2}{l^2 \sin^2 \theta},$$

and since the sum of the squares of the first two of Eqs. (1) gives

$$l^2 \sin^2 \theta = A^2\omega_i^2 + B^2\omega_j^2,$$

there results finally

$$\begin{aligned}\psi' &= l\frac{A\omega_i^2 + B\omega_j^2}{A^2\omega_i^2 + B^2\omega_j^2} = \frac{D(D\omega_l^2 - C\omega_k^2)}{D^2\omega_l^2 - C^2\omega_k^2}\omega_l,\\ &= \frac{D}{C}\left[1 + \frac{D(C - D)\omega_l^2}{D^2\omega_l^2 - C^2\omega_k^2}\right]\omega_l. \end{aligned}\tag{4}$$

Thus ψ' is always positive, and if the extreme values of ω_k^2 from Eq. (89.5) are substituted, it is found that

$$\frac{\omega_l}{B} < \frac{\psi'}{D} < \frac{\omega_l}{A}, \qquad \text{or} \qquad \frac{l}{B} < \psi' < \frac{l}{A}.$$

The angle of precession ψ always increases, and the rate of precession always lies between the two limits just indicated. If A and B differ but little, the precessional rate is nearly constant.

The angle ψ is determined by a quadrature, which, however, contains an elliptic function. It will not be attempted here. Jacobi has shown how to integrate it in Vol. 39 of *Crelle's Journal* (1850), and how to determine the nine direction cosines as functions of the time. Since γ_1, γ_2, and γ_3 do not depend upon ψ their values in terms of τ can be written down at once. Since [Eq. (1)]

$$A\omega_i = l\gamma_1, \qquad B\omega_j = l\gamma_2, \qquad C\omega_k = l\gamma_3, \qquad \text{and} \qquad l = D\omega_l,$$

it follows that

$$\left.\begin{aligned} \gamma_1 &= \frac{A}{D}\frac{\omega_i}{\omega_l} = \sqrt{\frac{A(C-D)}{D(C-A)}}\operatorname{cn}\tau, \\ \gamma_2 &= \frac{B}{D}\frac{\omega_j}{\omega_l} = \sqrt{\frac{B(C-D)}{D(C-B)}}\operatorname{sn}\tau, \\ \gamma_3 &= \frac{C}{D}\frac{\omega_k}{\omega_l} = \sqrt{\frac{C(D-A)}{D(C-A)}}\operatorname{dn}\tau. \end{aligned}\right\} \tag{5}$$

91. Particular Values of D.—It was observed in Sec. 88 that if D coincides with C, the cone degenerates into the ζ-axis. The instantaneous axis is fixed in the body, and coincides with one of the principal axes of inertia. Hence

$$\omega_i = 0, \qquad \omega_j = 0, \qquad \omega_k = \omega.$$

Either one of the integrals in Eqs. (89.1) shows that ω_k, and therefore ω also, is constant.

If D coincides with A, the cone degenerates with the ξ-axis, and the body again spins with uniform angular speed about a principal axis; this time the ξ-axis.

If D is equal to the mean axis of inertia B, the cone opens up into the two planes

$$\frac{\zeta}{\xi} = \frac{\omega_k}{\omega_i} = \pm\sqrt{\frac{A(B-A)}{C(C-B)}},$$

and the instantaneous axis moves in that one of the two planes in which it happens to be initially. From Eqs. (89.2) it is seen that

$$f^2 = g^2 = \omega_l^2,$$

and that

$$k^2 = 1.$$

The elliptic functions reduce to hyperbolic functions as will be shown. The definition of τ becomes

$$\tau = \int_0^s \frac{ds}{1 - s^2} = \sqrt{\frac{(C - B)(B - A)}{AC}}\,\omega_l(t - t_0).$$

Consequently,

$$s = \tanh \tau = \frac{e^\tau - e^{-\tau}}{e^\tau + e^{-\tau}},$$

and then

$$\omega_i = \sqrt{\frac{B(C - B)}{A(C - A)}}\,\omega_l \operatorname{sech} \tau,$$

$$\omega_j = \omega_l \tanh \tau,$$

$$\omega_k = \sqrt{\frac{B(B - A)}{C(C - A)}}\,\omega_l \operatorname{sech} \tau.$$

The expression for the square of the angular velocity, ω^2, becomes

$$\omega^2 = \frac{B}{C}\left[1 + (C - B)\left(\frac{\tanh^2 \tau}{B} + \frac{\operatorname{sech}^2 \tau}{A}\right)\right]\omega_l^2.$$

As the time increases indefinitely so also does τ, and

$$\tanh \tau \to +1, \qquad \operatorname{sech} \tau \to 0.$$

Hence

$$\omega_i \to 0, \qquad \omega_k \to 0; \qquad \omega_j \to \omega_l, \qquad \omega \to \omega_l.$$

The instantaneous axis approaches the η-axis asymptotically and the η-axis at the same time approaches the fixed z-axis asymptotically, for

$$\gamma_1 = \frac{A}{B}\frac{\omega_i}{\omega_l}, \qquad \gamma_2 = \frac{\omega_j}{\omega_l}, \qquad \gamma_3 = \frac{C}{B}\frac{\omega_k}{\omega_l},$$

and, in the limit,

$$\gamma_1 = \gamma_3 = 0, \qquad \gamma_2 = 1.$$

The rate of precession also has the limiting value ω_l, as is seen readily from Eq. (4).

92. The Ellipsoid of Inertia Is a Spheroid.—If $B = A$, the ellipsoid of inertia is a spheroid about the ζ-axis, and, since $C > A$, the spheroid is oblate; but in what follows it does not matter whether the spheroid is oblate or prolate. It is seen from the equations of Sec. 89 that as $B \to A$, f^2 remains finite, while g^2 tends toward infinity. Therefore $k^2 \to 0$, and the elliptic functions degenerate into circular functions; that is,

$$\operatorname{sn} \tau \to \sin \tau, \qquad \operatorname{cn} \tau \to \cos \tau,$$

and

$$\tau \to \sqrt{\frac{D(C - A)(D - A)}{A^2C}}\,\omega_l(t - t_0).$$

Consequently

$$\left.\begin{aligned} \omega_i &= \sqrt{\frac{D(C - D)}{A(C - A)}}\,\omega_l \cos \tau, \\ \omega_j &= \sqrt{\frac{D(C - D)}{A(C - A)}}\,\omega_l \sin \tau, \\ \omega_k &= \sqrt{\frac{D(D - A)}{C(C - A)}}\,\omega_l. \end{aligned}\right\} \tag{1}$$

Thus ω_k is a constant, as is evident from the third Euler equation [Eqs. (88.2)]. It is also evident from an inspection of Eqs. (1) that $\omega^2 = \omega_i^2 + \omega_j^2 + \omega_k^2$ is constant, and, indeed,

$$\omega = \sqrt{\frac{D(A - D + C)}{AC}}\,\omega_l. \tag{2}$$

From the third of Eqs. (90.1) it is found that the Eulerian angle θ, the inclination, is constant, and that

$$\sin \theta = \sqrt{\frac{A(C - D)}{D(C - A)}}, \qquad \cos \theta = \sqrt{\frac{C(D - A)}{D(C - A)}}.$$

The expression for φ in Eq. (90.2) becomes

$$\cot \varphi = \tan \tau,$$

so that

$$\varphi = \frac{\pi}{2} - \tau, \qquad \text{and} \qquad \varphi' = -\sqrt{\frac{D(C - A)(D - A)}{A^2C}}\,\omega_l; \tag{3}$$

and finally, as is seen from Eq. (90.4),

$$\psi' = \frac{D\omega_l}{A},$$

and the body precesses uniformly. Thus θ, φ', and ψ' are constants.

It was pointed out in Sec. 85 that $\boldsymbol{\omega}$ is the vector sum of $\boldsymbol{\theta}'$, $\boldsymbol{\varphi}'$, and $\boldsymbol{\psi}'$. Since $\boldsymbol{\theta}'$ is zero, $\boldsymbol{\omega}$ is the diagonal of the parallelogram constructed on $\boldsymbol{\varphi}'$ and $\boldsymbol{\psi}'$, Fig. 47. The vector $\boldsymbol{\psi}'$ coincides in direction with the z-axis and is therefore fixed in space. The vector $\boldsymbol{\varphi}'$ coincides in direction with the ζ-axis which makes the constant angle θ with the z-axis. As the body precesses the ζ-axis describes a right circular cone about the z-axis with the generating angle θ. Since φ' and ψ' are constants, $\boldsymbol{\omega}$ also makes a constant angle with the z-axis and therefore $\boldsymbol{\omega}$ also describes a right circular cone about the z-axis. The angle between the instantaneous axis $\boldsymbol{\omega}$ and the ζ-axis also is constant so that the instantaneous axis describes a cone in the body.

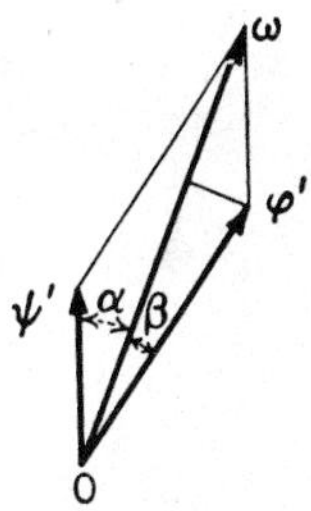

FIG. 47.

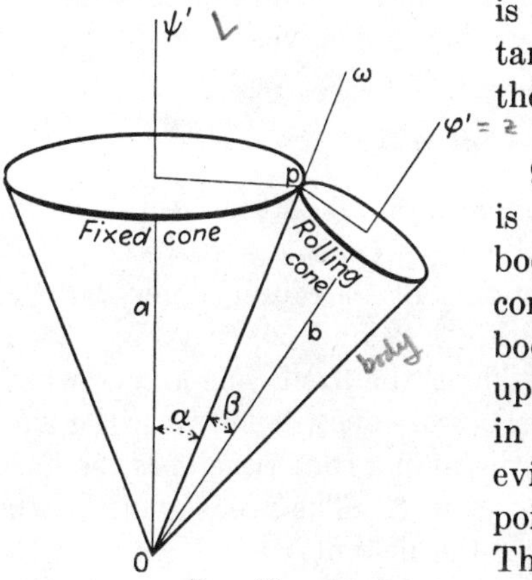

FIG. 48.

93. The Rolling Cones.—It is an interesting fact that the body moves just as though the cone which $\boldsymbol{\omega}$ describes in the body rolled without slipping upon the cone which $\boldsymbol{\omega}$ describes in fixed space. This is made evident in Fig. 48. Let p be a point on the instantaneous axis. Through p pass a plane perpendicular to $\boldsymbol{\psi}'$ cutting the axis at a distance a from the apex; then pass a second plane through p perpendicular to $\boldsymbol{\varphi}'$, cutting the axis at a distance b from the axis. Let the generating angles of the two cones be α and β respectively. Suppose the body cone rolls on the fixed cone and that in the interval of time dt the plane through $\boldsymbol{\psi}'$ and $\boldsymbol{\varphi}'$ turns through the angle $\psi'\,dt$. Then the point of contact p of the the two circles describes an arc on the circle of the fixed cone equal to $a \tan \alpha\psi' \, dt$, since the radius of the circle is $a \tan \alpha$. It also describes an arc of the same length ds on the circle of the body cone; that is

$$ds = a \tan \alpha\psi' \, dt.$$

It is evident from Fig. 48 that

$$a \sec \alpha = b \sec \beta,$$

and from Fig. 47 that

$$\psi' \sin \alpha = \varphi' \sin \beta.$$

Hence

$$a\psi' \tan \alpha = b\varphi' \tan \beta,$$

and

$$ds = b\varphi' \tan \beta \, dt.$$

Since the radius of the circle on the body cone is $b \tan \beta$, the angle through which the body cone has turned around its axis is $\varphi' \, dt$. The rolling motion therefore gives a displacement $\boldsymbol{\psi}' \, dt$ plus a displacement $\boldsymbol{\varphi}' \, dt$, and since

$$\boldsymbol{\varphi}' \, dt + \boldsymbol{\psi}' \, dt = \boldsymbol{\omega} \, dt,$$

the resulting displacement in the interval of time dt is just the same as though the angular velocity were $\boldsymbol{\omega}$.

Figure 48 does not represent the only possibility, however. It is easy to imagine cases like Figs. 49 and 50. In Fig. 48 the rolling, or body, cone lies outside of the fixed cone and $\boldsymbol{\omega}$, which lies in the line of contact of the two cones, is between the axes of the two cones. In Fig. 49 the rolling cone envelopes the fixed cone but still rolls on the outside of it. The z-axis, which is the direction of $\boldsymbol{\psi}'$, lies between $\boldsymbol{\omega}$, the instantaneous axis, and the ζ-axis, in which lies the vector $\boldsymbol{\varphi}'$. In Fig. 50 the ζ-axis lies between the z-axis and the instantaneous axis and the body cone rolls on the inside of the fixed cone.

By the terms z-axis and ζ-axis is meant the positive end of these axes. With this understanding it is easy to show that, Fig. 49 corresponds to the case developed in Sec. 92. According to the conventions there made ψ' and ω_k are positive and by

Eq. (92.3), φ' is negative. These are the conditions which are satisfied in Fig. 49, as is seen from the parallelogram of angular velocities in the figure. If it had been assumed that $C < A$ instead of $C > A$, φ' would have been positive and the cones

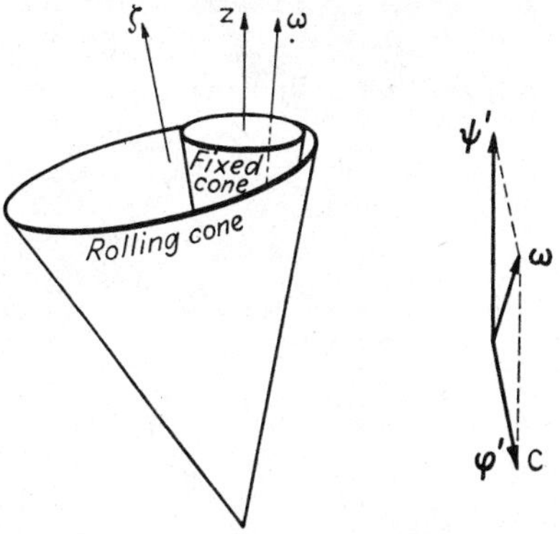

FIG. 49.

would have been as in Fig. 48. In order to have a case like Fig. 50 it is necessary to have ψ' negative, if φ' and ω_k are positive; or ψ' positive if both φ' and ω_k are negative.

The difference between φ' positive and φ' negative for ψ' positive in both cases is brought out in Figs. 51 and 52, cones being replaced by cylinders. Let z be the axis of the fixed cylinder and ζ the axis of the rolling cylinder in both figures. Since ψ' is positive in both cases the ζ-axis makes a circuit in the positive direction about the z-axis. Let O be the point of contact at the beginning of a circuit and let the arc $O1$ be equal to the circumference of the fixed cylinder. At the end of the first circuit, when ζ has returned to its initial position the point 1 is in contact with the fixed cylinder. It is seen in Fig. 51 that the rolling cylinder has turned through an angle corresponding to the arc $O1$ about the ζ-axis in a positive direction, while

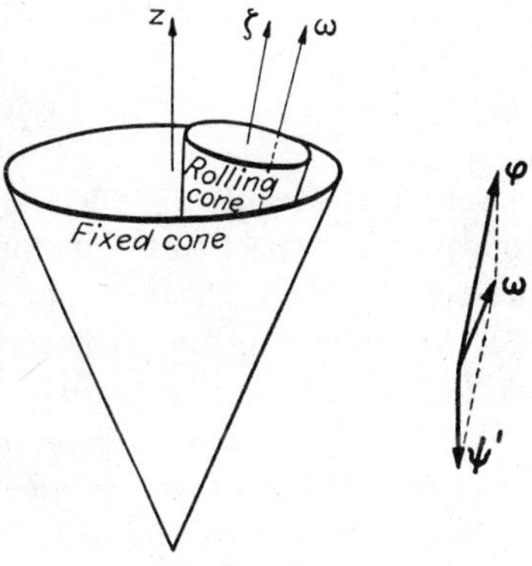

FIG. 50.

in Fig. 52, it has turned through the angle corresponding to the arc $O1$ in the negative direction.

POINSOT'S METHOD[1]

94. General Theorems.—Consider the ellipsoid of inertia at the fixed point O. The instantaneous axis pierces the surface at a point m which Poinsot called the *pole.* Let the distance $\overline{Om}$

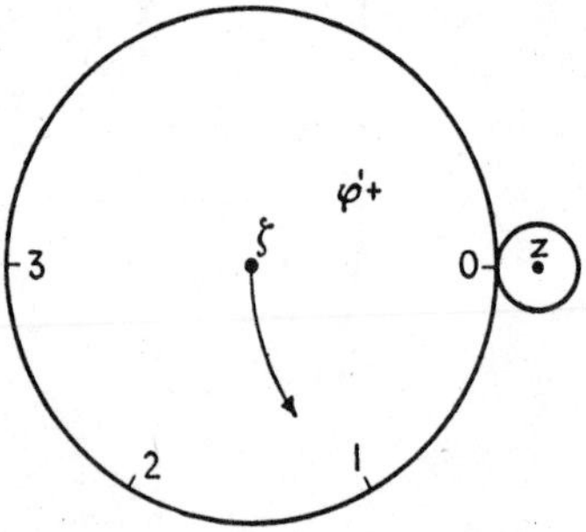

FIG. 51.

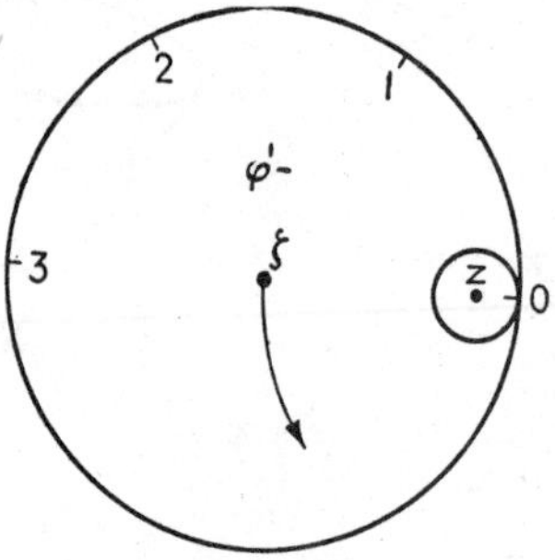

FIG. 52.

be denoted by ρ. Without making any assumptions as to the nature of the forces that are acting, the following theorems are easily derived.

Theorem I.—The vis viva of the body is ω^2/ρ^2.

The term *vis viva* means twice the kinetic energy. By Eq. (83.4)

$$2T = I\omega^2,$$

where T is the kinetic energy, I is the moment of inertia of the body with respect to the instantaneous axis, and ω is the angular velocity. Since the moment of inertia of the body, I, is equal to $1/\rho^2$ [Sec. 20], the theorem follows immediately.

Theorem II.—The plane which is tangent to the ellipsoid of inertia at the pole m is perpendicular to the vector **L** *that represents the total moment of momentum.*

The direction cosines of the instantaneous axis are

$$\frac{\omega_i}{\omega}, \quad \frac{\omega_j}{\omega}, \quad \text{and} \quad \frac{\omega_k}{\omega}.$$

[1] "Journal de Liouville," vol. 16 (1851).

Therefore the coordinates of the pole m are

$$x_m = \rho\frac{\omega_i}{\omega}, \qquad y_m = \rho\frac{\omega_j}{\omega}, \qquad z_m = \rho\frac{\omega_k}{\omega}. \tag{1}$$

The equation of the ellipsoid of inertia is

$$Ax^2 + By^2 + Cz^2 = 1,$$

and therefore the equation of the tangent plane at the pole is

$$Ax_m\xi + By_m\eta + Cz_m\zeta = 1,$$

where ξ, η, and ζ are the running coordinates of the plane. Hence, by substitution from Eqs. (1), the equation of the tangent plane becomes

$$A\omega_i\xi + B\omega_j\eta + C\omega_k\zeta = \frac{\omega}{\rho}. \tag{2}$$

The direction cosines of the normal to this plane are proportional to

$$A\omega_i, \qquad B\omega_j, \qquad C\omega_k,$$

and so also are the direction cosines of **L**, for, Eq. (82.6),

$$\mathbf{L} = A\omega_i\mathbf{i} + B\omega_j\mathbf{j} + C\omega_k\mathbf{k}.$$

Hence the tangent plane at m is perpendicular to **L**.

Let d be the perpendicular distance from the point O to the plane that is tangent at the pole m. Let h be the vis viva and l the total moment of momentum. Then:

Theorem III.—The perpendicular distance from the point O to the plane tangent at the pole is equal to the square root of the vis viva divided by the total moment of momentum; or, in formula,

$$d = \frac{\sqrt{h}}{l}. \tag{3}$$

By the usual formula of analytic geometry, the perpendicular distance from the origin to the plane

$$A\omega_i\xi + B\omega_j\eta + C\omega_k\zeta = \frac{\omega}{\rho}.$$

is

$$d = \frac{\omega}{\rho} \frac{1}{\sqrt{A^2\omega_i^2 + B^2\omega_j^2 + C^2\omega_k^2}} = \frac{\sqrt{h}}{l},$$

by Eq. (88.5) and Theorem I.

95. Application to Euler's Case.—The above theorems are independent of the nature of the forces and are always valid. If they are applied to Euler's case in which the applied forces are equivalent to a single force which passes through the fixed point, and if the notation of Sec. 88 is used, the vis viva is constant, and $h = D\omega_l^2$. Therefore

$$\frac{\omega}{\rho} = \sqrt{h} = \sqrt{D}\omega_l. \tag{1}$$

Since the moment of the forces that are acting is zero, the moment of momentum is constant, and the vector **L** is fixed both in magnitude, l, and in direction. On taking,

$$l = D\omega_l, \tag{2}$$

as in Sec. 88, there follows from Theorem III

$$d = \frac{\sqrt{h}}{l} = \frac{1}{\sqrt{D}}, \quad \text{or} \quad D = \frac{1}{d^2}; \tag{3}$$

thus

$$A = \frac{1}{a^2}, \quad B = \frac{1}{b^2}, \quad C = \frac{1}{c^2}, \quad D = \frac{1}{d^2}, \tag{4}$$

where a, b, and c are the principal semiaxes, and d is the perpendicular from the origin to the plane which is tangent to the ellipsoid of inertia at the pole m. It follows from Eqs. (3) and (2) that d and ω_l are constants. Since d is constant and the tangent plane is perpendicular to a fixed line, **L,** by Theorem II, it follows that the tangent plane is fixed in space. Its point of contact with the ellipsoid of inertia is the pole m through which the instantaneous axis passes.

Since

$$\omega = \sqrt{h}\,\rho, \tag{5}$$

the angular velocity about the instantaneous axis is proportional to the distance of the pole m from the fixed point O.

96. The Polhode and the Herpolhode.—The path of the pole on the ellipsoid of inertia was called the *polhode*[1] by Poinsot, and the path which the pole describes on the fixed plane was called the *herpolhode*.[2] The cone which is fixed in the body [Eq. (88.6)] has the instantaneous axis as a generator and the polhode as a directrix. The cone which is fixed in space has the instantaneous axis as a generator and the herpolhode as a directrix, but as the herpolhode is not, in general, a closed curve, the cone which is fixed in space is not a closed cone.

In order to obtain the motion it is necessary merely to roll the first cone upon the second in such a way that the angular velocity at each instant shall be proportional to ρ, the distance

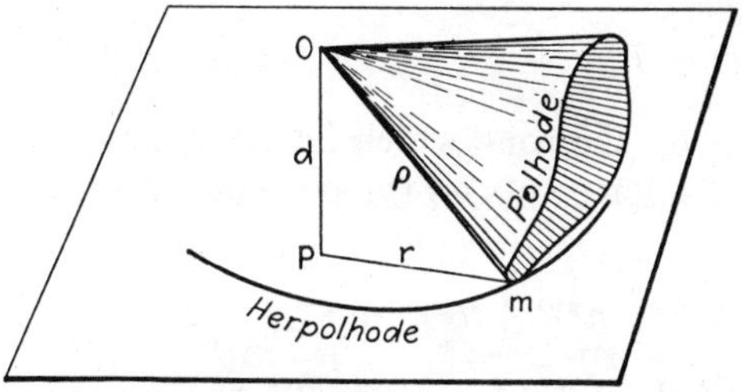

Fig. 53.

of the pole from the fixed point. The argument is given in detail in Sec. 93 for the case in which the cones are right circular cones. In the general case in which the cones are not right circular the true cones can be replaced at any instant by the osculating right circular cones and then the argument of Sec. 93 suffices to show that the motion is merely the rolling of one cone upon the other.

Suppose a material cone is constructed similar to the cone which is fixed in the body, terminating at the surface of the ellipsoid of inertia, so that the edge of the cone is a polhode (Fig. 53). Let $\overline{OP} = d$ be the distance of the fixed point O from the fixed plane P. Let the apex of this cone pivot on the point O and let the edge of the cone roll on the plane P. If the cone rolls in such a way that its angular velocity is proportional to

[1] πόλος axis, ὁδός path.

[2] The serpentine path.

the generator $\overline{Om}$ with the proper factor of proportionality, then the cone of the model will move just like the cone which is fixed in the moving body. On the fixed plane P it will trace out the herpolhode, since the corresponding arcs of the polhode and herpolhode are equal.

97. The Polhode in Rectangular Coordinates.—The equation of the ellipsoid of inertia is

$$A\xi^2 + B\eta^2 + C\zeta^2 = 1, \qquad (1)$$

and the equation of the cone described in the body by the instantaneous axis is [Eq. (88.6)]

$$A(A - D)\xi^2 + B(B - D)\eta^2 + C(C - D)\zeta^2 = 0. \qquad (2)$$

This last equation can be written

$$A^2\xi^2 + B^2\eta^2 + C^2\zeta^2 = D(A\xi^2 + B\eta^2 + C\zeta^2);$$

and for points on the cone which lie also on the surface of the ellipsoid, that is, for points on the polhode, this becomes, by Eq. (1),

$$A^2\xi^2 + B^2\eta^2 + C^2\zeta^2 = D. \qquad (3)$$

By virtue of the relations in Eq. (95.4) these equations define the polhodes as the intersections of the ellipsoid

$$\frac{\xi^2}{a^2} + \frac{\eta^2}{b^2} + \frac{\zeta^2}{c^2} = 1$$

with the family of ellipsoids

$$\frac{\xi^2}{a^4} + \frac{\eta^2}{b^4} + \frac{\zeta^2}{c^4} = \frac{1}{d^2}; \qquad (4)$$

where a, b, and c are the principal semiaxes of the ellipsoid of inertia, and d is the perpendicular distance from the center to the tangent plane. It is evident that d cannot be larger than the largest of the three principal semiaxes or smaller than the least. This gives a geometric interpretation to the inequalities that limited D in Sec. 88. When $D = A$, $d = a$ and the fixed plane is tangent to the ellipsoid of inertia at the extremity of the ξ-axis.

If

$$A < B < C, \qquad \text{then} \qquad a > b > c,$$

and d has its maximum value. The cone has shrunk down upon the ξ-axis. The polhode is reduced to a point, and the herpolhode also. The instantaneous axis is fixed in the body and fixed also in space, and the body spins with uniform angular speed about it.

Similarly, if

$$D = C, \qquad \text{then} \qquad d = c,$$

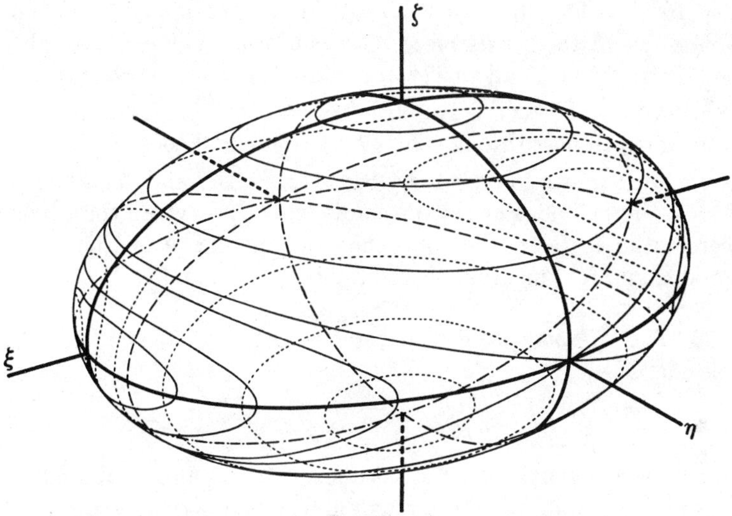

FIG. 54.

and d has its minimum value. The cone shrinks down upon the ζ-axis, which is fixed in the body and in space, and again the body spins with constant angular speed.

But if $D = B$, the cone opens up into the two planes

$$\zeta = \pm\sqrt{\frac{A(B - A)}{C(C - B)}}\,\xi,$$

[Eq. (88.7)]. These two planes, which pass through the η-axis, intersect the ellipsoid of inertia in two ellipses that intersect in the η-axis on the ellipsoid. These two ellipses, which are themselves polhodes, separate the polhodes on the surface of the ellipsoids into two classes; in one class the curves are closed around the ξ-axis, and in the other they are closed around the ζ-axis. Since the polhodes are the intersection of the surface of the ellipsoid with a cone, Eq. (3), whose apex is at the center of the ellipsoid, and since the cone has two nappes, there are two curves on the ellipsoid for each value of d. They are, of course, symmetrically placed on the ellipsoid. Which one of these two polhodes belongs to the motion under consideration depends upon the initial conditions. The pole m can follow but one of them.

In Fig. 54 polhodes of both classes are drawn for the ellipsoid in which $a = 4$, $b = 3$, and $c = 2$, as seen from the point $\xi = 7$, $\eta = 10$, $\zeta = 5$. For $d = 2$ the polhodes are merely the two points where the ζ-axis pierces the surface. For $d = 2.05$ the polhodes are the small curves about the ζ-axis, the next ones are for $d = \sqrt{5}$ and $\sqrt{7}$. For $d = \sqrt{9} = 3$ the polhodes are the ellipses which pass through the η-axis. The polhodes around the ξ-axis are drawn for $d = \sqrt{10}, \sqrt{12}, \sqrt{14}$; and finally, for $d = 4$, the polhodes are again points, this time where the ξ-axis pierces the surface. For one class of polhodes d lies between b and c, and for the other class d lies between a and b.

98. The Herpolhode.—The radius vector of the herpolhode (see Fig. 53) is

$$r = \sqrt{\rho^2 - d^2}.$$

Since d is constant and ρ has both a maximum and a minimum, r also has a minimum and a maximum. The herpolhode, therefore, lies between two concentric circles. It is a transcendental curve in general, but it has been shown by Hess[1] that it is always concave toward the origin and the name herpolhode (snakelike) given it by Poinsot was not justified, although in Poinsot's own diagram it was serpentine.

A few facts with respect to it, however, are fairly obvious. If $d = a$, or $d = c$, the herpolhode reduces to a point, since then the instantaneous axis is fixed both in the body and in space. If $d = b$, the polhode is one of the two ellipses that passes through the η-axis [Fig. 54], and the herpolhode is a spiral about the origin since the limiting value of r is zero. This spiral has infinitely

[1] A simple proof of this is given by Lecornu, *Bull. de la Société Mathématique de France*, 34, p. 40 (1906).

many turns about the origin, but its length is finite since it is equal to the length of the corresponding arc of the polhode.

If the ellipsoid of inertia is a spheroid, the polhode and the herpolhode are circles.

99. Stability of the Rotation about the Principal Axes.—The concept of the polhodes furnishes a ready answer to the question of stability of the rotation of the body when it is around one of the principal axes. It was shown in Sec. 60 that if a body is spinning about a principal axis of inertia it will continue to do so indefinitely with a uniform angular speed. It is natural to ask whether an infinitesimal disturbance would or would not result in a finite change in the state of rotation. If it does not for *any* infinitesimal disturbance, the motion is stable; otherwise it is unstable. The question is similar to that which arises in the equilibrium of a rigid body, which was discussed at I, **168.** If the axis of rotation is a principal axis, its state of rotation is a steady one. The polhode is a point. Suppose the axis of rotation is slightly displaced. The polhode of the new state of rotation is one in the neighborhood of the original one, the point polhode. In the case of the ξ-, or the ζ-axis, the polhodes are small closed curves, and in following these curves the axis of rotation departs only infinitesimally from its initial position; the motion is therefore stable. But if the η-axis was the initial axis of rotation, the polhodes in its neighborhood are all convex toward the axis. A very small displacement of the axis to one of these polhodes would result eventually in a large displacement of the axis of rotation and therefore the rotation about this axis is unstable.

This result can be summed up into the single statement: *If a body is rotating about a principal axis which is one of either maximum moment of inertia or minimum moment of inertia, the state of motion is stable; but if the axis of rotation is the intermediate principal axis, the state of motion is unstable.*

100. The Motion of the Invariable Axis in the Body.—It will be remembered that the total moment of momentum of the body **L** is constant. The axis through the fixed point O which is parallel to **L** is therefore fixed in space, but as the instantaneous axis does not coincide with it, this fixed axis which can be called the *invariable axis,* moves in the body, and indeed describes a cone.

It coincides in direction with the perpendicular d to the fixed plane.

Using the notation of Sec. 90, its direction cosines with respect to the axes which are fixed in the body are $\gamma_1, \gamma_2, \gamma_3$. It follows then from Eqs. (90.1) that

$$\frac{\gamma_1^2}{A} + \frac{\gamma_2^2}{B} + \frac{\gamma_3^2}{C} = \frac{1}{l^2}(A\omega_i^2 + B\omega_j^2 + C\omega_k^2) = \frac{h}{l^2}$$

and therefore, by Sec. 94,

$$a^2\gamma_1^2 + b^2\gamma_2^2 + c^2\gamma_3^2 = d^2. \tag{1}$$

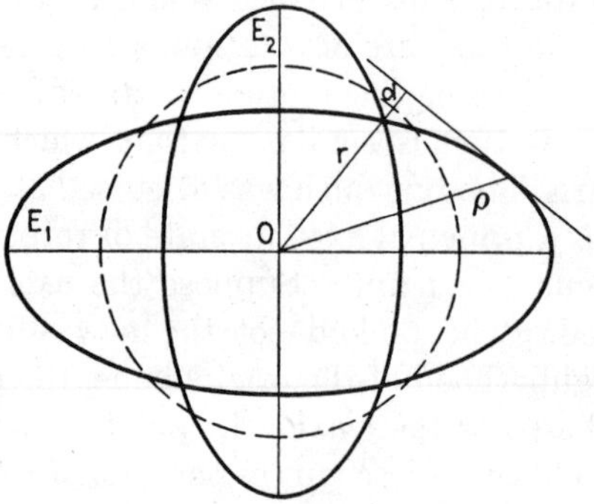

FIG. 55.

The coordinates of a point on this line at a distance r from O are

$$\xi = r\gamma_1, \qquad \eta = r\gamma_2, \qquad \zeta = r\gamma_3.$$

Multiply Eq. (1) by r^2 and then take $r = 1/d$. There results the equation

$$a^2\xi^2 + b^2\eta^2 + c^2\zeta^2 = 1, \tag{2}$$

which is called the reciprocal ellipsoid (E_2), Sec. 27, since its axes are the reciprocals of the axes of the ellipsoid of inertia (E_1). The two ellipsoids are not similar, although they have the same eccentricities. The longest axis of E_1 coincides in direction with the shortest of E_2; the shortest axis of E_1 coincides in direction with the longest axis of E_2; and the two intermediate axes have the same direction. In Fig. 55 two reciprocal ellipses are drawn, the broken line circle being the unit circle. Reciprocal ellipses, however, are similar.

The invariable axis pierces the surface of the reciprocal ellipsoid in the direction of d at a distance $1/d$ from O. Since d is constant throughout the motion, the curve traced by the invariable axis on the reciprocal ellipsoid is given by the two equations

$$a^2\xi^2 + b^2\eta^2 + c^2\zeta^2 = 1,$$

and

$$\xi^2 + \eta^2 + \zeta^2 = \frac{1}{d^2}.$$

The cone described by the axis is obtained multiplying the second equation by d^2, and subtracting from the first. Its equation is therefore

$$(a^2 - d^2)\xi^2 + (b^2 - d^2)\eta^2 + (c^2 - d^2)\zeta^2 = 0.$$

101. The Polhodes in Elliptic Coordinates.—The elliptic coordinates of a point ξ, η, ζ referred to an ellipsoid whose semiaxes are a, b, and c are the three roots q_1, q_2, and q_3 of the cubic equation which is obtained from the equation of confocal conicoids,

$$\frac{\xi^2}{a^2 - q} + \frac{\eta^2}{b^2 - q} + \frac{\zeta^2}{c^2 - q} = 1, \tag{1}$$

by clearing of fractions (I, **353**), namely,

$$(b^2 - q)(c^2 - q)\xi^2 + (c^2 - q)(a^2 - q)\eta^2 + (a^2 - q)(b^2 - q)\zeta^2 - \\ (a^2 - q)(b^2 - q)(c^2 - q) \equiv (q - q_1)(q - q_2)(q - q_3) = 0. \tag{2}$$

The coefficient of q^3 is $+1$ in both members of the identity. If the terms in q^3 are removed, and the other terms are taken to the left side, there remains an equation of the second degree that has three roots. It is therefore an identity in q and the coefficient of each power of q vanishes separately. From the coefficients of q^0, q^1, and q^2 it is found that

$$(E_1) \qquad b^2c^2\xi^2 + c^2a^2\eta^2 + a^2b^2\zeta^2 = a^2b^2c^2 - q_1q_2q_3, \tag{3}$$

$$(E_2) \quad (b^2 + c^2)\xi^2 + (c^2 + a^2)\eta^2 + (a^2 + b^2)\zeta^2 = \\ a^2b^2 + b^2c^2 + c^2a^2 - (q_1q_2 + q_2q_3 + q_3q_1), \tag{4}$$

$$(S) \qquad \xi^2 + \eta^2 + \zeta^2 = a^2 + b^2 + c^2 - (q_1 + q_2 + q_3). \tag{5}$$

If the order of magnitudes of the axes is

$$a > b > c.$$

then

$$a^2 \geqq q_1 \geqq b^2 \geqq q_2 \geqq c^2 \geqq q_3;$$

and

$$q_3 = 0$$

is the original ellipsoid, as is seen from Eq. (3). More generally,

$$q_1q_2q_3 = \text{constant}$$

represents an ellipsoid similar to the original;

$$q_1q_2 + q_2q_3 + q_3q_1 = \text{constant}$$

is another ellipsoid; and finally,

$$q_1 + q_2 + q_3 = \text{constant}$$

represents a sphere. The intersection of these surfaces with the original ellipsoid, E_1, is obtained by setting $q_3 = 0$ in Eqs. (4) and (5), that is,

$$(b^2 + c^2)\xi^2 + (c^2 + a^2)\eta^2 + (a^2 + b^2)\zeta^2 = a^2b^2 + b^2c^2 + c^2a^2 - q_1q_2, \tag{6}$$

in which

$$q_1q_2 = \text{constant};$$

and

$$\xi^2 + \eta^2 + \zeta^2 = a^2 + b^2 + c^2 - (q_1 + q_2), \tag{7}$$

with

$$q_1 + q_2 = \text{constant}.$$

The equations which define the polhodes on the ellipsoid of inertia are [Eq. (97.4)]

$$\left.\begin{aligned} \frac{\xi^2}{a^2} + \frac{\eta^2}{b^2} + \frac{\zeta^2}{c^2} &= 1, \\ \text{and} \qquad \frac{\xi^2}{a^4} + \frac{\eta^2}{b^4} + \frac{\zeta^2}{c^4} &= \frac{1}{d^2}. \end{aligned}\right\} \tag{8}$$

If the first of Eqs. (8) is multiplied by $(b^2c^2 + c^2a^2 + a^2b^2)$ and the second is multiplied by $-a^2b^2c^2$, and the two are then added, there results

$$(b^2 + c^2)\xi^2 + (c^2 + a^2)\eta^2 + (a^2 + b^2)\zeta^2 = b^2c^2 + c^2a^2 + a^2b^2 - \frac{a^2b^2c^2}{d^2}, \quad (9)$$

which equation also defines the polhodes on the ellipsoid. A comparison of Eqs. (6) and (9) shows that the equation of the polhodes in elliptic coordinates is simply

$$q_1q_2 = \frac{a^2b^2c^2}{d^2}, \qquad q_3 = 0.$$

Equation (7) gives

$$\rho^2 = a^2 + b^2 + c^2 - (q_1 + q_2).$$

The parameter of the family of polhodes is, of course, d.

If the equation of the reciprocal ellipsoid is

$$\frac{x^2}{\alpha^2} + \frac{y^2}{\beta^2} + \frac{z^2}{\gamma^2} = 1,$$

with

$$\alpha = \frac{l^2}{a}, \qquad \beta = \frac{l^2}{b}, \qquad \gamma = \frac{l^2}{c},$$

where l is an arbitrary length (not to be confused with the letter l which represents the magnitude of the vector **L**) this ellipsoid also has its system of elliptic coordinates which can be denoted by p_1, p_2, p_3, and the order of magnitudes can be written

$$\gamma^2 \geqq p_1 \geqq \beta^2 \geqq p_2 \geqq \alpha^2 \geqq p_3.$$

In this system $p_3 = 0$ is the reciprocal ellipsoid itself, and there are two other equations similar to Eqs. (4) and (5). In this system it is interesting to notice that it is the second family of surfaces [corresponding to Eq. (5)] whose intersection with the reciprocal ellipsoid gives the curves traced by the invariable axis on the reciprocal ellipsoid (Sec. 100).

A one to one correspondence between the points of the ellipsoid of inertia and the points of the reciprocal ellipsoid can be set up by taking

$$p_1 = \frac{l^4}{q_2}, \qquad p_2 = \frac{l^4}{q_1}.$$

It is evident, by taking the product of these two expressions, that if

$$q_1q_2 = \frac{a^2b^2c^2}{d^2}, \qquad \text{then} \qquad p_1p_2 = \frac{l^8d^2}{a^2b^2c^2},$$

and if δ is defined by the relation,

$$\delta = \frac{l^2}{d},$$

then

$$p_1p_2 = \frac{\alpha^2\beta^2\gamma^2}{\delta^2}.$$

The polhodes on the ellipsoid of inertia transform into the curves that would be polhodes on the reciprocal ellipsoid if the reciprocal ellipsoid were regarded as an ellipsoid of inertia.

The correspondence between the points of the two surfaces, generally, is

$$x^2 = \frac{l^4b^2c^2}{a^4q_1q_2}\xi^2, \qquad y^2 = \frac{l^4c^2a^2}{b^4q_1q_2}\eta^2, \qquad z^2 = \frac{l^4a^2b^2}{c^4q_1q_2}\zeta^2;$$

and

$$\frac{x^2y^2z^2\delta^3}{\alpha^3\beta^3\gamma^3} = \frac{\xi^2\eta^2\zeta^2d^3}{a^3b^3c^3}$$

is invariant.

II. LAGRANGE'S CASE. THE CENTER OF GRAVITY OF THE BODY LIES ON THE POLAR AXIS OF THE SPHEROID OF INERTIA

102. The Ellipsoid of Inertia Is a Spheroid.—It was observed in Sec. 86 that when no restrictions are made there are but two known integrals of the differential equations of motion of a rigid body that is spinning about a fixed point under the action of its own weight. It has been seen that when the fixed point is at the center of gravity, Euler's case, the problem can be completely integrated whatever the shape of the central ellipsoid of inertia may be. It was shown by Lagrange in the ninth section of the "Mécanique Analytique" that the equations can also be completely integrated when the central ellipsoid of inertia is a spheroid and the fixed point lies anywhere on the axis of revolution of this central ellipsoid.

Assuming that this condition is satisfied, the ellipsoid of inertia at the fixed point also is a spheroid, and the center of gravity of the body lies on its axis of revolution.

103. The Differential Equations.—As before, let the x-, y-, z-axes with origin at the fixed point O be fixed in space with the z-axis vertical, and let the ξ-, η-, ζ-axes, which have the **i**-, **j**-, **k**-directions coincide with the principal axes of inertia at the point O, and be fixed in the body. Of course, any diameter of the equator of the ellipsoid of inertia at O is a principal axis.

The two general integrals are the energy integral [Eq. (86.5)]

$$A\omega_i^2 + B\omega_j^2 + C\omega_k^2 = h - 2Mg\bar{z}, \tag{1}$$

where $\bar{z}$ is the height of the center of gravity above the horizontal plane through the point O; and the moment of momentum with respect to the z-axis integral [Eq. (85.7)]

$$A\omega_i\gamma_1 + B\omega_j\gamma_2 + C\omega_k\gamma_3 = K, \tag{2}$$

where K is the constant of integration, and γ_1, γ_2, γ_3 are the cosines of the angles between the z-axis and the ξ-, η-, ζ-axes respectively, which, expressed in terms of Euler's angles, (Sec. 52) have the values

$$\left.\begin{aligned} \gamma_1 &= \sin\theta\sin\varphi, \\ \gamma_2 &= \sin\theta\cos\varphi, \\ \gamma_3 &= \cos\theta. \end{aligned}\right\} \tag{3}$$

To these can be added Euler's third equation [Eq. (85.3)]

$$C\omega_k' + (B - A)\omega_i\omega_j = N_k. \tag{4}$$

By hypothesis, the center of gravity lies on the ζ-axis; therefore N_k, which is the moment of the weight with respect to the ζ-axis, vanishes. Also, by hypothesis, the ζ-axis is the axis of revolution of the spheroid of inertia at O; therefore A and B are equal. It follows from Eq. (4), then, that

$$\omega_k = \text{constant}. \tag{5}$$

Equations (1) and (2) can now be written

$$\left.\begin{aligned} \omega_i^2 + \omega_j^2 &= \alpha - a\cos\theta, \\ \sin\theta(\omega_i\sin\varphi + \omega_j\cos\varphi) &= \beta - b\omega_k\cos\theta, \end{aligned}\right\} \tag{6}$$

where, since

$$\bar{z} = \bar{\zeta} \cos \theta,$$

the constants a, b, α, and β have the values

$$\left.\begin{aligned} \alpha &= \frac{h - C\omega_k^2}{A}, & a &= \frac{2Mg\bar{\zeta}}{A}, \\ \beta &= \frac{K}{A}, & b &= \frac{C}{A}. \end{aligned}\right\} \tag{7}$$

The constants a and b depend only on the body itself and the position of the fixed point. If it is agreed that the positive end of the ζ-axis passes through the center of gravity, they are both positive. The constants α and β, however, are equivalent to constants of integration, and therefore are arbitrary. The angular velocity ω_k also is a constant of integration, but since the motion reduces to that of a compound pendulum for $\omega_k = 0$, it will be assumed in what follows that ω_k is not zero.

The system of differential equations is made complete by adding to Eqs. (6), which are equivalent to Euler's equations, Eqs. (85.4), which are

$$\left.\begin{aligned} \omega_i &= \psi' \sin \theta \sin \varphi + \theta' \cos \varphi, \\ \omega_j &= \psi' \sin \theta \cos \varphi - \theta' \sin \varphi, \\ \omega_k &= \psi' \cos \theta \qquad\qquad + \varphi'. \end{aligned}\right\} \tag{8}$$

104. Reduction of the Differential Equations.—The elimination of ω_i and ω_j from Eqs. (103.8) by means of Eqs. (103.6) gives the three equations

$$\left.\begin{aligned} \psi'^2 \sin^2 \theta + \theta'^2 &= \alpha - a \cos \theta, \\ \psi' \sin^2 \theta &= \beta - b\omega_k \cos \theta, \\ \psi' \cos \theta + \varphi' &= \omega_k, \end{aligned}\right\} \tag{1}$$

in which the only variables are the angles of Euler, θ, φ, and ψ.

If ψ' is eliminated between the first and second of Eqs. (1), there is obtained

$$(\beta - b\omega_k \cos \theta)^2 + \theta'^2 \sin^2 \theta = \sin^2 \theta(\alpha - a \cos \theta),$$

an equation that depends upon θ alone. This equation is simplified somewhat by taking

$$u = \cos \theta, \qquad u_4 = \frac{\beta}{b\omega_k} = \frac{K}{C\omega_k}. \tag{2}$$

It then becomes

$$u'^2 = (\alpha - au)(1 - u^2) - b^2\omega_k^2(u_4 - u)^2 = af(u). \qquad (3)$$

The second equation of Eqs. (1) now is

$$\psi' = b\omega_k \frac{u_4 - u}{1 - u^2}, \qquad (4)$$

and the third,

$$\varphi' = \omega_k\left(1 - bu\frac{u_4 - u}{1 - u^2}\right). \qquad (5)$$

Equation (3) shows that u is an elliptic function of t. If this equation is solved, so that u is a known function of t, Eqs. (4) and (5) show that φ and ψ are obtained by quadratures.

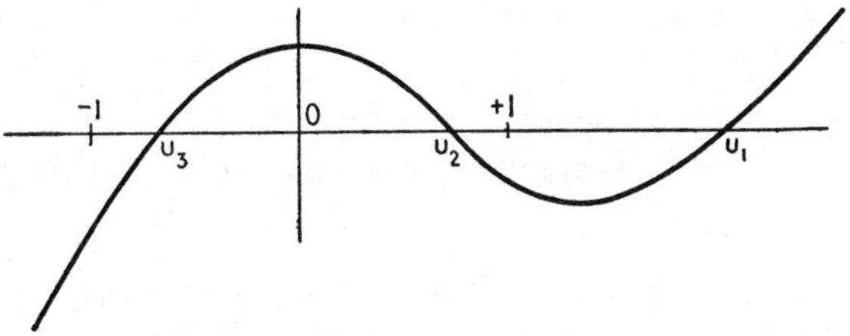

FIG. 56.

The polynomial $f(u)$ in Eq. (3) is negative for $u = -\infty, -1$, and $+1$, and positive for $u = +\infty$. Since u is the cosine of θ, and for real motion θ is real, there are two real roots, u_3 and u_2, between $u = -1$ and $u = +1$, and a third root, u_1 greater than $+1$. The character of the graph of $f(u)$ is therefore like that shown in Fig. 56, and the polynomial $f(u)$ has the form

$$f(u) = (u - u_3)(u - u_2)(u - u_1), \qquad (6)$$

with

$$-1 < u_3 < u_2 < +1 < u_1.$$

Since

$$u'^2 = af(u), \qquad \text{and} \qquad u^2 < 1,$$

it is evident (I, **254**) that u oscillates between the values u_2 and u_3.

105. The Constants of Integration Expressed in Terms of the Three Roots.—The constants of integration are α, u_4, and ω_k, and the three roots of $f(u)$ are u_1, u_2, and u_3. If the polynomials in Eq. (104.3) and (104.6) are expanded in powers of u, a comparison of the coefficients shows that

$$\left.\begin{aligned} u_1 + u_2 + u_3 &= \frac{\alpha}{a} + \frac{b^2\omega_k^2}{a}, \\ u_1u_2 + u_2u_3 + u_3u_1 &= 2u_4\frac{b^2\omega_k^2}{a} - 1, \\ u_1u_2u_3 &= -\frac{\alpha}{a} + \frac{b^2\omega_k^2}{a}u_4^2. \end{aligned}\right\} \qquad (1)$$

Let $f(+1)$ be $-p_1$ and $f(-1)$ be $-p_2$. Then

$$\left.\begin{aligned} &f(+1) = +(1 - u_1)(1 - u_2)(1 - u_3) = -p_1, \\ &f(-1) = -(1 + u_1)(1 + u_2)(1 + u_3) = -p_2, \\ &\text{where } p_1 = \frac{b^2\omega_k^2}{a}(u_4 - 1)^2, \quad \text{and} \quad p_2 = \frac{b^2\omega_k^2}{a}(u_4 + 1)^2 \end{aligned}\right\} \qquad (2)$$

are two positive numbers. If u_4 is positive, $p_2 > p_1$; and if u_4 is negative $p_2 < p_1$. By addition and subtraction of Eqs. (2), it is found that

$$\left.\begin{aligned} \tfrac{1}{2}(p_2 - p_1) &= 1 + (u_1u_2 + u_2u_3 + u_3u_1), \\ \tfrac{1}{2}(p_2 + p_1) &= (u_1 + u_2 + u_3) + u_1u_2u_3; \end{aligned}\right\} \qquad (3)$$

and by division that

$$\frac{p_1}{p_2} = \left(\frac{u_4 - 1}{u_4 + 1}\right)^2 = \frac{u_1 - 1}{u_1 + 1}\frac{1 - u_2}{1 + u_2}\frac{1 - u_3}{1 + u_3}. \qquad (4)$$

From the first of these two equations [Eqs. (4)] there is obtained

$$u_{41} = \frac{\sqrt{p_2} + \sqrt{p_1}}{\sqrt{p_2} - \sqrt{p_1}}, \qquad \text{and} \qquad u_{42} = \frac{\sqrt{p_2} - \sqrt{p_1}}{\sqrt{p_2} + \sqrt{p_1}}. \qquad (5)$$

These two values of u_4 are both positive or both negative, but in either case the two are mutually reciprocal, that is

$$u_{41} \cdot u_{42} = +1, \qquad \text{with} \qquad u_{41}^2 > 1.$$

Thus, if u_1, u_2, and u_3 are given, there are two values of u_4 that satisfy all of the conditions of the problem.

If, however, u_2, u_3, and u_4 are given, u_1 is determined uniquely; for, let

$$s = \left(\frac{u_4 - 1}{u_4 + 1}\right)^2 \frac{1 + u_2}{1 - u_2}\frac{1 + u_3}{1 - u_3},$$

Eq. (4) then shows that

$$u_1 = \frac{1+s}{1-s},$$

and since $u_1 > +1$, it is necessary that $0 < s < 1$.

The three roots u_1, u_2, and u_3 are restricted by the conditions

$$-1 < u_3, u_2 < +1, \qquad \text{and} \qquad +1 < u_1.$$

For given values of u_2 and u_3, which are the limits of the variable u, the value of u_4 also is restricted. To show this, let

$$\frac{1-u_2}{1+u_2}\frac{1-u_3}{1+u_3} = \xi^2 \qquad \text{and} \qquad \frac{u_1-1}{u_1+1} = \eta^2 < 1.$$

Then Eq. (4) gives

$$\left(\frac{u_4-1}{u_4+1}\right)^2 = \xi^2\eta^2,$$

and

$$u_{41} = \frac{1+\xi\eta}{1-\xi\eta}, \qquad u_{42} = \frac{1-\xi\eta}{1+\xi\eta}.$$

If ξ is kept fixed while η runs over its entire range from $+1$ to zero, it is found that, if $\xi < 1$, both values of u_4 lie in the interval

$$\frac{1-\xi}{1+\xi} < u_4 < \frac{1+\xi}{1-\xi};$$

but if $\xi > 1$, both values of u_4 lie outside of the interval

$$-\frac{\xi+1}{\xi-1} < u < -\frac{\xi-1}{\xi+1}.$$

From the definition of ξ it is readily verified that $\xi \gtrless 1$ according as $u_2 + u_3 \lesseqgtr 0$.

From the second of Eqs. (1) there is derived

$$\frac{b^2\omega_k^2}{a} = \frac{1}{2u_4}(1 + u_1u_2 + u_2u_3 + u_3u_1),$$

or, by the first of Eqs. (3),

$$\frac{b^2\omega_k^2}{a} = \frac{p_2 - p_1}{4u_4}.$$

Since for given values of u_1, u_2, and u_3 there are two values of u_4, so, also, there are two values of ω_k^2, namely,

$$\left.\begin{aligned} \omega_k^2 &= \frac{a}{4b^2}(\sqrt{p_2} - \sqrt{p_1})^2, \qquad \text{if} \qquad u_4 = u_{41}, \\ \text{and} \\ \omega_k^2 &= \frac{a}{4b^2}(\sqrt{p_2} + \sqrt{p_1})^2, \qquad \text{if} \qquad u_4 = u_{42}. \end{aligned}\right\} \tag{6}$$

Finally, the first of Eqs. (1) gives

$$\alpha = a(u_1 + u_2 + u_3) - b^2\omega_k^2. \tag{7}$$

106. The Value of ω_k as a Function of u_1.—The value of ω_k likewise is restricted. By Eq. (105.1),

$$\omega_k^2 = \frac{a}{2b^2}\frac{1 + (u_2 + u_3)u_1 + u_2u_3}{u_4}. \tag{1}$$

If u_2 and u_3 are kept fixed, the value of ω_k varies in a definite manner with u_1, since u_4 is a function of u_1 [Eq. (105.3)]. If u_1 is equal to $+1$, so also is u_4, and Eq. (1) gives for this value of u_1

$$\omega_k^2 = \frac{a}{2b^2}(1 + u_2)(1 + u_3). \tag{2}$$

By differentiating Eq. (1) with respect to u_1 and then reducing by means of the formulas of Sec. 105, it is found that

$$\frac{d\omega_k^2}{du_1} = \frac{au_4}{2b^2}\left[(u_2 + u_3) \pm \frac{\sqrt{(1 - u_2^2)(1 - u_3^2)}}{\sqrt{u_1^2 - 1}}\right], \tag{3}$$

the upper sign to be used if $u_4 < 1$ and the lower if $u_4 > 1$. Consider the case in which $u_2 + u_3 > 0$. If u_1 increases from $+1$ to $+\infty$ along the series for which $u_4 < 1$, the derivative of ω_k^2 is everywhere positive. Therefore ω_k^2 increases steadily from the value given in Eq. (2) to $+\infty$, by Eq. (1).

Along the series for which $u_4 > 1$, however, the derivative is negative until the bracket in the right member of Eq. (3) vanishes, and this happens for

$$u_1 = \frac{1 + u_2u_3}{u_2 + u_3},$$

which is greater than +1, if $u_2 + u_3 > 0$; and ω_k^2 has decreased from the value given in Eq. (2) to its minimum value, namely,

$$\omega_k^2 = \frac{a}{b^2}\frac{1 + u_2 u_3}{u_4} = \frac{a}{b^2}(u_2 + u_3). \tag{4}$$

For larger values of u_1 the derivative is positive and ω_k^2 increases indefinitely with u_1.

107. Reduction of the Elliptic Integral to a Normal Form.—If the independent variable t is changed by the substitution

$$\frac{\sqrt{a}}{2}\,dt = d\tau_1,$$

the differential equation [Eq. (104.3)] becomes

$$\left.\begin{aligned}\left(\frac{du}{d\tau_1}\right)^2 &= 4\left[\left(\frac{\alpha}{a} - u\right)(1 - u^2) - \frac{b^2\omega_k^2}{a}(u_4 - u)^2\right]\\ &= 4(u - u_1)(u - u_2)(u - u_3).\end{aligned}\right\} \tag{1}$$

Let also a new dependent variable s be defined by the relations

$$s = u - u_0, \tag{2}$$

where

$$u_0 = \tfrac{1}{3}(u_1 + u_2 + u_3);$$

and further, let

$$u_1 - u_0 = e_1, \qquad u_2 - u_0 = e_2, \qquad u_3 - u_0 = e_3, \tag{3}$$

so that

$$e_1 > e_2 > e_3,$$

and

$$e_1 + e_2 + e_3 = 0.$$

The differential equation now becomes

$$\left(\frac{ds}{d\tau_1}\right)^2 = 4(s - e_1)(s - e_2)(s - e_3).$$

This is the normal form of Weierstrass[1] and the solution which

[1] See Schwarz, "Formeln und Lehrsätze zum Gebrauche der Elliptischen Funktionen," or Appell and Lacour, "Fonctions Elliptiques et Applications."

is infinite for $\tau_1 = 0$ is

$$s = u - u_0 = \wp\tau_1;$$

with

$$\wp 0 = \pm\infty, \qquad \wp\omega_1 = e_1, \qquad \wp\omega_2 = e_2, \qquad \wp\omega_3 = e_3. \tag{4}$$

Figure 57 shows the parallelogram of half periods. Starting at the origin and proceeding along the real axis, $\wp\tau_1$ decreases from $+\infty$ to e_1 as τ_1 increases from zero to ω_1 which is one half of the real period. If τ_1 moves from ω_1 to ω_2 parallel to the purely imaginary axis, $\wp\tau_1$ continues to be real and decreases from e_1 to e_2. As τ_1 moves parallel to the real axis from ω_2 to ω_3, the purely imaginary half period, $\wp\tau_1$ is real and decreases from e_2 to e_3; and finally as τ_1 moves along the purely imaginary axis from ω_3 to the origin, $\wp\tau_1$ decreases from e_3 to $-\infty$. Thus $\wp\tau_1$ is real along the boundary of the parallelogram of half periods, and, if τ_1 traces the boundary in a counterclockwise direction, $\wp\tau_1$ is always real and decreases steadily from $+\infty$ to $-\infty$.

Along the real axis from 0 to ω_1, $\wp'\tau_1$ (the derivative of $\wp\tau_1$) is real and negative; along the boundary from ω_1 to ω_2, $\wp'\tau_1$ is a pure imaginary, and $\wp'/i > 0$; along the boundary from ω_2 to ω_3, $\wp'\tau_1$ is real and positive, and along the purely imaginary axis between ω_3 and 0, $\wp'\tau_1$ is a pure imaginary and $\wp'/i < 0$.

Let w be the value of τ_1 for which $u = +1$, and v the value of τ_1 for which $u = -1$. Then [Eq. (2)]

$$\wp w = 1 - u_0, \qquad \wp v = -1 - u_0; \tag{5}$$

and since, by Eqs. (3) and (4),

$$\wp\omega_1 = u_1 - u_0, \qquad \wp\omega_2 = u_2 - u_0, \qquad \wp\omega_3 = u_3 - u_0,$$

it is evident that, in tracing the boundary of the parallelogram of half periods, these points are encountered in the following order:

$$\tau_1 = 0, \qquad \omega_1, \qquad w, \qquad \omega_2, \qquad \omega_3, \qquad v, \qquad 0,$$

corresponding to

$$u = +\infty, \qquad u_1, \qquad +1, \qquad u_2, \qquad u_3, \qquad -1, \qquad -\infty. \tag{6}$$

Thus w and v lie on the rectangle as indicated in Fig. 57; and, algebraically, have the form

$$w = \omega_1 + im_1 = \omega_2 - im_2, \qquad v = 0 + in_1 = \omega_3 - in_2,$$

where m_j and n_j are real positive constants. Furthermore, since the variable u lies between u_3 and u_2, the values of τ_1 that belong to the problem lie on the axis through the points ω_3 and ω_2; and therefore

$$\tau_1 = \omega_3 + \tau,$$

where τ is real. Equation (2) then gives

$$u = u_0 + \wp(\tau + \omega_3),$$

and for $\tau = 0$,

$$u_3 = u_0 + e_3.$$

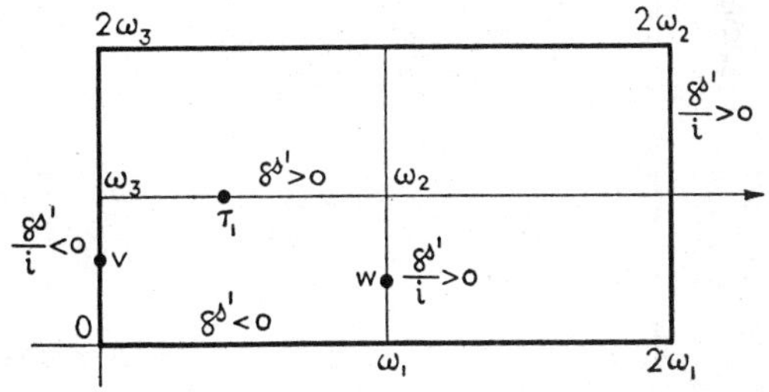

FIG. 57.

Hence[1]

$$u - u_3 = \wp(\tau + \omega_3) - e_3 = \left[\frac{\sigma_3}{\sigma}(\tau + \omega_3)\right]^2;$$

and since[2]

$$\frac{\sigma_3}{\sigma}(\tau + \omega_3) = \sqrt{(e_1 - e_3)(e_2 - e_3)}\frac{\sigma}{\sigma_3}(\tau),$$

$$e_j - e_k = u_j - u_k,$$

it is found, using the ϑ-functions,[3] that

$$u - u_3 = 4h^{\frac{1}{4}}\sqrt{(u_1 - u_3)(u_2 - u_3)} \times \left[\frac{\sin \xi - h^2 \sin 3\xi + h^6 \sin 5\xi + \cdots}{1 - 2h \cos 2\xi + 2h^4 \cos 4\xi - 2h^9 \cos 6\xi + \cdots}\right]^2; \quad (7)$$

[1] SCHWARZ, p. 21.
[2] *Idem.*, p. 27.
[3] *Idem.*, p. 62.

where

$$h = e^{\frac{\omega_3}{\omega_1}\pi i} \quad \text{and} \quad \xi = \frac{\tau\pi}{2\omega_1}.$$

In terms of Legendre's integrals[1]

$$\omega_1 = \frac{1}{\sqrt{u_1 - u_3}} \int_0^{\frac{\pi}{2}} \frac{d\varphi}{\sqrt{1 - k^2 \sin^2 \varphi}},$$

$$\omega_3 = \frac{i}{\sqrt{u_1 - u_3}} \int_0^{\frac{\pi}{2}} \frac{d\varphi}{\sqrt{1 - k_1^2 \sin^2 \varphi}};$$

with

$$k^2 = \frac{u_2 - u_3}{u_1 - u_3}, \qquad k_1^2 = \frac{u_1 - u_2}{u_1 - u_3}.$$

Since

$$\frac{\omega_3}{\omega_1}\pi i = -\frac{K_1}{K}\pi,$$

where K and K_1 are Legendre's complete elliptic integrals of the first kind for the moduli

$$k^2 = \frac{u_2 - u_3}{u_1 - u_3} \quad \text{and} \quad k_1^2 = 1 - k^2 = \frac{u_1 - u_2}{u_1 - u_3}$$

respectively, is always real and negative, it follows that $h < 1$, except for the case $u_1 = u_2$ in which it is equal to 1. The series used in Eq. (7) are convergent, therefore, for all values of the argument ξ, real or complex.

108. The Integration for the Angle of Precession.—On changing the independent variable from t to τ_1, Eq. (104.4) becomes

$$\frac{d\psi}{d\tau_1} = \frac{2b\omega_k}{\sqrt{a}} \frac{u_4 - u}{1 - u^2},$$

or again, by resolving the right member into its elements,

$$\frac{d\psi}{d\tau_1} = \frac{b\omega_k}{\sqrt{a}}\left(\frac{u_4 + 1}{u + 1} - \frac{u_4 - 1}{u - 1}\right).$$

[1] SCHWARZ, p. 61.

After multiplying by $2i$, $(i = \sqrt{-1})$, this equation takes the form

$$2i\frac{d\psi}{d\tau_1} = \frac{2b\omega_k i}{\sqrt{a}}\left(\frac{u_4 + 1}{u + 1} - \frac{u_4 - 1}{u - 1}\right), \tag{1}$$

and since this equation remains unaltered if the signs of u_4, ω_k, and u are changed, it is sufficient to consider only the case in which u_4 is positive.

Since

$$\frac{du}{d\tau_1} = \frac{ds}{d\tau_1} = \wp'\tau_1,$$

and

$$\wp(\tau + \omega_3) + u_0 = u, \qquad \wp w + u_0 = +1, \qquad \wp v + u_0 = -1,$$

it is seen from Eq. (107.1) that

$$\left.\begin{aligned} \wp' w &= +\frac{2b\omega_k i}{\sqrt{a}}(u_4 - 1), \quad \text{if} \quad u_4 > 1, \\ \text{and} \qquad & \\ \wp' w &= -\frac{2b\omega_k i}{\sqrt{a}}(u_4 - 1), \quad \text{if} \quad u_4 < 1, \end{aligned}\right\} \tag{2}$$

since, Sec. 107,

$$\frac{\wp' w}{i} > 0.$$

Likewise

$$\wp' v = -\frac{2b\omega_k i}{\sqrt{a}}(u_4 + 1), \quad \text{if} \quad u_4 > 0, \tag{3}$$

since

$$\frac{\wp' v}{i} < 0.$$

This assumes, of course, that ω_k is positive. If it is negative, the signs must be reversed.

Now

$$u + 1 = (u - u_0) + (1 + u_0) = \wp(\tau + \omega_3) - \wp v,$$

and

$$u - 1 = (u - u_0) - (1 - u_0) = \wp(\tau + \omega_3) - \wp w;$$

consequently Eq. (1) becomes

$$\left.\begin{aligned}
&(a)\ 2i\frac{d\psi}{d\tau} = -\frac{\wp' w}{\wp(\tau+\omega_3)-\wp w} - \frac{\wp' v}{\wp(\tau+\omega_3)-\wp v}, \quad \text{if} \quad u_4 > 1,\\
&\text{and}\\
&(b)\ 2i\frac{d\psi}{d\tau} = +\frac{\wp' w}{\wp(\tau+\omega_3)-\wp w} - \frac{\wp' v}{\wp(\tau+\omega_3)-\wp v}, \quad \text{if} \quad u_4 < 1.
\end{aligned}\right\} \quad (4)$$

These expressions are in the normal form of Weierstrass for elliptic integrals of the third kind,[1] and integration gives

$$\left.\begin{aligned}
&(a)\ \psi = \frac{1}{2i}\log\frac{\sigma(v+\tau+\omega_3)\sigma(w+\tau+\omega_3)}{\sigma(v-\tau-\omega_3)\sigma(w-\tau-\omega_3)} - \frac{\tau}{i}\left(\frac{\sigma'}{\sigma}(v) + \frac{\sigma'}{\sigma}(w)\right)\\
&\qquad\qquad + \text{constant},\\
&\text{or}\\
&(b)\ \psi = \frac{1}{2i}\log\frac{\sigma(v+\tau+\omega_3)\sigma(w-\tau-\omega_3)}{\sigma(v-\tau-\omega_3)\sigma(w+\tau+\omega_3)} - \frac{\tau}{i}\left(\frac{\sigma'}{\sigma}(v) - \frac{\sigma'}{\sigma}(w)\right)\\
&\qquad\qquad + \text{constant}.
\end{aligned}\right\} \quad (5)$$

If the constants of integration are chosen in such a way that $\psi = \psi_0$ for $\tau = 0$, these expressions reduce to[2]

$$\left.\begin{aligned}
&(a)\ \psi - \psi_0 = \frac{1}{2i}\log\frac{\sigma_3(\tau+v)\sigma_3(\tau+w)}{\sigma_3(\tau-v)\sigma_3(\tau-w)} - \frac{\tau}{i}\left(\frac{\sigma'}{\sigma}(v) + \frac{\sigma'}{\sigma}(w)\right),\\
&\text{or}\\
&(b)\ \psi - \psi_0 = \frac{1}{2i}\log\frac{\sigma_3(\tau+v)\sigma_3(\tau-w)}{\sigma_3(\tau-v)\sigma_3(\tau+w)} - \frac{\tau}{i}\left(\frac{\sigma'}{\sigma}(v) - \frac{\sigma'}{\sigma}(w)\right),
\end{aligned}\right\} \quad (6)$$

according as $u_4 > 1$ or $u_4 < 1$.

109. Transformation to the Theta Functions.—It was observed in Sec. 107 that

$$\left.\begin{aligned}
w &= \omega_1 + im_1 = \omega_2 - im_2,\\
v &= 0 + in_1 = \omega_3 - in_2,
\end{aligned}\right\} \quad (1)$$

[1] SCHWARZ, p. 95.

[2] *Idem*, p. 26.

where m_1, m_2, n_1, and n_2 are real, positive numbers, and

$$\left.\begin{aligned} m_1 + m_2 &= -\omega_3 i, \\ n_1 + n_2 &= -\omega_3 i. \end{aligned}\right\} \tag{2}$$

Since v and w are complex numbers, the form of $\psi - \psi_0$ in Eqs. (108.6) is complex notwithstanding the fact that $\psi - \psi_0$ is real. It is necessary therefore to transform these equations into others that are real and better suited for computation.

For this purpose take first the terms which depend upon v or w only, and consider the function

$$f(r) = \frac{1}{2i} \log \frac{\sigma_3(\tau + r)}{\sigma_3(\tau - r)} - \frac{\tau}{i} \frac{\sigma'}{\sigma}(r).$$

Let the Jacobi H and Θ functions be defined by the equations

$$\left.\begin{aligned} \vartheta_0(s) &= 1 - 2h \cos 2s + 2h^4 \cos 4s - 2h^9 \cos 6s + \cdots, \\ \vartheta_1(s) &= 2h^{\frac{1}{4}} \sin s - 2h^{\frac{9}{4}} \sin 3s + 2h^{\frac{25}{4}} \sin 5s + \cdots, \\ \vartheta_2(s) &= 2h^{\frac{1}{4}} \cos s + 2h^{\frac{9}{4}} \cos 3s + 2h^{\frac{25}{4}} \cos 5s + \cdots, \\ \vartheta_3(s) &= 1 + 2h \cos 2s + 2h^4 \cos 4s + 2h^9 \cos 6s + \cdots. \end{aligned}\right\} \tag{3}$$

Then for any argument u[1]

$$\left.\begin{aligned} &\sigma_k(u) = C_{k+1} e^{\frac{2\eta_1\omega_1 s^2}{\pi^2}} \vartheta_{k+1}(s), \qquad k = 0, 1, 2, 3, \\ &\text{provided} \\ &s = \frac{u\pi}{2\omega_1}, \qquad \eta_1 = \frac{\sigma'}{\sigma}(\omega_1), \end{aligned}\right\} \tag{4}$$

and C_{k+1} is a certain constant which is of no importance here. In this notation $\sigma_0(u)$ is the same as $\sigma(u)$, and $\vartheta_4 \equiv \vartheta_0$.

Now take

$$\xi = \frac{\tau\pi}{2\omega_1}, \qquad \zeta = \frac{r\pi}{2\omega_1}, \qquad \mu_j = \frac{m_j\pi}{2\omega_1}, \qquad \text{and} \qquad \nu_j = \frac{n_j\pi}{2\omega_1};$$

then

$$\frac{\sigma_3(\tau + r)}{\sigma_3(\tau - r)} = e^{\frac{8\eta_1\omega_1\xi\zeta}{\pi^2}} \frac{\vartheta_0(\xi + \zeta)}{\vartheta_0(\xi - \zeta)},$$

[1] SCHWARZ, p. 62.

and

$$\frac{\sigma'}{\sigma}(r) = \frac{4\eta_1\omega_1\zeta}{\pi^2}\cdot\frac{\pi}{2\omega_1} + \frac{\pi}{2\omega_1}\frac{\vartheta_1'}{\vartheta_1}(\zeta).$$

In the left member of this last equation the accent means differentiation with respect to u, and in the right member differentiation with respect to s. This accounts for the factor $\pi/(2\omega_1)$. From these equations it follows that

$$f(r) = \frac{1}{2i}\log\frac{\vartheta_0(\xi+\zeta)}{\vartheta_0(\xi-\zeta)} - \frac{\xi}{i}\frac{\vartheta_1'}{\vartheta_1}(\zeta). \tag{5}$$

For the terms in w,

$$\zeta = \frac{\pi}{2} + i\mu_1 \qquad \text{or} \qquad \zeta = \frac{\pi}{2} + \frac{\omega_3\pi}{2\omega_1} - i\mu_2;$$

and for the terms which depend upon ν,

$$\zeta = i\nu_1 \qquad \text{or} \qquad \zeta = \frac{\omega_3\pi}{2\omega_1} - i\nu_2.$$

There are, therefore, four values for the argument ζ in Eq. (5), and accordingly four different expressions for $f(r)$ when $f(r)$ is expressed in a form that is real. When the argument u in Eqs. (4) is increased, or decreased, by a half period, ω_1, ω_2, or ω_3, the argument s is increased, or decreased, by the amounts

$$p_1 = \frac{\pi}{2}, \qquad p_2 = \frac{\pi}{2} + \frac{\omega_3\pi}{2\omega_1}, \qquad \text{or} \qquad p_3 = \frac{\omega_3\pi}{2\omega_1}.$$

Now[1]

$$\begin{aligned}
\vartheta_0(s \pm p_1) &= \vartheta_3(s), & \vartheta_1(s + p_1) &= \vartheta_2(s),\\
\vartheta_0(s \pm p_2) &= e^{\mp is - \frac{1}{2}p_3 i}\vartheta_2(s), & \vartheta_1(s + p_2) &= e^{-is - \frac{1}{2}p_3 i}\vartheta_3(s),\\
\vartheta_0(s \pm p_3) &= e^{\mp i(s-p_1) - \frac{1}{2}p_3 i}\vartheta_1(s), & \vartheta_1(s + p_3) &= e^{-i(s-p_1) - \frac{1}{2}p_3 i}\vartheta_0(s),
\end{aligned}$$

by means of which Eq. (5) can be reduced when the four values of ζ, namely, $i\mu_1 + p_1$, $-i\mu_2 + p_2$, $-i\nu_2 + p_3$, and $i\nu_1 + 0$, are substituted in succession in it. There results from these substitutions

[1] These formulas can be derived from the properties of the H and Θ functions of Jacobi. See, for example, APPELL and LACOUR, "Fonctions Elliptiques," p. 404.

$$\begin{aligned}
f(\omega_1 + im_1) &= \frac{1}{2i} \log \frac{\vartheta_3(\xi + i\mu_1)}{\vartheta_3(\xi - i\mu_1)} - \frac{\xi}{i} \frac{\vartheta_2'}{\vartheta_2}(i\mu_1), \\
f(\omega_2 - im_2) &= \frac{1}{2i} \log \frac{\vartheta_2(\xi - i\mu_2)}{\vartheta_2(\xi + i\mu_2)} + \frac{\xi}{i} \frac{\vartheta_3'}{\vartheta_3}(i\mu_2), \\
f(\omega_3 - in_2) &= \frac{1}{2i} \log - \frac{\vartheta_1(\xi - i\nu_2)}{\vartheta_1(\xi + i\nu_2)} + \frac{\xi}{i} \frac{\vartheta_0'}{\vartheta_0}(i\nu_2), \\
f(0 + in_1) &= \frac{1}{2i} \log \frac{\vartheta_0(\xi + i\nu_1)}{\vartheta_0(\xi - i\nu_1)} - \frac{\xi}{i} \frac{\vartheta_1'}{\vartheta_1}(i\nu_1).
\end{aligned}$$

If $x + iy = \rho e^{i\lambda}$ is any complex number

$$\frac{x + iy}{x - iy} = e^{2i\lambda},$$

where

$$\tan \lambda = \frac{y}{x}.$$

Accordingly, since $\vartheta_k(\xi \pm i\eta) = \vartheta_{k1} \pm i\vartheta_{k2}$, where ϑ_{k1} and ϑ_{k2} are real, is a complex number,

$$\frac{\vartheta_k(\xi + i\eta)}{\vartheta_k(\xi - i\eta)} = e^{2i\lambda_k},$$

where

$$\tan \lambda_k = \frac{\vartheta_{k2}}{\vartheta_{k1}},$$

and λ_k is real. Then

$$\frac{1}{2i} \log \frac{\vartheta_k(\xi + i\eta)}{\vartheta_k(\xi - i\eta)} = \pm\lambda_k, \tag{6}$$

the signs to be chosen so that λ_k is positive. Likewise

$$\frac{\vartheta_k'}{\vartheta_k}(i\beta) = \pm iq_k, \tag{7}$$

where q_k is a real, positive number.

On substituting the complex arguments in the ϑ-functions, Eq. (3), and then separating the real and imaginary parts, it is found that

$$\left.\begin{aligned}
\tan \lambda_0 &= \frac{2h \sinh 2\nu_1 \sin 2\xi - 2h^4 \sinh 4\nu_1 \sin 4\xi + 2h^9 \sinh 6\nu_1 \sin 6\xi - \cdots}{1 - 2h \cosh 2\nu_1 \cos 2\xi + 2h^4 \cosh 4\nu_1 \cos 4\xi - 2h^9 \cosh 6\nu_1 \cos 6\xi + \cdots}, \\
\tan \lambda_1 &= \frac{\cosh \nu_2 \sin \xi - h^2 \cosh 3\nu_2 \sin 3\xi + h^6 \cosh 5\nu_2 \sin 5\xi - \cdots}{\sinh \nu_2 \cos \xi - h^2 \sinh 3\nu_2 \cos 3\xi + h^6 \sinh 5\nu_2 \cos 5\xi - \cdots}, \\
\tan \lambda_2 &= \frac{\sinh \mu_2 \sin \xi + h^2 \sinh 3\mu_2 \sin 3\xi + h^6 \sinh 5\mu_2 \sin 5\xi + \cdots}{\cosh \mu_2 \cos \xi + h^2 \cosh 3\mu_2 \cos 3\xi + h^6 \cosh 5\mu_2 \cos 5\xi + \cdots}, \\
\tan \lambda_3 &= \frac{2h \sinh 2\mu_1 \sin 2\xi + 2h^4 \sinh 4\mu_1 \sin 4\xi + 2h^9 \sinh 6\mu_1 \sin 6\xi + \cdots}{1 + 2h \cosh 2\mu_1 \cos 2\xi + 2h^4 \cosh 4\mu_1 \cos 4\xi + 2h^9 \cosh 6\mu_1 \cos 6\xi + \cdots}.
\end{aligned}\right\} \tag{8}$$

Also

$$\left.\begin{aligned}
q_0 &= \frac{4h \sinh 2\nu_2 - 8h^4 \sinh 4\nu_2 + 12h^9 \sinh 6\nu_2 - \cdots}{1 - 2h \cosh 2\nu_2 + 2h^4 \cosh 4\nu_2 - 2h^9 \cosh 6\nu_2 + \cdots},\\
q_1 &= \frac{\cosh \nu_1 - 3h^2 \cosh 3\nu_1 + 5h^6 \cosh 5\nu_1 - \cdots}{\sinh \nu_1 - h^2 \sinh 3\nu_1 + h^6 \sinh 5\nu_1 - \cdots},\\
q_2 &= \frac{\sinh \mu_1 + 3h^2 \sinh 3\mu_1 + 5h^6 \sinh 5\mu_1 + \cdots}{\cosh \mu_1 + h^2 \cosh 3\mu_1 + h^6 \cosh 5\mu_1 + \cdots},\\
q_3 &= \frac{4h \sinh 2\mu_2 + 8h^4 \sinh 4\mu_2 + 12h^9 \sinh 6\mu_2 + \cdots}{1 + 2h \cosh 2\mu_2 + 2h^4 \cosh 4\mu_2 + 2h^9 \cosh 6\mu_2 + \cdots},
\end{aligned}\right\} \tag{9}$$

which are real.

From Eq. (108.6a) it is seen that if $u_4 > 1$,

$$\psi - \psi_0 = f(v) + f(w).$$

Equation (108.6b) is obtained from Eq. (108.6a) merely by changing w into $-w$, and, since $f(-w) = -f(w)$, it is evident that Eq. (108.6b) becomes $\psi - \psi_0 = f(v) - f(w)$. Now

$$\left.\begin{aligned}
f(v) &= f(0 + in_1) = f(\omega_3 - in_2)\\
&= q_1\xi + \lambda_0 = q_0\xi + \lambda_1,\\
&\text{and}\\
f(w) &= f(\omega_1 + im_1) = f(\omega_3 - im_2)\\
&= -q_3\xi + \lambda_2 = +q_2\xi - \lambda_3,
\end{aligned}\right\} \tag{10}$$

so that there are four forms of the solution in each case, namely,

$$\left.\begin{aligned}
&\textit{Case a: } u_4 > 1\\
\psi - \psi_0 &= (q_1 - q_3)\xi + (\lambda_0 + \lambda_2),\\
&= (q_1 + q_2)\xi + (\lambda_0 - \lambda_3),\\
&= (q_0 - q_3)\xi + (\lambda_1 + \lambda_2),\\
&= (q_0 + q_2)\xi + (\lambda_1 - \lambda_3).\\
&\textit{Case b: } u_4 < 1\\
\psi - \psi_0 &= (q_1 + q_3)\xi + (\lambda_0 - \lambda_2),\\
&= (q_1 - q_2)\xi + (\lambda_0 + \lambda_3),\\
&= (q_0 + q_3)\xi + (\lambda_1 - \lambda_2),\\
&= (q_0 - q_2)\xi + (\lambda_1 + \lambda_3).
\end{aligned}\right\} \tag{11}$$

The choice of form depends upon the positions of the points v and w. Since

$$m_1 + m_2 = n_1 + n_2 = -\omega_3 i,$$

it is evident, on multiplying through by $\pi/(2\omega_1)$, that

$$\mu_1 + \mu_2 = \nu_1 + \nu_2 = -\frac{\omega_3 \pi i}{2\omega_1} = -\frac{1}{2}\log_e h,$$

and therefore, unless

$$\mu_1 = \mu_2 = -\tfrac{1}{4}\log_e h,$$

either μ_1 or μ_2 is less than this value, and the choice will naturally be the smaller one; and similarly for ν_1 and ν_2.

It will be observed that for $\xi = \pi/2$

$$\lambda_1 = \lambda_2 = \frac{\pi}{2}, \qquad \lambda_0 = \lambda_3 = 0.$$

Consequently, by setting $\xi = \pi/2$ in Eqs. (10), it is found that

$$q_1 - q_0 = 1 \qquad \text{and} \qquad q_2 + q_3 = 1;$$

and therefore

$$\lambda_1 = \xi + \lambda_0, \qquad \lambda_2 = \xi - \lambda_3.$$

110. The Precession Has the Same Sign as ω_k. An interesting proof that the precession for a complete period has the same sign as ω_k has been given by Hadamard.[1] From Eq. (104.3) it is seen that

$$dt = \frac{du}{\sqrt{a(u_1 - u)(u_2 - u)(u - u_3)}} = \frac{du}{\sqrt{af(u)}}, \tag{1}$$

the positive sign being taken before the radical as u increases from u_3 to u_2; and, by the elimination of dt between Eqs. (104.3) and (104.4), for the complete half period

$$\psi - \psi_0 = \frac{b\omega_k}{\sqrt{a}}\int_{u_3}^{u_2} \frac{u_4 - u}{1 - u^2}\frac{du}{\sqrt{f(u)}}. \tag{2}$$

If $u_4 > u_2$ the integrand is positive always; therefore the integral is positive and $\psi - \psi_0$ has the same sign as ω_k. But if u_4 lies between u_2 and u_3, the integrand changes sign at $u = u_4$,

[1] J. Hadamard, *Bulletin des Sciences Mathématiques*, 2 Series (1895), Vol. 19, 1, p. 228.

and it is not immediately evident that the integral is positive. To see that this is true, consider the integrand I as a function of the complex variable u. Its Rieman surface consists of two sheets with poles at $+1$ and -1, and branch points at u_1, u_2, u_3, and ∞. The function is made single valued on this surface by cuts along the real axis: the first cut joins u_2 and u_3, and the second cut joins u_1 to $+\infty$. Now let two circuits C_1 and C_2 be constructed as shown in Fig. 58. The first consists of a circle with

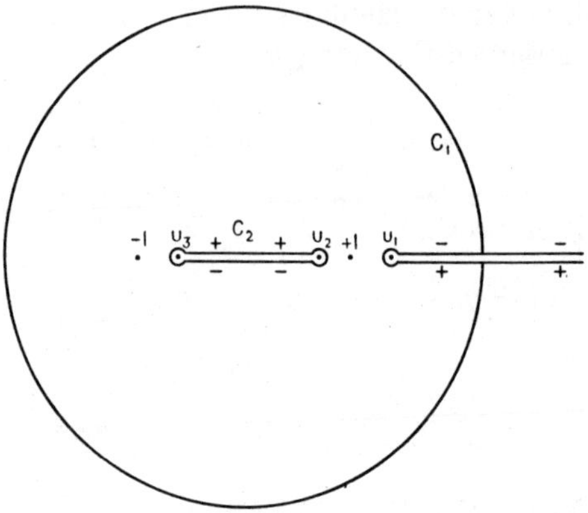

FIG. 58.

large radius about the origin and a narrow lane with a small circle about u_1. The second consists of a narrow lane joining u_2 and u_3 with small circles about these points.

Within the region which is bounded by these two circuits the integrand I is single valued with poles at -1 and $+1$. By Cauchy's theorem the value of the integral taken around the boundary is equal to the sum of the residues of I at the two poles. Let these residues be denoted by $R(-1)$ and $R(+1)$. Then

$$R(-1) = \frac{u_4 + 1}{2} \frac{1}{\sqrt{f(-1)}} = \frac{u_4 + 1}{2i\sqrt{(1 + u_1)(1 + u_2)(1 + u_3)}},$$

and

$$R(+1) = \frac{u_4 - 1}{2} \frac{1}{\sqrt{f(+1)}} = \frac{u_4 - 1}{2i\sqrt{(u_1 - 1)(1 - u_2)(1 - u_3)}}.$$

Since u_4 is less than unity, these residues have opposite signs, and by Eq. (105.4) they are numerically equal. Hence

$$R(+1) + R(-1) = 0,$$

and the value of the integral taken around the entire boundary is zero. Therefore

$$\int_{c_2} = \int_{c_1}, \tag{3}$$

and, since the integral around the large circle vanishes by itself, Eq. (3) reduces to

$$\int_{u_3}^{u_2} I\,du = \int_{u_1}^{+\infty} I\,du.$$

But I is positive for all values of u greater than u_1; therefore the integral is positive, and the precession has the same sign as ω_k.

111. The Integration for the Angle of Spin.—On replacing t by τ, Eq. (104.5) becomes

$$\begin{aligned}\frac{d\varphi}{d\tau} &= \frac{2\omega_k}{\sqrt{a}}\left(1 - bu\frac{u_4 - u}{1 - u^2}\right)\\ &= \frac{2\omega_k}{\sqrt{a}}(1 - b) + \frac{b\omega_k}{\sqrt{a}}\left(\frac{u_4 + 1}{u + 1} + \frac{u_4 - 1}{u - 1}\right).\end{aligned} \tag{1}$$

By the same substitutions that were used in Sec. 108, this equation becomes

$$\left.\begin{aligned}(a)\quad 2i\frac{d\varphi}{d\tau} &= \frac{4\omega_k i}{\sqrt{a}}(1 - b) + \frac{\wp' w}{\wp(\tau + \omega_3) - \wp w} - \frac{\wp' v}{\wp(\tau + \omega_3) - \wp v},\\ (b)\quad 2i\frac{d\varphi}{d\tau} &= \frac{4\omega_k i}{\sqrt{a}}(1 - b) - \frac{\wp' w}{\wp(\tau + \omega_3) - \wp w} - \frac{\wp' v}{\wp(\tau + \omega_3) - \wp v}.\end{aligned}\right\} \tag{2}$$

In case (a) $u_4 > 1$, and in case (b) $u_4 < 1$.

Since

$$\frac{2\omega_k}{\sqrt{a}}(1 - b)\tau = \frac{4\omega_k\omega_1}{\sqrt{a}\,\pi}(1 - b)\xi = q_0\xi,$$

if

$$\frac{4\omega_k\omega_1}{\sqrt{a}\,\pi}(1 - b) = q_0,$$

a comparison of Eqs. (2) with Eqs. (108.4) shows that

$$\text{and}\qquad \left.\begin{aligned}(\varphi - \varphi_0)_a &= q_0\xi + (\psi - \psi_0)_b,\\ (\varphi - \varphi_0)_b &= q_0\xi + (\psi - \psi_0)_a,\end{aligned}\right\} \qquad (3)$$

where the subscripts a and b are used to indicate that $u_4 > 1$ and $u_4 < 1$ respectively.

Equations (3) are formal only, in the sense that the formulas are the same, but if the u_4 that is greater than unity is the reciprocal of the u_4 that is less than unity, not only are the expressions formally the same but they are numerically the same, if the u_2 and u_3 of the one are the same as the u_2 and u_3 of the other.

If u_1, u_2, and u_3 are given, there are two values of u_4 which satisfy all of the conditions of the problem, and these two values of u_4 are mutually reciprocal. The elliptic functions defined in Sec. 106 depend upon u_1, u_2, and u_3 but not upon u_4. On the surface it would appear that the two expressions for $\wp'\omega$ in Eqs. (108.2) depend upon u_4, and so they do formally. But, taking the positive values of ω_k from Eq. (105.6),

$$\frac{2b\omega_k}{\sqrt{a}} = \sqrt{p_2} - \sqrt{p_1} \qquad \text{if} \qquad u_4 > 1,$$

and

$$\frac{2b\omega_k}{\sqrt{a}} = \sqrt{p_2} + \sqrt{p_1}, \qquad \text{if} \qquad u_4 < 1.$$

The corresponding values of u_4 are [Eq. (105.5)]

$$u_{41} = \frac{\sqrt{p_2} + \sqrt{p_1}}{\sqrt{p_2} - \sqrt{p_1}} \qquad \text{and} \qquad u_{42} = \frac{\sqrt{p_2} - \sqrt{p_1}}{\sqrt{p_2} + \sqrt{p_1}}.$$

If these values are substituted in Eqs. (108.2), it is seen that the two expressions for $\wp' w$ are the same, namely,

$$\wp' w = 2i\sqrt{p_1} = 2\sqrt{(1 - u_1)(1 - u_2)(1 - u_3)}.$$

112. Determination of v and w.—There still remains the problem of determining v and w in terms of u_1, u_2, and u_3. It was shown in Sec. 105 that

$$v = in_1, \quad = \omega_3 - in_2, \qquad \text{and} \qquad w = \omega_1 + im_1, \quad = \omega_2 - im_2,$$

where m_j and n_j are real positive constants. Since

$$\wp\tau_1 = u - u_0,$$

and

$$e_k = u_k - u_0,$$

it follows that[1]

$$\wp\tau_1 - e_k = \left(\frac{\sigma_k}{\sigma}\tau_1\right)^2 = u - u_k,$$

so that

$$\frac{\sigma_k}{\sigma}(\tau_1) = \pm\sqrt{u - u_k}. \tag{1}$$

If τ_1 is equal to v, u is equal to -1. On taking $k = 3$, Eq. (1) becomes

$$\frac{\sigma_3}{\sigma}(in_1) = \frac{\sigma_3}{\sigma}(\omega_3 - in_2) = -i\sqrt{1 + u_3}. \tag{2}$$

If τ_1 is equal to w, u is equal to $+1$. On taking $k = 1$ and $k = 2$, it is found that Eq. (1) becomes

$$\frac{\sigma_1}{\sigma}(\omega_1 + im_1) = -i\sqrt{u_1 - 1}, \text{ and } \frac{\sigma_2}{\sigma}(\omega_2 - im_2) = +\sqrt{1 - u_2}. \tag{3}$$

Now[2]

$$\frac{\sigma_1}{\sigma}(+im_1 + \omega_1) = -\sqrt{(e_1 - e_2)(e_1 - e_3)}\frac{\sigma}{\sigma_1}(im_1),$$

$$\frac{\sigma_2}{\sigma}(-im_2 + \omega_2) = -i\sqrt{(e_1 - e_2)(e_2 - e_3)}\frac{\sigma}{\sigma_2}(im_2),$$

$$\frac{\sigma_3}{\sigma}(-in_2 + \omega_3) = -\sqrt{(e_1 - e_3)(e_2 - e_3)}\frac{\sigma}{\sigma_3}(in_2);$$

[1] SCHWARZ, p. 21.
[2] *Idem*, pp. 27, 62.

and

$$\begin{aligned}
\frac{\sigma_3}{\sigma}(in_1) &= \sqrt[4]{(e_1 - e_3)(e_2 - e_3)}\frac{\vartheta_0}{\vartheta_1}(i\nu_1), \\
\frac{\sigma}{\sigma_1}(im_1) &= \frac{1}{\sqrt[4]{(e_1 - e_2)(e_1 - e_3)}}\frac{\vartheta_1}{\vartheta_2}(i\mu_2), \\
\frac{\sigma}{\sigma_2}(im_2) &= \frac{1}{\sqrt[4]{(e_1 - e_2)(e_2 - e_3)}}\frac{\vartheta_1}{\vartheta_3}(i\mu_2), \\
\frac{\sigma}{\sigma_3}(in_2) &= \frac{1}{\sqrt[4]{(e_1 - e_3)(e_2 - e_3)}}\frac{\vartheta_1}{\vartheta_0}(i\nu_2).
\end{aligned}$$

Since

$$e_j - e_k = u_j - u_k,$$

and the expansions of the theta functions are given in Eqs. (109.3), it is found without further difficulty that

$$\frac{\sqrt[4]{(u_1 - u_3)(u_2 - u_3)}}{2h^{\frac{1}{4}}\sqrt{1 + u_3}} = \frac{\sinh \nu_1 - h^2 \sinh 3\nu_1 + h^6 \sinh 5\nu_1 - \cdots}{1 - 2h \cosh 2\nu_1 + 2h^4 \cosh 4\nu_1 - 2h^9 \cosh 6\nu_1 + \cdots}, \tag{4}$$

$$\frac{\sqrt{1 + u_3}}{2h^{\frac{1}{4}}\sqrt[4]{(u_1 - u_3)(u_2 - u_3)}} = \frac{\sinh \nu_2 - h^2 \sinh 3\nu_2 + h^6 \sinh 5\nu_2 - \cdots}{1 - 2h \cosh 2\nu_2 + 2h^4 \cosh 4\nu_2 - 2h^9 \cosh 6\nu_2 + \cdots}, \tag{5}$$

$$\frac{\sqrt{u_1 - 1}}{\sqrt[4]{(u_1 - u_2)(u_1 - u_3)}} = \frac{\sinh \mu_1 - h^2 \sinh 3\mu_1 + h^6 \sinh 5\mu_1 - \cdots}{\cosh \mu_1 + h^2 \cosh 3\mu_1 + h^6 \cosh 5\mu_1 + \cdots}, \tag{6}$$

$$\frac{\sqrt{1 - u_2}}{2h^{\frac{1}{4}}\sqrt[4]{(u_1 - u_2)(u_2 - u_3)}} = \frac{\sinh \mu_2 - h^2 \sinh 3\mu_2 + h^6 \sinh 5\mu_2 - \cdots}{1 + 2h \cosh 2\mu_2 + 2h^4 \cosh 4\mu_2 + 2h^9 \cosh 6\mu_2 + \cdots}. \tag{7}$$

Since h is a known function of u_1, u_2, and u_3, the left members of these equations are known. The series in the right members converge with great rapidity so that there is little difficulty in solving them for μ_j and ν_j by the method of trial and error, but if h is small, so that terms of degree higher than the fourth can be neglected, the third equation can be reduced to a cubic equation in $\tanh \mu_1$, and the others to quartics in $\sinh \mu_2$ or $\sinh \nu_j$.

As for h, it, too, is readily computed by series.[1] Let

$$2l = \frac{\sqrt[4]{u_1 - u_3} - \sqrt[4]{u_1 - u_2}}{\sqrt[4]{u_1 - u_3} + \sqrt[4]{u_1 - u_2}}; \tag{8}$$

then

$$h = l + 2l^5 + 15l^9 + 150l^{13} + \cdots . \tag{9}$$

113. General Properties of the Motion.—A general description of the motion can be obtained from the properties of the differential equations without integration; and even though the integration can be effected, as has just been done, such a study of the motion is valuable.

Imagine a unit sphere drawn about the fixed point of the spinning body as a center. The ζ-axis, which is fixed in the body, pierces the unit sphere in a point, and as the ζ-axis moves about the z-axis, which is fixed in space, this point describes a curve C on the sphere. The principal point of the discussion that follows is to exhibit the character of this curve.

The differential equations referred to are given in Eqs. (104.3) and (104.4), namely,

$$\left.\begin{aligned} u'^2 &= (\alpha - au)(1 - u^2) - b^2\omega_k^2(u_4 - u)^2 = af(u), \\ &= a(u_1 - u)(u_2 - u)(u - u_3), \end{aligned}\right\}$$

and

$$\psi' = b\omega_k \frac{u_4 - u}{1 - u^2},$$

where

$$u = \cos\theta,$$

and

$$u_1 \geqq +1 \geqq u_2 \geqq u \geqq u_3 \geqq -1.$$

The extreme values of u are u_2 and u_3, corresponding to the extreme angles θ_2 and θ_3. Let two cones be constructed with the apex of each at the fixed point with generating angles θ_2 and θ_3 respectively. These two cones intersect the sphere in two circles C_2 and C_3. Since u_3 is less than u_2, the angle θ_3 is greater than the angle θ_2. Therefore the circle C_2 lies above the circle C_3, and the

[1] SCHWARZ, p. 61.

curve C lies on the sphere between these two circles, touching first one and then the other. In case the two circles C_2 and C_3 coincide, the curve C also is a circle, and

$$u = u_2 = u_3.$$

The ζ-axis in this case makes a constant angle with the z-axis; the rate of precession, ψ', is a constant; and Eq. (104.5) shows that the rate of spin, φ', likewise is constant.

If $u_2 \neq u_3$, let the point where the ζ-axis pierces the unit sphere be represented by the arc vector $z\zeta = \theta$ and the angle $xz\zeta$, which is the longitude, λ, of the pole of the $\xi\eta$-plane. The longitude

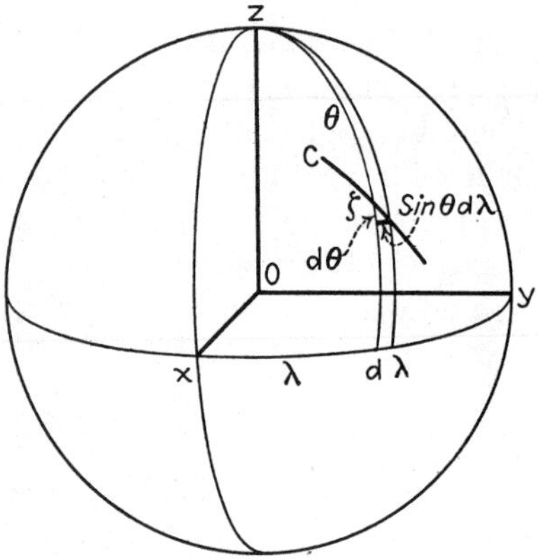

FIG. 59.

of the pole is 90° greater than the longitude of the node (the line of intersection of the $\xi\eta$-plane with the xy-plane), and since the longitude of the node is ψ, it follows that

$$\lambda = \psi + \frac{\pi}{2},$$

and

$$\lambda' = \psi'.$$

Since

$$u' = \sqrt{af(u)},$$

and

$$\lambda' = \psi' = b\omega_k \frac{u_4 - u}{1 - u^2},$$

there follows, by the elimination of t,

$$d\lambda = \frac{b\omega_k(u_4 - u)}{(1 - u^2)\sqrt{af(u)}}\,du, \tag{1}$$

which is the differential equation of the locus of ζ, or the curve C.

Let γ be the angle which the curve C makes with the arc vector $z\zeta$ (Fig. 59). It is seen from the figure that

$$\tan\gamma = \frac{d\lambda}{d\theta}\sin\theta,$$

or

$$\tan\gamma = -(1 - u^2)\frac{d\lambda}{du}.$$

Therefore, from Eq. (1),

$$\tan\gamma = -\frac{b\omega_k(u_4 - u)}{\sqrt{a(u - u_3)(u - u_2)(u - u_1)}}, \tag{2}$$

and it is evident that $\tan\gamma$ is infinite whenever u is equal to u_3 or u_2. Therefore the curve C is tangent to the circle C_3 or C_2 whenever u has one of its limiting values. This is certainly true unless the numerator of the right member of Eq. (2) vanishes at the same time that the denominator does; that is, u_4 is equal to either u_3 or u_2. In this event, $\tan\gamma$ vanishes instead of becoming infinite, for the numerator vanishes in the order one, while the denominator vanishes in the order one half. Thus the curve C has a cusp on the circle for which this happens.

If u_4 does not lie in the interval between u_3 and u_2, λ' never vanishes and never becomes infinite. It therefore never changes sign, and the ζ-axis moves around the z-axis always in the same direction. The curve is shown in Fig. 60 for $\theta_2 = 30°$ and $\theta_3 = 70°$, for which $u_2 = .8660$ and $u_3 = .3420$. The values of u_4 and u_1 are $u_4 = .91$ and $u_1 = 1.135$. The precession in the curve C is 266.°15 for the complete period.

If u_4 lies between u_3 and u_2, $d\lambda/du$ vanishes and changes sign at the point $u = u_4$. It has therefore one sign on the upper circle, and the opposite sign on the lower circle. The curve C, which is still tangent to C_2 and C_3, describes loops, as is shown in Fig. 61. In this figure $\theta_2 = 30°$ and $\theta_3 = 70°$, as before; but $u_1 = 2.096$ and $u_4 = .80$. The precession in the curve C is 99.°04.

Finally, if $u_4 = u_2$, the curve C has a cusp on the circle C_2, as is shown in Fig. 62. In this figure $\theta_2 = 30°$, $\theta_3 = 70°$, $u_1 = 1.3432$, $u_4 = u_2 = .8660$, and the precession in the curve C is 188.°37.

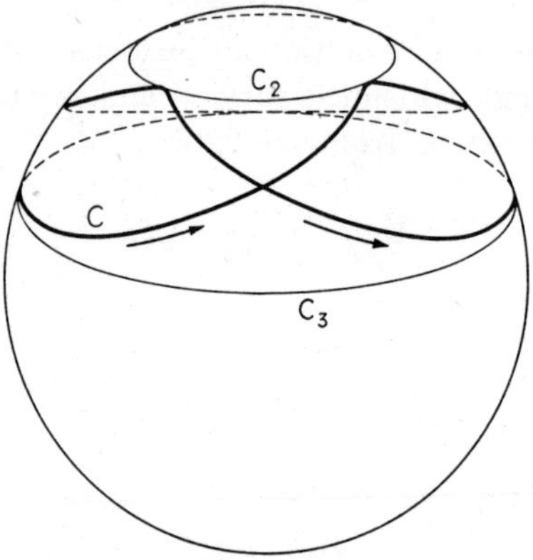

Fig. 60.

In these three diagrams $u_2 = .8660$ and $u_3 = .3420$ have been kept fixed. Therefore, Sec. 105, u_4 is limited to the range

$$.684 < u_4 < 1.462,$$

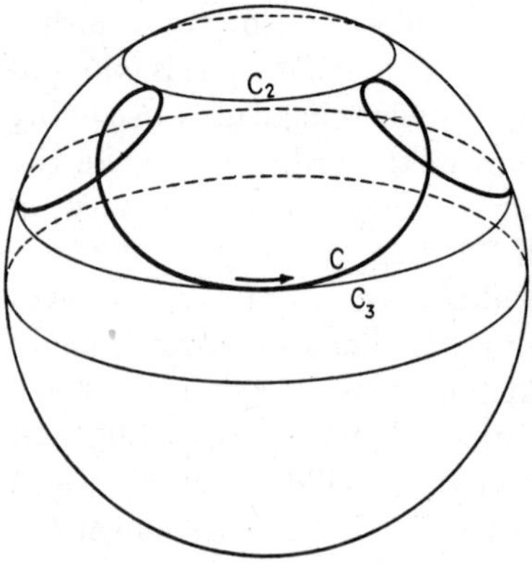

Fig. 61.

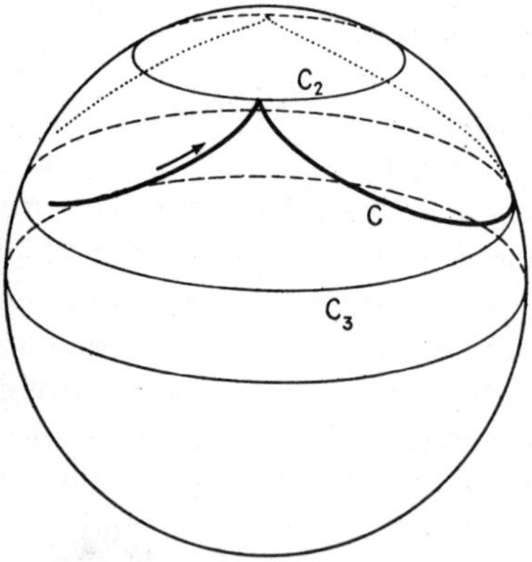

Fig. 62.

and u_4 cannot equal u_3. Indeed, u_4 can never equal u_3, and there can never be a cusp on the lower circle. In order to show that this is true, retake Eq. (105.4),

$$\left(\frac{1 - u_4}{1 + u_4}\right)^2 = \frac{u_1 - 1}{u_1 + 1}\frac{1 - u_2}{1 + u_2}\frac{1 - u_3}{1 + u_3}, \tag{3}$$

and set $u_4 = u_3$. A factor $(1 - u_3)/(1 + u_3)$ can then be removed, leaving

$$\frac{1 - u_3}{1 + u_3} = \frac{u_1 - 1}{u_1 + 1}\frac{1 - u_2}{1 + u_2}. \tag{4}$$

But this is impossible, for, since $u_3 < u_2$, necessarily

$$\frac{1 - u_3}{1 + u_3} > \frac{1 - u_2}{1 + u_2},$$

which contradicts Eq. (4), since

$$0 < \frac{u_1 - 1}{u_1 + 1} < +1.$$

Therefore u_4 cannot equal u_3, and there cannot be a cusp on the lower circle.

114. The Common Top.—Aside from element of friction, this theory applies, of course, to the common top when the point of the top is kept fixed, but not when the point slides as it will when spinning on a plate of glass. Suppose, by way of illustration that a rapidly spinning top is released gently so that its axis, initially at rest, makes an angle θ_0 with the vertical. At the initial instant, ω_k is the rate of spin and ω_i and ω_j are zero. If $u_0 = \cos\theta_0$, Eqs. (103.6) give

$$\alpha = au_0, \qquad \frac{\beta}{b\omega_k} \equiv u_4 = u_0,$$

and these values, substituted in Eq. (104.3) give

$$\begin{aligned} u'^2 &= a(u_0 - u)(1 - u^2) - b^2\omega_k^2(u_0 - u)^2 \\ &= (u_0 - u)[a(1 - u^2) - b^2\omega_k^2(u_0 - u)]. \end{aligned}$$

Thus u_0 is one of the roots of $f(u)$; the other u_j, that marks the limit of the variation of u, is a root of the bracket, that is

$$a(1 - u_j^2) - b^2\omega_k^2(u_0 - u_j) = 0;$$

whence

$$u_0 - u_j = \frac{a}{b^2\omega_k^2}(1 - u_j^2). \tag{1}$$

Since u_j^2 is less than unity, the right member of this expression is positive, and u_j is less than u_0. Hence

$$u_0 = u_2 \qquad \text{and} \qquad u_j = u_3,$$

and since u_4 also is equal to u_2, the case is one in which there is a cusp on the upper circle; also, the faster the spin, the smaller is the variation in u.

The expression for ψ',

$$\psi' = b\omega_k \frac{u_2 - u}{1 - u^2}, \tag{2}$$

shows that as the top falls it begins to precess, and the precession is always positive, or zero, if ω_k is positive.

If ω_k is large [Eq. (1)]

$$u_2 - u_3 = \frac{a}{b\omega_k}(1 - u_3^2),$$

shows that u_2 differs but little from u_3, so that the two circles C_2 and C_3 are very nearly together. The precession is slow; for, in view of the fact that

$$u_2 - u < u_2 - u_3 = \frac{a(1 - u_3^2)}{b^2\omega_k^2},$$

Eq. (2) gives

$$\psi' < \frac{a(1 - u_3^2)}{b\omega_k(1 - u^2)}.$$

The fraction

$$\frac{1 - u_3^2}{1 - u^2}$$

differs but little from unity, and therefore approximately

$$\psi' = \frac{a}{b\omega_k}.$$

Hence the faster the spin the slower the precession, and conversely.

As friction and air resistance diminish the rate of spin, ω_k decreases and the distance between the circles C_2 and C_3 increases. There is more vertical motion and precession becomes faster.

Finally the angle θ becomes so large that the top touches the ground and begins to roll.

The rate of spin of the top is given by the equation

$$\varphi' = \omega_k - u\psi'.$$

On the upper circle $\psi' = 0$, and $\varphi' = \omega_k$, which is the maximum value. On the lower circle ψ' has its maximum value, and therefore φ' its minimum value. The top spins fastest when most nearly vertical.

115. The Sleeping Top.—Suppose the upper circle C_2 shrinks to a point on the ζ-axis; then $u_2 = 1$, and

$$u' = \pm\sqrt{a(1 - u)(u_1 - u)(u - u_3)}. \tag{1}$$

Equation (105.4) shows that both values of u_4 also are equal to $+1$, and Eq. (105.1) that

$$\omega_k^2 = \frac{a}{2b^2}(1 + u_1)(1 + u_3). \tag{2}$$

If $u_3 = -1$, ω_k is zero, and the body becomes a compound pendulum in which the amplitude of the oscillation is π, and therefore an infinite time is required for a single oscillation; or, it hangs from the point of suspension in a state of rest (stable equilibrium) in which $u = -1$; or it stands upright on the fixed point in a state of rest (unstable equilibrium) in which $u = +1$.

If u_3 is different from -1 and fixed in value, the problem contains the single parameter u_1. The equation of precession becomes

$$\psi' = b\omega_k\frac{1 - u}{1 - u^2} = \frac{b\omega_k}{1 + u}, \tag{3}$$

and

$$\varphi' = \omega_k - u\psi'. \tag{4}$$

It is evident from Eq. (2) that ω_k^2 increases with u_1, and that its smallest value is given by $u_1 = 1$. For this value Eq. (1) becomes

$$u' = \pm\sqrt{a}(1 - u)\sqrt{u - u_3},$$

the general solution of which is

$$u - u_3 = (1 - u_3)\tanh^2 \tfrac{1}{2}\sqrt{1 - u_3^2}(t - t_0). \tag{5}$$

The top requires an infinite time to rise from C_3 to the vertical position for every $u_3 < 1$. But if $u_1 > 1$, the three roots of Eq. (1) are distinct, and the ζ-axis oscillates between the circle C_3 and the pole, but the time required is finite. Furthermore,

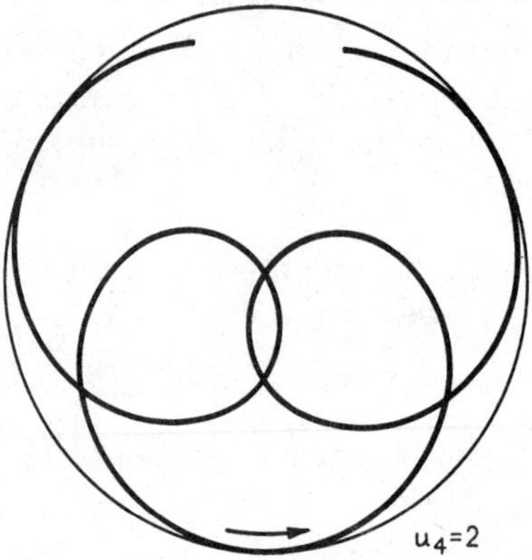

FIG. 63.

the ζ-axis does not approach the pole with a zero velocity; for, although u' [Eq. (1)] vanishes for $u = 1$,

$$\theta' = -\frac{u'}{\sqrt{1-u^2}} = \pm\sqrt{\frac{a(u_1 - 1)(u - u_3)}{1 + u}}$$

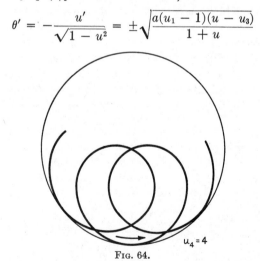

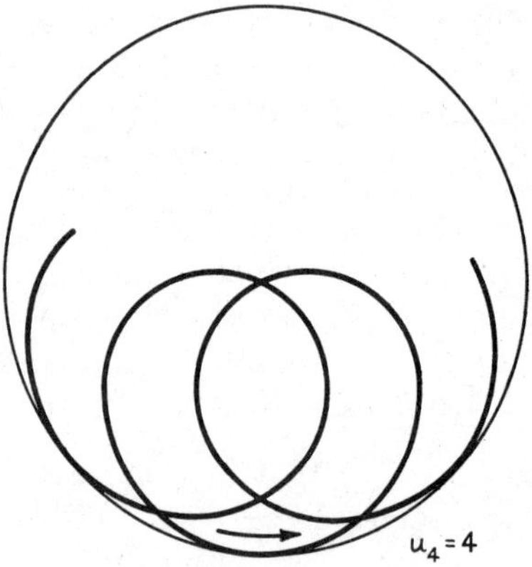

FIG. 64.

does not vanish. When the angle θ passes through zero the ascending node changes to the descending node, and if ψ designates always the ascending node, it is necessary to suppose that ψ jumps $\pm 180°$, and θ is then always positive. But if ψ always designates the same node, irrespective of its ascending or descending character, θ oscillates from $+\theta_3$ to $-\theta_3$ and back again, and there is no discontinuity.

In Figs. 63 and 64 the projections of the curves C upon the plane of the equator are shown for $\theta_2 = 0$ and $\theta_3 = 30°$. In Fig. 63 the value of u_1 is 2 and in Fig. 63 the value of u_1 is 4. In both cases $u_4 = 1$, Eqs. (105.4).

Finally if u_3 also is equal to $+1$, the oscillations cease and the top remains stationary in the vertical. It is said to "sleep." Equations (85.4) show that $\omega_i = \omega_j = 0$, and Eq. (2) then shows that

$$\omega = \omega_k = \frac{1}{b}\sqrt{a(1 + u_1)}.$$

The motion is evidently stable. The angles φ and ψ cease to have any significance and ω is the rate of spin.

116. The Steady State of Motion.—It has been noticed that if the circles C_2 and C_3 approach coincidence, u approaches a constant value, and so also do ψ' and φ'; the top spins and precesses in a steady state of motion and the axis of the top preserves a constant angle with the vertical. It will be of interest to examine the limiting values of these functions as u_2 tends toward u_3.

From the definition of l in Eq. (112.8) it will be observed that l and therefore h also vanishes if $u_2 = u_3$. Equation (107.7) gives at once

$$u = u_3;$$

since $\xi \rightarrow \sqrt{u_1 - u_3}\,\tau$, and $\sin \xi$ is finite. Equations (109.8) show that λ_0 and λ_3 also vanish, so that Eqs. (108.9) become

$$(a) \qquad \psi - \psi_0 = (q_1 + q_2)\sqrt{u_1 - u_3}\,\tau,$$

$$(b) \qquad \psi - \psi_0 = (q_1 - q_2)\sqrt{u_1 - u_3}\,\tau,$$

provided q_1 and q_2 remain finite.

Equation (112.6) reduces to

$$\tanh \mu_1 = \sqrt{\frac{u_1 - 1}{u_1 - u_3}}, \qquad (1)$$

and Eq. (112.4) gives

$$\sinh \nu_1 = \lim \frac{\sqrt[4]{(u_1 - u_3)(u_2 - u_3)}}{2h^{\frac{1}{4}}\sqrt{1 + u_3}};$$

or, on setting,

$$h = \frac{1}{2}\frac{\sqrt[4]{u_1 - u_3} - \sqrt[4]{u_1 - u_2}}{\sqrt[4]{u_1 - u_3} + \sqrt{u_1 - u_2}},$$

$$\sinh \nu_1 = \lim \frac{\sqrt[4]{u_1 - u_3}}{2\sqrt{1 + u_3}}\left[\frac{4(u_2 - u_3)\sqrt[4]{u_1 - u_3}}{\sqrt[4]{u_1 - u_3} - \sqrt[4]{u_1 - u_2}}\right]^{\frac{1}{4}}$$

$$= \frac{\sqrt[4]{u_1 - u_3}}{2\sqrt{1 + u_3}}\sqrt[4]{16}\sqrt[4]{u_1 - u_3} = \frac{\sqrt{u_1 - u_3}}{\sqrt{1 + u_3}},$$

from which it follows that at the limit

$$\coth \nu_1 = \sqrt{\frac{u_1 + 1}{u_1 - u_3}}. \tag{2}$$

From Eqs. (109.9) and Eqs. (1) and (2), it is found that the limiting values of q_1 and q_2 are

$$q_1 = \sqrt{\frac{u_1 + 1}{u_1 - u_3}}, \qquad q_2 = \sqrt{\frac{u_1 - 1}{u_1 - u_3}}.$$

Hence the expressions for the precession reduce to

$$\left.\begin{aligned}
(a)\quad \psi - \psi_0 &= [\sqrt{u_1 + 1} + \sqrt{u_1 - 1}]\tau \\
&= \frac{\sqrt{a}}{2}[\sqrt{u_1 + 1} + \sqrt{u_1 - 1}](t - t_0), \\
(b)\quad \psi - \psi_0 &= [\sqrt{u_1 + 1} - \sqrt{u_1 - 1}]\tau \\
&= \frac{\sqrt{a}}{2}[\sqrt{u_1 + 1} - \sqrt{u_1 - 1}](t - t_0);
\end{aligned}\right\} \tag{3}$$

which agree with the results obtained directly from Eq. (104.4).

Turning now to the angle of spin [Eq. (110.3)], it is found that

$$q_0\xi = \omega_k(1 - b)(t - t_0);$$

and, if the positive values of ω_k are taken from Eq. (106.6),

$$\left.\begin{aligned}
(a)\quad q_0\xi &= \frac{\sqrt{a}}{2}\left(\frac{1}{b} - 1\right) \times \\
&\quad [(1 + u_3)\sqrt{u_1 + 1} - (1 - u_3)\sqrt{u_1 - 1}](t - t_0), \\
(b)\quad q_0\xi &= \frac{\sqrt{a}}{2}\left(\frac{1}{b} - 1\right) \times \\
&\quad [(1 + u_3)\sqrt{u_1 + 1} + (1 - u_3)\sqrt{u_1 - 1}](t - t_0).
\end{aligned}\right\} \tag{4}$$

Hence

$$\varphi - \varphi_0 = \left\{ \begin{aligned} &\frac{\sqrt{a}}{2b}[(1 + u_3)\sqrt{u_1 + 1} \pm (1 - u_3)\sqrt{u_1 - 1}] \\ &\quad - \frac{\sqrt{a}u_3}{2}[\sqrt{u_1 + 1} \mp \sqrt{u_1 - 1}]\right\}(t - t_0), \end{aligned} \right. \tag{5}$$

the upper signs to be used in case b, $u_4 < 1$, and the lower signs to be used in case a, $u_4 > 1$.

The constants a and b depend only upon the body and the position of the fixed point. It will be observed that in the case of steady motion the precession depends only upon a and the root u_1 [Eqs. (3)]. The constant b and the root u_3 do not appear; but all four of these quantities appear in the rate of spin [Eq.(5)].

117. Jacobi's Theorem on Relative Motion.—At the end of the second volume of Jacobi's collected works there are three previously unpublished "Fragments" in which Jacobi develops certain phases of Lagrange's case of a spinning body. In the second of these "Fragments," B, there is stated without proof the following very remarkable theorem:

Jacobi's Theorem.—The rotation of any heavy body of revolution about any point of its axis can be replaced by the relative motion of two non-accelerated bodies (Euler's case) which are turning about the same fixed point and which in their rotations have the same invariable plane and the same mean oscillatory motion.

According to the editor of these "Fragments," E. Lottner, it would seem that just previous to his death Jacobi had in mind a complete memoir on Lagrange's case, but his studies were never completed. Nevertheless there was sufficient material in these "Fragments" to enable Lottner to construct a proof, which will be found in Vol. II, p. 510, of Jacobi's Collected Works; published in 1882. Jacobi's proof probably depended upon the properties of the elliptic functions.

In Vol. C of the *Comptes Rendus*, Halphan restated the theorem, remarking that Jacobi's statement was defective. In the *Journal de Mathématiques* (1885) the theorem is again restated by Darboux, as follows: *Consider a heavy body (P) of revolution fixed at the point O. At every instant a system C with axes Ox_1, Oy_1, Oz_1 moving about the point O can be determined in such a way that both the absolute motion of C and its motion relative to P shall* *be identical with the motion of a solid body, fixed at the point O, which is not acted upon by any applied force. In the first of these motions the invariable plane is a horizontal plane; and in the second it is the plane perpendicular to the axis of the body.*

Darboux continues,

However, it is necessary to understand that in the two motions of C the moments of inertia are different, and that they do not necessarily satisfy the inequalities which characterize the moments of inertia of a real body. They are motions which satisfy the equations of Euler where the constants A, B, and C can be regarded as taking any values whatever. On recalling the geometric representation of Poinsot it can be said that these motions would be reproduced not by making an ellipsoid of inertia roll on a plane, but any ellipsoid whatever or even any central surface of the second order.

The reader who is interested in pursuing the matter farther is referred to a volume entitled "*Résumé de la théorie du mouvement d'un corps solide autour d'un point fixe*" (1887) by A. de Saint-Germain and a note by Greenhill at the end of *l'Annuaire des Mathématiciens* (1902).

III. THE CASE OF MME. KOWALESKI

118. The Differential Equations.—If, aside from the constraint, the only force acting upon the body is its weight, the moment of all of the forces with respect to the fixed point O is

$$\mathbf{N} = M\mathbf{G} \times \mathbf{g} = +Mg\begin{vmatrix} \mathbf{i} & \mathbf{j} & \mathbf{k} \\ \gamma_1 & \gamma_2 & \gamma_3 \\ \bar{\xi} & \bar{\eta} & \bar{\zeta} \end{vmatrix},$$

where $\bar{\xi}$, $\bar{\eta}$, $\bar{\zeta}$ are the coordinates of the center of gravity, and γ_1, γ_2, γ_3 are the direction cosines of the ξ-, η-, ζ-axes with respect to the fixed z-axis. Hence Euler's equations [Eq. (85.3)] become

$$\left.\begin{aligned} A\omega_i' + (C - B)\omega_j\omega_k &= Mg(\gamma_2\bar{\zeta} - \gamma_3{}^{-}), \\ B\omega_j' + (A - C)\omega_k\omega_i &= Mg(\gamma_3\bar{\xi} - \gamma_1\bar{\zeta}), \\ C\omega_k' + (B - A)\omega_i\omega_j &= Mg(\gamma_1\bar{\eta} - \gamma_2\bar{\xi}). \end{aligned}\right\} \tag{1}$$

Since the center of gravity is fixed in the body, $\bar{\xi}$; $\bar{\eta}$, ζ are constants, and the only variables that occur in these equations, aside from the angular velocities ω_i, ω_j, ω_k, are the direction cosines γ_1, γ_2, and γ_3.

Consider a fixed point on the fixed z-axis at a unit distance from the fixed point O. Relative to the ξ-, η-, ζ-axes that are fixed in the body its coordinates are γ_1, γ_2, and γ_3. Its absolute velocity, which is zero, is the sum of its relative velocity plus the velocity of following (Sec. 80). Hence if $\boldsymbol{\varrho}$ is its position vector

$$\boldsymbol{\varrho}' + \boldsymbol{\omega} \times \boldsymbol{\varrho} = 0,$$

or

$$\boldsymbol{\varrho}' = \begin{vmatrix} \mathbf{i} & \mathbf{j} & \mathbf{k} \\ \gamma_1 & \gamma_2 & \gamma_3 \\ \omega_i & \omega_j & \omega_k \end{vmatrix};$$

and since

$$\boldsymbol{\varrho} = \gamma_1\mathbf{i} + \gamma_2\mathbf{j} + \gamma_3\mathbf{k},$$

it follows readily that

$$\left.\begin{aligned} \gamma_1' &= \gamma_2\omega_k - \gamma_3\omega_j, \\ \gamma_2' &= \gamma_3\omega_i - \gamma_1\omega_k, \\ \gamma_3' &= \gamma_1\omega_j - \gamma_2\omega_i. \end{aligned}\right\} \tag{2}$$

Equations (1) and (2) form a complete set of differential equations for the variables ω_i, ω_j, ω_k; γ_1, γ_2, and γ_3: but they are not sufficient to define the motion, since γ_1, γ_2, and γ_3 do not depend upon the angle of precession ψ. It is necessary to add the equation of precession, Eq. (85.5)

$$\sin\theta\,\psi' = \omega_i \sin\varphi + \omega_j \cos\varphi. \tag{3}$$

It is evident at once that Eqs. (2) admit the integral

$$\gamma_1^2 + \gamma_2^2 + \gamma_3^2 = 1. \tag{4}$$

which must be satisfied since γ_1, γ_2, and γ_3 are the direction cosines of a line.

Equations (1) admit two integrals that were derived in Sec. 86, namely the energy integral

$$A\omega_i^2 + B\omega_j^2 + C\omega_k^2 = -2Mg\bar{z} + \text{constant}, \tag{5}$$

and the integral of angular momentum

$$A\gamma_1\omega_i + B\gamma_2\omega_j + C\gamma_3\omega_k = \text{constant}. \tag{6}$$

Thus three of the six integrals for the system of Eqs. (1) and (2) are known for every case.

119. The Existence of a Fourth Integral.—It was discovered by Mme. Kowaleski that a fourth integral can be found if the conditions

$$A = B = 2C, \qquad \text{and} \qquad \bar{\zeta} = 0$$

are satisfied. Assuming these conditions, the ξ-axis can be directed so that it passes through the center of gravity and therefore $\bar{\eta}$ also is equal to zero. If in addition, the units are chosen so that

$$\frac{Mg\bar{\xi}}{C} = 1,$$

the differential equations [Eq. (118.1)] become

$$\left.\begin{aligned} 2\omega_i' &= +\omega_j\omega_k, & \gamma_1' &= \gamma_2\omega_k - \gamma_3\omega_j, \\ 2\omega_j' &= -\omega_k\omega_i + \gamma_3, & \gamma_2' &= \gamma_3\omega_i - \gamma_1\omega_k, \\ \omega_k' &= \quad 0 - \gamma_2, & \gamma_3' &= \gamma_1\omega_j - \gamma_2\omega_i, \end{aligned}\right\} \qquad (1)$$

in which the coefficients are purely numerical; and the integrals take the form

$$\left.\begin{aligned} 2\omega_i^2 + 2\omega_j^2 + \omega_k^2 &= C_1 - 2\gamma_1, \\ 2\gamma_1\omega_i + 2\gamma_2\omega_j + \gamma_3\omega_k &= C_2, \\ \gamma_1^2 + \gamma_2^2 + \gamma_3^2 &= 1. \end{aligned}\right\} \qquad (2)$$

If the second equation in the first column of Eqs. (1) is multiplied by $i = \sqrt{-1}$ and added to the first, and the same thing is done in the second column, there results

$$\left.\begin{aligned} 2(\omega_i + i\omega_j)' &= -i\omega_k(\omega_i + i\omega_j) + i\gamma_3, \\ (\gamma_1 + i\gamma_2)' &= -i\omega_k(\gamma_1 + i\gamma_2) + i\gamma_3(\omega_i + i\omega_j). \end{aligned}\right\} \qquad (3)$$

If the first of Eqs. (3) is multiplied by $(\omega_i + i\omega_j)$ and the second is subtracted from it, γ_3 is eliminated, and there results

$$\frac{d}{dt}[(\omega_i + i\omega_j)^2 - (\gamma_1 + i\gamma_2)] = -i\omega_k[(\omega_i + i\omega_j)^2 - (\gamma_1 + i\gamma_2)],$$

or again,

$$\frac{d}{dt}\log\,[(\omega_i + i\omega_j)^2 - (\gamma_1 + i\gamma_2)] = -i\omega_k.$$

Likewise, by changing i into $-i$,

$$\frac{d}{dt}\log\,[(\omega_i - i\omega_j)^2 - (\gamma_1 - i\gamma_2)] = +i\omega_k;$$

therefore, by addition,

$$\frac{d}{dt} \log [(\omega_i + i\omega_j)^2 - (\gamma_1 + i\gamma_2)][(\omega_i - i\omega_j)^2 - (\gamma_1 - i\gamma_2)] = 0.$$

By integration, it is seen that

$$[(\omega_i + i\omega_j)^2 - (\gamma_1 + i\gamma_2)][(\omega_i - i\omega_j)^2 - (\gamma_1 - i\gamma_2)] = c_3,$$

or, in a real form,

$$(\omega_i^2 - \omega_j^2 - \gamma_1)^2 + (2\omega_i\omega_j - \gamma_2)^2 = c_3,$$

which is a new algebraic integral.

In Mme. Kowaleski's memoir it is shown that $\omega_i, \omega_j, \omega_k; \gamma_1, \gamma_2, \gamma_3$ can be expressed in terms of two auxiliary functions s_1 and s_2 that are hyperelliptic functions of the time, but the demonstration is too long for insertion here. Her memoir will be found in Vol. 12 of *Acta Mathematica* (1888). In Vol. 17 of the same journal (1893), Fritz Kötter in dealing with the same problem has effected noteworthy simplifications, but the problem is still very complicated. A discussion of the problem by G. Kolossoff will be found in Vol. 56 of *Mathematische Annalen* (1903). Kolossoff reduces the problem to two differential equations, each of the second order, which can be regarded as the equations of motion of a particle which moves under the action of two forces which are directed toward two fixed points in the plane. These equations are integrated by the method of Hamilton-Jacobi.

A list of references to the literature of Mme. Kowaleski's problem is given by Whittaker.[1]

Problems

1. If the left members of Eqs. (4), (5), (6), and (7) in Sec. 112 are denoted by a_4, a_5, a_6, and a_7 respectively, show that, if $\nu_1 = \nu_2 = -\frac{1}{4} \log h$,

$$a_4 = a_5 = 1;$$

and if $\mu_1 = \mu_2 = -\frac{1}{4} \log h$,

$$a_6 = a_7 = \frac{1 - h^{\frac{1}{2}} - h^{\frac{3}{2}} + h^{\frac{6}{2}} + h^{\frac{10}{2}} - h^{\frac{15}{2}} - h^{\frac{21}{2}} + \cdots}{1 + h^{\frac{1}{2}} + h^{\frac{3}{2}} + h^{\frac{6}{2}} + h^{\frac{10}{2}} + h^{\frac{15}{2}} + h^{\frac{21}{2}} + \cdots}.$$

2. If the left number of Eq. (112.6) is denoted by a and if

$$x = \frac{4h^2}{1 + h^2}, \qquad t = \tanh \mu_1,$$

[1] "Analytical Dynamics," 3d ed., p. 166.

the solution of the cubic

$$t^3 - a(1 - x)t^2 - (1 - x)t + a = 0$$

gives the value of tanh μ_1 correctly up to terms of degree 6 in h.

3. If

$$s = \sinh \nu_1 \qquad \text{and} \qquad b = \frac{\sqrt[4]{(u_1 - u_3)(u_2 - u_3)}}{2h^{\frac{1}{4}}\sqrt{1 + u_3}},$$

the quartic equation

$$16bh^4s^4 + 4h^2s^3 - 4bh(1 - 4h^3)s^2 - (1 - 3h^2)s + b(1 - 2h + 2h^2) = 0$$

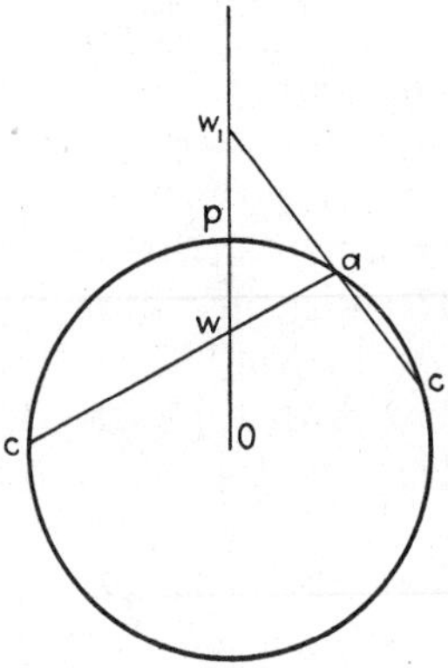

FIG. 65.

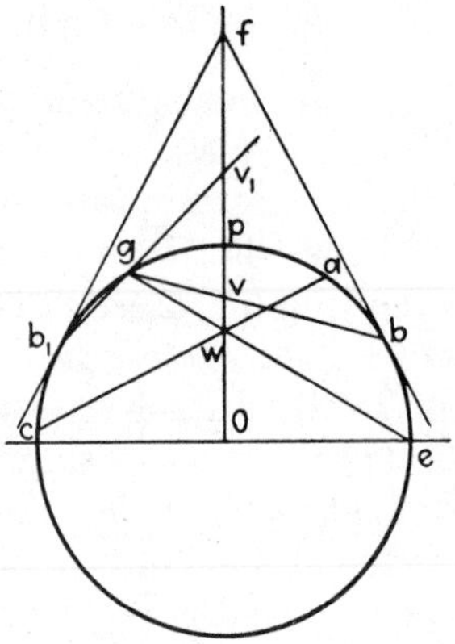

FIG. 66.

gives the correct value of sinh ν_1 up to terms of degree 5 in h. Show that the solution of this equation as a power series in h is

$$s = b(1 + s_1h + s_2h^2 + s_3h^3 + s_4h^4 + \cdots),$$

where

$$\begin{aligned} s_1 &= -2 - 4b^2, \\ s_2 &= +3 + 20b^2 + 32b^4, \\ s_3 &= -6 - 76b^2 - 272b^4 - 320b^6, \\ s_4 &= +11 + 256b^2 + 1{,}568b^4 + 3{,}904b^6 + 3{,}584b^8. \end{aligned}$$

4. In Fig. 65 O is the center of a circle of unit radius. The arc pa is equal to θ_2 and the arcs pc and pc_1 are each equal to θ_3. Draw the chord ca and the secant c_1a intersecting the line Op in the points w and w_1. Let u_4 be a point on the line Op, extended if necessary, such that the length Ou_4 is equal to the number u_4, Sec. 105. Prove that for $\xi < 1$ the point u_4 lies in the interval ww_1.

How is this construction modified for the case $\xi > 1$? (Bartky.)

5. Given u_1, u_2, and u_3, show that the two values of u_4 are given by the following geometrical construction (Fig. 66): With O as the center of a unit circle, draw Of equal to u_1, then the two tangents fb and fb_1, and the two arcs $pa = \theta_2$, $pc = \theta_3$. The chord ac intersects the line Op at w, just as in Fig. 65.

Take the arc $pe = 90°$, and let g be the point where the chord through e and w cuts the circle again. The two values of u_4 are the points of intersection of the chords bg and b_1g with the line Of.

This construction will serve for the determination of any one of the four quantities u_1, u_2, u_3, u_4, if the other three are given. (Bartky.)

6. If the fixed point is at the center of gravity, show that the cone

$$\frac{\xi^2}{a^2 - d^2} + \frac{\eta^2}{b^2 - d^2} + \frac{\zeta^2}{c^2 - d^2} = 0,$$

which is fixed in the body, rolls without slipping upon a plane through O parallel to the fixed plane. (Poinsot, p. 305.)

7. A uniform straight rod of length a is constrained to move on a right circular cone the generating angle of which is α, pivoting at the apex of the cone. If the axis of the cone makes an angle β with the vertical show that the angular motion of the rod around the axis of the cone is the same as that of a simple pendulum of length $\frac{2}{3}a \sin \alpha/\sin \beta$.

8. The coordinates of the extremity of the vector ω with respect to the axes fixed in the body are ω_i, ω_j, and ω_k. Since, in Lagrange's case, ω_k is constant, the terminus of α lies in a plane which is perpendicular to the ξ-axis and fixed in the body, and ω traces a curve in this plane, and a cone in the body. If ρ and υ are the polar coordinates of this curve, show that

$$\rho^2 = \alpha - au,$$

and

$$\rho^2\frac{d\upsilon}{dt} = \frac{1}{2}\omega_k(b - 2)\rho^2 + \frac{1}{2}b\omega_k(\alpha - au_4).$$

9. If ω_x, ω_y, and ω_z are the coordinates of the terminus of ω in fixed space, that is, relative to the set of fixed axes x, y, z, show that

$$\omega_x = +\varphi' \sin \theta \sin \psi + \theta' \cos \psi, \qquad \omega_y = -\varphi' \sin \theta \cos \psi + \theta' \sin \psi,$$
$$\omega_z = \varphi' \cos \theta + \varphi',$$

and then

$$(1 - b)\omega_k(\omega_x^2 + \omega_y^2 + \omega_z^2) + a\omega_z = (1 - b)(\alpha + \omega_k^2) + a\beta.$$

where a, b, and β are the constants defined in Eq. (103.7). This equation shows that in fixed space the terminus of ω traces a curve that lies on a sphere whose center lies on the z-axis below the origin. Since there is no motion of the instantaneous axis, the plane curve that is fixed in the body rolls without slipping on the spherical curve that is fixed in fixed space.

In the particular case in which the ellipsoid of inertia is a sphere, $b = 1$, and the above sphere becomes the plane $\omega_z = u_4$.

10. If a body is acted upon by no forces other than a couple whose axis is always parallel and proportional to the angular momentum, Euler's equations are

$$A\omega_i' + (C - B)\omega_j\omega_k = \lambda A\omega_i,$$
$$B\omega_j' + (A - C)\omega_k\omega_i = \lambda B\omega_j,$$
$$C\omega_k' + (B - A)\omega_i\omega_j = \lambda C\omega_k.$$

The transformation

$$\omega_i = e^{-\lambda t}\omega_i, \qquad \omega_j = e^{-\lambda t}\omega_j, \qquad \omega_k = e^{-\lambda t}\omega_k, \qquad \lambda\tau = 1 - e^{-\lambda t}$$

removes the right numbers of these equations without otherwise altering their form. (Greenhill, "Elliptic Functions," p. 106.)

11. A sphere which is homogeneous in concentric layers is turning about its center, which is fixed, under the action of no forces. A brake is applied to the surface at a point that is constant in fixed space. What are the equations of motion after the brake is applied?

Ans. If the z-axis in fixed space is chosen so as to pass through the brake, the equations of motion are

$$\begin{aligned} \omega_i' &= \mu[(\gamma_1^2 - 1)\omega_i + \gamma_1\gamma_2\omega_j + \gamma_1\gamma_3\omega_k], \\ \omega_j' &= \mu[\gamma_1\gamma_2\omega_i + (\gamma_2^2 - 1)\omega_j + \gamma_2\gamma_3\omega_k], \\ \omega_k' &= \mu[\gamma_1\gamma_3\omega_i + \gamma_2\gamma_3\omega_j + (\gamma_3^2 - 1)\omega_k], \end{aligned}$$

where μ is a positive constant, and

$$\gamma_1' = \gamma_2\omega_k - \gamma_3\omega_j, \qquad \gamma_2' = \gamma_3\omega_i - \gamma_1\omega_k, \qquad \gamma_3' = \gamma_1\omega_j - \gamma_2\omega_i.$$

These equations are interesting because they are linear in the ω's. There are two integrals, namely,

$$\gamma_1^2 + \gamma_2^2 + \gamma_3^2 = 1,$$

and

$$\gamma_1\omega_1 + \gamma_2\omega_2 + \gamma_3\omega_3 = c;$$

and since

$$\tfrac{1}{2}(\omega_i^2 + \omega_j^2 + \omega_k^2)' = -\mu(\gamma_1'^2 + \gamma_2'^2 + \gamma_3'^2),$$

the kinetic energy steadily decreases.

12. Show that the problem of a rigid body which is turning about a fixed point admits the integrals

$$\begin{aligned} A\omega_i^2 + B\omega_j^2 + C\omega_k^2 &= 2h, \\ (A\omega_i + a)^2 + (B\omega_j^2 + b)^2 + (C\omega_j + c)^2 &= k^2, \end{aligned}$$

if the equations of Euler are

$$\begin{aligned} A\omega_i' + (C - B)\omega_j\omega_k &= b\omega_k - c\omega_j, \\ B\omega_j' + (A - C)\omega_k\omega_i &= c\omega_i - a\omega_k, \\ C\omega_k' + (B - A)\omega_i\omega_j &= a\omega_j - b\omega_i, \end{aligned}$$

where a, b, and c are constants. Then show that the integration can be reduced to quadratures. (Volterra, 1895.)

13. In the problem of Mme. Kowaleski, show that by the use of the fourth integral the problem can be reduced to the form

$$\frac{d^2x}{d\tau^2} = \frac{\partial v}{\partial x}, \qquad \frac{d^2y}{d\tau^2} = \frac{\partial v}{\partial y},$$

when v is a function of x and y only. The problem is thus reduced to the motion of a single particle in a certain field of force.

14. Show that the equations of motion of a body turning about a fixed point can be reduced to quadratures if $A = B = 4C$ provided the momentum of the body about the vertical is zero. [Kolossoff, *Rend. del Circolo Matematico di Palermo* (1902).]

CHAPTER VIII

ROLLING MOTION

120. Historical.—The first general discussion of the motion of a rigid body that is so constrained as to be always touching a fixed plane was made by Poisson in 1838, and he assumed that the contact was smooth. A few years later, in volumes 5 and 8 of *Crelle's Journal*, Cournot introduced the element of friction. A particular case, that of a sphere, was discussed by Coriolis in 1835. In 1848 and 1852 Puiseux applied the equations of Poisson to the motion of a rigid body of revolution in contact, without friction, with a plane. In the *Quarterly Journal of Mathematics* for 1861 Slesser gave the equations of motion of a rigid body that is constrained to roll and pivot without sliding on a horizontal plane. Slesser's method is followed by Routh in his discussion of the rolling and pivoting of a sphere on any surface. Ferrers took up the case of a rolling hoop in the *Quarterly Journal of Mathematics* in 1872. Other writers on this subject have been Shouten (Amsterdam, 1889) Newmann, *Mathematische Annalen*, 1886, and Kortweg and Appell, *Rendiconti del Circolo Matematico di Palermo*, 1899.

121. The Rolling of a Sphere on a Given Surface.—As a first example of rolling motion consider Routh's case of a sphere that rolls and pivots on a given surface, but does not slide. Let the surface referred to a set of fixed axes be $f_0(x, y, z) = 0$; let the radius of the sphere be a and its mass be m. If a normal at each point of f_0 is drawn with the length a, the termini of these normals will form a new surface $f(x, y, z) = 0$, and the center of the rolling sphere will always lie in the surface f.

The motion will be referred to a moving trihedron, the origin of which is at the center of the sphere O. It is assumed that the sphere is homogeneous in concentric layers, or, perhaps more generally, the center of gravity is at O and the central ellipsoid of inertia is a sphere. The ζ-axis of the moving trihedron is the normal to f at O which coincides with the normal to f_0 at the point of contact. The ξ- and η-axes lie in the tangent plane of at O, Fig. 67.

The trihedron so defined moves, not only with respect to a fixed trihedron x, y, z of space, but also with respect to a trihedron that is fixed in the body of the sphere. The ξ-, η-, ζ-axes will be regarded as the **i**-, **j**-, **k**-directions of a vector system as usual. The angular velocity of the moving trihedron with respect to a system of axes of fixed space with origin at O will be denoted by $\boldsymbol{\theta}$, and the angular velocity of the sphere will be denoted by $\boldsymbol{\omega}$, so that, referred to the moving trihedron,

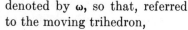

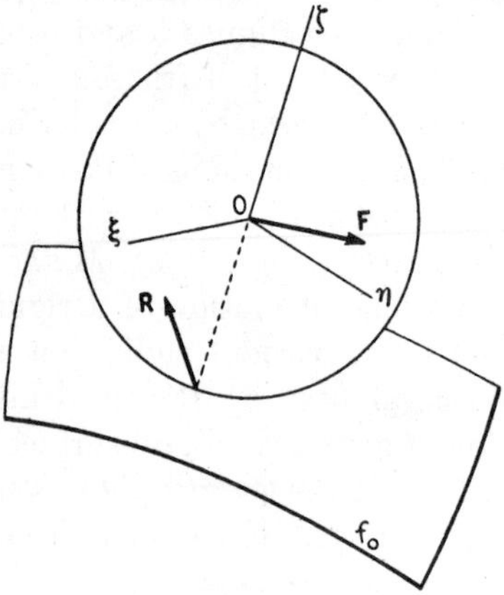

FIG. 67.

$$\boldsymbol{\theta} = \theta_i\mathbf{i} + \theta_j\mathbf{j} + \theta_k\mathbf{k},$$
$$\boldsymbol{\omega} = \omega_i\mathbf{i} + \omega_j\mathbf{j} + \omega_k\mathbf{k}.$$

Let the velocity of the point O with respect to fixed space be $\mathbf{s}$ which, when referred to the moving trihedron, is $\boldsymbol{\sigma}$. Then, by Sec. 80,

$$\mathbf{s}' = \boldsymbol{\sigma}' + \boldsymbol{\theta} \times \boldsymbol{\sigma}, \qquad (0)$$

Let $m\mathbf{R}$, acting at the point of contact, be the reaction of the surface f_0 on the sphere and $m\mathbf{F}$, acting at the center of the sphere, be the resultant of the applied forces. It is one of the hypotheses that $\mathbf{F}$ passes through O. The principle of momentum (Sec. 45) then gives the equation

$$\boldsymbol{\sigma}' + \boldsymbol{\theta} \times \boldsymbol{\sigma} = \mathbf{F} + \mathbf{R}. \qquad (1)$$

When the ellipsoid of inertia at the fixed point O is a sphere, the instantaneous angular velocity coincides in direction with the angular momentum. If k is the radius of gyration of the sphere, the principle of moment of momentum gives the equation

$$k^2(\boldsymbol{\omega}' + \boldsymbol{\theta} \times \boldsymbol{\omega}) = -a\,\mathbf{k} \times \mathbf{R}. \qquad (2)$$

To these two dynamical equations must be added a geometrical equation, or an equation of constraint, which expresses the fact that the point of contact with f_0 does not slide. In addition to the motion of translation $\boldsymbol{\sigma}$ which each particle shares with the entire sphere, there is a velocity due to rotation about the instantaneous axis. This velocity varies from point to point of the sphere. The position vector of the point of contact is $-a\mathbf{k}$, and its velocity due to rotation of the sphere is $-a(\boldsymbol{\omega} \times \mathbf{k})$. Since the particle at the point of contact is at rest, it follows that

$$\boldsymbol{\sigma} - a(\boldsymbol{\omega} \times \mathbf{k}) = 0; \tag{3}$$

and since O always lies in the tangent plane of f,

$$\sigma_k = \sigma_k{}' = 0. \tag{4}$$

A resolution of Eqs. (1), (2), and (3) into their **i**-, **j**-, and **k**-components gives the following system of differential equations

$$\text{Momentum} \quad \left.\begin{aligned} \sigma_i{}' + 0 - \theta_k\sigma_j &= F_i + R_i,\\ \sigma_j{}' + \theta_k\sigma_i - 0 &= F_j + R_j,\\ 0 + \theta_i\sigma_j - \theta_j\sigma_i &= F_k + R_k;\end{aligned}\right\} \tag{5}$$

$$\text{Angular momentum} \quad \left.\begin{aligned} \omega_i{}' + \theta_j\omega_k - \theta_k\omega_j &= +\frac{a}{k^2}R_j,\\ \omega_j{}' + \theta_k\omega_i - \theta_i\omega_k &= -\frac{a}{k^2}R_i,\\ \omega_k{}' + \theta_i\omega_j - \theta_j\omega_i &= 0;\end{aligned}\right\} \tag{6}$$

$$\text{Constraint} \quad \left.\begin{aligned} \sigma_i - a\omega_j &= 0,\\ \sigma_j + a\omega_i &= 0,\\ \sigma_k = \sigma_k{}' &= 0.\end{aligned}\right\} \tag{7}$$

122. Elimination of the Surface Reaction.—If Eq. (121.1) is multiplied by $a\mathbf{k}\times$ and then added to Eq. (121.2) the vector $\mathbf{R}$ is eliminated, with the result

$$\mathbf{k} \times (\boldsymbol{\sigma}' + \boldsymbol{\theta} \times \boldsymbol{\sigma}) + \frac{k^2}{a}(\boldsymbol{\omega}' + \boldsymbol{\theta} \times \boldsymbol{\omega}) = \mathbf{k} \times \mathbf{F}. \tag{1}$$

For convenience of notation, let $\mathbf{V}_{ij}$ be the projection of $\mathbf{V}$ (any vector) upon the **ij**-plane; then

$$-\mathbf{k} \times (\mathbf{k} \times \mathbf{V}) = \mathbf{V}_{ij}.$$

If Eq. (1) is multiplied by $-\mathbf{k}\times$, there results

$$(\boldsymbol{\sigma}' + \boldsymbol{\theta} \times \boldsymbol{\sigma})_{ij} - \frac{k^2}{a}[\mathbf{k} \times (\boldsymbol{\omega}' + \boldsymbol{\theta} \times \boldsymbol{\omega})] = \mathbf{F}_{ij}. \tag{2}$$

By Eq. (121.3)

$$-\mathbf{k} \times \boldsymbol{\omega}' = +\frac{\boldsymbol{\sigma}'}{a}, \qquad \omega_i = -\frac{\sigma_j}{a}, \qquad \omega_j = +\frac{\sigma_i}{a}; \tag{3}$$

and

$$\mathbf{k} \times (\boldsymbol{\theta} \times \boldsymbol{\omega}) = \omega_k \boldsymbol{\theta}_{ij} - \theta_k \boldsymbol{\omega}_{ij}.$$

But it is found also that

$$(\boldsymbol{\theta} \times \boldsymbol{\sigma})_{ij} = \theta_k(-\sigma_j \mathbf{i} + \sigma_i \mathbf{j}) = a\theta_k \boldsymbol{\omega}_{ij};$$

therefore

$$\mathbf{k} \times (\boldsymbol{\theta} \times \boldsymbol{\omega}) = \omega_k \boldsymbol{\theta}_{ij} - \frac{1}{a}(\boldsymbol{\theta} \times \boldsymbol{\sigma})_{ij},$$

and Eq. (5) becomes

$$\left(1 + \frac{k^2}{a^2}\right)(\boldsymbol{\sigma}' + \boldsymbol{\theta} \times \boldsymbol{\sigma})_{ij} = \mathbf{F}_{ij} + \frac{k^2}{a}\omega_k \boldsymbol{\theta}_{ij},$$

or

$$(\boldsymbol{\sigma}' + \boldsymbol{\theta} \times \boldsymbol{\sigma})_{ij} = \frac{a^2}{a^2 + k^2}\mathbf{F}_{ij} + \frac{k^2}{a^2 + k^2} a\omega_k \boldsymbol{\theta}_{ij}. \tag{4}$$

The left member of this equation is the **i**, **j**-component of the absolute acceleration of the center of the sphere. The center of the sphere, therefore, moves just as though it were free under the action of two forces, the first of which is the **i**, **j**-component of the resultant of the applied forces, and the second depends upon the angular velocities $\boldsymbol{\omega}_k$ and $\boldsymbol{\theta}_{ij}$.

The angular velocities $\boldsymbol{\theta}_i$, $\boldsymbol{\theta}_j$, and $\boldsymbol{\theta}_k$ are related to the linear velocities $\boldsymbol{\sigma}_i$ and $\boldsymbol{\sigma}_j$ of the center of the sphere and the curvatures of the surface. Let the ξ- and η-axes coincide in direction with the tangents to the lines of curvature, c_i and c_j, at each point. These directions change, of course, from point to point of the surface f. Let ρ_i be the radius of curvature of the normal plane section of f through the tangent to the curve c_i, taken positively if the center of curvature lies on the positive end of the **k**-axis; and ρ_j the radius of curvature of a normal plane section of f through the tangent to the curve c_j, taken positively if the center of curvature lies on the positive end of the k-axis. It will be verified without difficulty from Fig. 68 that

$$\boldsymbol{\sigma}_i = -\boldsymbol{\theta}_j \times \rho_i \mathbf{k},$$
$$\boldsymbol{\sigma}_j = -\boldsymbol{\theta}_i \times \rho_j \mathbf{k},$$

and therefore

$$\theta_i = +\frac{\sigma_j}{\rho_j}, \qquad \theta_j = -\frac{\sigma_i}{\rho_i}. \tag{5}$$

In order not to confuse the figure ρ_i and ρ_j are drawn negatively.

The angular velocity $\boldsymbol{\theta}_k$ depends upon the rate of change of direction of the tangents to the lines of curvature as the sphere

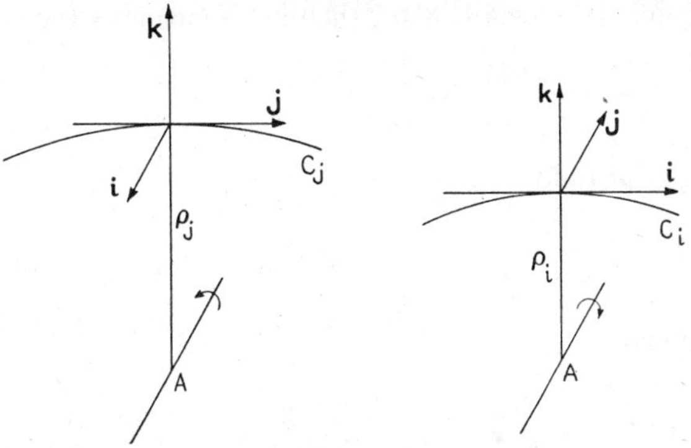

FIG. 68.

moves. Let c_{i0} be the orthogonal projection of c_i upon the tangent plane, and ρ_{i0} its radius of curvature taken positively if the center of curvature lies on the positive end of the j-axis and negatively if the center of curvature lies on the negative end of the j-axis. If an infinitesimal displacement $\boldsymbol{\sigma}_i\, dt$ of the center of the sphere is made, it is evident that the $\xi\eta$-axes rotate about the ζ-axis through an angle $\theta_k^{(i)}\, dt$, and that

$$\boldsymbol{\sigma}_i\, dt = -\boldsymbol{\theta}_k{}^i \times \rho_{i0}\mathbf{j}\, dt = +\rho_{i0}\theta_k{}^{(i)}\mathbf{i}\, dt;$$

therefore

$$\theta_k{}^{(i)} = +\frac{\sigma_i}{\rho_{i0}}.$$

From a similar displacement $\boldsymbol{\sigma}_j\, dt$, it is found that

$$\theta_k{}^{(j)} = -\frac{\sigma_j}{\rho_{j0}}.$$

In the displacement that actually occurs, $\boldsymbol{\delta}_{ij}\,dt = (\boldsymbol{\delta}_i + \boldsymbol{\delta}_j)\,dt$, the $\xi\eta$-axes rotate through the angle

$$\boldsymbol{\theta}_k\,dt = (\boldsymbol{\theta}_k{}^{(i)} + \boldsymbol{\theta}_k{}^{(j)})\,dt;$$

and therefore

$$\theta_k = \frac{\sigma_i}{\rho_{i0}} - \frac{\sigma_j}{\rho_{j0}}.$$

Now let α_i be the angle between the osculating plane of c_i and the normal plane of f through the tangent of c_i. If ρ is the radius of curvature of c_i in the osculating plane, ρ_i the radius of curvature in the normal plane, and ρ_{i0} the radius of curvature of c_{i0} in the tangent plane (see I, **335**), then by Meusnier's theorem[1]

$$\frac{\cos\alpha_i}{\rho} = \frac{1}{\rho_i}, \qquad \frac{\sin\alpha_i}{\rho} = \frac{1}{\rho_{i0}},$$

from which it follows that

$$\frac{1}{\rho_{i0}} = \frac{\tan\alpha_i}{\rho_i},$$

and similarly

$$\frac{1}{\rho_{j0}} = \frac{\tan\alpha_j}{\rho_j}.$$

Hence

$$\theta_k = \frac{\sigma_i\tan\alpha_i}{\rho_i} - \frac{\sigma_j\tan\alpha_j}{\rho_j}. \tag{6}$$

From Eqs. (3), (4), and the third of (121.6) it is seen also that

$$\omega_k' = \frac{\sigma_i\sigma_j}{a}\left(\frac{1}{\rho_i} - \frac{1}{\rho_j}\right). \tag{7}$$

Finally, the resolution of Eq. (4) into its components gives the two ordinary differential equations

$$\begin{aligned} \sigma_i' - \theta_k\sigma_j &= \frac{a^2}{a^2+k^2}F_i + \frac{k^2}{a^2+k^2}a\omega_k\theta_i, \\ \sigma_j' + \theta_k\sigma_i &= \frac{a^2}{a^2+k^2}F_j + \frac{k^2}{a^2+k^2}a\omega_k\theta_j. \end{aligned} \tag{8}$$

[1] EISENHART, "Differential Geometry," p. 118.

123. Integration of the Equations.—If the first of Eq. (122.8) is multiplied by σ_i, the second by σ_j, and the equations are then added, there results

$$\sigma_i\sigma_i' + \sigma_j\sigma_j' = \frac{a^2}{a^2 + k^2}(F_i\sigma_i + F_j\sigma_j) + \frac{k^2}{a^2 + k^2}a\omega_k(\theta_i\sigma_i + \theta_j\sigma_j). \tag{1}$$

From Eqs. (122.5) it is found that

$$\theta_i\sigma_i + \theta_j\sigma_j = \sigma_i\sigma_j\left(\frac{1}{\rho_j} - \frac{1}{\rho_i}\right) = -a\omega_k'.$$

In the first term of the right member of Eq. (1) $F_i\sigma_i + F_j\sigma_j$ represents the rate at which the applied forces are doing work. The component perpendicular to the plane does no work, since there is no displacement in that direction. That is, since $\sigma_k = 0$,

$$F_i\sigma_i + F_j\sigma_j = F_i\sigma_i + F_j\sigma_j + F_k\sigma_k$$

represents the entire work of the applied forces, and, if there exists a potential function V of the applied forces,

$$F_i\sigma_i + F_j\sigma_j = V'.$$

Equation (1) is therefore an exact differential, and since, by Eq. (122.3),

$$\sigma_i = +a\omega_j, \qquad \sigma_j = -a\omega_i,$$

the integral can be written

$$(a^2 + k^2)(\omega_i^2 + \omega_j^2) + k^2\omega_k^2 = 2V + c. \tag{2}$$

This integral is easily interpreted. Since at any instant the sphere is pivoting on the point of contact, the left member is twice the kinetic energy of the sphere. Equation (2) is therefore the energy integral. Further integration requires a knowledge of the given surface f.

Suppose the surface $f(x, y, z) = 0$, referred to its lines of curvature, is given by the parametric equations

$$x = x(u, v), \qquad y = y(u, v), \qquad z = z(u, v),$$

and that x_u is understood to mean $\partial x/\partial u$, etc. Then if the ξ-axis of the moving trihedron is tangent to the curve u-constant and the η-axis is tangent to the line v-constant, and if u and v are arc lengths along these curves,

$$\sigma_i = u' \quad \text{and} \quad \sigma_j = v';$$

therefore

$$\left.\begin{aligned} x' &= x_u\sigma_i + x_v\sigma_j, \\ y' &= y_u\sigma_i + y_v\sigma_j, \\ z' &= z_u\sigma_k + z_v\sigma_j. \end{aligned}\right\} \tag{3}$$

The position of the body in fixed space is determined by these three equations after the velocities σ_i and σ_j are known.

The surface reaction is found from Eq. (121.1) to be

$$\mathbf{R} = \boldsymbol{\sigma}' + \boldsymbol{\theta} \times \boldsymbol{\sigma} - \mathbf{F},$$

and the normal pressure is

$$R_k = +\mathbf{k} \cdot \boldsymbol{\theta} \times \boldsymbol{\sigma} - \mathbf{k} \cdot \mathbf{F}.$$

124. The Surface Is a Plane.—Important simplifications in the equations of motion occur when the surface on which the sphere rolls is a plane. Since the curvature of a plane is everywhere zero, the radii of curvatures ρ_i and ρ_j are everywhere infinite, and any set of rectangular axes in the plane can be taken as lines of curvature. From Eqs. (122.5) and (122.6) it is found that

$$\theta_i = \theta_j = \theta_k = 0, \tag{1}$$

and the moving trihedron does not rotate. Since

$$\boldsymbol{\theta} \times \boldsymbol{\sigma} = 0, \tag{2}$$

Equation (121.0) shows that σ' is the absolute acceleration. Equation (122.4) becomes

$$\boldsymbol{\sigma}_{ij}' = \frac{a^2}{a^2 + k^2}\mathbf{F}_{ij}. \tag{3}$$

Since the equation of motion of a particle, which is constrained to move in the plane and is acted upon by the same force, is

$$\boldsymbol{\sigma}_{ij}' = \mathbf{F}_{ij},$$

provided the mass of the particle is the same as the mass of the sphere, it is seen that the center of the sphere moves just as though it were a particle of the same mass, and the force acting upon it were the force that is actually acting multiplied by the constant factor

$$\frac{a^2}{a^2 + k^2}.$$

For a homogeneous sphere

$$k^2 = \frac{2}{5} \quad \text{and} \quad \frac{a^2}{a^2 + k^2} = \frac{5}{7}.$$

Hence the equation of motion of a homogeneous sphere that is rolling upon a fixed plane is

$$\boldsymbol{\sigma}_{ij}' = \tfrac{5}{7}\mathbf{F}_{ij}. \tag{4}$$

The equation of momentum, Eq. (121.1), gives the surface reaction

$$\left.\begin{aligned} \mathbf{R} &= \boldsymbol{\sigma}' - \mathbf{F} = \boldsymbol{\sigma}_{ij}' - \mathbf{F} \\ &= -\frac{k^2}{a^2 + k^2}\mathbf{F}_{ij} - \mathbf{F}_k, \end{aligned}\right\} \tag{5}$$

and the normal pressure of the sphere on the plane is $\mathbf{F}_k$.

The equation of angular momentum [Eq. (121.2)] becomes

$$\boldsymbol{\omega}' = \frac{a}{a^2 + k^2}(-F_j\mathbf{i} + F_i\mathbf{j}). \tag{6}$$

Example.—A homogeneous sphere rolls on a horizontal plane and is attracted toward a fixed point in the plane by a force that acts at its center and that in magnitude is directly proportional to the distance from the fixed point. It is required to describe the motion of the sphere.

Taking the fixed point as an origin, let $\mathbf{r}$ be the position vector of the center of the sphere, m the mass, and a the radius of the sphere. If n_1^2 is the factor of proportionality,

$$\mathbf{F} = -\frac{n_1^2}{m}\mathbf{r} + \mathbf{g},$$

when $\mathbf{g}$ is the acceleration of gravity. Let the k-axis be vertical, directed upward, so that

$$\mathbf{g} = -g\mathbf{k}.$$

Let

$$\boldsymbol{\varrho} = \mathbf{r}_{ij}, \qquad \text{and} \qquad n^2 = \frac{5}{7}\frac{n_1^2}{m};$$

then Eq. (4) becomes

$$\boldsymbol{\varrho}'' = -n^2\boldsymbol{\varrho},$$

which is the equation of simple harmonic motion, Eq. (13.2).

If the **i**- and **j**-directions are properly chosen the solution of this equation is

$$\boldsymbol{\varrho} = b \cos nt\, \mathbf{i} + c \sin nt\, \mathbf{j},$$

where b and c are constants and represent the semiaxes of the ellipse in which the motion occurs; also

$$F_i = -\tfrac{7}{5}bn^2 \cos nt, \qquad F_j = -\tfrac{7}{5}cn^2 \sin nt, \qquad F_k = -\tfrac{7}{5}an^2 - g.$$

Equation (6) now gives

$$\omega_i' = +\frac{c}{a}n^2 \sin nt,$$

$$\omega_j' = -\frac{b}{a}n^2 \cos nt,$$

$$\omega_k' = 0.$$

From these equations it follows that ω_k is constant, and

$$\omega_i = -\frac{c}{a}n \cos nt, \qquad \omega_j = -\frac{b}{a}n \sin nt,$$

the constants of integration vanishing since, by the equations of constraint [Eq. (121.7)]

$$\sigma_i = \rho_i' = a\omega_j, \qquad \sigma_j = \rho_j' = -a\omega_i.$$

With respect to the trihedron that moves with the sphere, the direction of the axes remaining fixed, the instantaneous axis of rotation of the sphere describes an elliptical cone. The reaction **R** is

$$\mathbf{R} = \tfrac{2}{5}n^2\boldsymbol{\varrho} + (\tfrac{7}{5}an^2 + g)\mathbf{k}.$$

In order that the motion be one of pure rolling

$$\frac{\tfrac{2}{5}n^2\rho}{\tfrac{7}{5}an^2 + g}$$

must always be less than the coefficient of friction. That is, the ellipse on which the sphere rolls must not be too large.

125. The Sphere Rolls and Slides.—A modification of the argument must be made if the state of motion of the sphere is such that both rolling and sliding occur. If Secs. 121 and 122 are re-examined with the idea that the sphere rolls and slides, it will be found that the equation of momentum, Eq. (121.1), and moment of momentum, Eq. (121.2) hold without any alteration; that is,

$$\boldsymbol{\sigma}' + \boldsymbol{\theta} \times \boldsymbol{\sigma} = \mathbf{F} + \mathbf{R}, \tag{1}$$

and

$$k^2(\boldsymbol{\omega}' + \boldsymbol{\theta} \times \boldsymbol{\omega}) = -a\mathbf{k} \times \mathbf{R}. \tag{2}$$

The angular velocities $\boldsymbol{\theta}_i$, $\boldsymbol{\theta}_j$, and $\boldsymbol{\theta}_k$ also have the same expressions, that is

$$\theta_i = \frac{\sigma_j}{\rho_j}, \qquad \theta_j = -\frac{\sigma_i}{\rho_i}, \qquad \theta_k = \frac{\sigma_i \tan \alpha_i}{\rho_i} - \frac{\sigma_j \tan \alpha_j}{\rho_j}, \tag{3}$$

as before, Eqs. (122.5).

The equation of constraint, however, Eq. (121.3) no longer holds, but becomes

$$\boldsymbol{\sigma} - a(\boldsymbol{\omega} \times \mathbf{k}) = -\mathbf{v}; \tag{4}$$

that is the velocity of the point of contact of the sphere with the surface is $-\mathbf{v}$, and not zero, as before. As an offset to this new variable, however, the frictional component of the surface reaction bears, in magnitude, a constant ratio to the normal component of $\mathbf{R}$, and has the direction of $\mathbf{v}$. Therefore, if $\mathbf{u}$ is a unit vector in the direction of $\mathbf{v}$, the frictional component $\mathbf{R}_{ij}$ of $\mathbf{R}$ is

$$\mathbf{R}_{ij} = \mu R_k \mathbf{u}, \tag{5}$$

where μ is the coefficient of sliding friction; and

$$\mathbf{R} = R_k(\mu\mathbf{u} + \mathbf{k}). \tag{6}$$

The surface reaction can be eliminated just as in Sec. 122, and the same equation, Eq. (122.2) results, namely,

$$(\boldsymbol{\sigma}' + \boldsymbol{\theta} \times \boldsymbol{\sigma})_{ij} - \frac{k^2}{a}[\mathbf{k} \times (\boldsymbol{\omega}' + \boldsymbol{\theta} \times \boldsymbol{\omega})] = \mathbf{F}_{ij}, \tag{7}$$

but the transformation of $\mathbf{k} \times (\boldsymbol{\omega}' + \boldsymbol{\theta} \times \boldsymbol{\omega})$ is different. This time

$$-a\mathbf{k} \times \boldsymbol{\omega}' = \mathbf{v}' + \boldsymbol{\sigma}',$$

and

$$-a\mathbf{k} \times (\boldsymbol{\theta} \times \boldsymbol{\omega}) = (\boldsymbol{\theta} \times \boldsymbol{\sigma})_{ij} + (\boldsymbol{\theta} \times \mathbf{v})_{ij} - a\omega_k\boldsymbol{\theta}_{ij},$$

where $\mathbf{v}'$ means the relative derivative

$$\mathbf{v}' = v_i'\mathbf{i} + v_j'\mathbf{j},$$

and not the total derivative

$$\mathbf{v}' = v_i'\mathbf{i} + v_j'\mathbf{j} + v_i\mathbf{i}' + v_j\mathbf{j}'.$$

Eq. (7) now reduces to

$$(\boldsymbol{\sigma}' + \boldsymbol{\theta} \times \boldsymbol{\sigma})_{ij} + \frac{k^2}{a^2 + k^2}(\mathbf{v}' + \boldsymbol{\theta} \times \mathbf{v}) = \frac{a^2}{a^2 + k^2}\mathbf{F}_{ij} + \frac{k^2}{a^2 + k^2}a\omega_k\boldsymbol{\theta}_{ij}, \quad (8)$$

which corresponds to Eq. (122.4).

Obviously, an energy integral exists only when $\mathbf{v} = 0$, but Eqs. (8) can be resolved into its two rectangular components just as in Sec. 122.

126. The Billiard Ball.—The game of billiards furnishes an ideal example of a sphere that rolls and slides upon a plane surface. In this case the plane upon which the ball rolls is horizontal and the cue ball, especially, rolls, slides, and pivots. The only forces that are acting on the ball are the weight of the ball $m\mathbf{g}$ and the reaction of the table $m\mathbf{R}$. Since the curvature of the table is zero, Eqs. (125.1, .2, .4, .8) reduce to

$$\boldsymbol{\sigma}' = \mathbf{g} + \mathbf{R}, \quad (1)$$

$$k^2\boldsymbol{\omega}' = -a\mathbf{k} \times \mathbf{R}, \quad (2)$$

$$-a\mathbf{k} \times \boldsymbol{\omega} = \boldsymbol{\sigma} + \mathbf{v}, \quad (3)$$

and

$$\boldsymbol{\sigma}' = -\frac{k^2}{a^2 + k^2}\mathbf{v}'. \quad (4)$$

The $\mathbf{k}$-direction is vertical upward. Hence

$$\mathbf{g} = -g\mathbf{k}, \qquad R_k = g,$$

and

$$\mathbf{R}_{ij} = g\mu\mathbf{u}.$$

Equation (1) becomes

$$\boldsymbol{\sigma}' = \mathbf{R}_{ij} = g\mu\mathbf{u}, \tag{5}$$

and this result combined with Eq. (4) gives

$$\mathbf{v}' = -\frac{a^2 + k^2}{k^2} g\mu\mathbf{u}. \tag{6}$$

But

$$\mathbf{v} = v\mathbf{u}, \qquad \text{and} \qquad \mathbf{v}' = v'\mathbf{u} + v\mathbf{u}',$$

and since $\mathbf{u}$ is a unit vector, $\mathbf{u}'$ is perpendicular to $\mathbf{u}$. Equation (6) therefore can be written

$$v'\mathbf{u} + v\mathbf{u}' = -\frac{a^2 + k^2}{k^2} g\mu\mathbf{u},$$

which shows that

$$\mathbf{u}' = 0, \qquad \text{and} \qquad v' = -\frac{a^2 + k^2}{k^2} g\mu.$$

The vector $\mathbf{u}$ therefore is fixed, not only in magnitude, but in direction also, and

$$\mathbf{v} = \mathbf{v}_0 - \frac{a^2 + k^2}{k^2} g\mu t\mathbf{u}, \tag{7}$$

where $\mathbf{v}_0$ is the initial value of $\mathbf{v}$. Likewise, from Eq. (5),

$$\boldsymbol{\sigma} = \boldsymbol{\sigma}_0 + g\mu t\mathbf{u}. \tag{8}$$

If $\mathbf{r}$ is the position vector of the center of the sphere (Sec. 121)

$$\boldsymbol{\sigma} = \mathbf{s} = \mathbf{r}'.$$

Integration of Eq. (8) gives, after replacing $\boldsymbol{\sigma}$ by $\mathbf{r}'$,

$$\mathbf{r} = \mathbf{r}_0 + t\boldsymbol{\sigma}_0 + \tfrac{1}{2}g\mu t^2\mathbf{u},$$

from which it is evident that, if $\boldsymbol{\sigma}_0$ is not collinear with $\mathbf{u}$, the path described by the center of the sphere is a parabola.

As for the instantaneous axis, it follows from Eq. (2) that ω_k, the component perpendicular to the table, is constant, since the vector $\mathbf{k} \times \mathbf{R}$ lies in the plane of the table. Rotation about the vertical axis is called pivoting, and since the contact of the ball with the table is regarded as a point, friction does not affect this component of the rotation. It would do so if the contact were regarded as a small area, which, actually, it is. On multiplying Eq. (3) by $\mathbf{k}\times$, it is found that

$$\boldsymbol{\omega}_{ij} = \frac{1}{a}\mathbf{k}\times(\boldsymbol{\sigma}+\mathbf{v})$$
$$= \boldsymbol{\omega}_{ij0} - \frac{a}{k^2}g\mu t\,\mathbf{k}\times\mathbf{u},$$

where

$$\boldsymbol{\omega}_{ij0} = \frac{1}{a}(\boldsymbol{\sigma}_0+\mathbf{v}_0).$$

This result follows also from Eq. (2), but, as Eq. (3) shows, the constant vector of integration is not arbitrary. The change of

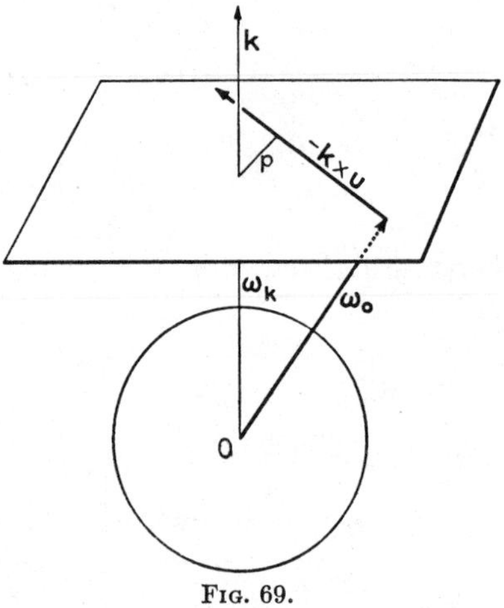

FIG. 69.

direction of the instantaneous axis with respect to a set of axes which has its origin at the center O of the sphere and fixed in direction is shown in Fig. 69. Since ω_k is constant, the horizontal plane through its terminus is at a fixed distance above the able. If $\boldsymbol{\omega}_0$ is the initial value of $\boldsymbol{\omega}$ and $-\mathbf{k}\times\mathbf{u}$ is a unit vector as represented in the diagram, the terminus of $\boldsymbol{\omega}$ moves from its initial position in the direction of $-\mathbf{k}\times\mathbf{u}$ with constant velocity. Consequently the terminus of $\boldsymbol{\omega}$ always lies in a fixed plane.

This motion of $\boldsymbol{\omega}$ continues until slipping ceases, which occurs at the instant

$$t = \frac{k^2v_0}{(a^2+k^2)g\mu}.$$

At this instant $\boldsymbol{\omega} = \boldsymbol{\omega}_s$, where

$$\boldsymbol{\omega}_s = \boldsymbol{\omega}_0 - \frac{av_0}{a^2 + k^2}\mathbf{k} \times \mathbf{u},$$

and the ball begins to roll. In the situation shown in the diagram the tensor of $\boldsymbol{\omega}$ decreases until the terminus of $\boldsymbol{\omega}$ reaches the perpendicular p from the vertical line through O, after which it increases, provided it passes that point. The value of t at this point is obtained by minimizing $\omega^2 = \boldsymbol{\omega} \cdot \boldsymbol{\omega}$, or by imposing upon $\boldsymbol{\omega}_{ij}$ the condition that it shall have the direction $-\mathbf{u}$. If $\boldsymbol{\omega}_m$ is the minimum value of $\boldsymbol{\omega}$, it is found that

$$\boldsymbol{\omega}_m = \boldsymbol{\omega}_0 - \frac{1}{a}(\mathbf{k} \cdot \mathbf{u} \times \boldsymbol{\sigma}_0)\mathbf{k} \times \mathbf{u}.$$

If $\mathbf{k} \cdot \mathbf{u} \times \boldsymbol{\sigma}_0$ is positive and

$$\frac{a^2 v_0}{a^2 + k^2} \gtrless g\mu\, \mathbf{k} \cdot \mathbf{u} \times \boldsymbol{\sigma},$$

the terminus of $\boldsymbol{\omega}$ will pass the minimum point and the spin will increase if the upper inequality sign holds, but will stop short of the minimum point if the lower sign holds. If $\mathbf{k} \cdot \mathbf{u} \times \boldsymbol{\sigma}_0$ is negative the terminus of $\boldsymbol{\omega}$ moves away from the minimum point and the rate of spin always increases. From this it is seen that the spin of the ball may steadily fall, steadily rise, or it may sink to a minimum and again rise; but it cannot rise to a maximum and then fall.

127. Euler's Angles for the Billiard Ball.—In order to complete the problem of the motion of a billiard ball, it is necessary to assign the position of the spot on the ball, or the several spots if there are that many, at any instant. This requires a determination of Euler's angles for the ball as functions of the time. From Problem 7, Chap. VI, it is found that

$$\left.\begin{aligned} \omega_i &= +\varphi' \sin\theta \sin\psi + \theta' \cos\psi, \\ \omega_j &= -\varphi' \sin\theta \cos\psi + \theta' \sin\psi, \\ \omega_k &= +\varphi' \cos\theta + \psi'. \end{aligned}\right\} \quad (1)$$

In the present case ω_i, ω_j and ω_k are known functions of the time, namely,

$$\left.\begin{aligned} \omega_i &= \omega_{i0} + qt \sin\lambda, \\ \omega_j &= \omega_{i0} - qt \cos\lambda, \\ \omega_k &= \omega_{k0}, \end{aligned}\right\} \quad (2)$$

where λ is the angle which the vector $\mathbf{u}$ makes with the vector $\mathbf{i}$, and accordingly

$$\mathbf{i}\cdot\mathbf{k}\times\mathbf{u} = -\mathbf{j}\cdot\mathbf{u} = -\sin\lambda,$$
$$\mathbf{j}\cdot\mathbf{k}\times\mathbf{u} = +\mathbf{i}\cdot\mathbf{u} = +\cos\lambda,$$

and, for brevity of notation,

$$q = \frac{a}{k^2}g\mu.$$

The solution of Eqs. (1) for θ', φ', and ψ' gives the differential equations

$$\left.\begin{aligned} \theta' &= (\omega_{i0} + qt\sin\lambda)\cos\psi + (\omega_{j0} - qt\cos\lambda)\sin\psi, \\ \sin\theta\varphi' &= (\omega_{i0} + qt\sin\lambda)\sin\psi - (\omega_{j0} - qt\sin\lambda)\cos\psi, \\ \psi' &= \omega_{k0} - \varphi'\cos\theta. \end{aligned}\right\} \quad (3)$$

In these equations ω_{i0}, ω_{j0}, ω_{k0}, q, and λ are constants. Notwithstanding the apparently simple character of these equations, a satisfactory solution of them has not been found. They can be solved, however, if $q = 0$, which is equivalent to the assumption that there is no friction. For this case the equations become

$$\left.\begin{aligned} \theta' &= \omega_{i0}\cos\psi + \omega_{j0}\sin\psi, \\ \sin\theta\phi' &= \omega_{i0}\sin\psi - \omega_{j0}\cos\psi, \\ \psi' &= \omega_{k0} - \varphi'\cos\theta. \end{aligned}\right\} \quad (4)$$

The instantaneous axis is fixed in the body, if the ζ-axis is taken to coincide with it, and if ω_{i0} and ω_{j0} are given the forms

$$\omega_{i0} = +\omega_{k0}\tan\theta_0\sin\psi_0,$$
$$\omega_{j0} = -\omega_{k0}\tan\theta_0\cos\psi_0,$$

the equations become

$$\begin{aligned} \theta' &= \omega_{k0}\tan\theta_0\sin(\psi_0 - \psi), \\ \sin\theta\varphi' &= \omega_{k0}\tan\theta_0\cos(\psi_0 - \psi), \\ \psi' &= \omega_{k0} - \varphi'\cos\theta, \end{aligned}$$

for which the particular solution

$$\theta = \theta_0, \qquad \psi = \psi_0, \qquad \varphi = \varphi_0 = \frac{\omega_k}{\cos\theta_0}t + \bar{\varphi}, \quad (5)$$

is evident. This solution contains but one constant of integration, namely $\bar{\varphi}$, but it is not difficult to derive the complete solution of Eqs. (4) from it. All that is necessary is to refer the motion to an arbitrary set of axes that are fixed in the body instead of referring it to a particular set.

In Fig. 70 let C, C_0, and C_1 be great circles on a unit sphere, the circle C is horizontal, C_0 is perpendicular to the axis of rotation, and C_1 is in the $\xi\eta$-plane of the arbitrary set of axes. Let P, P_0, and P_1 be the poles of these great circles; and N, N_0, N_1 the nodes, or points of intersection of the circles. The points where the x-, or ξ-, axes pierce the sphere are indicated by dots on the respective circles. Let the arc $N\varphi_0$ be $\bar{\varphi}$ and the arc $N\varphi$ be φ_1. These arcs may have any values whatever without affecting the spherical triangle NN_0N_1; they are constant throughout the motion, and so also is θ_1. The values of the sides and angles of this triangle are as indicated in the diagram, and likewise for the triangle formed by the three poles.

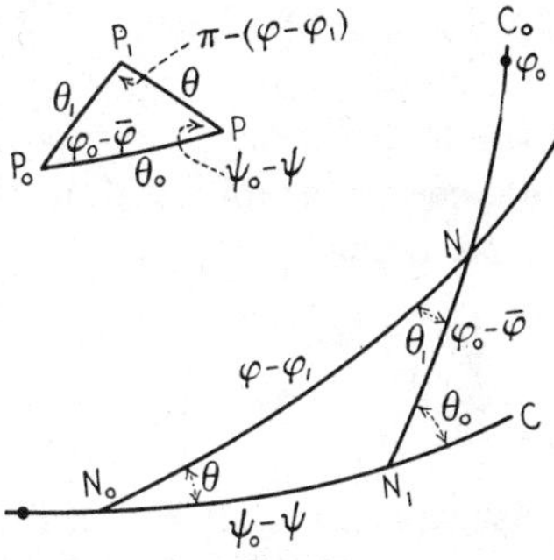

FIG. 70.

If Eqs. (52.3) are applied to the triangle PP_0P_1, it is found that

$$\left.\begin{aligned} \cos\theta &= +\cos\theta_0\cos\theta_1 + \sin\theta_0\sin\theta_1\cos(\varphi_0-\bar{\varphi}), \\ \cos(\varphi-\varphi_1)\sin\theta &= -\cos\theta_0\sin\theta_1 + \sin\theta_0\cos\theta_1\cos(\varphi_0-\bar{\varphi}), \end{aligned}\right\} \tag{6}$$

and

$$\frac{\sin(\varphi-\varphi_1)}{\sin\theta_0} = \frac{\sin(\varphi_0-\bar{\varphi})}{\sin\theta} = \frac{\sin(\psi_0-\psi)}{\sin\theta_1}. \tag{7}$$

These equations define the Eulerian angles of the arbitrary trihedron as functions of the time through φ_0, Eqs. (5). They contain the three arbitrary constants θ_1, φ_1, and $\bar{\varphi}$ that are necessary for the complete solution of Eqs. (4).

It follows therefore that, if ω_{i0}, ω_{j0}, and ω_{k0} were constants, the ball would spin uniformly about some axis that is fixed in the body, and the point of contact of the ball with the table would describe a small circle on the sphere. As the instantaneous axis moves toward or away from the vertical, it changes its position in the body and the small circle of the point of contact decreases or increases in size. Since Eqs. (6) and (7) are the complete solution of Eqs. (4), the complete solution of Eqs. (3) can be obtained from them by the method of variation of parameters (I, **381**).

128. Rolling and Slipping on an Inclined Plane.—The equations of motion for an inclined plane do not differ greatly from the equations of motion for the horizontal plane. For the horizontal plane the applied force is normal to the plane; for the inclined plane it is not. Let the inclination of the plane to the horizontal be α, let the **i**-direction be directed down the plane, and the **k**-direction be normal to the plane directed upward.

The equations of motion then are almost the same as in Sec. 126, namely,

$$\left.\begin{aligned} \boldsymbol{\sigma}' &= \mathbf{g} + \mathbf{R}, & -a\mathbf{k} \times \boldsymbol{\omega} &= \boldsymbol{\sigma} + \mathbf{v}, \\ k^2\boldsymbol{\omega}' &= -a\mathbf{k} \times \mathbf{R}, & \boldsymbol{\sigma}' + \frac{k^2}{a^2 + k^2}\mathbf{v}' &= \frac{a^2}{a^2 + k^2}\mathbf{g}_{ij}; \end{aligned}\right\} \tag{1}$$

the last equation only differing by virtue of the fact that there is a component of the weight in the **i**, **j**-plane, namely,

$$\mathbf{g}_{ij} = +g \sin \alpha \,\mathbf{i}.$$

The reaction of the plane on the sphere evidently is

$$\mathbf{R} = g \cos \alpha(\mu\mathbf{u} + \mathbf{k}),$$

where **u** is a unit vector in the direction of **v**, just as before.

The first of Eqs. (1) becomes

$$\boldsymbol{\sigma}' = \mu g \cos \alpha \,\mathbf{u} + g \sin \alpha \,\mathbf{i} \qquad (2$$

and if $\boldsymbol{\sigma}'$ is eliminated from the fourth of Eqs. (1) by means of this expression, it is found that

$$\mathbf{v}' = -g \sin \alpha \,\mathbf{i} - \frac{a^2 + k^2}{k^2}\mu g \cos \alpha \,\mathbf{u}. \tag{3}$$

For brevity of notation, let

$$\frac{a^2 + k^2}{k^2}\mu g \cos \alpha = m,$$

and

$$g \sin \alpha = n;$$

then

$$\mathbf{v}' = -m\mathbf{u} - n\mathbf{i}, \tag{4}$$

which, for $\alpha = 0$, reduces to Eq. (126.6). This equation shows that $\mathbf{v}'$ is not collinear with **u**, and therefore, while **u** is still a unit vector, its direction is not fixed. The component of $\mathbf{v}'$ in the direction of $\mathbf{u}$ is obtained by multiplying Eq. (4) by $\mathbf{u}\,\cdot$, and the component perpendicular to $\mathbf{u}$ is obtained by multiplying through by $-\mathbf{u}\times(\mathbf{u}\times$, Eq. (5.2).

Now if ρ, θ are the polar coordinates of the terminus of $\mathbf{v}$,

$$\mathbf{u}\cdot\mathbf{v}' = \rho',$$

and

$$-\mathbf{u}\times(\mathbf{u}\times\mathbf{v}') = \rho\theta'\mathbf{k}\times\mathbf{u},$$

$\mathbf{k}\times\mathbf{u}$ being the unit vector in the plane perpendicular to $\mathbf{u}$. On the right side of Eq. (4)

$$\mathbf{u}\cdot\mathbf{u} = 1, \qquad \mathbf{u}\cdot\mathbf{i} = \cos\theta$$
$$\mathbf{u}\times(\mathbf{u}\times\mathbf{u}) = 0, \qquad +\mathbf{u}\times(\mathbf{u}\times\mathbf{i}) = +\sin\theta\mathbf{k}\times\mathbf{u}.$$

The components of Eq. (4), therefore, give the differential equations

$$\left.\begin{aligned}\rho' &= -n\cos\theta - m,\\ \rho\theta' &= +n\sin\theta.\end{aligned}\right\} \tag{5}$$

By the elimination of the time between these two equations, there is obtained

$$\frac{d\rho}{\rho} = \left(-\cot\theta - \frac{m}{n}\operatorname{cosec}\theta\right)d\theta,$$

and, by integration, this becomes

$$\rho = \rho_0\left(\frac{\tan\frac{1}{2}\theta_0}{\tan\frac{1}{2}\theta}\right)^{\frac{m}{n}}\frac{\sin\theta_0}{\sin\theta}, \tag{6}$$

ρ_0 and θ_0 being the initial values of ρ and θ.

If Eq. (6) is substituted in the second of Eq. (5), it is found by a second integration that

$$t = \frac{1}{2}\rho_0\sin\theta_0\tan^{\frac{m}{n}}\frac{1}{2}\theta_0\times$$
$$\left[\frac{(\cot\frac{1}{2}\theta_0)^{m+n}}{m+n} + \frac{(\cot\frac{1}{2}\theta_0)^{m-n}}{m-n} - \frac{(\cot\frac{1}{2}\theta)^{m+n}}{m+n} - \frac{(\cot\frac{1}{2}\theta)^{m-n}}{m-n}\right]. \tag{7}$$

The second of Eqs. (5) also shows that θ always increases. The direction of $\mathbf{v}$ moves in the direction of the line of greatest slope upward, that is, the slip is downward. The limit of ρ, Eq. (6), as θ tends toward π is zero if $m/n > 1$, that is, if

$$\mu > \frac{k^2}{a^2 + k^2} \tan \alpha.$$

Slipping ceases, and the ball begins to roll (Sec. 124).

By direct integration of the fourth of Eq. (1) it is found that

$$(\boldsymbol{\sigma} - \boldsymbol{\sigma}_0) + \frac{k^2}{a^2 + k^2}(\mathbf{v} - \mathbf{v}_0) = \frac{a^2}{a^2 + k^2} gt \sin \alpha \mathbf{i}, \tag{8}$$

which determines $\boldsymbol{\sigma}$; and by multiplying the third of Eqs. (1) by $\mathbf{k} \times$ it is seen that

$$\boldsymbol{\omega} = \boldsymbol{\omega}_0 + \frac{a}{a^2 + k^2}[\mathbf{k} \times (\mathbf{v} - \mathbf{v}_0) + gt \sin \alpha \mathbf{j}].$$

A determination of Euler's angles does not seem very promising.

129. A Coin Rolls and Spins.—Some interesting results on the problem of rolling hoops and coins were given by Appell and Kortweg[1] in 1899.

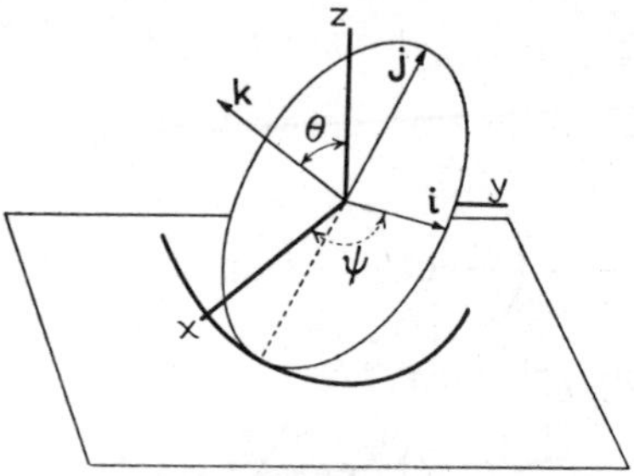

FIG. 71.

Let there be a set of axes T_1, movable with respect to fixed space and with respect to the coin, but having its origin always at the center of the coin, the ζ-, or $\mathbf{k}$-, axis perpendicular to its plane, and the ξ-, or $\mathbf{i}$-axis always horizontal. Let there be a second set of axes T_2, fixed with respect to the coin, with its origin also at the center of the coin and one of its axes perpendicular to its plane and therefore coinciding with the $\mathbf{k}$-axis. With respect to T_1 the trihedron T_2 merely turns about the $\mathbf{k}$-axis. If θ, φ, and ψ are Euler's angles for the axes that are fixed in the body, $\boldsymbol{\omega}$ the instantaneous rotation of T_2, and $\bar{\boldsymbol{\omega}}$ the instantaneous rotation of T_1, then

$$\boldsymbol{\omega} = \bar{\boldsymbol{\omega}} + \varphi' \mathbf{k}.$$

[1] *Rendiconti del Circolo Matematico di Palermo*, XIV, pp. 1, 7 (1899).

It is evident from Fig. 71 that

$$\bar{\omega}_i = \theta', \qquad \bar{\omega}_j = \psi' \sin \theta, \qquad \bar{\omega}_k = \psi' \cos \theta, \tag{1}$$

a result that can also be obtained by taking $\varphi \equiv 0$ in Eq. (85.4). The moment of momentum of the coin is

$$\mathbf{L} = \mathbf{\Lambda} = A\bar{\omega}_i\mathbf{i} + B\bar{\omega}_j\mathbf{j} + C\omega_k\mathbf{k}.$$

For the distinction between **L** and **Λ** the reader is referred to Sec. 84.

The principle of moment of momentum gives the equation

$$\mathbf{L}' = \mathbf{\Lambda}' + \bar{\boldsymbol{\omega}} \times \mathbf{\Lambda} = -a\mathbf{j} \times \mathbf{R}m, \tag{2}$$

if a is the radius of the coin, m its mass, and **R** is the acceleration due to the reaction of the plane. Since the **k**-axis is fixed in the coin and every axis in the plane of the coin is a principal axis, the moments of inertia with respect to these axes are constants, and $A = B$. The mass factor can be eliminated by taking

$$A = mA_1, \qquad B = mA_1, \qquad C = mC_1.$$

Then

$$\frac{1}{m}\mathbf{L}' = [A_1\bar{\omega}_i' + (C_1\omega_k - A_1\bar{\omega}_k)\bar{\omega}_j]\mathbf{i} + [A_1\bar{\omega}_j' + (A_1\bar{\omega}_k - C_1\omega_k)\bar{\omega}_i]\mathbf{j} + [C_1\omega_k']\mathbf{k}. \tag{3}$$

Since the point of contact of the coin is at rest, the equation of constraint is

$$\boldsymbol{\sigma} - a\boldsymbol{\omega} \times \mathbf{j} = 0. \tag{4}$$

In this equation $\boldsymbol{\omega}$ can be written

$$\boldsymbol{\omega} = \bar{\omega}_i\mathbf{i} + \bar{\omega}_j\mathbf{j} + \omega_k\mathbf{k},$$

and then

$$\boldsymbol{\sigma} - a\boldsymbol{\omega} \times \mathbf{j} = (\sigma_i + a\omega_k)\mathbf{i} + \sigma_j\mathbf{j} + (\sigma_k - a\bar{\omega}_i)\mathbf{k} = 0,$$

from which it is seen that

$$\sigma_i = -a\omega_k, \qquad \sigma_j = 0, \qquad \sigma_k = a\bar{\omega}_i. \tag{5}$$

From the principle of momentum it follows that the equation of motion for the center of gravity is

$$\boldsymbol{\sigma}' + \bar{\boldsymbol{\omega}} \times \boldsymbol{\sigma} = \mathbf{g} + \mathbf{R}, \tag{6}$$

where

$$\mathbf{g} = -g \sin \theta\mathbf{j} - g \cos \theta\mathbf{k}$$

is the acceleration of gravity.

If Eq. (6) is multiplied by $a\mathbf{j}\times$, Eq. (2) is multiplied by $1/m$, and the two equations are then added, $\mathbf{R}$ is eliminated, and there results

$$a\mathbf{j}\times\boldsymbol{\sigma}' + a\mathbf{j}\times(\bar{\boldsymbol{\omega}}\times\boldsymbol{\sigma}) + \frac{1}{m}\mathbf{L}' = a\mathbf{j}\times\mathbf{g}. \tag{7}$$

Since

$$\begin{aligned} a\mathbf{j}\times\boldsymbol{\sigma}' &= a\sigma_k'\mathbf{i} - a\sigma_i'\mathbf{k} \\ &= a^2\bar{\omega}_i'\mathbf{i} + a^2\omega_k'\mathbf{k}, \qquad \text{by Eq. (5),} \end{aligned}$$

and, since $\sigma_j = 0$,

$$a\mathbf{j}\times(\bar{\boldsymbol{\omega}}\times\boldsymbol{\sigma}) = -a\bar{\omega}_j\sigma_i\mathbf{i} - a\bar{\omega}_j\sigma_k\mathbf{k},$$

the components of Eq. (7) give the equations

$$\left.\begin{aligned} (a^2 + A_1)\bar{\omega}_i' + [(a^2 + C_1)\omega_k - A_1\bar{\omega}_k]\bar{\omega}_j &= -ag\cos\theta, \\ A_1\bar{\omega}_j' + [A_1\bar{\omega}_k - C_1\omega_k]\bar{\omega}_i &= 0, \\ (a^2 + C)\omega_k' - a^2\bar{\omega}_i\bar{\omega}_j &= 0. \end{aligned}\right\} \tag{8}$$

If $\omega_i = \theta' \neq 0$, the time can be eliminated from the last two of these equations, since

$$\omega_j' = \frac{d\bar{\omega}_j}{d\theta}\theta' = \bar{\omega}_i\frac{d\bar{\omega}_j}{d\theta},$$

and

$$\omega_k' = \frac{d\omega_k}{d\theta}\theta' = \bar{\omega}_i\frac{d\omega_k}{d\theta}.$$

After removing the factor $\bar{\omega}_i$ and replacing $\bar{\omega}_k$ by $\bar{\omega}_j \cot\theta$, they become

$$\left.\begin{aligned} A_1\frac{d\bar{\omega}_j}{d\theta} + A_1\bar{\omega}_j\cot\theta - C_1\omega_k &= 0, \\ (a^2 + C_1)\frac{d\omega_k}{d\theta} - a^2\bar{\omega}_j &= 0. \end{aligned}\right\} \tag{9}$$

These equations define $\bar{\omega}_j$ and ω_k as functions of θ. If $\bar{\omega}_j$ is eliminated between them, there results a single equation of the second order for ω_k, namely,

$$\frac{d^2\omega_k}{d\theta^2} + \cot\theta\frac{d\omega_k}{d\theta} - \frac{a^2C_1}{A_1C_1 + a^2A_1}\omega_k = 0. \tag{10}$$

If the independent variable is changed by the substitution

$$\cos^2\theta = s, \qquad \text{and if} \qquad p = \frac{a^2C_1}{4A_1(a^2 + C_1)},$$

Eq. (9) becomes

$$s(1 - s)\frac{d^2\omega_k}{ds^2} + \left(\frac{1}{2} - \frac{3}{2}s\right)\frac{d\omega_k}{d\theta} - p\omega_k = 0. \tag{11}$$

The differential equation of the hypergeometric series of Gauss[1] is

$$x(1 - x)\frac{d^2y}{dx^2} + [\gamma - (1 + \alpha + \beta)x]\frac{dy}{dx} - \alpha\beta y = 0; \tag{12}$$

and its complete solution, if γ is not an integer, is

$$y = MF(\alpha, \beta, \gamma; x) + Nx^{1-\gamma}F(\alpha_1, \beta_1, \gamma_1; x), \tag{13}$$

where

$$\alpha_1 = \alpha + 1 - \gamma, \qquad \beta_1 = \beta + 1 - \gamma, \qquad \gamma_1 = 2 - \gamma,$$

and

$$F(\alpha, \beta, \gamma; x) = 1 + \frac{\alpha\beta}{1 \cdot \gamma}x + \frac{\alpha(\alpha + 1)\beta(\beta + 1)}{1 \cdot 2 \quad \gamma(\gamma + 1)}x^2 + \cdot \cdot \cdot . \tag{14}$$

It is evident then from Eq. (11) that

$$\omega_k = MF(\alpha, \beta, \gamma; \cos^2 \theta) + N \cos \theta F(\alpha_1, \beta_1, \gamma_1; \cos^2 \theta), \tag{15}$$

where M and N are constants of integration, and that

$$\gamma = \tfrac{1}{2}, \qquad \alpha + \beta = \tfrac{1}{2}, \qquad \alpha\beta = p;$$
$$\alpha = \tfrac{1}{4} + \tfrac{1}{4}\sqrt{1 - 16p}, \qquad \beta = \tfrac{1}{4} - \tfrac{1}{4}\sqrt{1 - 16p}.$$

For a coin that can be regarded as a thin, homogeneous, circular disk $p = \frac{1}{3}$, and for a hoop that can be regarded as a homogeneous circular circumference $p = \frac{1}{4}$. In both cases α and β are conjugate complex numbers.

After having determined ω_k as a function of θ, $\bar{\omega}_j$ is obtained from the second of Eq. (9),

$$\bar{\omega}_j = \left(1 + \frac{C_1}{a^2}\right)\frac{d\omega_k}{d\theta}.$$

The first of Eq. (8) then gives, by integration,

$$\bar{\omega}_i^2 = K - \frac{(a^2+C_1)^2}{a^2(a^2+A_1)}\omega_k^2 - \frac{2ag \sin \theta}{a^2+A_1} + \frac{2A_1(a^2+C_1)^2}{a^4(a^2+A_1)}\int\left(\frac{d\omega_k}{d\theta}\right)^2 \cot \theta \, d\theta.$$

Finally, the time is defined as a function of θ by the first of Eqs. (1),

[1] "Werke," III, p. 207.

$$t - t_0 = \int \frac{d\theta}{\bar{\omega}_i},$$

and Eqs. (5) give the linear velocities also as functions of θ.

It should be remarked that since there is no loss of energy,

$$\sigma_i^2 + \sigma_j^2 + \sigma_k^2 + A_1(\bar{\omega}_i^2 + \bar{\omega}_j^2) + C_1\omega_k^2 = h - 2ga \sin \theta,$$

where h is a constant. It will be remembered of course that

$$\omega_i = \bar{\omega}_i, \qquad \omega_j = \bar{\omega}_j,$$

but the distinction in notation has been preserved for the sake of clarity.

A Particular Solution.—It is natural to enquire whether the coin or hoop can roll with constant speed around a circle. In such a motion $\bar{\omega}_i$, $\bar{\omega}_j$, and ω_k are constants, and Eqs. (8) reduce to

$$\left.\begin{aligned} [(a^2 + C_1)\omega_k - A_1\bar{\omega}_k]\bar{\omega}_j &= -ag \cos \theta_0, \\ [A_1\bar{\omega}_k - C_1\omega_k]\bar{\omega}_i &= 0, \\ a^2\bar{\omega}_i\bar{\omega}_j &= 0. \end{aligned}\right\} \tag{16}$$

The last two of these equations are satisfied by $\bar{\omega}_i = 0$. The vector $\bar{\boldsymbol{\omega}}$ is vertical, positive upward. Hence

$$\bar{\omega}_j = \bar{\omega} \sin \theta_0, \qquad \bar{\omega}_k = \bar{\omega} \cos \theta_0.$$

Since the angular motion of the center of gravity is constant, $\bar{\omega}$ is constant, and therefore θ_0 is constant. Likewise $\psi' = \bar{\omega}$ is constant and also φ' is constant. The first of Eqs. (16) gives

$$\omega_k = \left(A_1 \sin \theta_0 - \frac{ag}{\bar{\omega}^2}\right)\frac{\bar{\omega} \cot \theta_0}{a^2 + C_1}. \tag{17}$$

The linear velocity of the center of gravity is, by Eq. (5),

$$\sigma_i = -a\omega_k, \qquad \sigma_j = 0, \qquad \sigma_k = 0.$$

Thus $\boldsymbol{\sigma}$ is constant; then Eq. (6) gives

$$\mathbf{R} = -a\omega_k\bar{\omega}\,\mathbf{h} - \mathbf{g}, \tag{18}$$

where

$$\mathbf{h} = \cos \theta\,\mathbf{j} - \sin \theta\,\mathbf{k}$$

is a horizontal unit vector that is always directed toward the axis of the circle on which the coin rolls.

From Eq. (17) it is found that

$$-\varphi' = \left[(a^2 + C_1 - A_1) \sin \theta_0 + \frac{ag}{\bar{\omega}^2}\right]\frac{\bar{\omega} \cot \theta_0}{a^2 + C_1}, \tag{19}$$

so that φ' is opposite in sign to $\bar{\omega}$. The angular velocity of the center of gravity as it moves in its circle is $\bar{\omega}$, and if ρ is the radius of this circle, $\rho\bar{\omega} = \sigma_i = -a\omega_k$. Hence

$$\rho = \left(\frac{ag}{\bar{\omega}^2} - A_1 \sin \theta_0\right)\frac{a\bar{\omega} \cot \theta_0}{a^2 + C_1}.$$

The radius of the circle on which the coin rolls is

$$r = \rho + a \cos \theta_0 = \left[(a^2 + C_1 - A_1) \sin \theta_0 + \frac{ag}{\bar{\omega}^2}\right]\frac{a \cot \theta_0}{a^2 + C_1}. \quad (20)$$

An examination of these equations shows that two of the four constants, r, φ', $\bar{\omega}$, and θ_0, can be chosen at will; the other two are then determined. For example, the radius of the circle on which the coin rolls and the inclination of the coin θ_0 can be chosen, then Eq. (20) determines $\bar{\omega}$, and Eq. (19) determines φ'.

If r is kept fixed and θ_0 tends toward zero, $\bar{\omega}$ tends toward infinity. The limit cannot, of course be attained physically, for R_h [Eq. (18)] also tends toward infinity.

If $\bar{\omega}$ is kept finite and θ_0 tends toward $\pi/2$, r tends toward zero, and the coin merely spins, the rate of spin being arbitrary. But if θ_0 tends toward $\pi/2$, and at the same time $\bar{\omega}$ tends toward zero in such a way that

$$\frac{\cos \theta}{\bar{\omega}} = Q,$$

where Q is an arbitrarily chosen constant, then r tends toward infinity, and φ' is arbitrary. The coin rolls uniformly along a straight line. In the particular case in which φ' also is zero, the coin stands at rest in an equilibrium that is, of course, unstable.

130. Other Forms of the Hypergeometric Series.—The hypergeometric series that were given in the last section are convenient when $\cos \theta$ is small, that is when the coin or hoop is nearly in a vertical plane. They are not convenient when the angle θ is small and the coin is nearly horizontal. For this case a series in the sine of θ converges more rapidly.

If the transformation

$$x = 1 - t$$

is made in the differential equation of the hypergeometric series, Eq. (129.12), the equation becomes

$$t(1-t)\frac{d^2y}{dt^2} + [1+\alpha+\beta-\gamma-(1+\alpha+\beta)t]\frac{dy}{dt} - \alpha\beta y = 0; \quad (1)$$

and if the substitutions

$$\alpha_2 = \alpha, \qquad \beta_2 = \beta, \qquad \gamma_2 = 1 + \alpha + \beta - \gamma$$

are made, the equation is unaltered in form. Since, however, in the present case

$$\alpha + \beta = \tfrac{1}{2} \qquad \text{and} \qquad \gamma = \tfrac{1}{2},$$

γ_2 is equal to 1, and Eq. (1) does not admit two distinct hypergeometric series as solutions. It does, however, admit one such series as a solution and, since $t = \sin^2\theta$, one solution for Eq. (129.10) is

$$\omega_k = M_2F(\alpha_2, \beta_2, 1; \sin^2\theta).$$

A second independent solution is[1]

$$\omega_k = N_2 \log \sin^2\theta F(\alpha_2, \beta_2, 1; \sin^2\theta) + N_2G(\alpha_2, \beta_2, 1; \sin^2\theta)$$

where

$$G = \frac{\alpha_2\beta_2}{1\cdot\gamma}\left(\frac{1}{\alpha_2} + \frac{1}{\beta_2} - \frac{1}{1} - \frac{1}{\gamma_2}\right)\sin^2\theta + \cdots,$$

the G series being the same as the F series, with the omission of the constant term, except that each coefficient is multiplied by a factor, called the adjunct which consists of the sum of the reciprocals of the factors of the numerator diminished by the sum of the reciprocals of the factors of the denominators. The complete solution, therefore, can be written

$$\omega_k = [M_2 + 2N_2 \log \sin\theta]F(\alpha_2, \beta_2, 1; \sin^2\theta) + N_2G(\alpha_2, \beta_2, 1; \sin^2\theta).$$

Kortweg gives another form of the series[2] in which the arguments are $2\sin^2\frac{1}{2}\theta$ and $2\cos^2\frac{1}{2}\theta$, thus avoiding the logarithmic terms that indicate the character of the solution in the neighborhood of $\theta = 0$.

131. A Body of Any Shape on a Horizontal Plane.—With the experience derived from the previous examples, it is not a difficult

[1] Johnson, "Ordinary and Partial Differential Equations," p. 202.
[2] Appell, "Mécanique Rationelle," 4th ed., Vol. II, p. 254.

matter to write down the differential equations of motion for a body of any shape that rolls or rolls and slides on a horizontal plane under the action of gravity and the reaction of the plane.

Let the moving trihedron of reference have its origin O at the center of gravity of the body and its axes have the directions of the principal moments of inertia. It is therefore fixed in the body. With respect to this set of axes the surface of the body can be denoted by

$$\varphi(\xi, \eta, \zeta) = 0. \tag{1}$$

Let the position vector with respect to O of the point of contact with the plane be $\mathbf{r}$, and let $\mathbf{n}$ be a unit vector that has the direction of the *outward* normal to the surface at the point of contact, and therefore

$$\mathbf{n} = \frac{\dfrac{\partial\varphi}{\partial\xi}\mathbf{i} + \dfrac{\partial\varphi}{\partial\eta}\mathbf{j} + \dfrac{\partial\varphi}{\partial\zeta}\mathbf{k}}{\sqrt{(\partial\varphi/\partial\xi)^2 + (\partial\varphi/\partial\eta)^2 + (\partial\varphi/\partial\zeta)^2}}. \tag{2}$$

Let $\boldsymbol{\sigma}$ and $\boldsymbol{\Lambda}$ be the absolute velocity of the center of gravity and the moment of momentum of the body referred to O; and finally, let $\mathbf{R}$ be the reaction of the plane. For simplicity of notation the mass of the body will be taken as the unit of mass.

The principles of momentum and the moment of momentum then give the two equations

$$\boldsymbol{\sigma}' + \boldsymbol{\omega} \times \boldsymbol{\sigma} = g\mathbf{n} + \mathbf{R}, \tag{3}$$

and

$$\boldsymbol{\Lambda}' + \boldsymbol{\omega} \times \boldsymbol{\Lambda} = \mathbf{r} \times \mathbf{R}. \tag{4}$$

Since the plane is horizontal, the normal at the point of contact is always vertical, and the outward normal is directed downward, so that, if $\mathbf{g}$ is the acceleration of gravity,

$$\mathbf{g} = g\mathbf{n}.$$

With respect to fixed space $\mathbf{n}$ is constant, therefore

$$\mathbf{n}' + \boldsymbol{\omega} \times \mathbf{n} = 0. \tag{5}$$

Equations (3), (4), and (5) hold in all cases provided φ is of such a nature that there is but one point of contact with the plane, and at that point there is a definite tangent plane.

Pure Rolling.—The equation of constraint, however, depends upon the character of the motion. If the motion is a pure rolling and pivoting, the point of contact of the body is at rest relative to the horizontal plane. Its velocity of translation is $\boldsymbol{\delta}$ and its velocity due to the instantaneous rotation is $\boldsymbol{\omega} \times \mathbf{r}$. Hence

$$\boldsymbol{\delta} + \boldsymbol{\omega} \times \mathbf{r} = 0.$$

Rolling and Sliding.—If the body is sliding and rolling, the absolute velocity of the particle of the body that is in contact with the plane is not zero, and the equation of constraint is

$$\boldsymbol{\delta} + \boldsymbol{\omega} \times \mathbf{r} = -\mathbf{v},$$

where $-\mathbf{v}$ is the absolute velocity of the particle in contact with the plane. The negative sign is attached because the frictional component of $\mathbf{R}$ is opposite to the direction of motion; $\mathbf{R}_{ij}$ has the same direction as $\mathbf{v}$, and $\mathbf{R} \cdot \mathbf{v}$ is positive.

As long as the body is sliding the reaction of the horizontal plane makes a constant angle ϵ with the normal, where ϵ is the angle of friction, and

$$\mathbf{R} \cdot \mathbf{n} = R \cos \epsilon.$$

Since the three vectors $\mathbf{R}$, $\mathbf{n}$, and $\mathbf{v}$ lie in the same plane, their scalar triple product, Sec. 4, vanishes, that is

$$\mathbf{V} \cdot \mathbf{R} \times \mathbf{n} = 0.$$

Smooth Contact.—In the case in which there is no friction the particle in contact with the plane moves in the plane, and the equation of constraint is

$$\mathbf{n} \cdot [\boldsymbol{\delta} + \boldsymbol{\omega} \times \mathbf{r}] = 0.$$

The reaction is normal to the horizontal plane, and therefore

$$\mathbf{R} = -R\mathbf{n}.$$

Since all of the forces that are acting upon the body are collinear with $\mathbf{n}$, the components of $\boldsymbol{\delta}$ that are parallel to the plane are constants. It is only the component that is perpendicular to the plane that varies.

Problems

1. In the illustrative example of Sec. 124, show that a horizontal plane section of the cone described by the instantaneous axis is an ellipse similar to that described by the center of the sphere but turned through an angle of 90°. Show also that the surface described by the instantaneous axis in fixed space is of the fourth degree.

2. If a sphere is rolling on a curved surface the normal pressure of the surface on the sphere is

$$R_k = \frac{\sigma_i^2}{\rho_i} + \frac{\sigma_j^2}{\rho_j} - F_k.$$

Compare this expression with the normal pressure of a surface on a particle which is sliding on a surface (I. **333**).

3. Show that a necessary and sufficient condition that the pivoting of the sphere about the normal is constant, (ω_k = constant), is that the center of the sphere is moving along a line of curvature.

4. If the moving trihedron defined in Sec. 121 moves in such a way that the ξ-axis is always tangent to the path described by the center of gravity of the sphere instead of being tangent to one of the lines of curvature, if ρ is the radius of curvature of a normal section of the surface through the tangent to the path at the center of gravity and if τ is the radius of geodetic torsion,[1] then σ_j and ω_i are always zero, and

$$\theta_i = \frac{\sigma}{\tau}, \qquad \theta_j = \frac{\sigma}{\rho}, \qquad \text{and} \qquad \theta_k = \frac{\sigma}{\rho}\tan\alpha,$$

where, as before, α is the angle between the osculating plane and the normal plane. The components of Eq. (122.4) now give the equations

$$\sigma' = \frac{a^2}{a^2 + k^2}F_i + \frac{k^2}{a^2 + k^2}a\omega_k\frac{\sigma}{\tau},$$

$$\frac{\sigma^2}{\rho}\tan\alpha = \frac{a^2}{a^2 + k^2}F_j + \frac{k^2}{a^2 + k^2}a\omega_k\frac{\sigma}{\rho};$$

and the third of Eqs. (121.6) becomes

$$a\omega_k' = -\frac{\sigma^2}{\tau}.$$

5. If $\sigma \not\equiv 0$, prove that the angular velocity ω_k is constant when and only when the center of gravity of the sphere moves along a line of curvature.

6. Show that if a homogeneous sphere is moving along a line of curvature without spin about the normal to the surface, the **j**-component of the applied force is equal to the **j**-component of the centrifugal force regarding the mass of the sphere as concentrated into a particle at the center of gravity, multiplied by $\frac{7}{5}$.

7. If there are no applied forces, show that

$$\sigma^2\left(\frac{2}{7} + \tan^2\alpha\right) = \text{constant}, \qquad a\omega_k = \frac{7}{2}\sigma\tan\alpha,$$

$$\frac{d}{ds}\log\left(\frac{2}{7} + \tan^2\alpha\right) = -\frac{2}{\tau}\tan\alpha$$

and that the path will be a geodesic if and only if the path is a plane curve. Under these circumstances the velocity, $\dot{s}$, of the center of gravity is constant.

8. A sphere of radius a rolls without slipping on the inside of a spherical bowl the radius of which is $a + b$. If the center of the bowl is taken as the

[1] Eisenhart, "Differential Geometry," p. 138.

origin of a rectangular coordinate system with the z-axis vertical, the coordinates of the center of the rolling sphere are

$$x = b\cos\varphi\cos\psi, \qquad y = b\cos\varphi\sin\psi, \qquad z = b\sin\varphi.$$

Let the moving trihedron have its **k**-direction toward the center of the bowl, the **i**-direction along the meridian toward the north pole, and the **j**-direction tangent to the circle of latitude at the center of the rolling sphere. Prove the following formulas:

$$\sigma_i = b\varphi', \qquad \sigma_j = b\cos\varphi\psi', \qquad \sigma_k = 0;$$

$$\rho_i = \rho_j = b, \qquad \alpha_i = 0, \qquad \alpha_j = \varphi;$$

$$\theta_i = \frac{\sigma_j}{b}, \qquad \theta_j = -\frac{\sigma_i}{b}, \qquad \theta_k = -\frac{\sigma_j}{b}\tan\varphi;$$

$$\omega_i = -\frac{\sigma_j}{a}, \qquad \omega_j = +\frac{\sigma_i}{a}, \qquad \omega_k = \text{constant};$$

$$F_i = -g\cos\varphi, \qquad F_j = 0, \qquad F_k = +g\sin\varphi;$$

$$\sigma_i' + \frac{\sigma_j^2}{b}\tan\varphi = -\frac{a^2}{a^2+k^2}g\cos\varphi + \frac{k^2}{a^2+k^2}\frac{a}{b}\omega_k\sigma_j,$$

$$\sigma_j' - \frac{\sigma_i\sigma_j}{b}\tan\varphi = 0 - \frac{k^2}{a^2+k^2}\frac{a}{b}\omega_k\sigma_i;$$

$$\sigma_i^2 + \sigma_j^2 = \frac{2ga^2}{a^2+k^2}(z_0 - z),$$

$$\sigma_j\cos\varphi = \frac{k^2\omega_k}{a^2+k^2}\frac{a}{b}(z_1 - z),$$

where z_0 and z_1 are constants of integration, and

$$R_k = \frac{g}{b(a^2+k^2)}\{2a^2z_0 - (3a^2+k^2)z\}.$$

Then

$$z'^2 = \frac{2ga^2}{b^2(a^2+k^2)}(z_0 - z)(b^2 - z^2) - \frac{k^2\omega_k}{a^2+k^2}\frac{a}{b}(z_1 - z)^2,$$

$$\psi' = \frac{k^2a\omega_k}{a^2+k^2}\frac{z_1 - z}{b^2 - z^2}.$$

Compare the last two equations with those of the spherical pendulum, I, **341**.

9. If the coefficient of sliding friction is $\frac{1}{5}$ and the initial speed of sliding is 11.27 feet per second, a billiard ball will slide for one half of a second before it begins to roll.

10. If P is the point of contact of a billiard ball on the table and Q is the center of oscillation of the ball with respect to P, show that the particle of the ball that is at Q has a velocity **v** that is constant throughout the motion, and that in the purely rolling motion the velocity of the center of the ball is $\frac{5}{7}$**v.**

11. If the initial velocity of the center of the ball is **v**, the straight-line path of the pure rolling intersects the initial line which has the direction **v** at a point P_1 which is at a distance $vT/2$ from the initial point, T being the time of sliding.

12. On any surface of revolution the lines of curvature are the meridians and the parallels of latitude. Discuss the equations of motion of a sphere rolling on the inside of such a surface.

13. A homogeneous right circular cylinder whose altitude is equal to the diameter of the base rolls on a rough horizontal plane with its axis inclined 45° to the vertical. If n is the angular velocity of the cylinder about its axis and m is the angular velocity of its center of gravity, show that

$$\frac{m}{n} = 30\sqrt{\frac{2}{31}}.$$

14. If v is the speed of the center of gravity of a coin that is rolling along a straight line (the edge of the coin being regarded as a line), show that $v^2 > \frac{1}{3}ag$, and for a hoop $v^2 > \frac{1}{4}ag$.

15. If a cone of any shape is rolling on a fixed plane, it has but one degree of freedom, and the energy integral gives the differential equation of motion. Suppose the cone is a heavy right circular cone with the generating angle β, the length of the generator being l, and that it rolls on a plane whose inclination to the plane of the horizon is α.

If θ is the angle between the line of greatest slope on the plane and the line of contact with the cone, show that the angle θ satisfies the differential equation

$$\theta'' + \frac{g \sin \alpha}{l(\frac{1}{5} + \cos^2 \beta)} \sin \theta = 0,$$

which is the equation of motion of a simple pendulum of length

$$l(\tfrac{1}{5} + \cos^2 \beta) \operatorname{cosec} \alpha.$$

16. A heavy, solid, homogeneous cylinder of radius r and mass m rolls on the inside of a cylindrical shell of radius R and mass M which is supported by its axis and turns freely about it. If θ is the angle which the plane through the two axes makes with the vertical plane through the axis of the cylindrical shell show that the angle θ satisfies the differential equation

$$\theta'' + \frac{2M + m}{3M + m} \frac{g}{R - r} \sin \theta = 0,$$

which is the equation of motion of a simple pendulum of length

$$\frac{3M + m}{2M + m}(R - r).$$

17. A sphere of radius r rolls down the cycloid

$$x = a(2\theta + \sin 2\theta), \qquad y = -a(1 + \cos 2\theta).$$

Show that the speed of its center at the lowest point is given by the equation

$$v^2 = \tfrac{10}{7}g(2a - r).$$

CHAPTER IX

IMPULSIVE FORCES

132. Definitions.—When the force to which a body is subjected rises from zero to great magnitude and then sinks back to zero again in an interval of time that is very short, the force is said to be an *impulsive* one. Various names are used to denote this type of action: for example, a baseball struck by a bat is said to have received a *blow;* two balls on a billiard table are said to *collide;* the countryside is said to have received a *shock* from an earthquake; a bullet is driven from a gun by an *explosion;* we speak of the *impact* of a bullet on its target; etc. The chief characteristic of impulsive forces being the extremely short interval of time during which they act, an interval so short that the action is over with before the object has sensibly left its initial position. Also the force is so great that the ordinary forces that are acting, such as gravity, are completely negligible during the brief interval of the impulse.

Consider a particle, or a mass that is not rotating. If $\mathbf{r}$ is its position vector and m is its mass, the equation of momentum is

$$m\mathbf{r}'' = \mathbf{F}, \tag{1}$$

where $\mathbf{F}$ is the sum of all of the forces that are acting on it. The time integral

$$m\mathbf{r}' - m\mathbf{r}_0' = \int_{t_0}^{t} \mathbf{F}\, dt \tag{2}$$

measures the change in momentum of the particle, or body, in the interval of time $t - t_0$. If $\mathbf{F}$ is an impulsive force and the time interval $t - t_0$ is very short, the integral

$$\mathbf{I} = \int_{t_0}^{t} \mathbf{F}\, dt$$

is called the *impulse.* It has the dimensions of momentum MLT^{-1}, and must be distinguished from $\mathbf{F}$ which is the impulsive force. Equation (2) states that *the change in the momentum of the particle, or mass, is equal to the impulse which it has received.*

Similarly, if **L** is the moment of momentum of a particle, or mass, which is acted upon by an impulsive force **F** at a point whose position when referred to a point of fixed space, or to the center of gravity of the mass, is **r**, then, by Sec. 45,

$$\mathbf{L}' = \mathbf{r} \times \mathbf{F},$$

and since **r** does not change sensibly during the impact,

$$\mathbf{L} - \mathbf{L}_0 = \mathbf{r} \times \int_{t_0}^{t} \mathbf{F}\, dt = \mathbf{r} \times \mathbf{I};$$

that is, *the change in the moment of momentum of a particle, or mass, due to an impact, is equal to the moment of the impulse.*

133. General Theorems for Impulsive Forces.—Notwithstanding the fact that impulsive forces are singled out as a class and given a name, they are still forces, and the general theorems for systems of free particles that were derived in Chapter III still hold, provided only the individual particles of the system act upon one another only in the lines that join them. Indeed, if

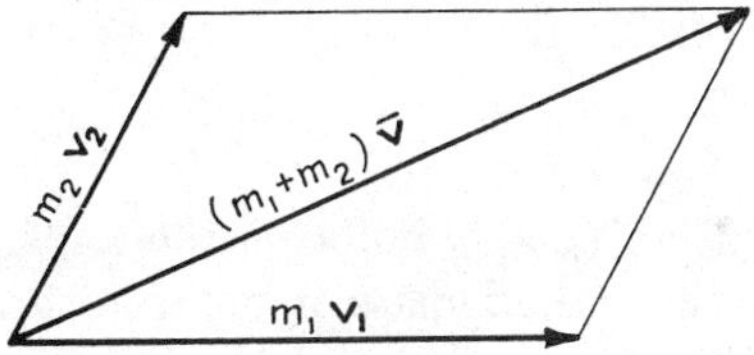

FIG. 72.

all of the particles that participate in an impulsive action are regarded as a system by itself, it can be regarded as an isolated system, since other forces that are acting upon the system are negligible during the action of the impulse. Since for every isolated system the momentum and the moment of momentum are constant, it follows that the momentum and the moment of momentum of the system are not altered by an impulsive action, for the forces of an impulse belong to the class of *interior* forces. A reference to Sec. 34 will show that this is not the case, in general, with the energy of the system. The exterior kinetic energy is not altered by interior forces, but the interior kinetic energy can be altered by interior forces.

As an example, consider two masses m_1 and m_2 that are moving with the velocities $\mathbf{v}_1$ and $\mathbf{v}_2$, but are not rotating, Fig. 72.

Suppose these two masses collide and unite into a single mass $m_1 + m_2$ that has the velocity $\mathbf{v}$ and is not rotating, as, for example, a bullet shot into the center of gravity of a block of wood. If the velocities, referred to the center of gravity of the system, are $\mathbf{u}_1$ and $\mathbf{u}_2$, and $\bar{\mathbf{v}}$ is the velocity of the center of gravity itself,

$$\mathbf{v}_1 = \bar{\mathbf{v}} + \mathbf{u}_1, \qquad \mathbf{v}_2 = \bar{\mathbf{v}} + \mathbf{u}_2. \tag{1}$$

The expression for the momentum of the system,

$$m_1\mathbf{v}_1 + m_2\mathbf{v}_2 = (m_1 + m_2)\bar{\mathbf{v}},$$

shows that

$$m_1\mathbf{u}_1 + m_2\mathbf{u}_2 = 0. \tag{2}$$

If T is the total kinetic energy, T_e and T_i the exterior and interior kinetic energies respectively, then

$$\begin{aligned} T &= \tfrac{1}{2}m_1\mathbf{v}_1 \cdot \mathbf{v}_1 + \tfrac{1}{2}m_2\mathbf{v}_2 \cdot \mathbf{v}_2, \\ T_e &= \tfrac{1}{2}(m_1 + m_2)\bar{\mathbf{v}} \cdot \bar{\mathbf{v}}, \\ T_i &= \tfrac{1}{2}m_1\mathbf{u}_1 \cdot \mathbf{u}_1 + \tfrac{1}{2}m_2\mathbf{u}_2 \cdot \mathbf{u}_2. \end{aligned}$$

It will be found readily from Eqs. (1) and (2) that

$$T = T_e + T_i.$$

Before the collision $T_i \neq 0$, but after the collision, owing to the hypothesis that the united mass is not rotating, $T_i = 0$, since $\mathbf{u}_1 = \mathbf{u}_2 = 0$. The total kinetic energy is reduced to T_e which remains unaltered, since $m_1 + m_2$ and $\bar{v}$ remain unaltered.

In accordance with the principle of the conservation of energy, this amount of energy, T_i, appears in vibrations or in molecular motions whose total momentum is zero, or in some other form, such as radiation, for example.

134. Head-on Collision of Two Elastic Spheres.—A collision between two spheres will be called a *head-on* collision if the motion of each relative to their common center of gravity lies in the straight line that joins their centers. It is assumed that the center of gravity of each sphere is at the geometric center. Under this assumption the impulse of collision acts at the points of contact of the two spheres and in the line of centers. Vector notation is not necessary since the motion is entirely straight-line motion.

Let m_1 and m_2 be the masses of the two spheres, v_1 and v_2 their velocities relative to their common center of gravity before impact, u_1 and u_2 their velocities after impact, and let the impulse of collision be written

$$I = \frac{m_1 m_2}{m_1 + m_2} v. \tag{1}$$

Then, if the notation

$$M = \frac{m_1 m_2}{m_1 + m_2}, \qquad \mu_1 = \frac{m_1}{m_1 + m_2}, \qquad \mu_2 = \frac{m_2}{m_1 + m_2}, \tag{2}$$

be adopted,

$$\left. \begin{aligned} u_1 &= v_1 + \mu_2 v, \\ u_2 &= v_2 - \mu_1 v. \end{aligned} \right\} \tag{3}$$

The momentum relative to their common center of gravity is

$$m_1 v_1 + m_2 v_2 = 0, \tag{4}$$

and the vis viva before collision is

$$V = m_1 v_1^2 + m_2 v_2^2.$$

After collision the vis viva is

$$U = m_1 u_1^2 + m_2 u_2^2,$$

which by virtue of Eqs. (3) becomes

$$U = V + M[v^2 + 2v(v_1 - v_2)]. \tag{5}$$

Now, by Eq. (4),

$$v_2 = -\frac{m_1}{m_2} v_1, \qquad M(v_1 - v_2) = m_1 v_1, \qquad \text{and} \qquad MV = m_1^2 v_1^2,$$

so that, on multiplying through by M, Eq. (5) becomes

$$MU = (Mv + m_1 v_1)^2. \tag{6}$$

Suppose the kinetic energy is altered by the collision and that

$$U = e^2 V,$$

e^2 being a positive number. Equation (6) then reduces to

$$e^2 m_1^2 v_1^2 = (Mv + m_1 v_1)^2,$$

whence

$$Mv = (-1 \pm e) m_1 v_1,$$

and, Eqs. (3),

$$u_1 = \pm ev_1, \qquad u_2 = \pm ev_2.$$

The hypothesis used in this analysis has been merely that the kinetic energy has been altered by the collision. If a bullet were shot through the center of a wooden sphere, the bullet and the sphere would continue in their original directions and the positive sign would be taken before e in the above expressions; but if the spheres rebound and separate, the negative sign must be taken, since, by hypothesis, the velocities have changed sign. In either case, if $e = 1$, there is no loss of kinetic energy; but obviously work is done by the bullet in boring its way through the sphere in the first case, and one can scarcely doubt but that vibrations are set up in the spheres in the second case, and these vibrations absorb a certain amount of kinetic energy. On the other hand if there were an explosive at the point of contact e might be greater than one, the increase of kinetic energy coming from the explosive. In any event, whether e is greater or less than one the speeds of the two spheres after collision are proportional to their speeds before impact. If $e = 0$, the two spheres unite and the interior kinetic energy is reduced to zero, just as in the example considered in the previous section.

It was found by Newton from experiments on balls of different kinds that for any two given spheres the value of e is less than unity and is independent of the relative velocity, provided this velocity is not high enough to deform the spheres permanently or to break them, and this experience of Newton's has been confirmed by others. In a general way the harder the two balls are, the more nearly e approaches unity.

The impact begins when the first two points of the spheres are in contact. As the impact proceeds the contact widens into an area owing to an elastic deformation of the spheres. The velocities relative to the center of gravity of the system are rapidly reduced to zero, at which time there is a maximum deformation of the spheres. The elastic forces that have been called into play by the deformation then begin to restore the figures of the spheres. This restoration of the figures drives the centers of the spheres apart and acts until the surfaces are no longer in contact. The forces of restitution could equal the forces of compression only if the spheres had no residual vibrations of any kind. This is a conceivable possibility, but does not seem very probable. In this event e, which is called the *coefficient of restitution* is equal to one, but in general the forces of restitution are smaller than the forces of compression in the ratio $e:1$.

It is also doubtful if e is independent of the relative sizes of the two spheres. During the interval of compression a compression wave is set up in both spheres. If the spheres are of the same size and the same material, the two periods are the same and both waves participate in driving the spheres apart, but if the periods are different as is the case when the two spheres are very unequal, the wave in the smaller sphere will return first and effect a separation before the return of the longer period wave. More energy remains therefore in the larger sphere in the form of vibration, and e is smaller than when the two spheres are of the same size.

135. Glancing Collision of Two Smooth Spheres.—Let the motion be referred to the center of gravity of the system. If $\mathbf{v}_1$ and $\mathbf{v}_2$ are the velocities before collision and $\mathbf{u}_1$ and $\mathbf{u}_2$ the velocities after collision, then, by the principle of momentum,

$$\left.\begin{aligned} m_1\mathbf{v}_1 + m_2\mathbf{v}_2 &= 0, \\ \text{and} \qquad m_1\mathbf{u}_1 + m_2\mathbf{u}_2 &= 0. \end{aligned}\right\} \tag{1}$$

The velocities $\mathbf{v}_1$ and $\mathbf{v}_2$ are collinear but the centers of the two spheres do not move in the same straight line. Likewise $\mathbf{u}_1$ and $\mathbf{u}_2$ are collinear, Fig. 73.

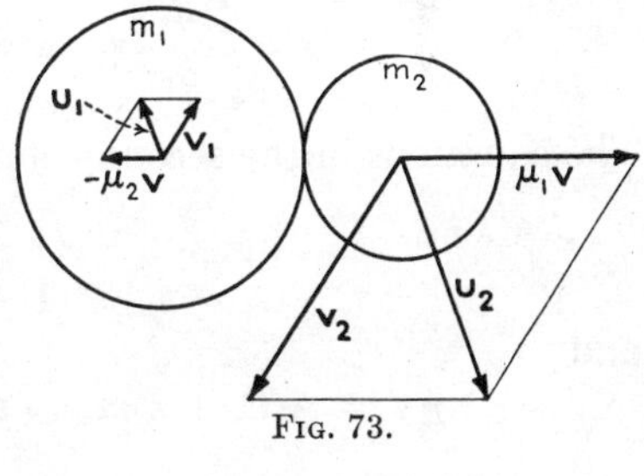

Fig. 73.

Let $\mathbf{a}$ be a unit vector in the line joining the centers of the spheres at the instant of impact, directed from the center of m_2 toward the center of m_1. Since the spheres are smooth, the impulse acts in the line of centers and it can be written

$$\mathbf{I} = \pm\frac{m_1m_2}{m_1 + m_2}v\mathbf{a},$$

the positive sign giving the impulse on m_1 and the negative sign on m_2; and as before

$$M = \frac{m_1m_2}{m_1 + m_2}, \quad \mu_1 = \frac{m_1}{m_1 + m_2}, \quad \mu_2 = \frac{m_2}{m_1 + m_2}, \quad \mu_1 + \mu_2 = 1.$$

The equations of momenta, then, are

$$\left.\begin{aligned} m_1\mathbf{u}_1 &= m_1\mathbf{v}_1 + Mv\mathbf{a}, \\ m_2\mathbf{u}_2 &= m_2\mathbf{v}_2 - Mv\mathbf{a}, \end{aligned} \quad \text{whence} \quad \begin{aligned} \mathbf{u}_1 &= \mathbf{v}_1 + \mu_2 v\mathbf{a}, \\ \mathbf{u}_2 &= \mathbf{v}_2 - \mu_1 v\mathbf{a}. \end{aligned}\right\} \tag{2}$$

The difference between the equations in the last column gives

$$\mathbf{u}_2 - \mathbf{u}_1 = \mathbf{v}_2 - \mathbf{v}_1 - v\mathbf{a},$$

and on multiplying through by $\cdot\,\mathbf{a}$, it is found that

$$v = (\mathbf{v}_2 - \mathbf{v}_1) \cdot \mathbf{a} - (\mathbf{u}_2 - \mathbf{u}_1) \cdot \mathbf{a}.$$

Since the impulse acts in the line of centers, the components of the velocities perpendicular to this line are not altered, but by Sec. 134 the components in the line are multiplied by $-e$, where e is the coefficient of restitution. Hence

$$(\mathbf{u}_2 - \mathbf{u}_1) \cdot \mathbf{a} = -e(\mathbf{v}_2 - \mathbf{v}_1) \cdot \mathbf{a},$$

and

$$v = (1 + e)(\mathbf{v}_2 - \mathbf{v}_1) \cdot \mathbf{a}.$$

From Eqs. (1) it is found that

$$\mathbf{v}_2 - \mathbf{v}_1 = \frac{\mathbf{v}_2}{\mu_1} = -\frac{\mathbf{v}_1}{\mu_2},$$

so that the expression for v can also be written

$$v = \frac{1 + e}{\mu_1}\mathbf{v}_2 \cdot \mathbf{a} = -\frac{1 + e}{\mu_2}\mathbf{v}_1 \cdot \mathbf{a}. \tag{3}$$

The equations in the second column of Eqs. (2) then become

$$\left.\begin{aligned} \mathbf{u}_1 &= \mathbf{v}_1 - (1 + e)\mathbf{v}_1 \cdot \mathbf{a}\ \mathbf{a}, \\ \mathbf{u}_2 &= \mathbf{v}_2 - (1 + e)\mathbf{v}_2 \cdot \mathbf{a}\ \mathbf{a}. \end{aligned}\right\} \tag{4}$$

and

$$\pm I = +(1 + e)m_2\mathbf{v}_2 \cdot \mathbf{a} = -(1 + e)m_1\mathbf{v}_1 \cdot \mathbf{a}.$$

By taking the dot product of $\mathbf{u}_1$ into itself it is found that

$$\mathbf{u}_1 \cdot \mathbf{u}_1 = \mathbf{v}_1 \cdot \mathbf{v}_1 - (1 - e^2)(\mathbf{v}_1 \cdot \mathbf{a})^2.$$

If now $\mathbf{b}$ is a unit vector that has the direction of $\mathbf{v}_1$, this equation can be written

$$u_1^2 = v_1^2[1 - (1 - e^2)(\mathbf{b} \cdot \mathbf{a})^2],$$

or

$$u_1 = \epsilon v_1; \qquad \text{and similarly} \qquad u_2 = \epsilon v_2,$$

where

$$\epsilon = \sqrt{1 - (1 - e^2)(\mathbf{b} \cdot \mathbf{a})^2}.$$

Thus the ratio of the speeds with respect to the center of mass after collision is the same as before collision, which is evident more directly from Eqs. (1). The letter ϵ is independent of v_1 and v_2, but varies, of course, with **a** and **b**. It is equal to e if **a** and **b** are collinear, and equal to 1 if they are mutually perpendicular.

If $m_2 = \infty$ and $\mathbf{v}_2 = 0$, the second of Eqs. (4) shows that $\mathbf{u}_2 = 0$. The mass m_2 can be regarded as a solid surface and $\mathbf{v}_1$ as the velocity of m_1 with respect to this surface. The first of Eqs. (4) is then the equation of rebound of an elastic sphere from a solid surface.

136. The Stroke of a Billiard Cue.—In the game of billiards the cue ball is started into motion by a sharp blow with the cue. The tip of the cue is well chalked so as to make the coefficient of friction of the cue with the ball as large as possible, in the neighborhood of unity, perhaps. The ball rolls on a hard level surface which is covered with broadcloth and is therefore inelastic. The coefficient of friction between the ball and the table is small. Experiments carried out by Morin at the request of Poisson showed that the laws of friction are the same under impulsive forces as they are under forces of smaller magnitudes. Assuming that this is true and that there is no slippage at the tip of the cue, it is desired to find the state of motion of the ball due to the stroke of the cue at the instant after impact.

Let M be the mass and a the radius of the ball, and $M\mathbf{u}$ the impulse of the stroke. The velocity $\mathbf{u}$ may have any direction subject to the restriction that its vertical component must be downward, or zero, but not upward. Let $M\mathbf{t}$ be the reaction of the table. This also is an impulse, so that the ball is subjected to two simultaneous impulses. If slippage occurs between the ball and the table, as is usually the case when the motion is not one of pure rolling, the impulse $M\mathbf{t}$ lies on the cone of friction whose apex is at C and whose generating angle is ϵ. Finally, let **i, j, k** be a system of mutually orthogonal unit vectors, and let **r** with origin at the center of the sphere be the position vector of the point of application P of the impulse (Fig. 74). The system of unit vectors is chosen so that the **ij**-plane through the center of the sphere is horizontal and the **ki**-plane is parallel to the vector **u**.

The elements of the problem that are given are a, M, **u**, **r**, and ϵ. It is required to find the reaction of the table **t**, the velocity of the center of the sphere, **v** and the angular velocity, or rate of spin, $\boldsymbol{\omega}$. As a matter of notation, let

$$\mathbf{u} = u(u_i\mathbf{i} + u_j\mathbf{j} + u_k\mathbf{k}), \qquad \mathbf{v} = v(v_i\mathbf{i} + v_j\mathbf{j} + v_k\mathbf{k}),$$
$$\mathbf{r} = a(r_i\mathbf{i} + r_j\mathbf{j} + r_k\mathbf{k}), \qquad \mathbf{t} = t(t_i\mathbf{i} + t_j\mathbf{j} + t_k\mathbf{k}),$$
$$\boldsymbol{\omega} = \omega(\omega_i\mathbf{i} + \omega_j\mathbf{j} + \omega_k\mathbf{k}),$$

so that u_i, u_j, u_k, etc. are the direction cosines of the vectors, and u, v, r, etc. are their tensors.

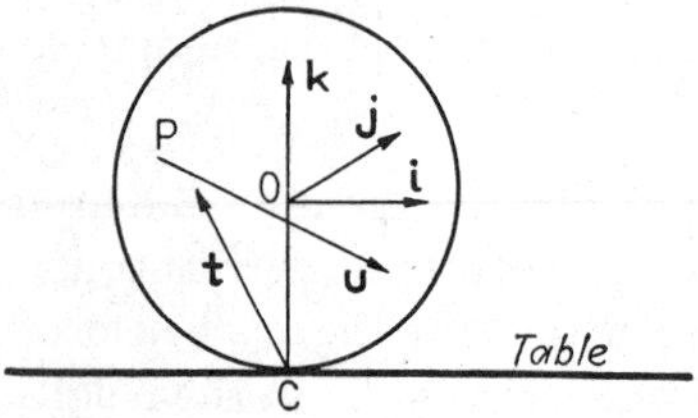

FIG. 74.

Since the table is hard and inelastic, the upward, or vertical, component of **t** is equal in magnitude and opposite in sign to the vertical component of **u**, that is,

$$tt_k = -uu_k,$$

and, since **t** lies on the cone of friction,

$$t_k = \cos\epsilon.$$

Hence

$$t = -\frac{u_k}{\cos\epsilon}u.$$

From the manner in which the **i**, **j**, **k**-vectors were chosen

$$u_j = 0.$$

The velocity of the center of the sphere, then, is

$$\mathbf{v} = \mathbf{u} + \mathbf{t} = u\left[\left(u_i - \frac{t_iu_k}{\cos\epsilon}\right)\mathbf{i} - \left(\frac{t_ju_k}{\cos\epsilon}\right)\mathbf{j}\right].$$

The sum of the moments of the two impulses with respect to the center of the sphere is the change in the moment of momentum of the ball. Since initially the ball was at rest, the change in the moment of momentum is the same as the moment of momentum of the ball after impact. The radius of gyration of the ball is $\sqrt{\frac{2}{5}}a$. Therefore

$$\tfrac{2}{5}a^2\boldsymbol{\omega} = \mathbf{r} \times \mathbf{u} - a\mathbf{k} \times \mathbf{t},$$

since **r** is the point of application of **u** and $-a\mathbf{k}$ is the point of application of **t**. The evaluation of this expression gives

$$\omega = \frac{5}{a}\frac{u}{}\left[\left(r_j u_k - \frac{t_j u_k}{\cos\epsilon}\right)\mathbf{i} + \left(r_k u_i - r_i u_k + \frac{t_i u_k}{\cos\epsilon}\right)\mathbf{j} - r_j u_i \mathbf{k}\right].$$

The velocity of the point of contact C of the ball with the table is $\mathbf{v} - a\,\omega \times \mathbf{k}$. Since the frictional component of **t** is in the same straight line as this velocity, but opposite in direction,

$$\mathbf{u} + \mathbf{t} - \frac{5}{2a}(\mathbf{r} \times \mathbf{u}) \times \mathbf{k} + \frac{5}{2a}(\mathbf{k} \times \mathbf{t}) \times \mathbf{k} = l\,\mathbf{k} \times (\mathbf{k} \times \mathbf{t}),$$

where l is some constant, and $-\mathbf{k} \times (\mathbf{k} \times \mathbf{t})$ is the projection of **t** on the **ij**-plane. If it is agreed to consider only the components of the vectors that lie in the **ij**-plane, this equation can be written in the simplified form

$$\mathbf{u} + \frac{5}{2a}\mathbf{k} \times (\mathbf{r} \times \mathbf{u}) = m\mathbf{t},$$

where m is some constant. The evaluation of this expression gives

$$u\left[u_i + \frac{5}{2}(r_i u_k - r_k u_i)\right]\mathbf{i} + \frac{5}{2}u r_j u_k \mathbf{j} = -mu\frac{u_k}{\cos\epsilon}[t_i\mathbf{i} + t_j\mathbf{j}].$$

The ratio of the coefficients of **j** to **i** in this equation gives

$$\frac{5r_j u_k}{(2 - 5r_k)u_i + 5r_i u_k} = \frac{t_j}{t_i} = \tan\beta, \text{ say},$$

and this equation, combined with the equation

$$t_i^2 + t_j^2 = \sin^2\epsilon,$$

which exists by virtue of the fact that $t_k = \cos\epsilon$, determines t_i and t_j; namely

$$t_i = \sin\epsilon\cos\beta,$$
$$t_j = \sin\epsilon\sin\beta,$$
$$t_k = \cos\epsilon.$$

Hence, if μ is the coefficient of friction,

$$\mathbf{t} = -uu_k[\mu\cos\beta\,\mathbf{i} + \mu\sin\beta\,\mathbf{j} + \mathbf{k}].$$

If the stroke of the cue is horizontal, $u_k = 0$, $u_i = 1$ and **t** vanishes; and, if $r_i = \cos\varphi\cos\theta$, $r_j = \cos\varphi\sin\theta$, $r_k = \sin\varphi$, then

$$\mathbf{v} = u\,\mathbf{i}, \qquad \omega = \tfrac{5}{2}u(\sin\varphi\,\mathbf{j} - \cos\varphi\sin\theta\,\mathbf{k}).$$

The ball spins about the **j**-axis in the forward direction if φ is positive and in the negative direction if φ is negative, provided $\theta = \pi$. If $\theta > \pi$, there is in addition a positive spin about the vertical axis, and if $\theta < \pi$ a negative spin. Whatever φ or θ may be the center of the ball moves in the direction of the stroke, but the spin depends upon both φ and θ.

If the stroke is nearly vertical, as in a massé shot, if $\theta = \pi$ and

$$\frac{u_i}{u_k} < \frac{t_i}{\cos \epsilon} = \mu,$$

the ball will not slip either on the table or at the tip, and the ball does not move at all, for friction will not give a negative motion.

137. The Rebound from a Rail.—As in the preceding section, let M be the mass of the ball and a its radius. Let $\mathbf{v}_1$ be the velocity of the center of the ball just before contact with the rail and $\mathbf{v}_2$ the velocity just after contact; let $\boldsymbol{\omega}_1$ be the spin before contact and $\boldsymbol{\omega}_2$ the spin just after contact; let $M\mathbf{r}$ be the impulse of the rail and $M\mathbf{t}$ the impulse of the table, and finally, let **i**, **j**, and **k** be a system of unit vectors with **i** parallel to the rail, **j** perpendicular to the rail, but parallel to the table, and **k** vertical, directed upward (Fig. 75) so that

$$\begin{aligned} \mathbf{v}_1 &= v_{1i}\mathbf{i} + v_{1j}\mathbf{j} + 0\ \mathbf{k}, & \boldsymbol{\omega}_1 &= \omega_{1i}\mathbf{i} + \omega_{1j}\mathbf{j} + \omega_{1k}\mathbf{k},\\ \mathbf{v}_2 &= v_{2i}\mathbf{i} + v_{2j}\mathbf{j} + v_{2k}\mathbf{k}, & \boldsymbol{\omega}_2 &= \omega_{2i}\mathbf{i} + \omega_{2j}\mathbf{j} + \omega_{2k}\mathbf{k},\\ \mathbf{r} &= r_i\mathbf{i} + r_j\mathbf{j} + r_k\mathbf{k}, & \mathbf{t} &= t_i\mathbf{i} + t_j\mathbf{j} + t_k\mathbf{k}. \end{aligned}$$

In order not to complicate the problem unnecessarily it will be assumed that the rail lies in the horizontal plane through the center of the ball, that the coefficient of friction μ with the table is the same as that with the rail, and that there is slippage at both points of contact.

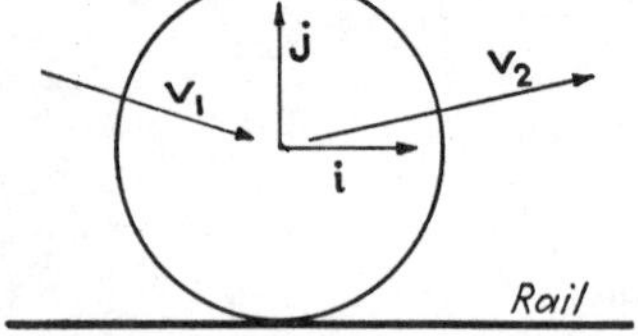

FIG. 75.

The friction between the ball and the rail, and also between the ball and the table, is opposite in direction to the velocities of the points of contact of the ball. As these velocities change their directions, in general, during the impact, a rigorous treatment of this change would require a complete theory of the elasticity of the materials in use, which is out of the question here. Furthermore, since the rail is made of rubber, the contact of the ball with the rail is by no means a point. An approximate solution, therefore, is all that can be undertaken. Of course, the solution of every mechanical problem is, in reality, the solution of an idealized problem, and is therefore but an approximation to any concrete application, and the degree of the approximation in every case is a worthy subject of enquiry. In the present case it will be assumed that the friction throughout the impact has the same direction as at the first instant of contact, the change of direction being ignored. This is not the best approximation that could be made, but it is, perhaps, the simplest one.

Let P be the point of contact with the rail and C the point of contact with the table. The velocity of the particle of the ball at P is

$$\mathbf{v}_1 + a\,\mathbf{j} \times \boldsymbol{\omega}_1,$$

and the component of this velocity in the plane perpendicular to $\mathbf{j}$ is

$$\mathbf{w} = (v_{1i} + a\omega_{1k})\mathbf{i} - a\omega_{1i}\mathbf{k};$$

by taking

$$\begin{aligned} v_{1i} + a\omega_{1k} &= w \cos\alpha, \\ 0 - a\omega_{1i} &= w \sin\alpha, \end{aligned}$$

the expression for $\mathbf{w}$ becomes

$$\mathbf{w} = w(\mathbf{i}\cos\alpha + \mathbf{k}\sin\alpha).$$

Similarly the velocity at the point C is

$$\mathbf{v}_1 + a\,\mathbf{k} \times \boldsymbol{\omega}_1,$$

and the component in the plane of the table is

$$\mathbf{u} = (v_{1i} - a\omega_{1j})\mathbf{i} + (v_{1j} + a\omega_{1i})\mathbf{j};$$

by taking

$$\begin{aligned} v_{1i} - a\omega_{1j} &= u \cos\beta, \\ v_{1j} + a\omega_{1i} &= u \sin\beta, \end{aligned}$$

the expression for $\mathbf{u}$ becomes

$$\mathbf{u} = u(\mathbf{i}\cos\beta + \mathbf{j}\sin\beta).$$

It will be observed that if the state of the ball just before impact is given, the angles α and β may be regarded as known.

If e is the coefficient of restitution with the rail, the normal impulse of the rail gives

$$v_{2j} = -ev_{1j}, \qquad r_j = -(1 + e)v_{1j},$$

which is positive since v_{1j} is necessarily negative. The frictional impulse is then

$$-r_j\mathbf{w} = (1 + e)v_{1j}\mu[\mathbf{i} \cos \alpha + \mathbf{j} \sin \alpha].$$

Hence

$$\mathbf{r} = (1 + e)v_{1j}[\mathbf{i}\mu \cos \alpha - \mathbf{j} + \mathbf{k}\mu \sin \alpha].$$

Similarly,

$$\mathbf{t} = t_k[-\mathbf{i}\mu \cos \beta - \mathbf{j}\mu \sin \beta + \mathbf{k}].$$

The principle of momentum

$$\mathbf{v}_2 = \mathbf{v}_1 + \mathbf{r} + \mathbf{t}$$

gives

$$\mathbf{v}_2 = [v_{1i} + (1 + e)v_{1j}\mu \cos \alpha - t_k\mu \cos \beta]\mathbf{i} - [ev_{1j} - t_k\mu \sin \beta]\mathbf{j} + [t_k + (1 + e)v_{1j}\mu \sin \alpha]\mathbf{k}.$$

In case the ball does not lose contact with the table the coefficient of k vanishes, and

$$t_k = -(1 + e)v_{1j}\mu \sin \alpha,$$

which must be positive. Hence $\sin \alpha$ must be positive and ω_{1i} must be negative. This value of t_k makes

$$\mathbf{v}_2 = [v_{1i} + (1 + e)v_{1j}\mu(\cos \alpha + \mu \sin \alpha \cos \beta)]\mathbf{i} + [-e + (1 + e)\mu^2 \sin \alpha \sin \beta]v_{1j}\mathbf{j}. \quad (1)$$

The principle of moment of momentum then gives

$$k^2\boldsymbol{\omega}_2 = k^2\boldsymbol{\omega}_1 - a\mathbf{j} \times \mathbf{r} - a\mathbf{k} \times \mathbf{t},$$

which, after evaluation, becomes

$$\boldsymbol{\omega}_2 = \boldsymbol{\omega}_1 + \frac{5}{2a}v_{1j}\mu[\sin \alpha\{(-1 + \mu \sin \beta)\mathbf{i} + \mu \cos \beta\, \mathbf{j}\} + \cos \alpha\, \mathbf{k}]. \quad (2)$$

In case $\sin \alpha$ is negative, t_k changes sign and also becomes negative; that is, a downward constraint is necessary to hold the ball on the table, but as no such constraint exists the ball loses contact with the table and jumps.

A solution of closer approximation can be obtained by assuming the lines of friction are a mean between their initial and final directions, that is,

$$\mathbf{w} = [\tfrac{1}{2}(v_{1i} + v_{2i}) + \tfrac{1}{2}a(\omega_{1k} + \omega_{2k})]\mathbf{i} - \tfrac{1}{2}a(\omega_{1i} + \omega_{2i})\mathbf{k},$$
$$\mathbf{u} = [\tfrac{1}{2}(v_{1i} + v_{2i}) - \tfrac{1}{2}a(\omega_{1j} + \omega_{2j})]\mathbf{i} + [\tfrac{1}{2}(v_{1j} + v_{2j}) + \tfrac{1}{2}(\omega_{1i} + \omega_{2i})]\mathbf{j},$$

but the resulting equations, though solvable, are more complicated.

138. General Equations of Impact.—The general equations for the impact, or collision, of any two bodies can easily be written down, although the working out of a solution in a given particular case may be very complicated.

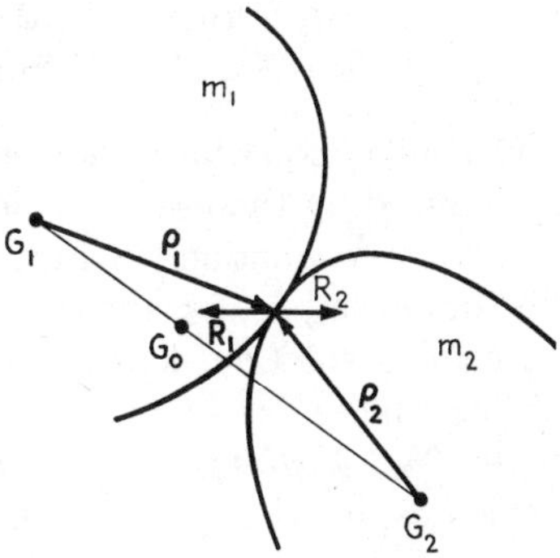

FIG. 76.

With subscripts 1 and 2 to distinguish the two bodies and G_0 the common center of gravity of the two masses, let

m be the mass.
G the center of gravity,
C the particle of m at the point of impact,
$\boldsymbol{\rho}$ the point of impact referred to G,
$\mathbf{v}$ the velocity of G with respect to G_0 before impact,
$\mathbf{u}$ the velocity of G with respect to G_0 after impact,
$\boldsymbol{\omega}$ the angular velocity before impact,
$\bar{\boldsymbol{\omega}}$ the angular velocity after impact,
A, B, C, D, E, F the moments and products of inertia of m at G.

Reference to Fig. 76 will make this notation clear. The impulse of the impact will be denoted by **R**, with the component **N** normal to the surfaces at the point of contact and the component **T** in the tangent plane.

Since other forces that are acting during the collision are of no importance, the principle of momentum gives the two equations

$$\left.\begin{aligned} m_1\mathbf{u}_1 &= m_1\mathbf{v}_1 + \mathbf{R}_1, \\ m_2\mathbf{u}_2 &= m_2\mathbf{v}_2 + \mathbf{R}_2, \end{aligned} \qquad \text{and} \qquad \mathbf{R}_1 + \mathbf{R}_2 = 0.\right\} \qquad (1)$$

Likewise the principle of angular momentum gives the equations

$$\left.\begin{aligned} I_{1a}\bar{\omega}_1 &= I_{1b}\omega_1 + \rho_1 \times \mathbf{R}_1, \\ I_{2a}\bar{\omega}_2 &= I_{2b}\omega_2 + \rho_2 \times \mathbf{R}_2, \end{aligned}\right\} \tag{2}$$

where I_{1a} and I_{1b} are the moments of inertia of m_1 at G_1 with respect to the instantaneous axis of rotation immediately after and before impact. Since, by Eqs. (82.5), the components of $I_{1a}\bar{\omega}_1 - I_{1b}\omega_1$ are

$$\left.\begin{aligned} A_1(\bar{\omega}_{1i} - \omega_{1i}) - F_1(\bar{\omega}_{1j} - \omega_{1j}) - E_1(\bar{\omega}_{1k} - \omega_{1k}), \\ B_1(\bar{\omega}_{1j} - \omega_{1j}) - D_1(\bar{\omega}_{1k} - \omega_{1k}) - F_1(\bar{\omega}_{1i} - \omega_{1i}), \\ C_1(\bar{\omega}_{1k} - \omega_{1k}) - E_1(\bar{\omega}_{1i} - \omega_{1i}) - D_1(\bar{\omega}_{1j} - \omega_{1j}), \end{aligned}\right\} \tag{3}$$

and similar equations with subscript 2, no new unknowns are introduced by the use of the letters I_{1a}, I_{1b}, I_{2a}, and I_{2b}.

The four equations in Eqs. (1) and (2) contain five unknown vectors u_1, u_2, $\bar{\omega}_1$, $\bar{\omega}_2$, and $\mathbf{R}$. The fifth equation which is necessary for a solution depends upon the nature of the bodies and their surfaces.

A. The Bodies Are Inelastic and Perfectly Rough.—The velocities of the particles C_1 and C_2 just after impact are respectively

$$\mathbf{u}_1 + \bar{\omega}_1 \times \rho_1,$$

and

$$\mathbf{u}_2 + \bar{\omega}_2 \times \rho_2.$$

If the bodies are inelastic and perfectly rough, the two particles C_1 and C_2 do not separate after collision and their relative velocity is zero. The fifth condition is therefore

$$\mathbf{u}_2 - \mathbf{u}_1 + \bar{\omega}_2 \times \rho_2 - \bar{\omega}_1 \times \rho_1 = 0.$$

B. The Bodies Are Inelastic and Perfectly Smooth.—Imagine a rectangular system of unit vectors **i**, **j**, **k** in which **k** is parallel to the normal of the surfaces at the point of impact and **i** and **j** are parallel to the tangent plane.

If the two bodies are inelastic and perfectly smooth, the **i**- and **j**-components of the relative velocity of C_1 and C_2 are unaltered; or, perhaps more simply, the **i**- and **j**-components of the momenta are unaltered. But the **k**-component of velocity of C_2 with respect to C_1 is reduced to zero. The fifth condition is therefore represented by the three equations

$$(\mathbf{u}_1 - \mathbf{v}_1) - (\mathbf{u}_1 - \mathbf{v}_1) \cdot \mathbf{k} = 0,$$
$$(\mathbf{u}_2 - \mathbf{v}_2) - (\mathbf{u}_2 - \mathbf{v}_2) \cdot \mathbf{k} = 0,$$
$$(\mathbf{u}_2 - \mathbf{u}_1 + \bar{\omega}_2 \times \varrho_2 - \omega_1 \times \varrho_1) \cdot \mathbf{k} = 0.$$

C. The Bodies Are Elastic and Perfectly Smooth.—At the instant of greatest compression the **k**-component of the velocity of C_2 with respect to C_1 is zero, and the magnitude of the impulse up to this instant can be computed just as in case *B*. This value multiplied by $1 + e$, where e is the coefficient of restitution, gives the entire magnitude of the impulse; and since its direction is normal to the surfaces, the impulse **R** is entirely known, and Eqs. (1) and (2) are sufficient.

D. The Bodies Are Elastic and Partially Rough.—If the collision is of such a character that slippage occurs, the limiting value of friction is called into play, and the impulse lies on the cone of friction. The direction of slip may change during the impact, or it may even cease. If, however, the slip is always in the same direction and μ is the coefficient of friction, the magnitude of the frictional impulse is μN; and the normal component **N** of the impulse is computed just as in case *C*. The frictional impulse lies in the tangential plane and its direction is opposite to the relative motion of its point of contact.

There are, of course, other possibilities, for example, the bodies may collide at two or more points simultaneously or even in areas. What happens shortly after the impact depends upon the surfaces of the bodies at points other than those at which collision occurs. The bodies may separate immediately like the billiard balls; one or both bodies may be given a violent spin; a lead bullet striking the concave side of a steel target may slide so far that it is completely worn out; the surfaces may roll upon each other, or roll and slide; etc.

Problems

1. A loaded freight car of mass m_1 moving with a speed v_1 collides and unites with a stationary empty car of mass m_2. The two cars then move together with a speed v. Show that

$$v = \frac{m_1}{m_1 + m_2} v_1.$$

2. A nail, driven into a beam by a 2-lb. hammer moving 20 feet per second, advances one fourth of an inch at each blow. Assuming that the resistance of the beam to the nail is constant show that its value is 600 lb. and its duration is 1/480 second.

3. A sphere is thrown against a vertical wall which it strikes at right angles. Neglecting the rotation of the sphere and the resistance of the air, show that, if a is the distance to the wall and e is the coefficient of restitution, the ball will strike the ground at a distance ae from the wall.

4. A ball strikes a horizontal floor at an angle of 45° and rebounds at an angle of 45°. Show that

$$\mu = \frac{1 - e}{1 + e}.$$

Discuss the change in rotation of the ball.

5. A heavy cylinder of height h and diameter d rests on a horizontal board. If the board is started suddenly into motion with the acceleration α, show that the cylinder will remain at rest relative to the board if and only if α is less than both μg and gd/h.

6. Two spheres s_1 and s_2 of the same mass m are acted upon by an impulse I and by a constant force F respectively in the same direction along the line joining them. The sphere s_1 is at a distance a behind s_2. In order that s_1 may overtake s_2 show that it is necessary that

$$\mathrm{I}^2 > 2amF.$$

7. An elastic ball falls from rest at a height h and rebounds repeatedly. If e is the coefficient of restitution show that the ball will come to a state of rest in

$$\frac{1 + e}{1 - e}\sqrt{\frac{2h}{g}} \text{ sec.,}$$

and the total distance which it will have traveled is

$$\frac{1 + e^2}{1 - e^2} \text{ ft.}$$

8. Two equal elastic spheres moving in the same straight line collide with velocities relative to the ground of

$$-v \quad \text{and} \quad \frac{1 + e}{1 - e}v.$$

show that the faster of the two is reduced to a state of rest.

9. Show that the greatest possible change in the direction of motion of the cue ball when it strikes an object ball at rest occurs when the direction of projection of the cue ball makes angle

$$\sin^{-1} \frac{a}{c}\sqrt{\frac{1 - e}{3 - e}}$$

with the line joining the centers of the balls, a being the diameter of the balls and c the initial distance between the centers of the balls. Assume that the balls are smooth.

10. A stiff uniform rod of length $2a$ and weight w is pivoted at its center point slightly out of contact with the floor and a weight w_1 is placed on one end of it. A second weight w_2 falls from a height h_2 and strikes the rod at a distance c from the pivot, thus throwing w_1 upward. Show that the height h_1 to which w_1 rises is

$$h_1 = \left(\frac{w_2}{w_1 + w_2 + \frac{1}{3}w}\frac{c}{a}\right)^2 h_2.$$

11. A uniform thin plate of mass μ per unit area is bounded by the axis ON of a parabola $y^2 = 4ax$, an arc of the parabola OP, and an ordinate NP. The corner of the plate at O is the vertex of the parabola. If the plate is at rest with the point O fixed and a blow of impulse B perpendicular to the plate is struck at P, show that the plate will begin to turn about the line OQ, where Q is a point on the ordinate NP such that

$$NQ = \tfrac{7}{25}NP,$$

and that the instantaneous angular velocity is

$$\frac{75}{26}\frac{B}{\mu ac^3}OQ,$$

where

$$c = ON.$$

12. Given a plane and an ellipsoid. There exist two parallel planes that are tangent to the ellipsoid. The straight line through the points of tangency passes through the center of the ellipsoid and is called the diametral line of the plane with respect to the ellipsoid.

If an impulsive force acts upon a rigid body that has one point fixed, the impulse and the constraint of the fixed point together form an impulsive couple. Show that the instantaneous axis of rotation (the axis about which such a body begins to turn) is the diametral line of the plane of the couple with respect to the ellipsoid of inertia of the body at the fixed point.

Thus the instantaneous axis is perpendicular to the plane of the couple only when the plane of the couple is parallel to a principal plane of inertia of the body at the fixed point.

13. An entirely free body that is acted upon by an impulse begins to turn about some axis. The line in which the impulse acts is called the *line of percussion*, and the line about which the body turns is called the *spontaneous axis of rotation*. Prove the following statements:

(*a*) The line of percussion is perpendicular to the plane that passes through the spontaneous axis and through the center of gravity.

(*b*) The spontaneous axis is a principal axis of inertia at the point where it is cut by a plane through the line of percussion perpendicular to the spontaneous axis. Therefore a line that does not contain anywhere a principal point (Sec. 26) cannot be a spontaneous axis for any impulse.

(*c*) The perpendicular distance between the line of percussion and the spontaneous axis is equal to the distance of the center of oscillation (Sec. 61) from the axis of suspension.

(*d*) If the spontaneous axis is parallel to a principal axis at the center of gravity, the line of percussion passes through the center of oscillation.

14. A free inelastic plate of any form, turning in its own plane about an instantaneous center of rotation S, strikes a fixed point P on the line through the center of gravity G and S. Show that there are two points, P_1 and P_2, equidistant from S, for which the magnitude of the blow is a maximum and that the magnitudes of these blows are inversely proportional to the distances of P_1 and P_2 from G.

15. A tripod with three uniform equal legs at right angles with one another is dropped from a height h and the three feet strike a smooth inelastic floor. Show that if the legs are freely jointed at the top the velocity of the center of gravity is diminished on striking by one-half.

16. To one end of a uniform rod that lies on a smooth horizontal table an impulse parallel to the table, and applied at that end, imparts a velocity $\mathbf{v}$. If $\mathbf{i}$ and $\mathbf{j}$ are unit vectors parallel to the table in the direction of the rod and perpendicular to it and $\mathbf{w}$ is the velocity imparted to the other end of the rod, show that

$$\mathbf{w} \cdot \mathbf{i} = \mathbf{v} \cdot \mathbf{i} \qquad \text{and} \qquad \mathbf{w} \cdot \mathbf{j} = -\tfrac{1}{2}\mathbf{v} \cdot \mathbf{j}.$$

CHAPTER X

THE DIFFERENTIAL EQUATIONS OF ANALYTICAL DYNAMICS

139. The Generalized Coordinates of Lagrange.—In the preceding chapters a free use has been made of vector notation and a free appeal has been made to the intuition. These methods have led in the end to certain differential equations, the solution of which, after all, presents the essential difficulties of the problem. In the present chapter analytic methods, due to Lagrange, lead to the differential equations in nearly every case with a minimum use of the intuition. Indeed Lagrange states in the preface to his "Mécanique Analytique" that no diagrams are to be found in his book.

In Chapter III, Sec. 28, it was shown that a system of n free particles leads to $3n$ differential equations each of the second order and in Chapter IV that a rigid body may be regarded as a system of free particles subject to $3n - 6$ constraints, and therefore a rigid body that is entirely free has six degrees of freedom—that is, the position and orientation of the body are completely specified by six independent parameters.

It is possible to generalize this and to say that any material system can be regarded as a system of free particles subject to $3n - k$ independent constraints, and having therefore k degrees of freedom. That is to say, the coordinates of the particles x_i, y_i, z_i can be expressed by means of k parameters, or by means of k parameters and the time if the constraints depend upon the time in a known way. These parameters are known as the *generalized coordinates of Lagrange.*

Consider, for example, a single rigid body the coordinates of whose particles are x_i, y_i, z_i with respect to some fixed trihedron of reference. Imagine another trihedron with origin at the center of gravity of the body, rigidly attached to the body. With respect to this trihedron the coordinates of the particles are ξ_i, η_i, ζ_i which, no matter how the body may move, remain fixed constants throughout the motion. If x, y, z are the coordinates of the center of gravity of the body with respect to the fixed trihedron of reference, the equations of transformation are

$$\left.\begin{aligned} x_i &= x + \alpha_1\xi_i + \alpha_2\eta_i + \alpha_3\zeta_i, \\ y_i &= y + \beta_1\xi_i + \beta_2\eta_i + \beta_3\zeta_i, \\ z_i &= z + \gamma_1\xi_i + \gamma_2\eta_i + \gamma_3\zeta_i; \end{aligned}\right\} \tag{1}$$

where $\alpha_1, \alpha_2, \ldots, \gamma_3$ are the nine direction cosines that define the orientation of the trihedron that is attached to the body with respect to the fixed reference trihedron. These direction cosines can be regarded as functions of the three Eulerian angles φ, ψ, and θ, as in Sec. 52 where the functional relationship is given. If the direction cosines in Eq. (1) are replaced by their values from Sec. 52, all of the coordinates x_i, y_i, and z_i, are expressed in terms of the six independent parameters $x, y, z; \varphi, \psi, \theta$, and if the values of these parameters at any instant are known, Eq. (1) gives the position of each particle of the body. It is desirable therefore to have the differential equations of these parameters which are the Lagrange coordinates in this case.

I. HOLONOMIC SYSTEMS

140. The Differential Equations of Lagrange.—Each particle of any system must satisfy a set of differential equations of the form

$$\left.\begin{aligned} m_i x_i'' &= X_i, \\ m_i y_i'' &= Y_i, \qquad i = 1, \cdots, n. \\ m_i z_i'' &= Z_i, \end{aligned}\right\} \tag{1}$$

where X_i Y_i and Z_i represent the components of the resultant of all of the forces, both interior and exterior, that are acting upon it, Sec. 28. While these equations must be satisfied, they are not independent if constraints exist. Suppose that constraints do exist and that the system has only k ($<3n$) degrees of freedom. Then there exist equations of transformation that relate the coordinates x_i, y_i, and z_i and the k parameters (Lagrangian coordinates) that are needed to express the k degrees of freedom, as in Eqs. (139.1). Let these equations be

$$\left.\begin{aligned} x_i &= \varphi_i(q_1, \cdots, q_k; t), \\ y_i &= \psi_i(q_1, \cdots, q_k; t), \\ z_i &= \omega_i(q_1, \cdots, q_k; t), \end{aligned}\right\} \tag{2}$$

which may or may not contain the time: it is immaterial. In the following analysis, it will be understood that

$$\frac{\partial x_i}{\partial q_j} \equiv \frac{\partial \varphi_i}{\partial q_j}, \qquad \frac{\partial y_i}{\partial q_j} \equiv \frac{\partial \psi_i}{\partial q_j}, \qquad \frac{\partial z_i}{\partial q_j} \equiv \frac{\partial \omega_i}{\partial q_j}.$$

If the first of Eqs. (1) is multiplied by $\partial x_i/\partial q_j$, the second by $\partial y_i/\partial q_j$, and the third by $\partial z_i/\partial q_j$ and the three equations are then added, there is obtained

$$m_i\left(\frac{\partial x_i}{\partial q_j}x_i'' + \frac{\partial y_i}{\partial q_j}y_i'' + \frac{\partial z_i}{\partial q_j}z_i''\right) = Q_{ij}, \qquad i = 1, \cdots, n. \tag{3}$$

where, for brevity of notation,

$$Q_{ij} = X_i\frac{\partial x_i}{\partial q_j} + Y_i\frac{\partial y_i}{\partial q_j} + Z_i\frac{\partial z_i}{\partial q_j}. \tag{4}$$

It will be verified without much difficulty that Eq. (3) can be written in the form

$$\left.\begin{aligned} &\frac{d}{dt}\left[m_i\left(\frac{\partial x_i}{\partial q_j}x_i' + \frac{\partial y_i}{\partial q_j}y_i' + \frac{\partial z_i}{\partial q_j}z_i'\right)\right] \\ &\qquad - m_i\left[x_i'\left(\frac{\partial x_i}{\partial q_j}\right)' + y_i'\left(\frac{\partial y_i}{\partial q_j}\right)' + z_i'\left(\frac{\partial z_i}{\partial q_j}\right)'\right] = Q_{ij}, \end{aligned}\right\} \tag{5}$$

where, as usual,

$$\left(\frac{\partial x_i}{\partial q_j}\right)' \equiv \frac{d}{dt}\left(\frac{\partial x_i}{\partial q_j}\right), \text{ etc.}$$

If the equations of transformation are differentiated with respect to the time, it is seen that

$$\left.\begin{aligned} x_i' &= \sum_{j=1}^{k}\frac{\partial x_i}{\partial q_j}q_j' + \frac{\partial x_i}{\partial t}, \\ y_i' &= \sum_{j=1}^{k}\frac{\partial y_i}{\partial q_j}q_j' + \frac{\partial y_i}{\partial t}, \\ z_i' &= \sum_{j=1}^{k}\frac{\partial z_i}{\partial q_j}q_j' + \frac{\partial z_i}{\partial t}. \end{aligned}\right\} \tag{6}$$

From these equations it is found that

$$\left.\begin{array}{l}\dfrac{\partial x_i'}{\partial q_j'} = \dfrac{\partial x_i}{\partial q_j}, \qquad \dfrac{\partial y_i'}{\partial q_j'} = \dfrac{\partial y_i}{\partial q_j}, \qquad \dfrac{\partial z_i'}{\partial q_j'} = \dfrac{\partial z_i}{\partial q_j}, \\ \text{and the equations} \\ \left(\dfrac{\partial x_i}{\partial q_j}\right)' = \dfrac{\partial x_i'}{\partial q_j}, \qquad \left(\dfrac{\partial y_i}{\partial q_j}\right)' = \dfrac{\partial y_i'}{\partial q_j}, \qquad \left(\dfrac{\partial z_i}{\partial q_j}\right)' = \dfrac{\partial z_i'}{\partial q_j'},\end{array}\right\} \qquad (7)$$

result from the identities

$$\frac{\partial x_i'}{\partial q_j} \equiv \sum_{l=1}^{k} \frac{\partial^2 x_i}{\partial q_l\, \partial q_j} q_l' + \frac{\partial^2 x_i}{\partial t\, \partial q_j} \equiv \left(\frac{\partial x_i}{\partial q_j}\right)'.$$

By virtue of the equalities in Eqs. (7), Eqs. (5) can now be written

$$\frac{d}{dt}\left[m_i\left(x_i'\frac{\partial x_i'}{\partial q_j'} + y_i'\frac{\partial y_i'}{\partial q_j'} + z_i'\frac{\partial z_i'}{\partial q_j'}\right)\right] - m_i\left[x_i'\frac{\partial x_i'}{\partial q_j} + y_i'\frac{\partial y_i'}{\partial q_j} + z_i'\frac{\partial z_i}{\partial q_j}\right] = Q_{ij};$$

and if the sum of these equations with respect to the letter i is taken, there results

$$\left.\begin{array}{l}\dfrac{d}{dt}\displaystyle\sum_{i=1}^{n}\left[m_i\left(x_i'\frac{\partial x_i'}{\partial q_j'} + y_i'\frac{\partial y_i'}{\partial q_j'} + z_i'\frac{\partial z_i'}{\partial q_j'}\right)\right] \\ \qquad\qquad\qquad\qquad j = 1, \cdots, k. \\ \qquad - \displaystyle\sum_{i=1}^{n} m_i\left[x_i'\frac{\partial x_i'}{\partial q_j} + y_i'\frac{\partial y_i'}{\partial q_j} + z_i'\frac{\partial z_i'}{\partial q_j}\right] = \sum_{i=1}^{n} Q_{ij}.\end{array}\right\} \qquad (8)$$

Since the kinetic energy of the system is

$$T = \tfrac{1}{2}\sum_{i=1}^{n} m_i(x_i'^2 + y_i'^2 + z_i'^2),$$

it is readily seen that Eqs. (8) become

$$\left(\frac{\partial T}{\partial q_j'}\right)' - \frac{\partial T}{\partial q_j} = \sum_{i=1}^{n} Q_{ij} = Q_j, \qquad j = 1, \cdots, k. \qquad (9)$$

if, for brevity

$$Q_j = \sum_{i=1}^{n} Q_{ij} = \sum_{i=1}^{n}\left(X_i\frac{\partial x_i}{\partial q_j} + Y_i\frac{\partial y_i}{\partial q_j} + Z_i\frac{\partial z_i}{\partial q_j}\right). \qquad (10)$$

Equations (9) are the general form of the equations of Lagrange. They are valid for all systems in which the constraints are expressible in an integral form, or, if they are in a differential form, these differential forms are integrable. Systems of this type are called *holonomic*. If the constraints are expressed in non-integrable differential forms, or if the equations of transformation involve the derivatives, $q_1', \ldots, q_k'$, it is readily seen that the above analysis does not hold and the system is *non-holonomic*. An example of such a system is a sphere rolling upon any given surface, for instance, a plane. In this case the point of contact describes a curve upon the sphere and upon the given surface, and one of the constraints is that there is no slipping. This requires that an arc element on the sphere be equal to the corresponding arc element of the curve on the given surface. That is, the constraint is differential in form, and this differential form is non-integrable.

It is evident from Eqs. (6) that the x_i', y_i', and z_i' are linear functions of $q_1', \ldots, q_k'$ and therefore T is quadratic in the q''s. Furthermore T is homogeneous of the second degree in the q''s if the time does not occur explicitly in the equations of transformation, that is, if the constraints are not moving constraints; otherwise T is quadratic but non-homogeneous.

141. There Exists a Potential Function.—The equations of Lagrange have a very simple form when there exists a potential function for the exterior forces.

The forces X_i, Y_i, Z_i [Eqs. (140.1)] that act upon the individual particles of the system are divisible into two classes: the interior forces and the exterior forces. Therefore

$$X_i = X_i^{(1)} + X_i^{(2)}, \qquad Y_i = Y_i^{(1)} + Y_i^{(2)}, \qquad Z_i = Z_i^{(1)} + Z_i^{(2)};$$

and [Eq. (140.10)]

$$Q_j = \sum\left(X_i^{(1)}\frac{\partial x_i}{\partial q_j} + Y_i^{(1)}\frac{\partial y_i}{\partial q_j} + Z_i^{(1)}\frac{\partial z_i}{\partial q_j}\right) + \sum\left(X_i^{(2)}\frac{\partial x_i}{\partial q_j} + Y_i^{(2)}\frac{\partial y_i}{\partial q_j} + Z_i^{(2)}\frac{\partial z_i}{\partial q_j}\right),$$

the interior forces being represented by the superscript 1, and the exterior by superscript 2.

The components of the vector that represents the displacement of the particle at x_i, y_i, z_i, are (I, **350**)

$$dx_i = \frac{\partial x_i}{\partial q_j} dq_j, \qquad dy_i = \frac{\partial y_i}{\partial q_j} dq_j, \qquad dz_i = \frac{\partial z_i}{\partial q_j} dq_j,$$

assuming that q_j alone varies, the other parameters remaining fixed. The components of the resultant of the interior forces that are acting on this particle are $X_i^{(1)}$, $Y_i^{(1)}$, and $Z_i^{(1)}$. Hence

$$\sum_{i=1}^{n} \left(X_i^{(1)} \frac{\partial x_i}{\partial q_j} + Y_i^{(1)} \frac{\partial y_i}{\partial q_j} + Z_i^{(1)} \frac{\partial z_i}{\partial q_j} \right) dq_j$$

represents the work done on the system by the interior forces in an infinitesimal displacement due to a change dq_j in the parameter q_j; or, for short, an infinitesimal displacement in the q_j direction.

It was shown in Sec. 48 that the work done on the particles of a rigid body by the interior forces is zero, and therefore for a rigid body

$$\sum_{i=1}^{n} \left(X_i^{(1)} \frac{\partial x_i}{\partial q_j} + Y_i^{(1)} \frac{\partial y_i}{\partial q_j} + Z_i^{(1)} \frac{\partial z_i}{\partial q_j} \right) = 0.$$

This result can be extended to systems of rigid bodies that are connected by pivots, or sliding and pure rolling contact in so far as the friction of pivoting, sliding or rolling can be ignored; in these cases either there is no displacement, as in pivoting and rolling, or the displacements are perpendicular to the pressures as in the case of sliding. For all such cases of articulated systems of rigid bodies the work done by the interior forces vanishes.

The work done by the exterior forces is, of course,

$$\sum_{i=1}^{n} \left(X_i^{(2)} \frac{\partial x_i}{\partial q_j} + Y_i^{(2)} \frac{\partial y_i}{\partial q_j} + Z_i^{(2)} \frac{\partial z_i}{\partial q_j} \right) dq_j = Q_j \, dq_j.$$

For the sake of a name, therefore, it is convenient to call Q_j the component of the force in the q_j direction. Aside from a certain factor, this is strictly correct in the case of a single particle (I, **350**). In the case of systems of many particles dq_j represents a change in configuration of the system due to an infinitesimal change in the coordinate q_j, the other q's remaining fixed. Since $Q_j\,dq_j$ is the work done by the forces acting in this change of configuration, it is convenient to retain the language that is applicable to a single particle, and say that the Q_j are the components of the resultant force in the q_j direction.

If there exists a potential function $U(x_1, y_1, z_1; x_2, y_2, z_2; \ldots ; t)$, of the exterior forces, so that

$$X_i^{(2)} = \frac{\partial U}{\partial x_i}, \qquad Y_i^{(2)} = \frac{\partial U}{\partial y_i}, \qquad Z_i^{(2)} = \frac{\partial U}{\partial z_i}, \qquad i = 1, \cdots, n,$$

then, for all systems in which the work done by the interior forces vanishes,

$$Q_j = \sum_{i=1}^{n}\left(\frac{\partial U}{\partial x_i}\frac{\partial x_i}{\partial q_j} + \frac{\partial U}{\partial y_i}\frac{\partial y_i}{\partial q_j} + \frac{\partial U}{\partial z_i}\frac{\partial z_i}{\partial q_j}\right) = \frac{\partial U}{\partial q_j}.$$

Under these circumstances the equations of Lagrange [Eqs. (140.9)] become

$$\left(\frac{\partial T}{\partial q_j'}\right)' - \left(\frac{\partial T}{\partial q_j}\right) = \frac{\partial U}{\partial q_j},$$

or

$$\left(\frac{\partial T}{\partial q_j'}\right)' - \frac{\partial (T + U)}{\partial q_j} = 0, \qquad j = 1, \cdots, k. \tag{1}$$

If a new function L is defined by the relation

$$L = T + U, \tag{2}$$

the equations of Lagrange can be written

$$\left.\begin{aligned} &\left(\frac{\partial L}{\partial q_j'}\right)' - \frac{\partial L}{\partial q_j} = 0, \qquad j = 1, \cdots, k; \\ \text{for} \\ &\frac{\partial T}{\partial q_j'} = \frac{\partial L}{\partial q_j'}, \end{aligned}\right\} \tag{3}$$

since U does not depend upon $q_1', q_2', \ldots, q_k'$. The function L is called the *kinetic potential*, or the *Lagrangian function*. Since U, the potential function, is the negative of the potential energy, it is seen that *the Lagrangian function is the difference between the kinetic and the potential energies of the system.*

If one knows how to write down the kinetic and potential energies in terms of the parameters adopted, $q_1, \ldots, q_k$ and their derivatives $q_1', \ldots, q_k'$, Eqs. (3) furnish the scheme for deriving the differential equations of motion. It will be noticed that the constraints do not appear in the equations; that is, *the constraints have been eliminated.*

Equations (3) apply only to holonomic systems; that is, to systems for which the equations of transformation appear in finite form and independent of the velocities; or, if they are in differential form, these forms are integrable. Otherwise the system is non-holonomic, and Eqs. (3) are not valid in general even when they can be formed.

142. The Energy and Other Integrals.—Suppose the constraints are independent of the time. Then the equations of transformation also are independent of the time, and Eqs. (140.6) are both linear and homogeneous in $q_1', \ldots, q_k'$; and the expression for the kinetic energy T is homogeneous and quadratic in these letters.

Let Eqs. (141.3) be multiplied by q_j' and then summed with respect to the letter j. There results

$$\sum\left(\frac{\partial L}{\partial q_j'}\right)' q_j' - \sum\frac{\partial L}{\partial q_j} q_j' = 0. \tag{1}$$

Now

$$\sum\left(\frac{\partial L}{\partial q_j'}\right)' q_j' = \sum\left(\frac{\partial T}{\partial q_j'}\right)' q_j' = \sum\left(q_j'\frac{\partial T}{\partial q_j'}\right)' - \sum\frac{\partial T}{\partial q_j'} q_j''$$

and

$$\sum\frac{\partial L}{\partial q_j} q_j' = \sum\frac{\partial T}{\partial q_j} q_j' + \sum\frac{\partial U}{\partial q_j} q_j'.$$

Hence

$$\sum\left(\frac{\partial L}{\partial q_j'}\right)' q_j' - \sum\frac{\partial L}{\partial q_j} q_j' = \sum\left(q_j'\frac{\partial T}{\partial q_j'}\right)' - \sum\frac{\partial T}{\partial q_j'} q_j'' - \sum\frac{\partial T}{\partial q_j} q_j' - \sum\frac{\partial U}{\partial q_j} q_j' = \sum\left(q_j'\frac{\partial T}{\partial q_j'}\right)' - T' - U'.$$

Since T is a homogeneous quadratic form in $q_1', \ldots, q_k'$, it follows from Euler's theorem on homogeneous functions that

$$\sum q_j' \frac{\partial T}{\partial q_j'} = 2T.$$

Hence

$$\sum \left(\frac{\partial L}{\partial q_j'}\right)' q_j' - \sum \frac{\partial L}{\partial q_j} q_j' = T' - U'$$

is an exact differential; and, by integration,

$$T - U = E = \text{constant}. \tag{2}$$

Since T is the kinetic energy and $-U$ is the potential energy, the total energy E is constant. Equation (2) is the energy integral.

It is evident, at once, from Eqs. (141.3) that if for any j

$$\frac{\partial L}{\partial q_j} \equiv 0,$$

the remaining part of the differential equation is an exact differential, and that

$$\frac{\partial L}{\partial q_j'} = \beta_j = \text{constant} \tag{3}$$

is an integral. Under these conditions q_j is called an *ignorable* or *cyclic* coordinate because it does not occur in L. For each ignorable coordinate, there is a corresponding integral.

143. Systems That Are Constrained to Rotate Uniformly.— If any holonomic system is placed upon a table that is rotating uniformly, it will still be holonomic when referred to the rotating table and Lagrange's equations are still valid. Let the axis of rotation be taken as the z-axis, then

$$\begin{aligned} x_i &= \rho_i \cos(\theta_i + \omega t) \\ y_i &= \rho_i \sin(\theta_i + \omega t) \\ z_i &= \zeta_i \end{aligned}$$

in which the angular velocity ω is constant. The polar coordinates ρ and θ then refer to a polar axis that is at rest relatively to the table. The kinetic energy becomes

$$\begin{aligned} T &= \tfrac{1}{2}\Sigma m_i(x_i'^2 + y_i'^2 + z_i'^2) \\ &= \tfrac{1}{2}\Sigma m(\zeta_i'^2 + \rho_i'^2 + \rho_i^2\theta_i'^2) + \omega\Sigma m_i\rho_i^2\theta_i' + \tfrac{1}{2}\omega^2\Sigma m_i\rho_i^2 \\ &= T_2 + \omega T_1 + \omega^2 T_0. \end{aligned}$$

In this expression T_2 represents the terms homogeneous of degree 2, T_1 homogeneous of degree 1, and T_0 homogeneous of degree zero in the accented letters. If the equations of transformation do not otherwise contain the time, T_2 will be a homogeneous function of degree 2 in $q_1', \ldots, q_k'$, T_1 and T_0 will be homogeneous of degree 1 and 0 respectively in the same letters, and all three in general will be functions of the coordinates $q_1, \ldots q_k$.

The equations of Lagrange then become

$$\left[\left(\frac{\partial T_2}{\partial q_j'}\right)' - \frac{\partial T_2}{\partial q_j}\right] + \omega\left[\left(\frac{\partial T_1}{\partial q_j'}\right)' - \frac{\partial T_1}{\partial q_j}\right] = \frac{\partial U}{\partial q_j} + \omega^2\frac{\partial T_0}{\partial q_j}.$$

If the coefficient of ω in this equation vanishes and if a new potential function U_2 is taken such that

$$U_2 = U + \omega^2 T_0,$$

the above equation reduces to the previous form

$$\left(\frac{\partial T_2}{\partial q_j'}\right)' - \frac{\partial T_2}{\partial q_j} = \frac{\partial U_2}{\partial q_j}.$$

The motion of the system is just the same as though the table were at rest and the term $+\frac{1}{2}\omega^2\Sigma m\rho^2$ were added to the potential function, or $-\frac{1}{2}\omega^2\Sigma m\rho^2$ were added to the potential energy, and these are called the centrifugal force terms.

The coefficient of ω vanishes if every θ_i' vanishes, for then $T_1 \equiv 0$. This is impossible for a rigid body that is actually moving with respect to the table except for a translation parallel to the axis, but it is possible for discrete particles, or a straight rod or a thin plane sheet. The coefficient also vanishes if T_1 is an exact differential, say

$$T_1 = S',$$

for then

$$\left(\frac{\partial T_1}{\partial q_j'}\right)' = \left(\frac{\partial S'}{\partial q_j'}\right)' = \left(\frac{\partial S}{\partial q_j}\right)' = \frac{\partial S'}{\partial q_j} = \frac{\partial T_1}{\partial q_j},$$

and this condition is always satisfied if $k = 1$, for then T_1 has the form

$$T_1 = f(q_1)q_1'.$$

144. Reduction of the Order of the Differential Equations When There Are Ignorable Coordinates.—In 1876 Routh showed that if the system has s ($<k$) ignorable coordinates the resulting integrals can be used to reduce the order of the differential equations by s and still preserve the Lagrange form of the equations. It is the purpose of the present section to exhibit this reduction.

It will be supposed that the notation has been chosen in such a way that the integrals [Eqs. (142.3)] are

$$\frac{\partial L}{\partial q_j'} = \beta_j, \qquad j = 1, 2, \cdots s. \tag{1}$$

These equations are linear in $q_1', \ldots, q_s'$, and are independent of $q_1, \ldots, q_s$. Equations (1), therefore, can be solved for $q_1', \ldots, q_s'$ in terms of $\beta_1, \ldots, \beta_s$ and $q_{s+1}, \ldots, q_k$. Now form the function

$$R = L - \sum_{j=1}^{s} q_j' \frac{\partial L}{\partial q_j'}, \tag{2}$$

and eliminate $q_1', \ldots, q_s'$ from it, so that R becomes a function of $q_{s+1}, \ldots, q_k;\ q_{s+1}', \ldots, q_k';\ \beta_1, \ldots, \beta_s$.

If the letters q_r, q_r', β_r are given small arbitrary variations the functions L and R also will receive small variations, so that

$$\delta R = \delta L - \delta \sum_{j=1}^{s} q_j' \frac{\partial L}{\partial q_j'}.$$

Since L does not contain $q_1, \ldots, q_s$,

$$\delta L = \sum_{j=s+1}^{k} \frac{\partial L}{\partial q_j} \delta q_j + \sum_{j=1}^{s} \frac{\partial L}{\partial q_j'} \delta q_j' + \sum_{j=s+1}^{k} \frac{\partial L}{\partial q_j'} \delta q_j',$$

and since by Eqs. (1),

$$\delta\left(\frac{\partial L}{\partial q_j'}\right) = \delta\beta_j, \qquad j = 1, \cdots, s,$$

it is seen that

$$\delta \sum_{j=1}^{s} q_j' \frac{\partial L}{\partial q_j'} = \sum_{j=1}^{s} \frac{\partial L}{\partial q_j'} \delta q_j' + \sum_{j=1}^{s} q_j' \delta\beta_j,$$

and therefore

$$\delta R = \sum_{j=s+1}^{k} \frac{\partial L}{\partial q_j}\delta q_j + \sum_{j=s+1}^{k} \frac{\partial L}{\partial q_j'}\delta q_j' - \sum_{j=1}^{s} q_j'\delta\beta_j. \tag{3}$$

But if the variations are formed directly from R,

$$\delta R = \sum_{j=s+1}^{k} \frac{\partial R}{\partial q_j}\delta q_j + \sum_{j=s+1}^{k} \frac{\partial R}{\partial q_j'}\delta q_j' + \sum_{j=1}^{s} \frac{\partial R}{\partial \beta_j}\delta\beta_j. \tag{4}$$

Therefore, if the variations in Eqs. (3) and (4) are the same,

$$0 = \sum_{j=s+1}^{k}\left(\frac{\partial L}{\partial q_j} - \frac{\partial R}{\partial q_j}\right)\delta q_j + \sum_{j=s+1}^{k}\left(\frac{\partial L}{\partial q_j'} - \frac{\partial R}{\partial q_j'}\right)\delta q_j' - \sum_{j=1}^{s}\left(q_j' + \frac{\partial R}{\partial \beta_j}\right)\delta\beta_j;$$

and, since the variations are arbitrary, it follows that

$$\frac{\partial L}{\partial q_j'} = \frac{\partial R}{\partial q_j'}, \qquad \frac{\partial L}{\partial q_j} = \frac{\partial R}{\partial q_j}, \qquad j = s + 1, \cdots, k,$$

and

$$q_j' = -\frac{\partial R}{\partial \beta_j}, \qquad j = 1, \cdots, s.$$

The equations of motion [Eqs. (141.3)] therefore become

$$\left(\frac{\partial R}{\partial q_j'}\right)' - \frac{\partial R}{\partial q_j} = 0, \qquad j = s + 1, \cdots, k,$$

$$q_j = -\int \frac{\partial R}{\partial \beta_j} dt, \qquad j = 1, \cdots, s. \tag{5}$$

Thus, if the dynamical system has k degrees of freedom and s ignorable coordinates, the problem can be reduced to one with $k - s$ degrees of freedom and s quadratures.

145. The Integral of Angular Momentum.—Without assuming the existence of an energy integral, suppose a dynamical system has the kinetic energy T. Suppose further that a variation of the coordinate q_1, the other q's remaining constant, corresponds to a rotation of the entire system about a fixed axis and that q_1 is an ignorable coordinate; that is, q_1 does not enter in T, and $Q_1 = 0$. Then Eq. (140.9) gives

$$\left(\frac{\partial T}{\partial q_1'}\right)' = 0, \qquad \text{or} \qquad \frac{\partial T}{\partial q_1'} = \text{constant}.$$

Let the fixed axis be taken as the z-axis of a rectangular coordinate system, then

$$\frac{\partial T}{\partial q_1'} = \sum m\left(x'\frac{\partial x}{\partial q_1} + y'\frac{\partial y}{\partial q_1} + z'\frac{\partial z}{\partial q_1}\right).$$

Passing to polar coordinates, let

$$x = r\cos\theta, \qquad y = r\sin\theta, \qquad z = z,$$

so that

$$\frac{\partial x}{\partial q_1} = -r\sin\theta = -y, \qquad \frac{\partial y}{\partial q_1} = r\cos\theta = +x, \qquad \frac{\partial z}{\partial q_1} = 0.$$

Then

$$\frac{\partial T}{\partial q_1'} = \sum m(xy' - yx') = \sum mr^2\omega = \text{angular momentum}.$$

The angular momentum is constant. Hence the theorem: *Whenever a system can be rotated as if it were rigid about a fixed axis without violating any of the constraints and without altering any of the forces that are acting on it, then the moment of momentum of the system about this axis is constant.*

Again, suppose that q_1, having the same meaning as before, is not an ignorable coordinate. The kinetic energy will not depend upon q_1, although it does depend upon q_1', since

$$T = \tfrac{1}{2}\Sigma m_i(x_i'^2 + y_i'^2 + z_i'^2) = \tfrac{1}{2}\Sigma m_i(r_i'^2 + r^2\theta_i'^2 + z'^2),$$

does not depend upon the angles θ_i. The Lagrange equation [Eq. (140.9)] for the coordinate q_1 becomes

$$\left(\frac{\partial T}{\partial q_1'}\right)' = Q_1.$$

Since $Q_1\,dq_1$ is the work done in an infinitesimal rotation, Q_1 is the couple that is acting on the system, or the sum of the moments of all of the forces, including the constraints, with respect to the fixed axis. Since $\partial T/\partial q_1'$ is the angular momentum, as has just been seen, the theorem on angular momentum (I, **32**) again presents itself, namely: *the time rate of change of the* *angular momentum about any fixed axis is equal to the sum of the moments of all of the forces with respect to that axis.*

146. Reduction of the Order of the Differential Equations by Means of the Energy Integral.—In 1900 Whittaker effected a reduction in the order of the differential equations by means of the energy integral in a manner somewhat similar to that of Routh (Sec. 144) for the ignorable coordinates, the Lagrange form of the differential equations being preserved.

If the time does not occur explicitly, the kinetic energy is a homogeneous quadratic form in $q_1', \ldots, q_k'$, and the energy equation [Eq. (142.2)] can be written

$$\sum q_j' \frac{\partial L}{\partial q_j'} - L = E, \tag{1}$$

since

$$\sum q_j' \frac{\partial L}{\partial q_j'} = 2T \qquad \text{and} \qquad L = T + U.$$

If the substitution

$$q_j' = p_j q_1', \qquad j = 2, \cdots, k, \tag{2}$$

is made, equation (1) can be solved for q_1' as a function of the letters $p_2, \ldots, p_k; q_1, \ldots, q_k$, or it can be regarded as defining such a function implicitly. By the same substitutions the Lagrangian function L passes over into another function W_1, so that

$$L(q_1', \cdots q_k'; q_1, \cdots, q_k) = W_1(q_1'; p_2, \cdots p_k; q_1, \cdots, q_k).$$

Now

$$\left.\begin{aligned} \frac{\partial L}{\partial q_1'} &= \frac{\partial W_1}{\partial q_1'} - \sum_{j=2}^{k} \frac{q_j'}{q_1'^2}\frac{\partial W_1}{\partial p_j}, \\ \frac{\partial L}{\partial q_j'} &= \frac{1}{q_1'}\frac{\partial W_1}{\partial p_j}, \qquad j = 2, \cdots, k, \\ \frac{\partial L}{\partial q_j} &= \frac{\partial W_1}{\partial q_j}, \qquad j = 1, \cdots, k. \end{aligned}\right\} \tag{3}$$

Let the function

$$W = \sum_{j=1}^{k} \frac{\partial L}{\partial q_j'}\frac{q_j'}{q_1'}$$

be formed and the substitutions Eq. (2) made in it. By the use of Eqs. (3), it is found that

$$W = \frac{\partial W_1}{\partial q_1'}; \tag{4}$$

and the energy equation becomes

$$q_1' \frac{\partial W_1}{\partial q_1'} - W_1 = E.$$

If this expression is differentiated with respect to p_j and q_j respectively, and it is remembered that q_1' is a function of these letters, it is seen that

$$\left.\begin{aligned} q_1'\left(\frac{\partial^2 W_1}{\partial q_1'^2}\frac{\partial q_1'}{\partial p_j} + \frac{\partial^2 W_1}{\partial q_1'\,\partial p_j}\right) &= \frac{\partial W_1}{\partial p_j}, \\ q_1'\left(\frac{\partial^2 W_1}{\partial q_1'^2}\frac{\partial q_1'}{\partial q_j} + \frac{\partial^2 W_1}{\partial q_1'\,\partial q_j}\right) &= \frac{\partial W_1}{\partial q_j}. \end{aligned}\right\} \tag{5}$$

Likewise, from Eq. (4),

$$\left.\begin{aligned} \frac{\partial W}{\partial p_j} &= \frac{\partial^2 W_1}{\partial q_1'^2}\frac{\partial q_1'}{\partial p_j} + \frac{\partial^2 W_1}{\partial q_1'\,\partial p_j}, \\ \frac{\partial W}{\partial q_j} &= \frac{\partial^2 W_1}{\partial q_1'^2}\frac{\partial q_1'}{\partial q_j} + \frac{\partial^2 W_1}{\partial q_1'\,\partial q_j}. \end{aligned}\right\} \tag{6}$$

A comparison of Eqs. (5) and (6) shows that

$$\frac{\partial W}{\partial p_j} = \frac{1}{q_1'}\frac{\partial W_1}{\partial p_j},$$

and

$$\frac{\partial W}{\partial q_j} = \frac{1}{q_1'}\frac{\partial W_1}{\partial q_j};$$

and then, from Eqs. (3),

$$\frac{\partial W}{\partial p_j} = \frac{\partial L}{\partial q_j'}, \qquad \text{and} \qquad \frac{\partial W}{\partial q_j} = \frac{1}{q_1'}\frac{\partial L}{\partial q_j}, \qquad j = 2, \cdots, k.$$

The equations of Lagrange [Eqs. (141.3)] then become

$$\frac{d}{dq_1}\left(\frac{\partial W}{\partial p_j}\right) - \frac{\partial W}{\partial q_j} = 0, \qquad j = 2, \cdots, k. \tag{7}$$

Since the time does not occur explicitly in L, it does not occur in W. After forming the derivatives $\partial W/\partial p_j$, the letters p_j can be replaced by their equivalents

$$p_j = \frac{q_j'}{q_1'} = \frac{dq_j}{dq_1}.$$

It is then seen that Eqs. (7) are Lagrange equations for a new system in which W is the kinetic potential and q_1 plays the rôle of the time. If these equations can be solved, $q_2, \cdots, q_k$ will be expressed as funct ons of q_1, and these values substituted in the energy equation [Eq. (5)] will give q_1 as a function of the time by a quadrature. Thus by means of Whittaker's transformation, the energy integral reduces a dynamical system with k degrees of freedom to another system with $k - 1$ degrees of freedom, and a quadrature.

147. Motion with Reversed Forces.—Suppose there is given a dynamical system in which the constraints are independent of the time and the forces depend only on position. Lagrange's equations are then

$$\left(\frac{\partial T}{\partial q_j'}\right)' - \frac{\partial T}{\partial q_j} = Q_j, \qquad j = 1, \cdots, k. \tag{1}$$

Under the hypotheses made, T is a homogeneous quadratic function of $q_1', \cdots, q_k'$, and Q_j depends only upon $q_1, \cdots q_k$. Suppose also that the solutions of these equations are

$$\left.\begin{aligned} q_j &= f_j(\alpha_1, \cdots, \alpha_k; \beta_1, \cdots, \beta_k; t), \\ q_j' &= f_j'(\alpha_1, \cdots, \alpha_k; \beta_1, \cdots, \beta_k; t), \end{aligned}\right\} \tag{2}$$

where the α's and β's are constants such that

$$q_j(0) = \alpha_j, \qquad q_j'(0) = \beta_j, \qquad j = 1, \cdots, k. \tag{3}$$

Suppose further that t is changed into $i\tau$, $i = \sqrt{-1}$. Since $(\partial T/\partial q_j')'$ and $(\partial T/\partial q_j)$ are homogeneous of degree -2 in dt, and Q_j is independent of dt, the differential equations (1) become

$$\frac{d}{d\tau}\left(\frac{\partial T_1}{\partial \dot{q}_j}\right) - \frac{\partial T_1}{\partial q_j} = -Q_j, \tag{4}$$

where

$$-T_1(\dot{q}_1, \cdots, \dot{q}_k) \equiv T(q_1', \cdots, q_k'),$$

the accents denoting differentiation with respect to t and the dot differentiation with respect to τ. On account of the homogeneity of T, T_1 is precisely the same function of the arguments

$\dot{q}_1, \ldots, \dot{q}_k$ that T is of $q_1', \ldots, q_k'$. The solutions however become

$$q_j = f_j(\alpha_1, \cdots, \alpha_k; \beta_1, \cdots, \beta_k; i\tau), \qquad (5)$$
$$\dot{q}_j = \dot{f}_j(\alpha_1, \cdots, \alpha_k; \beta_1, \cdots, \beta_k; i\tau);$$

and the initial values are

$$q_j(0) = \alpha_j, \qquad \dot{q}_j(0) = i\beta_j, \qquad j = 2, \cdots, k. \qquad (6)$$

Equations (4) differ from Eqs. (1) only in that the forces are reversed. If t is the time in Eqs. (1) and τ is regarded as the time in Eqs. (4), Eqs. (2) are the solutions of Eqs. (1) and Eqs. (5) are the solutions of Eqs. (4). If the letters α and β have the same values in the two cases and if the initial values are real in both cases, it is necessary that $\beta_j = 0$ for every j; that is, the system must start from rest. Under these conditions the solution for] Eqs. (4) is obtained from Eqs. (2) merely by changing t into it, and since Eqs. (5) also are real, it follows that q_j is an even function of t and q_j' is an odd function.

For example, the simple pendulum (Fig. 77) oscillates in the arc BAD of the vertical circle with a certain period P_1, the pendulum being at rest at the points B and D. If the forces be reversed, or, its equivalent, if the circle be rotated through 180° about a horizontal axis through the center O, the pendulum oscillates in the arc BCD with a certain other period P_2. Consequently, if θ represents the angle which the pendulum rod makes with the vertical, θ is a periodic function of the time, say

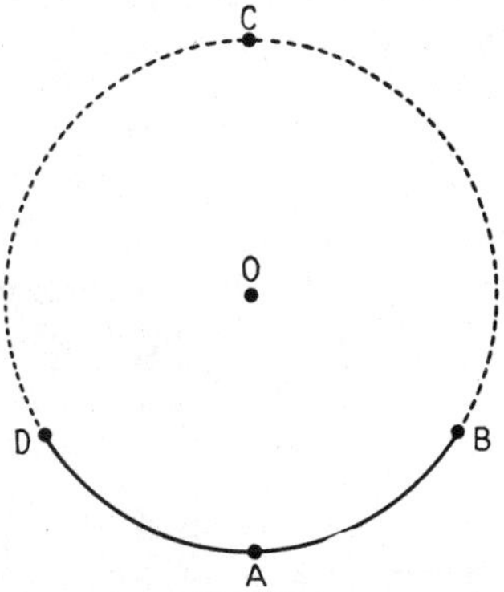

FIG. 77.

$$\theta = \varphi(t),$$

and $\varphi(t)$ has the real period P_1. If the forces are reversed

$$\theta = \varphi(it)$$

is real with the period P_2. Thus $\varphi(t)$ is a doubly periodic function of t with the periods P_1 and iP_2. Therefore $\varphi(t)$ cannot be functionally simpler than an elliptic function. If it were known that $\varphi(t)$ is a uniform function, this would be sufficient to show that it is an elliptic function, which is actually the case. (See also I, **306**.)

148. Lagrange's Equations for Impulses.—The changes in the momenta or the velocities that occur during an impulse are very simply derived from the Lagrangian equations of motion, which are

$$\left(\frac{\partial T}{\partial q_j'}\right)' - \left(\frac{\partial T_1}{\partial q_j}\right) = Q_j; \qquad j = 1, \cdots, k.$$

for on multiplying through by dt and integrating from 0 to t, there results

$$\int_0^t \left(\frac{\partial T}{\partial q_j'}\right)' dt - \int_0^t \frac{\partial T}{\partial q_j} dt = \int_0^t Q_j \, dt.$$

The first term is immediately integrable and represents the change that occurs in $\partial T/\partial q_j'$ during the impulse; that is

$$\left.\frac{\partial T}{\partial q_j'}\right|_{t=t} - \left.\frac{\partial T_1}{\partial q_j'}\right|_{t=0},$$

the first term representing the values at the end of the impulse, and the second the values at the beginning. The second integral vanishes, for the integrand $\partial T/\partial q_j$ is finite and the interval of integration is infinitely short. The third integral,

$$\int_0^t Q_j \, dt = I_j,$$

is the impulse in the q_j direction, or the q_j-component of the impulse.

Hence for impulses, the equations of Lagrange become simply

$$\left.\frac{\partial T}{\partial q_j'}\right|_{t=t} - \left.\frac{\partial T}{\partial q_j'}\right|_{t=0} = I_j, \qquad j = 1, \cdots, k.$$

These equations are linear in the q_j''s, since T is quadratic in these letters. The determinant does not vanish, as is shown in Sec. 162. The equations can therefore be solved, and the changes in the momenta that occur during the impulse can be determined.

149. The Atwood Machine.—As a simple problem illustrative of Lagrange's method consider the Atwood machine in which a rope with weights of mass m_1 and m_2 attached at each end is placed over a pulley of radius a and moment of inertia mk^2 with respect to the axis. Determine the motion when the system is released from a state of rest under the assumption that there is no friction, and that the rope is without mass.

Let the free ends of the rope initially be of length l_1 and l_2, and let θ be the angle of rotation of the pulley. The kinetic energies of the two weights are evidently

$$\tfrac{1}{2}m_1a^2\theta'^2 \qquad \text{and} \qquad \tfrac{1}{2}m_2a^2\theta'^2$$

respectively, and the kinetic energy of the pulley due to its rotation is [Eq. (49.1)]

$$\tfrac{1}{2}mk^2\theta'^2;$$

therefore

$$T = \tfrac{1}{2}[(m_1 + m_2)a^2 + mk^2]\theta'^2.$$

The potential energies of the two weights with respect to the level of the axis of the pulley are

$$-m_1g(l_1 + a\theta) \qquad \text{and} \qquad -m_2g(l_2 - a\theta),$$

and the potential energy of the wheel is constant and equal to zero. Hence

$$U = m_1g(l_1 + a\theta) + m_2g(l_2 - a\theta),$$

and

$$L = \tfrac{1}{2}[(m_1 + m_2)a^2 + mk^2]\theta'^2 + m_1g(l_1 + a\theta) + m_2g(l_2 - a\theta).$$

The system has but one degree of freedom, and Lagrange's equation,

$$\left(\frac{\partial L}{\partial \theta'}\right)' = \frac{\partial L}{\partial \theta},$$

gives the differential equation

$$[(m_1 + m_2)a^2 + mk^2]\theta'' = (m_1 - m_2)ga,$$

or

$$\theta'' = \frac{(m_1 - m_2)ga}{(m_1 + m_2)a^2 + mk^2}.$$

The motion is therefore a uniformly accelerated one.

150. The Double Pendulum.—To a simple pendulum of mass m_1 and length l_1 is attached a second one of mass m_2 and length l_2.

Determine the equations of motion under the assumption that the system is constrained to move in a vertical plane (Fig. 78).

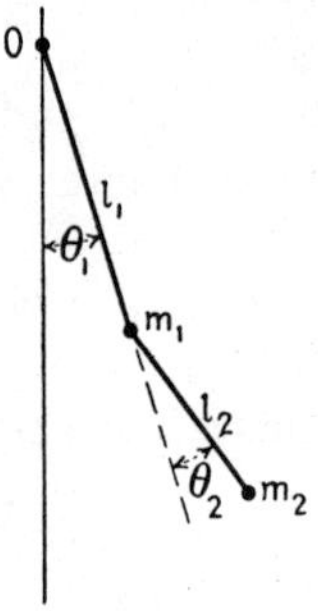

FIG. 78.

Let O be the fixed point of suspension of l_1; let θ_1 be the angle which l_1 makes with the vertical, and θ_2 the angle which l_2 makes with l_1. If O is the origin of a rectangular system of coordinates with the y-axis vertical, the equations of transformation are

$$\begin{aligned} x_1 &= +l_1 \sin \theta_1, \\ x_2 &= +l_1 \sin \theta_1 + l_2 \sin (\theta_1 + \theta_2), \\ y_1 &= -l_1 \cos \theta_1, \\ y_2 &= -l_1 \cos \theta_1 - l_2 \cos (\theta_1 + \theta_2); \end{aligned}$$

from which, since

$$\begin{aligned} T &= \tfrac{1}{2} m_1 (x_1'^2 + y_1'^2) + \tfrac{1}{2} m_2 (x_2'^2 + y_2'^2), \\ U &= -m_1 g y_1 - m_2 g y_2, \end{aligned}$$

is readily derived

$$\begin{aligned} T = \tfrac{1}{2}[m_1 l_1^2 + m_2(l_1^2 + 2l_1 l_2 \cos \theta_2 + l_2^2)]\theta_1'^2 \\ + m_2[l_1 l_2 \cos \theta_2 + l_2^2]\theta_1'\theta_2' + \tfrac{1}{2} m_2 l_2^2 \theta_2'^2, \\ U = (m_1 + m_2) l_1 g \cos \theta_1 + m_2 l_2 g \cos (\theta_1 + \theta_2). \end{aligned}$$

The Lagrangian function is

$$L = T + U.$$

Hence

$$\begin{aligned} \frac{\partial L}{\partial \theta_1'} &= [m_1 l_1^2 + m_2(l_1^2 + 2l_1 l_2 \cos \theta_2 + l_2^2)]\theta_1' + \\ &\qquad\qquad m_2[l_1 l_2 \cos \theta_2 + l_2^2]\theta_2', \\ \frac{\partial L}{\partial \theta_2'} &= m_2[l_1 l_2 \cos \theta_2 + l_2^2]\theta_1' + m_2 l_2^2 \theta_2', \\ -\frac{\partial L}{\partial \theta_1} &= (m_1 + m_2) l_1 g \sin \theta_1 + m_2 l_2 g \sin (\theta_1 + \theta_2), \\ -\frac{\partial L}{\partial \theta_2} &= m_2 l_1 l_2 \sin \theta_2 \theta_1'^2 + m_2 l_1 l_2 \sin \theta_2 \theta_1' \theta_2' + m l_2 g \sin (\theta_1 + \theta_2). \end{aligned}$$

The differential equations of Lagrange

$$\left(\frac{\partial L}{\partial \theta_1'}\right)' - \frac{\partial L}{\partial \theta_1} = 0, \qquad \left(\frac{\partial L}{\partial \theta_2'}\right)' - \frac{\partial L}{\partial \theta_2} = 0,$$

now become the differential equations of motion,

$$[m_1l_1^2 + m_2(l_1^2 + 2l_1l_2 \cos \theta_2 + l_2^2)]\theta_1'' - 2m_2l_1l_2 \sin \theta_2\theta_1'\theta_2' - m_2l_1l_2 \sin \theta_2\theta_2'^2 + m_2[l_1l_2 \cos \theta_2 + l_2^2]\theta_2'' + (m_1 + m_2)l_1g \sin \theta_1 + m_2l_2g \sin (\theta_1 + \theta_2) = 0, \quad (1)$$

and

$$m_2[l_1l_2 \cos \theta_2 + l_2^2]\theta_1'' + m_2l_2^2\theta_2'' + m_2l_1l_2 \sin \theta_2\theta_1'^2 + m_2l_2g \sin (\theta_1 + \theta_2) = 0. \quad (2)$$

Since there are no ignorable coordinates, no integrals can be obtained from this source. The energy integral

$$T - U = \text{constant},$$

holds, and this is the only integral that is evident.

If $l_2 = 0$, the double pendulum reduces to the simple pendulum. The second equation [Eq. (2)] is satisfied identically, and the first [Eq. (1)] reduces to

$$(m_1 + m_2)l_1^2\theta_1'' + (m_1 + m_2)l_1g \sin \theta = 0,$$

which, after removal of the factor $(m_1 + m_2)l_1$, is seen to be the equation for the simple pendulum. Likewise, if $l_1 = 0$, the double pendulum becomes a simple pendulum. In this event it is seen that Eqs. (1) and (2) become identical, namely,

$$m_2l_2^2(\theta_1'' + \theta_2'') + m_2l_2g \sin (\theta_1 + \theta_2) = 0.$$

The equations again reduce to the equation of motion of a simple pendulum, since $\theta_1 + \theta_2$ is the angle which l_2 makes with the vertical. Evidently, θ_1 can be taken equal to zero.

151. The Motion of a Rigid Body about a Fixed Point.—A single point of a rigid body is fixed in position, but the body otherwise is free to move. Find the equations of motion.

This problem was treated in Chapter VI, and the discussion there led to the establishment of Euler's equations [Eqs. (85.3)]. In the present section the approach is through the method of Lagrange.

Let O be the fixed point, which will be taken as the origin of a trihedron ξ, η, ζ that is rigidly attached to the body, and also as the origin of a trihedron x, y, z that is regarded as fixed in space. In order to define the position of the body in space it is necessary merely to define the position of the moving trihedron ξ, η, ζ with respect to the fixed trihedron x, y, z, and, as is shown in Sec. 52, this is conveniently done by means of the three angles of Euler, θ, φ, ψ, where θ is the angle between the z- and the ζ-axes, ψ is the angle between the x-axis and the line OK (Fig. 24) the ascending node of $\xi\eta$-plane on the xy-plane, and φ, called the angle of rotation, is the angle between the line of nodes OK and the ξ-axis. These three angles will be taken as the coordinates of Lagrange.

If the ξ-, η-, and ζ-axes coincide with the principal axes of inertia of the body at the point O (Sec. 20), the kinetic energy of the body is, by Eq. (83.2),

$$T = \tfrac{1}{2}(A\omega_\xi^2 + B\omega_\eta^2 + C\omega_\zeta^2),$$

where, as before, A, B, and C are the principal moments of inertia of the body at the point O, and ω_ξ, ω_η, and ω_ζ are the angular velocities which, expressed in terms of the Eulerian angles and their derivatives are [Eqs. (85.4)]

$$\left.\begin{aligned} \omega_\xi &= \psi' \sin\theta \sin\varphi + \theta' \cos\varphi, \\ \omega_\eta &= \psi' \sin\theta \cos\varphi - \theta' \sin\varphi, \\ \omega_\zeta &= \psi' \cos\theta + \varphi'. \end{aligned}\right\} \tag{1}$$

Taking Lagrange's equations in the form

$$\left(\frac{\partial T}{\partial q_i'}\right)' - \frac{\partial T}{\partial q_i} = Q_i,$$

and identifying the coordinate q_i with the coordinate φ, it follows that

$$\left(\frac{\partial T}{\partial \varphi'}\right)' - \frac{\partial T}{\partial \varphi} = Q_\varphi. \tag{2}$$

Now

$$\frac{\partial T}{\partial \varphi'} = \frac{\partial T}{\partial \omega_\zeta} \cdot \frac{\partial \omega_\zeta}{\partial \varphi'} = C\omega_\zeta,$$

since φ' enters in T only through ω_ζ, and

$$\frac{\partial T}{\partial \varphi} = \frac{\partial T}{\partial \omega_\xi}\frac{\partial \omega_\xi}{\partial \varphi} + \frac{\partial T}{\partial \omega_\eta}\frac{\partial \omega_\eta}{\partial \varphi} = (A - B)\omega_\xi\omega_\eta,$$

for

$$\frac{\partial T}{\partial \omega_\xi} = A\omega_\xi, \qquad \frac{\partial \omega_\xi}{\partial \varphi} = +\psi' \sin\theta\cos\varphi - \theta' \sin\varphi = +\omega_\eta,$$

$$\frac{\partial T}{\partial \omega_\eta} = B\omega_\eta, \qquad \frac{\partial \omega_\eta}{\partial \varphi} = -\psi' \sin\theta \sin\varphi - \theta' \cos\varphi = -\omega_\xi.$$

Hence Eq. (1) gives

$$C\omega_\zeta' + (B - A)\omega_\xi\omega_\eta = N_\zeta, \tag{3}$$

in agreement with the third equation of Eqs. (85.3). Since the product of $Q_\varphi\, d\varphi$ is the work done on the body in an infinitesimal displacement $d\varphi$, ψ and θ remaining constant, Q_φ, evidently, is the φ-, or ζ-, component of the couple that is acting on the body. It is represented by N_ζ in Eq. (3) in conformity with the notation in Eqs. (85.3).

Equation (3) does not contain the coordinates φ, ψ, θ explicitly, and the symmetry with respect to the angular velocities gives the other two equations of Euler,

$$\left.\begin{aligned} A\omega_\xi' + (C - B)\omega_\eta\omega_\zeta &= N_\xi, \\ B\omega_\eta' + (A - C)\omega_\zeta\omega_\xi &= N_\eta, \end{aligned}\right\} \tag{4}$$

without computation. The actual computation of these equations by the method of Lagrange is much more laborious than is the derivation of Eq. (2), but it involves no particular difficulties if it is recognized that

$$\left.\begin{aligned} N_\xi \sin\theta &= Q_\psi \sin\varphi + Q_\theta \cos\varphi \sin\theta - Q_\varphi \cos\theta \sin\varphi, \\ N_\eta \sin\theta &= Q_\psi \cos\varphi - Q_\theta \sin\varphi \sin\theta - Q_\varphi \cos\theta \cos\varphi, \\ N_\zeta &= \qquad\qquad\qquad\qquad\qquad\qquad + Q_\varphi; \end{aligned}\right\} \tag{5}$$

for which a study of Fig. 46 is recommended, Q_θ being the couple about the line OK, Q_ψ the couple about the z-axis, and Q_φ the couple about the ζ-axis.

152. Motion of a Top on a Smooth Horizontal Plane.—It will be assumed that the top is the common top of revolution and that the ζ-axis coincides with the axis of the top. The central ellipsoid of inertia is then one of revolution with $A = B$. If l is the distance from the point of the top to the center of gravity, the height of the center of gravity above the plane is $l \cos\theta$, and its potential energy is $Mgl \cos\theta$.

Since the plane is smooth the components of the velocity of the center of gravity parallel to the plane are constants which for the present purpose can be taken equal to zero. The z-component of the velocity of the center of gravity is $-l\theta' \sin\theta$.

Hence the exterior kinetic energy (Sec. 35) is $\frac{1}{2}Ml^2\theta'^2 \sin^2\theta$. The interior kinetic energy is, as in the previous section,

$$\tfrac{1}{2}(A\omega_\xi^2 + B\omega_\eta^2 + C\omega_\zeta^2);$$

and the angular velocities are related to the Eulerian angles just as in Eqs. (151.1).

The Lagrangian function is therefore

$$L = \tfrac{1}{2}Ml^2\theta'^2 \sin^2\theta + \tfrac{1}{2}A(\psi'^2 \sin^2\theta + \theta'^2) + \tfrac{1}{2}C(\psi' \cos\theta + \theta')^2 - Mgl\cos\theta.$$

It will be observed from this expression that ψ and φ are ignorable coordinates; and therefore

$$\frac{\partial L}{\partial \psi'} = A\psi' \sin^2\theta + C\cos\theta\,(\psi'\cos\theta + \theta') = c_1, \tag{1}$$

$$\frac{\partial L}{\partial \varphi'} = C(\psi'\cos\theta + \varphi') = c_2, \tag{2}$$

are integrals; and, in addition to these two, there is the energy integral

$$\tfrac{1}{2}Ml^2\theta'^2 \sin^2\theta + \tfrac{1}{2}A(\psi'^2\sin^2\theta + \theta'^2) + \tfrac{1}{2}C(\psi'\cos\theta + \varphi')^2 + Mgl\cos\theta = c_3. \tag{3}$$

Inasmuch as these three integrals are sufficient to determine the motion it is not necessary to write down the differential equations of motion.

Equations (1) and (2) are linear in φ' and ψ' and their solution gives

$$\psi' = \frac{c_1 - c_2\cos\theta}{A\sin^2\theta}, \tag{4}$$

$$\varphi' = \frac{(A\sin^2\theta + C\cos^2\theta) - Cc_1\cos\theta}{AC\sin^2\theta}. \tag{5}$$

The elimination of φ' and ψ' between Eqs. (1), (2), and (3) gives

$$(Ml^2\sin^2\theta + A)\theta'^2 + \frac{(c_1 - c_2\cos\theta)^2}{A\sin^2\theta} + 2Mgl\cos\theta = 2c_3 - \frac{c_2^2}{C},$$

and by taking

$$\cos\theta = x,$$

$$A = Ma^2, \qquad C = Mc^2, \qquad c_1 = M\gamma_1^2, \qquad c_2 = M\gamma_2^2,$$

$$2c_3 - \frac{c_2^2}{C} = M\gamma_3^2,$$

it reduces readily to the equation

$$a^2[a^2 + l^2(1 - x^2)]x'^2 = a^2\gamma_3^2 - (\gamma_1^2 - \gamma_2^2 x)^2 - 2a^2 glx(1 - x^2). \quad (6)$$

The variables are separable in this equation, but x is, in general, a hyperelliptic function of the time. After θ has been expressed as a function of the time, Eqs. (4) and (5) give ψ and φ as functions of the time by two quadratures. The entire problem is therefore reduced to three quadratures.

II. NON-HOLONOMIC SYSTEMS

153. Example—the Rolling Sphere.—Let x, y, z be the coordinates of the center of the sphere and φ, ψ, and θ its Eulerian angles. If U is its potential function, the Lagrangian function L is

$$L = \tfrac{1}{2}M(x'^2 + y'^2 + z'^2) + \tfrac{1}{2}(A\omega_\xi^2 + B\omega_\eta^2 + C\omega_\zeta^2) + U \quad (1)$$

where the angular velocities ω_ξ, ω_η, and ω_ζ are related to φ, ψ, θ; φ', ψ', θ' as in Eqs. (151.1).

If the sphere is entirely free, the system is holonomic, and the equations of motion are formed in accordance with the method of Lagrange; the sphere has six degrees of freedom. If the sphere is constrained to be always in contact with the xy-plane and the contact is smooth, it is necessary to write merely

$$z = a, \qquad z' = 0, \quad (2)$$

and the degrees of freedom are reduced from six to five. The constraint [Eq. (2)] leaves the system holonomic; but if the sphere is constrained to a pure rolling contact, or rolling and pivoting, it is necessary to formulate the fact that the velocity of the particle of the sphere in contact with the xy-plane is always zero. These conditions are given in Eqs. (121.7) in the form

$$\sigma_x - a\omega_y = 0, \qquad \sigma_y + a\omega_x = 0, \qquad \sigma_z = 0, \quad (3)$$

where $\boldsymbol{\sigma}$ is the velocity of the center of the sphere, and therefore

$$\sigma_x = x', \qquad \sigma_y = y', \qquad \sigma_z = z',$$

and ω_x, ω_y, ω_z are the components of the instantaneous angular velocity with respect to the x-, y-, and z-axes. Now

and

$$\left.\begin{aligned}\omega_x &= \alpha_1\omega_\xi + \alpha_2\omega_\eta + \alpha_3\omega_\zeta,\\ \omega_y &= \beta_1\omega_\xi + \beta_2\omega_\eta + \beta_3\omega_\zeta,\end{aligned}\right\} \tag{4}$$

where the α's and β's are the direction cosines, as in Sec. 52 where their expressions in terms of Euler's angles are given. On substituting in their values and inserting the values of ω_ξ, ω_η, and ω_ζ from Eqs. (151.1), Eqs. (3) become

$$\begin{aligned} x' - a\theta' \sin\psi + a\varphi' \sin\theta \cos\psi &= 0,\\ y' + a\theta' \cos\psi + a\varphi' \sin\theta \sin\psi &= 0, \end{aligned} \tag{5}$$

or, on multiplying through by dt,

$$\begin{aligned} dx - a \sin\psi\, d\theta + a \sin\theta \cos\psi\, d\varphi &= 0,\\ dy + a \cos\psi\, d\theta + a \sin\theta \sin\psi\, d\varphi &= 0. \end{aligned} \tag{6}$$

Only such displacements as satisfy Eqs. (6) are possible, or, if preferred, only such velocities as satisfy Eqs. (5). There are two of these constraints in addition to the constraint in Eq. (2), and the degrees of freedom of the sphere are reduced to three. As Eqs. (6) are not exact differentials it is not possible to express the admissible geometric positions and orientations of the sphere by means of three independent parameters. Hence the system is non-holonomic, and the equations of Lagrange cannot be used without modification.[1]

154. An Extension of Lagrange's Equations for Non-holonomic Systems.—Let x, y, z be the coordinates of any particle of mass m, and n the number of degrees of freedom, so that the coordinates $q_1, \ldots, q_n$ can be regarded as entirely free. Suppose further that for any arbitrary variations (t constant)

$$\left.\begin{aligned}\delta x &= a_1\delta q_1 + a_2\delta q_2 + \cdots + a_n\delta q_n,\\ \delta y &= b_1\delta q_1 + b_2\delta q_2 + \cdots + b_n\delta q_n,\\ \delta z &= c_1\delta q_1 + c_2\delta q_2 + \cdots + c_n\delta q_n.\end{aligned}\right\} \tag{1}$$

[1] The first extension of Lagrange's equations to non-holonomic systems was made by Ferrers, *Quarterly Journal of Mathematics* XII, (1873). See also C. Neumann, *Berichte der königl. Gesellschaft der Wissenschaften zu Leipzig* (1888); and Vierkandt, "Monatshefte für Mathematik und Physik," III, (1892); Hadamard, *Société des Sciences de Bordeaux*, 1895; Carvallo, *Journal de l'École Polytechnique*, 1900; Kortweg, *Nieuw Archief*, 1899.

In these equations the coefficients $a_1, a_2, \ldots, c_n$ are functions of the coordinates $q_1, q_2, \ldots, q_n$ and the time, and possibly k other parameters $p_1, \ldots, p_k$ whose variations are related to the variations of the q's by the equations

$$\begin{aligned} \delta p_1 &= \alpha_{11}\delta q_1 + \alpha_{21}\delta q_2 + \cdots + \alpha_{n1}\delta q_n \\ &\cdots\cdots\cdots\cdots\cdots\cdots, \\ \delta p_k &= \alpha_{1k}\delta q_1 + \alpha_{2k}\delta q_2 + \cdots + \alpha_{nk}\delta q_n. \end{aligned} \tag{2}$$

Under these conditions the displacement of the particle that occurs in its motion in the interval of time dt is given by the equations

$$\begin{aligned} dx &= a_1\, dq_1 + a_2\, dq_2 + \cdots + a_n\, dq_n + a_0\, dt, \\ dy &= b_1\, dq_1 + b_2\, dq_2 + \cdots + b_n\, dq_n + b_0\, dt, \\ dz &= c_1\, dq_1 + c_2\, dq_2 + \cdots + c_n\, dq_n + c_0\, dt; \end{aligned} \tag{3}$$

and the changes that take place in the p's are given by the equations

$$\begin{aligned} dp_1 &= \alpha_{11}\, dq_1 + \alpha_{21}\, dq_2 + \cdots + \alpha_{n1}\, dq_n + \alpha_{01}\, dt, \\ &\cdots\cdots\cdots\cdots\cdots\cdots\cdots, \\ dp_k &= \alpha_{1k}\, dq_1 + \alpha_{2k}\, dq_2 + \cdots + \alpha_{nk}\, dq_n + \alpha_{0k}\, dt, \end{aligned} \tag{4}$$

the added coefficients $a_0, b_0, c_0, \alpha_0, \ldots \alpha_{0k}$ vanishing if the constraints are independent of the time.

It follows then that

$$\left.\begin{aligned} x' &= a_1q_1' + a_2q_2' + \cdots + a_nq_n' + a_0, \\ y' &= b_1q_1' + b_2q_2' + \cdots + b_nq_n' + b_0, \\ z' &= c_1q_1' + c_2q_2' + \cdots + c_nq_n' + c_0; \end{aligned}\right\} \tag{5}$$

also

$$\left.\begin{aligned} p_1' &= \alpha_{11}q_1' + \alpha_{21}q_2' + \cdots + \alpha_{n1}q_n' + \alpha_{01}, \\ &\cdots\cdots\cdots\cdots\cdots\cdots\cdots \\ p_k' &= \alpha_{1k}q_1' + \alpha_{2k}q_2' + \cdots + \alpha_{nk}q_n' + \alpha_{0k}. \end{aligned}\right\} \tag{6}$$

From Eqs. (3) and (5) it is seen that

$$\frac{\partial x}{\partial q_j} = \frac{\partial x'}{\partial q_j'} = a_j, \qquad \frac{\partial y}{\partial q_j} = \frac{\partial y'}{\partial q_j'} = b_j, \qquad \frac{\partial z}{\partial q_j} = \frac{\partial z'}{\partial q_j'} = c_j; \tag{7}$$

but, unlike Eqs. (140.7),

$$\left(\frac{\partial x}{\partial q_j}\right)' \neq \frac{\partial x'}{\partial q_j}, \qquad \left(\frac{\partial y}{\partial q_j}\right)' \neq \frac{\partial y'}{\partial q_j}, \qquad \left(\frac{\partial z}{\partial q_j}\right)' \neq \frac{\partial z'}{\partial q_j},$$

for

$$\left.\begin{aligned}\left(\frac{\partial x}{\partial q_j}\right)' &= a_j' = \sum_{i=0}^{n}\frac{\partial a_j}{\partial q_i}q_i' + \sum_{i=1}^{k}\frac{\partial a_j}{\partial p_i}p_i', \cdots,\\ \text{and}\qquad \frac{\partial x'}{\partial q_j} &= \sum_{i=0}^{n}\frac{\partial a_i}{\partial q_j}q_i' + \sum_{i=0}^{n}\sum_{s=1}^{k}\frac{\partial a_i}{\partial p_s}\frac{\partial p_s}{\partial q_j}q_i', \cdots,\end{aligned}\right\} \qquad (8)$$

in which q_0 is to be taken equal to t.

It is possible however to write

$$\left(\frac{\partial x}{\partial q_j}\right)' = \frac{\partial x'}{\partial q_j} + \xi_j, \qquad \left(\frac{\partial y}{\partial q_j}\right)' = \frac{\partial y'}{\partial q_j} + \eta_j, \qquad \left(\frac{\partial z}{\partial q_j}\right)' = \frac{\partial z'}{\partial q_j} + \zeta_j, \qquad (9)$$

where ξ_j, η_j, and ζ_j are functions that can be obtained by taking the difference between the equations in the two lines of Eqs. (8). It is needless to write out their forms explicitly; it is sufficient to notice that they are linear in $q_1', \ldots, q_n'$.

The equations of motion for each particle are

$$mx'' = X, \qquad my'' = Y, \qquad mz'' = Z.$$

Let the first of these equations be multiplied by $\partial x/\partial q_j$, the second by $\partial y/\partial q_j$, the third by $\partial z/\partial q_j$ and the three equations then added. On summing these equations over all of the particles, there results

$$\begin{aligned}\sum m\left(x''\frac{\partial x}{\partial q_j} + y''\frac{\partial y}{\partial q_j} + z''\frac{\partial z}{\partial q_j}\right) &=\\ \sum\left(X\frac{\partial x}{\partial q_j} + Y\frac{\partial y}{\partial q_j} + Z\frac{\partial z}{\partial q_j}\right) &= Q_j, \qquad j = 1, \cdots, n. \qquad (10)\end{aligned}$$

where Q_j has the same significance as in the holonomic case. The transformation of the left member proceeds just as in Sec. 140, except for the added terms in ξ_j, η_j, and ζ_j.

On setting

$$T = \tfrac{1}{2}\Sigma m(x'^2 + y'^2 + z'^2),$$

and

$$W_j = \Sigma m(\xi_j x' + \eta_j y' + \zeta_j z'),$$

Eqs. (10) become

$$\left(\frac{\partial T}{\partial q_j'}\right)' - \frac{\partial T}{\partial q_j} - W_j = Q_j, \qquad j = 1, \cdots, n, \tag{11}$$

which are the same as for the holonomic case with the addition of the term $-W_j$. These terms are somewhat troublesome to compute since the function $m(\xi_j x' + \eta_j y' + \zeta_j z')$ must be formed for each particle and then summed over the entire system.

155. The Equations of Motion for a Homogeneous Sphere Rolling on a Plane.—It will be assumed that the center of gravity of the sphere is at its center and that the central ellipsoid of inertia also is a sphere, conditions that are satisfied if the sphere is homogeneous, or homogeneous in concentric layers. It will be assumed also that the applied forces act at the center of the sphere. With these assumptions the principal moments of inertia are equal, and

$$A = B = C = Mk^2, \tag{1}$$

where M is the mass of the sphere and k is the radius of gyration with respect to a diameter.

The potential function U depends upon the position of the sphere, but not upon its orientation; that is U is a function of x and y, the coordinates of its center, but not upon the Eulerian angles θ, φ, and ψ. The z-axis is perpendicular to the plane so that the z-coordinate of the sphere is

$$z = a, \qquad z' = 0.$$

If the values of the angular velocities, given in Eqs. (151.1), are substituted in Eq. (153.1), the Lagrangian function is found to be

$$L = \tfrac{1}{2}M(x'^2 + y'^2) + \tfrac{1}{2}Mk^2(\theta'^2 + \varphi'^2 + \psi'^2 + 2\varphi'\psi' \cos\theta) + U;$$

and the constraints are, Eqs. (153.5),

$$\left.\begin{aligned} x' &= +a\theta' \sin\psi - a\varphi' \sin\theta \cos\psi, \\ y' &= -a\theta' \cos\psi - a\varphi' \sin\theta \sin\psi. \end{aligned}\right\} \tag{2}$$

Since the sphere has only three degrees of freedom, three of the five variables x, y, θ, φ, and ψ can be regarded as primary and two as secondary. For example, if θ, φ, and ψ are regarded as entirely free, or primary, the coordinates x and y are secondary; or if x, y, and ψ are primary, then θ and φ are secondary. The problem will be considered for both cases.

The Equations for Euler's Angles.—In accordance with the method of Sec. 154 the equations of Lagrange become

$$\left.\begin{aligned} \left(\frac{\partial T}{\partial \theta'}\right)' - \frac{\partial T}{\partial \theta} - W_\theta &= \frac{\partial U}{\partial \theta}, \\ \left(\frac{\partial T}{\partial \varphi'}\right)' - \frac{\partial T}{\partial \varphi} - W_\varphi &= \frac{\partial U}{\partial \varphi}, \\ \left(\frac{\partial T}{\partial \psi'}\right)' - \frac{\partial T}{\partial \psi} - W_\psi &= \frac{\partial U}{\partial \psi}. \end{aligned}\right\} \tag{3}$$

From Eqs. (2) it is seen that

$$x'^2 + y'^2 = a^2(\theta'^2 + \varphi'^2 \sin^2 \theta),$$

and therefore the kinetic energy T can be expressed in terms of the Eulerian angles and their derivatives alone. Its expression is

$$T = \tfrac{1}{2}Ma^2(\theta'^2 + \varphi'^2 \sin^2 \theta) + \\ \tfrac{1}{2}Mk^2(\theta'^2 + \varphi'^2 + \psi'^2 + 2\varphi'\psi' \cos \theta). \tag{4}$$

The equations of transformation for the individual particles are given in Eqs. (139.1). Let these equations be written

$$x_i = x + A_i, \qquad y_i = y + B_i, \qquad z_i = a + C_i, \tag{5}$$

where

$$\begin{aligned} A_i &= \alpha_1\xi_i + \alpha_2\eta_i + \alpha_3\zeta_i, \\ B_i &= \beta_1\xi_i + \beta_2\eta_i + \beta_3\zeta_i, \\ C_i &= \gamma_1\xi_i + \gamma_2\eta_i + \gamma_3\zeta_i. \end{aligned}$$

The direction cosines $\alpha_1, \ldots, \gamma_3$ are functions of θ, φ, and ψ alone, (Sec. 52), and

$$\sum_i m_iA_i = \sum_i m_iB_i = \sum_i m_iC_i = 0,$$

the sum being extended over the entire sphere. Any partial derivative of these sums with respect to θ, φ, and ψ also vanishes. From Eqs. (5) and (2) it follows that

$$x_i' = \left(\frac{\partial A_i}{\partial \theta} + a \sin \psi\right)\theta' + \left(\frac{\partial A_i}{\partial \varphi} - a \sin \theta \cos \psi\right)\varphi' + \frac{\partial A_i}{\partial \psi}\psi'$$

$$
\begin{aligned}
y_i' &= \left(\frac{\partial B_i}{\partial \theta} - a\cos\psi\right)\theta' + \left(\frac{\partial B_i}{\partial \varphi} - a\sin\theta\sin\psi\right)\varphi' + \frac{\partial B_i}{\partial \psi}\psi',\\
z_i' &= \frac{\partial C_i}{\partial \theta}\theta' + \frac{\partial C_i}{\partial \varphi}\varphi' + \frac{\partial C_i}{\partial \psi}\psi'.
\end{aligned}
$$

From these expressions it is found that

$$
\begin{aligned}
\xi_\theta &= +a\cos\theta\cos\psi\,\varphi' + a\cos\psi\,\psi',\\
\eta_\theta &= +a\cos\theta\sin\psi\,\varphi' + a\sin\psi\,\psi',\\
\xi_\varphi &= -a\cos\theta\cos\psi\,\theta' + a\sin\theta\sin\psi\,\psi',\\
\eta_\varphi &= -a\cos\theta\sin\psi\,\theta' - a\sin\theta\cos\psi\,\psi',\\
\xi_\psi &= -a\cos\psi\,\theta' - a\sin\theta\sin\psi\,\varphi',\\
\eta_\psi &= -a\sin\psi\,\theta' + a\sin\theta\cos\psi\,\varphi',\\
\zeta_\theta &= \zeta_\varphi = \zeta_\psi = 0.
\end{aligned}
$$

These functions are the same for every particle. Hence in the formation of

$$
W_\theta = \Sigma m_i(\xi_\theta x_i' + \eta_\theta y_i' + \zeta_\theta z_i'), \qquad W_\varphi = \cdots, \text{ etc.},
$$

the terms that depend upon $\Sigma m_i A_i$, $\Sigma m_i B_i$, $\Sigma m_i C_i$ and their derivatives do so linearly, and therefore vanish. The partial derivatives that occur in x_i', y_i', and z_i', therefore, can be set equal to zero at once, and it is then found that

$$
\left.
\begin{aligned}
W_\theta &= -Ma^2[\sin\theta\cos\theta\,\varphi'^2 + \sin\theta\,\varphi'\psi'],\\
W_\varphi &= +Ma^2[\sin\theta\cos\theta\,\theta'\varphi' + \sin\theta\,\theta'\psi'],\\
W_\psi &= 0.
\end{aligned}
\right\} \tag{6}
$$

The remaining terms of the equations of motion are computed in the usual manner. The resulting equations are therefore

$$
\left.
\begin{aligned}
&M(a^2 + k^2)[\theta'' + \varphi'\psi'\sin\theta] = \frac{\partial U}{\partial \theta},\\
&Ma^2[\varphi''\sin^2\theta + \varphi'\theta'\sin\theta\cos\theta - \theta'\psi'\sin\theta] +\\
&\qquad\qquad Mk^2[\varphi'' + \psi''\cos\theta - \theta'\psi'\sin\theta] = \frac{\partial U}{\partial \varphi},\\
&Mk^2[\psi'' + \varphi''\cos\theta - \varphi'\theta'\sin\theta] = 0.
\end{aligned}
\right\} \tag{7}
$$

By eliminating ψ'' from the second equation, using its value from the third, the second of these equations takes the simpler form

$$
M(a^2 + k^2)[\varphi''\sin^2\theta + \varphi'\theta'\sin\theta\cos\theta - \theta'\psi'\sin\theta] = \frac{\partial U}{\partial \varphi}. \tag{8}
$$

The third of Eqs. (7) gives the integral

$$\psi' + \varphi' \cos \theta = c_1 \tag{9}$$

which expresses the fact that the moment of momentum about the diameter which is normal to the plane of motion is constant. This integral together with the equations of constraint, Eqs. (2), gives the three equations

$$\left.\begin{aligned} a\theta' &= x' \sin \psi - y' \cos \psi, \\ -a\varphi' \sin \theta &= x' \cos \psi + y' \sin \psi, \\ \psi' + \varphi' \cos \theta &= c_1, \end{aligned}\right\} \tag{10}$$

which define the orientation of the sphere when x' and y' are known.

The Equations for the Center of the Sphere.—Now let the primary variables be x, y, and ψ. Then the equations of motion are

$$\left.\begin{aligned} \left(\frac{\partial T}{\partial x'}\right)' - \frac{\partial T}{\partial x} - W_x &= \frac{\partial U}{\partial x}, \\ \left(\frac{\partial T}{\partial y'}\right)' - \frac{\partial T}{\partial y} - W_y &= \frac{\partial U}{\partial y}, \\ \left(\frac{\partial T}{\partial \psi'}\right)' - \frac{\partial T}{\partial \psi} - W_\psi &= 0; \end{aligned}\right\} \tag{11}$$

and the equations of constraint, Eqs. (2), become

$$\begin{aligned} \theta' &= +\frac{x'}{a} \sin \psi - \frac{y'}{a} \cos \psi, \\ \varphi' &= -\frac{x' \cos \psi}{a \sin \theta} - \frac{y' \sin \psi}{a \sin \theta}, \end{aligned} \tag{12}$$

so that

$$\begin{aligned} \frac{\partial \theta}{\partial x} &= +\frac{\sin \psi}{a}, & \frac{\partial \varphi}{\partial x} &= -\frac{\cos \psi}{a \sin \theta}, \\ \frac{\partial \theta}{\partial y} &= -\frac{\cos \psi}{a}, & \frac{\partial \varphi}{\partial y} &= -\frac{\sin \psi}{a \sin \theta}. \end{aligned} \tag{13}$$

In the equations of transformation, Eqs. (5),

$$x_i = x + A_i, \qquad y_i = y + B_i, \qquad z_i = a + C_i,$$

the variables x and y enter in A_i B_i and C_i implicitly through θ and φ, and this must always be remembered in forming the derivatives with respect to x and y. It will be found without much difficulty that

$$\left.\begin{aligned}
\xi_x &= \left[-\frac{\cos\theta}{\sin^2\theta}\right]\frac{\partial A_i}{\partial\varphi}\frac{y'}{a^2} + \left[\frac{\partial A_i}{\partial\theta}\cos\psi + \frac{\partial A_i}{\partial\varphi}\frac{\sin\psi}{\sin\theta}\right]\frac{\psi'}{a},\\
\xi_y &= \left[+\frac{\cos\theta}{\sin^2\theta}\right]\frac{\partial A_i}{\partial\varphi}\frac{x'}{a^2} + \left[\frac{\partial A_i}{\partial\theta}\sin\psi - \frac{\partial A_i}{\partial\varphi}\frac{\cos\psi}{\sin\theta}\right]\frac{\psi'}{a},\\
\xi_\psi &= \left[-\frac{\partial A_i}{\partial\theta}\cos\psi - \frac{\partial A_i}{\partial\varphi}\frac{\sin\psi}{\sin\theta}\right]\frac{x'}{a^2} + \\
&\qquad\left[-\frac{\partial A_i}{\partial\theta}\sin\psi + \frac{\partial A_i}{\partial\varphi}\frac{\cos\psi}{\sin\theta}\right]\frac{y'}{a^2}.
\end{aligned}\right\} \quad (14)$$

The expressions for η_x, η_y, and η_ψ are obtained merely by replacing A_i by B_i in Eqs. (14); and ζ_x, ζ_y and ζ_ψ are obtained by replacing A_i by C_i.

Since

$$x_i' = \left[a + \frac{\partial A_i}{\partial\theta}\sin\psi - \frac{\partial A_i}{\partial\varphi}\frac{\cos\psi}{\sin\theta}\right]\frac{x'}{a} + \left[-\frac{\partial A_i}{\partial\theta}\cos\psi - \frac{\partial A_i}{\partial\varphi}\frac{\sin\psi}{\sin\theta}\right]\frac{y'}{a} + \left[\frac{\partial A_i}{\partial\psi}\right]\psi'$$

and similar expressions, in which A_i is replaced by B_i and C_i, for y_i' and z_i', it is seen that

$$W_x = \Sigma m_i(\xi_x x_i' + \eta_x y_i' + \zeta_x\psi'), \qquad W_y = \cdots, \text{ etc.},$$

are quadratic in the partial derivatives of A_i, B_i and C_i. In forming the sum it will be remembered that the linear terms vanish, since $\Sigma m_i\xi_i = 0$, etc, and also the cross product terms of the form $\Sigma m_i\xi_i\eta_i$ vanish, since the products of inertia at the center of the sphere are equal to zero. There remain only the terms in the squares, and since

$$\Sigma m_i\xi_i^2 = \Sigma m_i\eta_i^2 = \Sigma m_i\zeta_i^2 = Mk^2$$

where k is the radius of gyration of the sphere with respect to a diameter, it is found that

$$\begin{aligned}
W_x = 0\,x'^2 &+ \frac{\sin\psi\cos\theta}{\sin^3\theta}\frac{k^2}{a^3}y'^2 + \frac{\sin\psi\cos\theta}{\sin\theta}\frac{k^2}{a}\psi'^2\\
&+ \frac{\cos\psi\cos\theta}{\sin^3\theta}\frac{k^2}{a^3}x'y' - \frac{\sin\psi\cos\psi\cos^2\theta}{\sin^2\theta}\frac{k^2}{a^2}x'\psi' -\\
&\qquad \frac{1+\sin^2\psi\cos^2\theta}{\sin^2\theta}\frac{k^2}{a^2}y'\psi',
\end{aligned}$$

$$W_y = -\frac{\cos\psi\cos\theta}{\sin^3\theta}\frac{k^2}{a^3}x'^2 + 0\,y'^2 - \frac{\cos\psi\cos\theta}{\sin\theta}\frac{k^2}{a}\psi'^2 - \frac{\sin\psi\cos\theta}{\sin^3\theta}\frac{k^2}{a^3}x'y' + \frac{1+\cos^2\psi\cos^2\theta}{\sin^2\theta}\frac{k^2}{a^2}x'\psi' + \frac{\sin\psi\cos\psi\cos^2\theta}{\sin^2\theta}\frac{k^2}{a^2}y'\psi',$$

$$W_\psi = \frac{\sin\psi\cos\psi\cos^2\theta}{\sin^2\theta}\frac{k^2}{a^3}x'^2 - \frac{\sin\psi\cos\psi\cos^2\theta}{\sin^2\theta}\frac{k^2}{a^3}y'^2 + 0\,\psi'^2 + \frac{(\sin^2\psi - \cos^2\psi)\cos^2\theta}{\sin^2\theta}\frac{k^2}{a^3}x'y' - \frac{\sin\psi\cos\theta}{\sin\theta}\frac{k^2}{a^2}x'\psi' + \frac{\cos\psi\cos\theta}{\sin\theta}\frac{k^2}{a^2}y'\psi'.$$

On eliminating θ' and φ' from the expression for the kinetic energy by means of Eqs. (12), it will be found that

$$T = M\frac{a^2+k^2}{2a^2}(x'^2 + y'^2) + \frac{1}{2}Mk^2\left(\psi' - \frac{x'}{a}\frac{\cos\psi\cos\theta}{\sin\theta} - \frac{y'}{a}\frac{\sin\psi\cos\theta}{\sin\theta}\right)^2;$$

and the equations of motion [Eqs. (11)] become

$$M\frac{a^2+k^2}{a^2}x'' - \frac{k^2}{a}\frac{\cos\psi\cos\theta}{\sin\theta}\times\left(\psi' - \frac{x'}{a}\frac{\cos\psi\cos\theta}{\sin\theta} - \frac{y'}{a}\frac{\sin\psi\cos\theta}{\sin\theta}\right)' = \frac{\partial U}{\partial x},$$

$$M\frac{a^2+k^2}{a^2}y'' - \frac{k^2}{a}\frac{\sin\psi\cos\theta}{\sin\theta}\times\left(\psi' - \frac{x'}{a}\frac{\cos\psi\cos\theta}{\sin\theta} - \frac{y'}{a}\frac{\sin\psi\cos\theta}{\sin\theta}\right)' = \frac{\partial U}{\partial y},$$

$$Mk^2\left(\psi' - \frac{x'}{a}\frac{\cos\psi\cos\theta}{\sin\theta} - \frac{y'}{a}\frac{\sin\psi\cos\theta}{\sin\theta}\right)' = 0.$$

The last equation gives the integral

$$\psi' - \frac{x'}{a}\frac{\cos\psi\cos\theta}{\sin\theta} - \frac{y'}{a}\frac{\sin\psi\cos\theta}{\sin\theta} = \psi' + \varphi'\cos\theta = \text{constant},$$

which is the same integral as in Eq. (9). Also, by virtue of the third equation, the first two equations reduce to

$$\left.\begin{aligned} Mx'' &= \frac{a^2}{a^2 + k^2}\frac{\partial U}{\partial x}, \\ My'' &= \frac{a^2}{a^2 + k^2}\frac{\partial U}{\partial y}, \end{aligned}\right\} \tag{15}$$

and as these equations do not contain any dependent variables other than x and y, they show that the center of the sphere moves just as though it were a free particle acted upon by the same forces as the sphere but reduced in the ratio $a^2 : a^2 + k^2$, a theorem that was proved otherwise in Sec. 124.

If Eqs. (15) can be solved, x' and y' become known functions of the time, and the problem is then reduced to the solution of Eqs. (10), which are of the third order.

156. Appell's Equations for Holonomic or Non-holonomic Systems.—In 1899 P. Appell gave a general form for the equations of motion that are valid whether the system is holonomic or non-holonomic.[1] The same hypotheses are made as in Sec. 124, and therefore the first six sets of equations of that section hold. Just as before, the equations of motion of the individual particles are

$$mx'' = X, \qquad my'' = Y, \qquad mz'' = Z. \tag{1}$$

On multiplying the first of these equations by δx, the second by δy, the third by δz, then adding and taking the sum over all of the particles, there is obtained

$$\Sigma m(x''\delta x + y''\delta y + z''\delta z) = \Sigma(X\delta x + Y\delta y + Z\delta z). \tag{2}$$

If in this equation δx, δy, and δz are replaced by their values from Eqs. (154.1) and it is remembered that $\delta q_1, \ldots, \delta q_n$ are entirely arbitrary, Eq. (2) is resolved into the following set of n-equations:

$$\left.\begin{aligned} \Sigma m(x''a_1 + y''b_1 + z''c_1) &= \Sigma(Xa_1 + Yb_1 + Zc_1), \\ \Sigma m(x''a_2 + y''b_2 + z''c_2) &= \Sigma(Xa_2 + Yb_2 + Zc_2), \\ &\cdots\cdots\cdots\cdots \\ \Sigma m(x''a_n + y''b_n + z''c_n) &= \Sigma(Xa_n + Yb_n + Zc_n). \end{aligned}\right\} \tag{3}$$

In the right member of Eq. (2)

$$\sum(X\delta x + Y\delta y + Z\delta z) = \sum_{j=1}^{n} Q_j \delta q_j,$$

[1] P. Appell, *Comptes Rendus*, Aug. 7, 1889; *Journal für Mathematik* 121; "Mécanique Rationelle," Vol. 2, chap. 24.

where

$$Q_j = \Sigma(Xa_j + Yb_j + Zc_j),$$

is the work done in the displacement; so that, just as before, Q_j is the component of the force in the q_j direction, Sec. 141. On differentiating Eqs. (154.5) with respect to the time there is obtained

$$\left.\begin{aligned} x'' &= a_1q_1'' + a_2q_2'' + \cdots + a_nq_n'' + (\cdots),\\ y'' &= b_1q_1'' + b_2q_2'' + \cdots + b_nq_n'' + (\cdots),\\ z'' &= c_1q_1'' + c_2q_2'' + \cdots + c_nq_n'' + (\cdots),\end{aligned}\right\} \qquad (4)$$

where the terms not written, (. . .), do not contain q_1'', q_2'', . . . , q_n''. From Eq. (4) it follows that

$$a_j = \frac{\partial x''}{\partial q_j''}, \qquad b_j = \frac{\partial y''}{\partial q_j''}, \qquad c_j = \frac{\partial z''}{\partial q_j''};$$

so that Eqs. (3) can be written

$$\sum m\left(x''\frac{\partial x''}{\partial q_j''} + y''\frac{\partial y''}{\partial q_j''} + z''\frac{\partial z''}{\partial q_j''}\right) = Q_j, \quad j = 1, \cdots, n. \qquad (5)$$

Now form the function

$$S = \tfrac{1}{2}\Sigma m(x''^2 + y''^2 + z''^2),$$

a function which, on account of its form, has received the name *the energy of acceleration of the system.* It is evident then that Eqs. (5) become

$$\frac{\partial S}{\partial q_j''} = Q_j, \qquad j = 1, \cdots, n, \qquad (6)$$

and these are Appell's equations.

In forming the function S it is necessary that it contain the second derivatives of q's only, since the q's are regarded as being entirely arbitrary. If it contains the second derivatives of the p's, these can be eliminated by means of Eqs. (154.6). The n equations in Eqs. (6) and the k equations in Eqs. (154.6) together form a system of $n + k$ equations that determine the $n + k$ letters p and q. It should be remarked that in computing S it is necessary to retain only those terms that contain the q_j'', since the other terms drop out in the process of differentiation. On comparing Eqs. (154.5) and (4), it is evident that the coefficients of the terms of the second degree in the q'''s in S are the same as the corresponding coefficients of the terms of the second degree in the q''s in the kinetic energy T; but this similarity does not extend, in general, to the linear terms.

157. Application of Appell's Equations to the Sphere Rolling on a Plane.—As an application of Appell's method of deriving the equations of motion, consider the sphere rolling on a plane, the problem treated in Sec. 155.

Let x_i, y_i, z_i be the coordinates of a particle of the sphere when referred to a set of fixed axes and ξ_i, η_i, ζ_i when referred to a system of axes that are rigidly attached to the sphere with origin at the center of the sphere. Then,

$$\begin{aligned} x_i &= x + \alpha_1\xi_i + \alpha_2\eta_i + \alpha_3\zeta_i, \\ y_i &= y + \beta_1\xi_i + \beta_2\eta_i + \beta_3\zeta_i, \\ z_i &= z + \gamma_1\xi_i + \gamma_2\eta_i + \gamma_3\zeta_i, \end{aligned}$$

where x, y, z are the coordinates of the center of the sphere relative to the fixed system and $\alpha_1, \alpha_2, \ldots, \gamma_3$ are the direction cosines as indicated in the table in Sec. 85. Throughout the motion ξ_i, η_i, and ζ_i are constants; hence on differentiating twice

$$\begin{aligned} x_i'' &= x'' + \alpha_1''\xi_i + \alpha_2''\eta_i + \alpha_3''\zeta_i, \\ y_i'' &= y'' + \beta_1''\xi_i + \beta_2''\eta_i + \beta_3''\zeta_i, \\ z_i'' &= z'' + \gamma_1''\xi_i + \gamma_2''\eta_i + \gamma_3''\zeta_i. \end{aligned}$$

With these expressions it is found that the energy of acceleration is

$$S = \tfrac{1}{2}\Sigma m_i(x_i''^2 + y_i''^2 + z_i''^2) = \tfrac{1}{2}M(x''^2 + y''^2) +$$
$$\tfrac{1}{4}Mk^2(\alpha_1''^2 + \alpha_2''^2 + \alpha_3''^2 + \beta_1''^2 + \beta_2''^2 + \beta_3''^2 + \gamma_1''^2 + \gamma_2''^2 + \gamma_3''^2),$$

where k is the radius of gyration of the sphere with respect to a diameter. Thus the acceleration energy, like the kinetic energy, is the sum of the exterior acceleration energy,

$$\tfrac{1}{2}M(x''^2 + y''^2),$$

and the interior acceleration energy; for the remainder of the expression is what the acceleration energy would be if the center of the sphere were fixed.

It is necessary to compute the interior acceleration energy in terms of Euler's angles, Sec. 52, and their derivative. For this purpose let

$$\alpha = -\cos\theta\sin\psi,$$
$$\beta = +\cos\theta\cos\psi,$$
$$\gamma = +\sin\theta;$$

which, since

$$\alpha\alpha_1 + \beta\beta_1 + \gamma\gamma_1 = \sin\varphi, \qquad \alpha\alpha_2 + \beta\beta_2 + \gamma\gamma_2 = \cos\varphi,$$
$$\alpha\alpha_3 + \beta\beta_3 + \gamma\gamma_3 = 0,$$

are the direction cosines of a line in the $\xi\eta$-plane that is perpendicular to the line OK, Fig. 24. Also let

$$\lambda = \cos\psi, \qquad \mu = \sin\psi.$$

Then

$$\alpha_1 = \alpha\sin\varphi + \lambda\cos\varphi, \qquad \alpha_2 = \alpha\cos\varphi - \lambda\sin\varphi,$$
$$\beta_1 = \beta\sin\varphi + \mu\cos\varphi, \qquad \beta_2 = \beta\cos\varphi - \mu\sin\varphi,$$
$$\gamma_1 = \gamma\sin\varphi, \qquad \gamma_2 = \gamma\cos\varphi,$$
$$\alpha_3 = \frac{d\alpha}{d\theta}, \qquad \beta_3 = \frac{d\beta}{d\theta}, \qquad \gamma_3 = \frac{d\gamma}{d\theta}.$$

After a straightforward, but somewhat lengthy, computation, it is found that the interior acceleration energy is

$$\begin{aligned}\tfrac{1}{2}Mk^2\{\theta''^2 + \varphi''^2 + \psi''^2 + 2\varphi''\psi''\cos\theta \\ + 2\sin\theta(\varphi'\psi'\theta'' - \psi'\theta'\varphi'' - \theta'\varphi'\psi'') \\ + \text{terms that do not contain the second derivatives}\}.\end{aligned} \tag{1}$$

By differentiation of the equations of constraint [Eqs. (155.2)] it is found that the exterior acceleration energy, insofar as it depends upon the second derivatives, is

$$\begin{aligned}\tfrac{1}{2}Ma^2\{\theta''^2 + \varphi''^2\sin^2\theta + 2\sin\theta(\varphi'\psi'\theta'' - \psi'\theta'\varphi'' \\ + \theta'\varphi'\varphi''\cos\theta) + \cdots\},\end{aligned} \tag{2}$$

and the sum of these two expressions is Appell's function S.

Since, by hypothesis, the potential function U depends only upon x and y, and by virtue of the equations of constraint,

$$\frac{\partial x}{\partial\psi} = 0, \qquad \frac{\partial y}{\partial\psi} = 0,$$

it follows at once that

$$\frac{1}{Mk^2}\frac{\partial S}{\partial\psi''} = \psi'' + \varphi''\cos\theta - \theta'\varphi'\sin\theta = 0; \tag{3}$$

and therefore

$$\psi' + \varphi' \cos\theta = c_1, \tag{4}$$

just as in Eq. (155.9).

By means of Eq. (3), the exterior acceleration energy, Eq. (2), can be given a variety of forms, and in particular the same form as Eq. (1) for the interior acceleration energy. Hence

$$\begin{aligned} S = \tfrac{1}{2}M(a^2 + k^2)\{&\theta''^2 + \varphi''^2 + \psi''^2 + 2\varphi''\psi'' \cos\theta \\ &+ 2 \sin\theta(\varphi'\psi'\theta'' - \psi'\theta'\varphi'' - \theta'\varphi'\psi'') \\ &+ \text{terms that do not contain the second derivatives}\}, \end{aligned} \tag{5}$$

and the equations of motion in terms of Euler's angles and their derivatives are

$$\frac{\partial S}{\partial \theta''} = M(a^2 + k^2)(\theta'' + \varphi'\psi' \sin\theta) = +a\left(\frac{\partial U}{\partial x} \sin\psi - \frac{\partial U}{\partial y} \cos\psi\right),$$

$$\frac{\partial S}{\partial \varphi''} = M(a^2 + k^2)(\varphi'' + \psi'' \cos\theta - \theta'\psi' \sin\theta) = -a\left(\frac{\partial U}{\partial x} \cos\psi + \frac{\partial U}{\partial y} \sin\psi\right) \sin\theta,$$

$$\frac{\partial S}{\partial \psi''} = M(a^2 + k^2)(\psi'' + \varphi'' \cos\theta - \theta'\varphi' \sin\theta) = 0.$$

The three degrees of freedom can also be represented by the letters x, y, and ψ as primary, with θ and φ as the secondary functions, namely,

$$\begin{aligned} a\theta' &= +x' \sin\psi - y' \cos\psi, \\ a\varphi' \sin\theta &= -x' \cos\psi - y' \sin\psi. \end{aligned}$$

With these letters Appell's function is

$$\begin{aligned} S = \frac{1}{2}M\left(\frac{a^2 + k^2}{a^2}\right)(&x''^2 + y''^2 + 0\,\psi''^2 \\ &+ \text{terms that do not contain second derivatives}); \end{aligned}$$

and the equations of motion for these variables are

$$\begin{aligned} \frac{\partial S}{\partial x''} &= M\left(\frac{a^2 + k^2}{a^2}\right)x'' = \frac{\partial U}{\partial x}, \\ \frac{\partial S}{\partial y''} &= M\left(\frac{a^2 + k^2}{a^2}\right)y'' = \frac{\partial U}{\partial y}, \\ \frac{\partial S}{\partial \psi''} &= 0 = 0. \end{aligned}$$

Thus the equations reduce to the equations of motion of the center of gravity, the ψ-equation reducing to an identity. Hence

$$Mx'' = \frac{a^2}{a^2 + k^2}\frac{\partial U}{\partial x}, \qquad My'' = \frac{a^2}{a^2 + k^2}\frac{\partial U}{\partial y},$$

just as in Eqs. (155.15).

158. The Motion Referred to Axes that Are Not Fixed in the Body.—That the motion is usually referred to axes that are fixed in the body is due to the fact that the moments of inertia are constants when referred to such axes, and when the principal axes of inertia are used, the products of inertia are zero. If the central ellipsoid of inertia is a sphere, or even a spheroid, both of these advantages can be retained even though the axes are not fixed in the body, and it may be desirable to choose such a set even though the moments of inertia are not constants.

Let the ξ-, η-, ζ-axes be referred to the center of gravity, let the moving trihedron have the instantaneous angular velocity $\boldsymbol{\theta}$ with respect to a set of fixed axes, and let **i**, **j**, and **k** be unit vectors having the direction of the ξ-, η-, and ζ-axes, so that

$$\boldsymbol{\theta} = \theta_i\mathbf{i} + \theta_j\mathbf{j} + \theta_k\mathbf{k}. \tag{1}$$

Let M be the mass of the body, **D** its momentum and **L** its moment of momentum when referred to axes fixed in space, and $\boldsymbol{\Delta}$ and $\boldsymbol{\Lambda}$ respectively when referred to the moving trihedron. Then by Eq. (80.7)

$$\mathbf{D}' = \boldsymbol{\Delta}' + \boldsymbol{\theta} \times \boldsymbol{\Delta}, \qquad \text{and} \qquad \mathbf{L}' = \boldsymbol{\Lambda}' + \boldsymbol{\theta} \times \boldsymbol{\Lambda}. \tag{2}$$

If **F** is the sum of all of the exterior forces that are acting upon the body, including the constraints, and **N** is the sum of their moments with respect to the center of gravity, the principles of momentum [Eqs. (30.5)] and moment of momentum [Eq. (32.5)] give the equations

$$\mathbf{D}' = \mathbf{F}, \qquad \text{and} \qquad \mathbf{L}' = \mathbf{N};$$

or, by Eqs. (2),

$$\boldsymbol{\Delta}' + \boldsymbol{\theta} \times \boldsymbol{\Delta} = \mathbf{F}, \qquad \boldsymbol{\Lambda}' + \boldsymbol{\theta} \times \boldsymbol{\Lambda} = \mathbf{N}. \tag{3}$$

If σ_i, σ_j, and σ_k are the components of the velocity of the center of gravity, the exterior kinetic energy is

$$T_e = \tfrac{1}{2}M(\sigma_i^2 + \sigma_j^2 + \sigma_k^2);$$

and if ω_i, ω_j, and ω_k are the components of the angular velocity of the body, the interior kinetic energy is [Eq. (83.2)]

$$T_i = \tfrac{1}{2}[A\omega_i^2 + B\omega_j^2 + C\omega_k^2 - 2D\omega_j\omega_k - 2E\omega_k\omega_i - 2F\omega_i\omega_j].$$

The total energy is therefore

$$T = T_i + T_e.$$

Since

$$\mathbf{D} = \boldsymbol{\Delta} = M(\sigma_i\mathbf{i} + \sigma_j\mathbf{j} + \sigma_k\mathbf{k}),$$

it can be written

$$\boldsymbol{\Delta} = \frac{\partial T}{\partial \sigma_i}\mathbf{i} + \frac{\partial T}{\partial \sigma_j}\mathbf{j} + \frac{\partial T}{\partial \sigma_k}\mathbf{k},$$

and, by Eq. (83.5),

$$\mathbf{L} = \boldsymbol{\Lambda} = \frac{\partial T}{\partial \omega_i}\mathbf{i} + \frac{\partial T}{\partial \omega_j}\mathbf{j} + \frac{\partial T}{\partial \omega_k}\mathbf{k}.$$

If these expressions for $\boldsymbol{\Delta}$ and $\boldsymbol{\Lambda}$ are substituted into Eqs. (3) and the equations are then resolved into their components, the following six scalar equations, which determine the motion, result:

$$\left.\begin{aligned}
\left(\frac{\partial T}{\partial \sigma_i}\right)' + \theta_j\frac{\partial T}{\partial \sigma_k} - \theta_k\frac{\partial T}{\partial \sigma_j} &= X, & \left(\frac{\partial T}{\partial \omega_i}\right)' + \theta_j\frac{\partial T}{\partial \omega_k} - \theta_k\frac{\partial T}{\partial \omega_j} &= N_i,\\
\left(\frac{\partial T}{\partial \sigma_j}\right)' + \theta_k\frac{\partial T}{\partial \sigma_i} - \theta_i\frac{\partial T}{\partial \sigma_k} &= Y, & \left(\frac{\partial T}{\partial \omega_j}\right)' + \theta_k\frac{\partial T}{\partial \omega_i} - \theta_i\frac{\partial T}{\partial \omega_k} &= N_j,\\
\left(\frac{\partial T}{\partial \sigma_k}\right)' + \theta_i\frac{\partial T}{\partial \sigma_j} - \theta_j\frac{\partial T}{\partial \sigma_i} &= Z, & \left(\frac{\partial T}{\partial \omega_k}\right)' + \theta_i\frac{\partial T}{\partial \omega_j} - \theta_j\frac{\partial T}{\partial \omega_i} &= N_k.
\end{aligned}\right\}\quad(4)$$

If the moving trihedron has its $\xi\eta$-plane tangent to the surface on which the center of a rolling sphere lies, with the ξ- and η-axes coinciding with the lines of curvature and the ζ-axis coinciding with the normal, Eqs. (4) reduce to the equations used in Sec. 121.

159. Sphere Rolling on a Surface of Revolution.—For a sphere whose center of gravity is at the center and whose central ellipsoid of inertia is a sphere, the kinetic energy is

$$T = \tfrac{1}{2}M(\sigma_i^2 + \sigma_j^2 + \sigma_k^2) + \tfrac{1}{2}Mk^2(\omega_i^2 + \omega_j^2 + \omega_k^2). \qquad (1)$$

If the surface on which the sphere rolls is one of revolution, the surface on which its center lies can be represented parametrically by the equations

$$x = f_1(\varphi)\cos\theta, \qquad y = f_1(\varphi)\sin\theta, \qquad z = f_2(\varphi). \qquad (2)$$

If the axis of the surface is vertical, θ is the azimuth of a point on the surface and φ is the angle which the normal to the surface directed inward makes with the vertical axis directed upward. The lines of curvature are then the meridians (θ = constant) and the circles of altitude (φ = constant). A right-handed trihedron is then defined by taking the ζ-axis along the inward normal, the ξ-axis tangent to a meridian directed upward, and the η-axis along a parallel in the positive direction of θ.

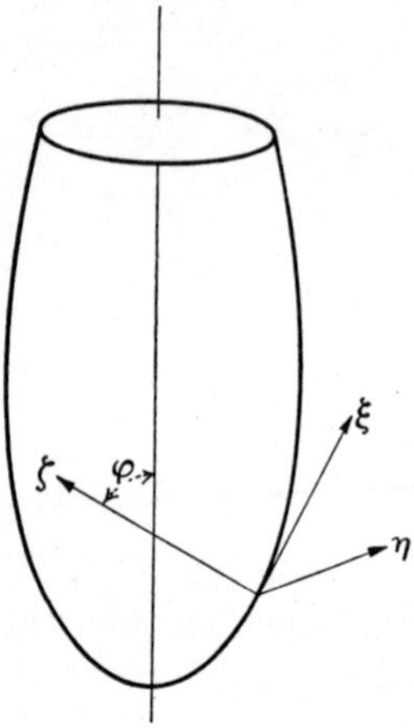

FIG. 79.

With this understanding as to the axes of reference, σ_i is the component of the velocity of the center of the sphere along a meridian, σ_j the component of motion along a parallel, and $\sigma_k \equiv 0$. Hence

$$\left.\begin{aligned} \sigma_i &= \varphi'\sqrt{\left(\frac{\partial f_1}{\partial \varphi}\right)^2 + \left(\frac{\partial f_2}{\partial \varphi}\right)^2}, \\ \sigma_j &= \theta' f_1. \end{aligned}\right\} \tag{3}$$

From the discussion in Sec. 122 the angular velocities θ_i, θ_j, θ_k are found to be

$$\theta_i = \frac{\sigma_j}{\rho_j}, \qquad \theta_j = -\frac{\sigma_i}{\rho_i}, \qquad \theta_k = \frac{\sigma_i \tan \alpha_i}{\rho_i} - \frac{\sigma_j \tan \alpha_j}{\rho_j}, \tag{4}$$

where ρ_i and ρ_j are the radii of curvature of the meridians and parallels respectively and α_i, α_j are the angles which the osculating planes make with normal planes through their tangents. For surfaces of revolution, evidently (Fig. 79)

$$\begin{aligned} \alpha_i &= 0, & \alpha_j &= 90 - \varphi, \\ \rho_i &= \frac{[(\partial f_1/\partial\varphi)^2 + (\partial f_2/\partial\varphi)^2]^{\frac{3}{2}}}{\dfrac{\partial f_1}{\partial \varphi}\dfrac{\partial^2 f_2}{\partial \varphi^2} - \dfrac{\partial f_2}{\partial \varphi}\dfrac{\partial^2 f_1}{\partial \varphi^2}}, & \rho_j &= f_1(\varphi). \end{aligned} \tag{5}$$

Hence

$$\left.\begin{aligned} \theta_i = \theta', \qquad \theta_j &= -\frac{\dfrac{\partial f_1}{\partial \varphi}\dfrac{\partial^2 f_2}{\partial \varphi^2} - \dfrac{\partial f_2}{\partial \varphi}\dfrac{\partial^2 f_1}{\partial \varphi^2}}{(\partial f_1/\partial\varphi)^2 + (\partial f_2/\partial\varphi)^2}\varphi', \\ \theta_k &= -\theta' \cot \varphi. \end{aligned}\right\} \tag{6}$$

The equations of motion [Eqs. (158.4)] are

$$\left.\begin{aligned} M(\sigma_i' - \theta_k\sigma_j) &= -Mg\sin\varphi + Mc_\xi, \\ M(\sigma_j' + \theta_k\sigma_i) &= \quad 0 \quad + Mc_\eta, \\ M(+\theta_i\sigma_j - \theta_j\sigma_i) &= -Mg\cos\varphi + 0, \end{aligned}\right\} \tag{7}$$

$$\left.\begin{aligned} Mk^2(\omega_i' + \theta_j\omega_k - \theta_k\omega_j) &= +aMc_\eta, \\ Mk^2(\omega_j' + \theta_k\omega_i - \theta_i\omega_k) &= -aMc_\xi, \\ Mk^2(\omega_k' + \theta_i\omega_j - \theta_j\omega_i) &= \quad 0; \end{aligned}\right\} \tag{8}$$

where Mc_ξ and Mc_η are the components of the frictional forces acting at the point of contact in the ξ and η directions respectively. The elimination of these quantities between Eqs. (7) and (8) and the removal of the factor M gives the set

$$\left.\begin{aligned} a(\sigma_i' - \theta_k\sigma_j) + k^2(\omega_j' + \theta_k\omega_i - \theta_i\omega_k) &= -ag\sin\varphi, \\ a(\sigma_j' + \theta_k\theta_i) - k^2(\omega_i' + \theta_j\omega_k - \theta_k\omega_j) &= \quad 0, \\ \theta_i\sigma_j - \theta_j\sigma_i &= -g\cos\varphi, \\ \omega_k' + \theta_i\omega_j - \theta_j\omega_i &= \quad 0; \end{aligned}\right\} \tag{9}$$

to which the constraint at the point of contact [Eq. (121.3)] adds the two equations

$$\sigma_i = a\omega_j, \qquad \sigma_j = -a\omega_i. \tag{10}$$

By the elimination of ω_i and ω_j, Eqs. (9) can be reduced somewhat, but as they cannot be integrated, in general, the matter will not be pursued farther. The only general integral is the energy integral. If the surface of revolution is a sphere, the motion of the center of the rolling sphere can be expressed in terms of elliptic integrals.

Problems

1. One end of a uniform bar of length $2l$ is constrained to move along a horizontal line and the other end along a vertical line. If the minimum distance between the two lines of constraint is $2a$, the radius of gyration of the bar with respect to its center is k, and the angle which the bar makes at any instant with a horizontal plane is φ, show that the energy equation is

$$\frac{1}{2}M(l^2 + k^2)\varphi'^2 = \frac{(h - Mgl\sin\varphi)(l^2\cos^2\varphi - a^2)}{(l^2 - a^2)\cos^2\varphi}.$$

By taking $x = \sin\varphi$ this reduces to an elliptic integral of type I, and φ is an elliptic function of the time.

2. A heavy uniform bar of length $2l$ slides down a helicoid, the equation of which is

$$x = r\cos\theta, \qquad y = r\sin\theta, \qquad z = b\theta,$$

pivoting at one end on the axis of the helicoid and always horizontal. Show that the equation of motion is

$$\theta'' = -\frac{3gb}{4l^2 + 3b^2}.$$

3. A uniform plank of length $2l$ and negligible thickness is balanced on a horizontal cylinder of radius a. If the plank is started to rocking (rolling without slipping) show that the energy equation gives

$$\theta'^2 = \frac{6g(h + 1 - \cos\theta - \theta\sin\theta)}{l^2 + 3a^2\theta^2},$$

where h is the constant of integration. If $\theta < 10°$, $1 - \cos\theta - \theta\sin\theta$ differs from $-\frac{1}{2}\theta^2$ by less than one per cent. Hence an approximate form for small oscillations is

$$\theta'^2 = \frac{3g(2h - \theta^2)}{l^2 + 3a^2\theta^2},$$

which defines θ as an elliptic function of the time.

4. A heavy rod of length of length $2l$, symmetrical and of radius of gyration k with respect to its center, moves with its two ends in contact with the interior of a smooth spherical surface of radius a. Find the equations of motion.

The Lagrangian function is found to be

$$L = \tfrac{1}{2}M\{b^2[\theta'^2 + \psi'^2\cos^2\theta] + k^2[\varphi'^2 + \theta'^2\sin^2\varphi + \psi'^2(1 - \sin^2\varphi\cos^2\theta)]\} - Mgb\sin\theta,$$

where b is the distance from the center of the sphere to the center of the rod, θ and ψ represent the altitude and azimuth of the radius of the sphere through the center of the rod, and φ the angle of rotation of the rod about this radius.

5. The surface on which a sphere rolls is a horizontal cylinder. Show that the projection of the center of the sphere on a plane perpendicular to the axis of the sphere coincides with the motion of a smooth sphere that merely slides on the cylinder in the perpendicular plane, the initial conditions being the same but the force reduced in the ratio $a^2 : a^2 + k^2$.

6. If a dynamical system possesses an energy integral and q_1, in the notation of Sec. 144, is an ignorable coordinate, show that the reduced system admits an integral of the same type as the energy integral, by means of which the system can again be reduced.

7. If the Lagrangian function of a dynamical system is

$$L = \tfrac{1}{2}f_1(q_2)q_1'^2 + \tfrac{1}{2}q_2^2 - f_2(q_2),$$

show that for the reduced system (Sec. 146)

$$W = \{2E - 2f_2(q_2)\}^{\frac{1}{2}}\{p_2^2 + f_1(q_2)\}^{\frac{1}{2}},$$

and that an integral of the energy type exists. Reduce the problem to quadratures. (Whittaker.)

8. *The Bifilar Pendulum.*—A uniform bar of length $2a$ and mass M is suspended at its extremities from two points O_1 and $O_2(\overline{O_1O_2} = 2a)$ in the same horizontal plane by two weightless strings of length l. If O is the mid-point of the line O_1O_2 and C is the mid-point of the bar, let α be the complement of the angle which the line OC makes with the line O_1O_2, θ one half of the angle between the bar and the line O_1O_2, and φ the angle of rotation of the entire system (as if rigid) about the line O_1O_2. Also let $\sigma = 2a/l$. Show that the Lagrangian function is

$$L = \frac{1}{2}Ml^2\left[\frac{\sigma^4 \sin^2\theta \cos^2\theta}{1 - \sigma^2 \sin^2\theta}\theta'^2 + (1 - \sigma^2\sin^2\theta)(\alpha'^2 + \varphi'^2\cos^2\alpha)\right]$$
$$+\frac{1}{6}Ma^2\left[\frac{4\cos^2\theta}{1 - \sin^2\theta\sec^2\alpha}\theta'^2 + \frac{\sin^2\theta\sin^2 2\theta\sec^4\alpha}{1 - \sin^2\theta\sec^2\alpha}\alpha'^2 + \varphi'^2\sin^2 2\theta\right.$$
$$+\frac{2\sin\theta\sin^2 2\theta\sec^2\alpha}{\sqrt{1 - \sin^2\theta\sec^2\alpha}}\alpha'\varphi' - \frac{8\cos\theta\sin^2\theta\tan\alpha}{\sqrt{1 - \sin^2\theta\sec^2\alpha}}\varphi'\theta'$$
$$\left.-\frac{8\sin^3\theta\cos\theta\sec^2\alpha\tan\alpha}{1 - \sin^2\theta\sec^2\alpha}\theta'\alpha'\right] - Mgl\cos\alpha\cos\varphi\sqrt{1 - \sigma^2\sin^2\theta},$$

and for infinitesimal oscillations about the position of equilibrium

$$L = \tfrac{1}{2}M[\tfrac{4}{3}a^2\theta'^2 + l^2(\alpha'^2 + \varphi'^2) + lg(\sigma^2\theta^2 + \alpha^2 + \varphi^2)].$$

9. If a homogeneous sphere rolls on an inclined plane, the inclination of which is α, the center of the sphere describes a parabola. If the initial horizontal velocity is v, show that the latus rectum of the parabola is $\frac{14}{5}v^2/(g\sin\alpha)$.

10. A homogeneous sphere rolls without slipping in a spherical bowl. Show that the complete solution for the center of the sphere can be obtained by means of elliptic integrals.

11. Show that the two following problems are mathematically equivalent:

(*a*) A uniform bar of length $2a$ is pivoted at one end to the rim of a wheel of radius $2a$, radius of gyration k, whose axle is horizontal and fixed. The other end of the bar is constrained to move on a straight horizontal line that passes through the axle and is perpendicular to it. The only force acting is gravity. Determine the motion.

(*b*) A circular disk is constrained to move in a vertical plane, but slides without friction on a horizontal plane. Determine the motion under the assumption that the center of gravity is not at the center of the disk and that the only force acting is gravity.

12. A thin circular disk rolls on a helicoid whose equations are

$$x = r\cos\theta, \qquad y = r\sin\theta, \qquad z = b\theta,$$

the z-axis of which is vertical. At every instant the disk is in a vertical plane and its center is at the distance a from the axis of the helicoid. If the radius of the disk is c show that the motion of the center of the disk satisfies the equation

$$\theta'' = -\frac{4gb}{6(a^2 + b^2) + c^2}.$$

Compare with Problem 2.

13. Four similar uniform heavy rods of the same length $2l$ are joined end to end by smooth hinges so as to form a rhomb. A smooth horizontal cylinder of radius a is placed inside the rhomb which is then allowed to rest on the cylinder in a plane perpendicular to the axis of the cylinder. In the position of equilibrium two of the sides of the rhomb are in contact with the cylinder and two are not. The rhomb is displaced from the configuration of equilibrium in such a way that the center of gravity is displaced vertically and is then released. If θ is the angle which the rods make with the horizontal at any instant, show that t is determined by a quadrature, namely,

$$t - t_0 = \frac{1}{2\sqrt{3lg}} \int \left[\frac{4l^2 + 3(2l \cos \theta + a \sin \theta)^2}{h - (2l \sin \theta - a \sec \theta)} \right] d\theta,$$

where h is a constant related to the total energy.

14. A uniform bar of mass M and length $2l$ slides without friction on a horizontal plane. Every particle of the bar is attracted toward the x-axis which lies in the plane, by a force which is proportional to its distance from the axis, γ^2 being the factor of proportionality. Show that the center of gravity of the bar describes a curve of the form

$$y = A \sin (\alpha x + \beta),$$

where A, α, and β are constants.

If θ is the angle which the bar makes with the x-axis,

$$\theta'^2 = \delta^2 - \gamma^2 \sin^2 \theta.$$

where δ is a constant of integration. Thus if $\delta^2 > \gamma^2$ the bar turns always in the same direction. It oscillates if $\delta^2 < \gamma^2$, and

$$\tan \tfrac{1}{2}\theta = \tanh \tfrac{1}{2}\gamma t,$$

if $\delta^2 = \gamma^2$. In this last case the bar becomes perpendicular to the axis asymptotically.

15. A uniform bar A_1B_1 pivots without friction in a vertical plane on its center point O_1. A second bar A_2B_2, also uniform and of the same mass, is attached to the first by two light strings of the same length at the ends of the bars, so that the two bars and the two strings form a parallelogram. The entire system is constrained to a vertical plane, but the initial state of motion is arbitrary in that plane provided the strings are kept taut.

(*a*) Show that the bar A_1B_1 rotates with uniform angular motion.

(*b*) Show that the point O_2, the center of the second bar A_2B_2, moves like a simple pendulum about the point O_1.

16. A homogeneous spherical shell of mass m_0 slides without friction on a horizontal plane. A particle of mass m slides without friction in the interior of the shell. Show that:

(*a*) The system has seven degrees of freedom.

(*b*) Since the actions of the particle and the plane on the shell pass through the center of the shell, the shell continues to rotate uniformly about the initial instantaneous axis.

(*c*) The center of gravity of the system moves uniformly along a straight line.

(*d*) If the system is referred to a rectangular trihedron, ξ, η, ζ, the $\xi\eta$-plane of which is the horizontal plane through the center C of the sphere and the origin at the projection g of the center of gravity G of the entire system on this plane, the ξ- and η-axes being fixed in direction; if θ is the angle which the line gC makes with the ξ-axis and φ the angle which the line CG makes with the vertical; and if

$$\lambda = \frac{m}{m_0 + m}R, \qquad \mu = \frac{m_0}{m_0 + m}R,$$

where R is the radius of the sphere, then the energy and moment of momentum with respect to the ζ-axis give the equations

$$\theta' \sin^2 \varphi = \text{constant},$$

$$(m_0\lambda^2 + m\mu^2)\theta'^2 \sin^2 \varphi + [(m_0\lambda^2 + m\mu^2) \cos^2 \varphi + mR^2 \sin^2 \varphi]\varphi'^2 = -2mgR \cos \varphi + \text{constant},$$

which, by the elimination of θ', gives t as a function of φ by a quadrature.

17. A straight homogeneous beam of length $2l$ and mass m_1 and a right circular cylinder of mass m_2 and radius r rest on a smooth horizontal plane. The beam lies across the cylinder in the vertical plane through its center of gravity and perpendicular to its axis with one end in contact with the plane. If all contacts are smooth, show that the motion can be reduced to a quadrature.

18. Two fixed points A and B on the axis of a homogeneous solid of revolution are constrained to slide without friction on two non-parallel lines L_1 and L_2, and the only force acting is gravity. Let the xy-plane bisect perpendicularly the common perpendicular to L_1 and L_2. If θ is the angle which the projection of AB on the xy-plane makes with the x-axis and φ is the angle of rotation of the body about AB, show that the motion is determined by the two equations.

$$\varphi = \theta \cos \lambda + \mu t + \nu$$

$$t = \int \sqrt{\frac{\alpha \cos 2\theta + \beta \sin 2\theta + \gamma}{a \cos \theta + b \sin \theta + c}}\, d\theta,$$

where λ, μ, ν; α, β, γ; a, b, c are constants.

19. Two heavy wheels of the same mass and diameters but with different radii of gyration are mounted on a light axle about which they turn freely without friction. The system is placed on a rough inclined plane on which the wheels roll without slipping. Determine the motion for arbitrary initial conditions.

Let k_1 and k_2 $(k_2 > k_1)$ be the radii of gyration, φ_1 and φ_2 the angles of rotation of the wheels about the axle, θ the angle which the axle makes with the line of greatest slope in the plane, r the radius of the wheels, a the distance between the wheels and α the angle of inclination of the plane with a horizontal plane. Show that θ satisfies the equation of the simple pendulum

$$l\theta'' = -g \sin \theta,$$

where

$$l = \frac{2a^2(r^2 + k_1^2)(r^2 + k_2^2) + r^2(k_1^2 + k_2^2)(2r^2 + k_1^2 + k_2^2)}{2a^2r(k_2^2 - k_1^2)\sin\alpha}.$$

Show further that the point p on the line of the axle at the fixed distance

$$d = \frac{a^2(2r^2 + k_1^2 + k_2^2) + 2r^2(k_1^2 + k_2^2)}{2a(k_2^2 - k_1^2)}$$

from the center of the axle describes an elastica curve (I, **228**), the curve assumed by a flexible rod when its ends are drawn together, with constant speed and that the line of the axle is always normal to this elastica curve, whose points of inflection lie on a horizontal line.

If the initial values of φ_1' and φ_2' satisfy the relation

$$\frac{\varphi_2'}{\varphi_1'} = \frac{a^2(r^2 + k_1^2) + r^2(k_1^2 + k_2^2)}{a^2(r^2 + k_2^2) + r^2(k_1^2 + k_2^2)},$$

the speed of the point p is zero and the center of the axle describes an arc of a circle of radius d, moving like a simple pendulum of length l. This is the case when the wheels are released on the plane from a state of rest.

Discuss the case when $k_1 = k_2$, and show that the motion is related to the cycloid.

20. *Lagrange's Equations with Multipliers.*—Suppose a configuration of any system is completely specified by n coordinates $q_1, \ldots, q_n$. If the system has n degrees of freedom, the system is holonomic and the equations of Lagrange, [Eqs. (140.9)] apply, namely,

$$\left(\frac{\partial T}{\partial q_j}\right)' - \frac{\partial T}{\partial q_j} = Q_j;$$

but if in addition there are constraints that are expressed by s non-integrable equations of the form

$$a_{i1}\,dq_1 + a_{i2}\,dq_2 + \cdots + a_{in}\,dq_n = 0, \qquad i = 1, \cdots, s \tag{1}$$

where the coefficients a_{ik} are functions of $q_1, \ldots, q_n$, then the system has $n - s$ degrees of freedom and the Q_j do not represent all the forces that are acting. Let F_j be the additional forces that are due to the constraints, so that the equations of motion are

$$\left(\frac{\partial T}{\partial q_j'}\right) - \frac{\partial T}{\partial q_j} = Q_j + F_j;$$

it will be assumed that these constraints do no work, so that

$$\Sigma F_j\,dq_j = 0.$$

Show that there exist multipliers $\lambda_1, \ldots, \lambda_s$ such that

$$F_j = \lambda_1 a_{1j} + \lambda_2 a_{2j} + \cdots + \lambda_s a_{sj}, \qquad j = 1, \cdots, n$$

and therefore the equations of motion can be written

$$\left(\frac{\partial T}{\partial q_j'}\right)' - \frac{\partial T}{\partial q_j} = Q_j + \lambda_1 a_{1j} + \lambda_2 a_{2j} + \cdots + \lambda_s a_{sj}, \qquad j = 1, \cdots, n.$$

These n-equations of motion and the s equations of constraint are sufficient to determine the $n + s$ unknowns $q_1, \ldots, q_n; \lambda_1, \ldots, \lambda_s$.

CHAPTER XI

THE CANONICAL EQUATIONS OF HAMILTON

160. Historical.—In following out certain analogies between the differential equations of dynamics and of optics Sir William R. Hamilton[1] was led in 1834 to a new form for the differential equations of dynamics, which on account of their simplicity of form, and also the fact that n differential equations each of the second order are replaced by $2n$ equations each of the first order, are called *canonical.*

The first step in Hamilton's transformation was made by Poisson[2] who derived half of Hamilton's equations in 1809, and in 1810 Lagrange[3] expressed the rate of change of the elements of a planetary orbit due to perturbations in the canonical form, but the development of the general theory is due to Hamilton who showed that the equations of motion for any conservative, holonomic, dynamical system can be expressed in this form. The extension to cases where the constraints depend upon the time was made by Ostrogradsky[4] and Donkin.[5] It was also shown by Ostrogradsky that all of the differential equations that arise in the calculus of variations in which there is but a single independent variable also can be expressed in the canonical form. Indeed, according to C. Lanczos,[6] the proper field of the canonical equations is the calculus of variations, and their occurrence in the field of mechanics is of an accidental nature. However this may be, the equations of Hamilton form the basis of most work in modern dynamics.

161. Derivation of Hamilton's Equations.—Suppose the system is holonomic and that there exists a force function U which

[1] *British Association Report,* p. 513 (1834); *Philosophical Transactions,* 1835, p. 95.

[2] *Journal de l'École Polytechnique,* Vol. 8; Cahier 15, p. 266.

[3] Oeuvres, Vol. 6, p. 814.

[4] *Mélanges de l'Académie de St. Pétersbourg,* 1848; *Mém. de l'Acad. de St. Pét.,* 6, p. 385, 1850.

[5] *Philosophical Transactions,* 1854, p. 71.

[6] *Annalen der Physik,* Bd. 20, p. 653 (1934).

may or may not contain the time explicitly. Then Lagrange's equations are

$$\left(\frac{\partial L}{\partial q_i'}\right)' = \frac{\partial L}{\partial q_i}, \qquad i = 1, \cdots, n. \tag{1}$$

It was Poisson's idea, and later Hamilton's, to introduce new variables, p_i, by the definitions

$$p_i = \frac{\partial L}{\partial q_i'} = \frac{\partial T}{\partial q_i'}, \tag{2}$$

where

$$L = T + U,$$

and T is the kinetic energy. In the right members of Eqs. (2) the q_i' occur linearly, so that Eqs. (2) can be solved for the q_i' as functions of the p_i, and these functions, as will be observed, are linear in the p_i.

A new function H, known as the Hamiltonian function, is introduced by the definition

$$H = \Sigma p_i q_i' - L, \tag{3}$$

and in this function the letters q_i' are replaced by their equivalent expressions in the letters p, so that H is to be regarded as a function of the letters p and q, while L is to be regarded as a function of the letters q' and q. Evidently

$$\begin{aligned} \frac{\partial H}{\partial p_i} &= q_i' + \sum_j p_j \frac{\partial q_j'}{\partial p_i} - \sum_j \frac{\partial L}{\partial q_j'}\frac{\partial q_j'}{\partial p_i} \\ &= q_i' + \sum_j \left(p_j - \frac{\partial L}{\partial q_j'}\right)\frac{\partial q_j'}{\partial p_i}, \qquad i = 1, \cdots, n, \end{aligned}$$

and since the parentheses vanish, by Eqs. (2), the interesting reciprocal relationships

$$\frac{\partial L}{\partial q_i'} = p_i \qquad \text{and} \qquad \frac{\partial H}{\partial p_i} = q_i' \tag{4}$$

are established.

Furthermore, from Eq. (3),

$$L + H - \Sigma p_i q_i' = 0$$

is a function of the letters q, q', and p. On differentiating with respect to these letters, regarding t, if it occurs explicitly, as a constant, there results

$$\sum_i \left\{ \frac{\partial}{\partial q_i}(L + H)\, dq_i + \left(\frac{\partial L}{\partial q_i'} - p_i \right) dq_i' + \left(\frac{\partial H}{\partial p_i} - q_i' \right) dp_i \right\} = 0,$$

which, by virtue of Eqs. (4), reduces to

$$\sum_i \left(\frac{\partial L}{\partial q_i} + \frac{\partial H}{\partial q_i} \right) dq_i = 0.$$

Since the differentials dq_i are independent and arbitrary, it follows that

$$\frac{\partial L}{\partial q_i} = -\frac{\partial H}{\partial q_i}.$$

Equations (1) now become

$$p_i' = -\frac{\partial H}{\partial q_i},$$

and these equations, together with the second set of Eqs. (4), are Hamilton's canonical equations, namely,

$$q_i' = \frac{\partial H}{\partial p_i}, \qquad p_i' = -\frac{\partial H}{\partial q_i}, \qquad i = 1, \cdots, n. \tag{5}$$

Since

$$\sum p_i q_i' = \sum q_i' \frac{\partial T}{\partial q_i'},$$

and T can be written

$$T = T_2 + T_1 + T_0,$$

where T_2, T_1, and T_0 are the terms in T that are homogeneous of degree two, one, and zero respectively in the q_i', it is evident from Euler's theorem on homogeneous functions that

$$\Sigma p_i q_i' = 2T_2 + T_1 + 0T_0,$$

and therefore

$$\begin{aligned} H = \Sigma p_i q_i' - L &= (2T_2 + T_1) - (T_2 + T_1 + T_0 + U) \\ &= T_2 - T_0 - U. \end{aligned}$$

If the equations of transformation, Eqs. (140.2), do not contain the time explicitly, $T_1 = T_0 = 0$, and

$$H = T - U,$$

which is the energy, provided U is a function of the coordinates $q_1, \cdots, q_n$ alone, that is it does not contain the time explicitly.

Suppose the time does not occur explicitly. If the first of Eqs. (5) is multiplied by p_i' and the second by $-q_i'$, and the two are then added and summed with respect to i, it is found that

$$\sum_i \left(\frac{\partial H}{\partial p_i} p_i' + \frac{\partial H}{\partial q_i} q_i' \right) = H' = 0.$$

Hence

$$H = h,$$

and this is the energy integral. If the time does occur in H explicitly, it is found that

$$H' = \frac{\partial H}{\partial t}.$$

The magnitudes denoted by the letters p_i are called *the generalized momenta* for reasons that are explained in I, **365.**

162. The Transformation Is Always Possible.—The transformation from the letters q_i' to the letters p_i defined by Eqs. (161.2) depends upon the non-vanishing of the determinant of the q''s in their right members. In order to get the proof that this transformation is always possible in a manageable form, it is desirable to revise the notation.

Instead of using $x_i, y_i, z_i, i = 1, \cdots, m$ as the coordinates of the m particles let these coordinates be denoted by the single letters $\xi_i, i = 1, \cdots, 3m$. The equations of transformation can then be written

$$\xi_i = \varphi_i(q_1, \cdots, q_n; t), \qquad i = 1, \cdots, 3m, \tag{1}$$

and the expression for the kinetic energy is

$$T = \tfrac{1}{2}\sum_{i=1}^{3m} m_i \xi_i'^2.$$

If, as a matter of notation,

$$\varphi_{ij} \equiv \frac{\partial \varphi_i}{\partial q_j}, \qquad \varphi_{i0} \equiv \frac{\partial \varphi_i}{\partial t},$$

the generalized momenta p_j are defined by the equations

$$p_j = \frac{\partial T}{\partial q_j'} = \sum_{i=1}^{3m} m_i \xi_i' \frac{\partial \xi_i'}{\partial q_j'} = \sum_{i=1}^{3m} m_i \varphi_{ij} \varphi_i',$$

or since

$$\varphi_i' = \sum_{k=1}^{n} \varphi_{ik} q_k' + \varphi_{i0},$$

the expressions for the p_j become

$$\left.\begin{aligned} p_j &= \sum_{i=1}^{3m} m_i \varphi_{ij} \sum_{k=1}^{n} \varphi_{ik} q_k' + \sum_{i=1}^{3m} m_i \varphi_{ij} \varphi_{i0}, \\ &\text{or,} \\ p_j &= \sum_{k=1}^{n} \sum_{i=1}^{3m} m_i \varphi_{ij} \varphi_{ik} q_k' + \sum_{i=1}^{3m} m_i \varphi_{ij} \varphi_{i0}. \end{aligned}\right\} \tag{2}$$

If the q's in Eqs. (1) are given small variations, the time regarded as constant, it is seen that

$$\delta \xi_i = \sum_{j=1}^{n} \varphi_{ij} \delta q_j, \qquad i = 1, \cdots, 3m;$$

and if the q's are true coordinates representing n real degrees of freedom, there will not exist any set of variations $\delta q_j, j = 1, \cdots, n$, for which $\delta \xi_i = 0, i = 1, \cdots, 3m$, except the set $\delta q_j = 0$ for every j. It is assumed therefore that

$$\sum_{j=1}^{n} \varphi_{ij} \delta q_j \not\equiv 0 \text{ for every } i, \tag{3}$$

unless every δq_j is zero. In other words, every change in the coordinates q implies some actual displacement of the system.

Equations (2) can be solved for the q''s in terms of the p's and q's if the determinant

$$\Delta = \left| \sum_{i=1}^{3n} m_i \varphi_{ij} \varphi_{ik} \right| \not\equiv 0.$$

Suppose this determinant is zero. Then there exist sets of δq_k, not all of which are zero, that satisfy the linear equations

$$\sum_{k=1}^{n} \left(\sum_{i=1}^{3m} m_i \varphi_{ij} \varphi_{ik} \right) \delta q_k = 0, \qquad j = 1, \cdots, n.$$

Multiply the jth equation of this set by δq_j, and then sum with respect to j. There results the single equation

$$\sum_{j=1}^{n}\sum_{k=1}^{n}\sum_{i=1}^{3m} m_i\varphi_{ij}\varphi_{ik}\delta q_j\delta q_k = 0,$$

which, by rearrangement, becomes

$$\sum_{i=1}^{3m} m_i\left(\sum_{j=1}^{n}\varphi_{ij}\delta q_j\right)\left(\sum_{k=1}^{n}\varphi_{ik}\delta q_k\right) = 0.$$

Save for notation, the two parentheses in this equation are not different. It can be written therefore

$$\sum_{i=1}^{3n} m_i\left(\sum_{j=1}^{n}\varphi_{ij}\delta q_j\right)^2 = 0,$$

and since the m_i are real and positive and the $\varphi_{ij}\delta q_j$ are real, this compels the relations

$$\Sigma\varphi_{ij}\delta q_j = 0, \qquad i = 1, \cdots, 3m,$$

which contradicts the hypothesis [Eqs. (3)] that this is not so.

It follows, therefore, that the determinant does not vanish identically, and that the transformation of Hamilton's is always possible.

163. An Equivalent Form of the Equations.—Suppose the equations of Hamilton [Eqs. (161.5)] have been completely integrated; that is, the variables p_i and q_i have been expressed as functions of the time t and $2n$ constants of integration $\alpha_1, \ldots,$ α_{2n} that satisfy the differential equations, whatever the α's may be. The functional determinant of the p's and q's with respect to the α's is not zero, for, if it were, there would exist one or more relations between the p's and q's, independent of the α's, and it would not be possible to choose the initial values arbitrarily.

If the p's and q's so determined are substituted in the Hamiltonian function, then H, too, becomes a function of t and the α's. Let H be differentiated with respect to any one of these constants of integration, say α_k. It is found then that

$$\frac{\partial H}{\partial \alpha_k} = \sum_{i=1}^{n}\frac{\partial H}{\partial p_i}\frac{\partial p_i}{\partial \alpha_k} + \sum_{i=1}^{n}\frac{\partial H}{\partial q_i}\frac{\partial q_i}{\partial \alpha_k}, \qquad k = 1, \cdots, 2n. \quad (1)$$

There exists also the identity

$$\frac{d}{dt}\sum_{i=1}^{n} q_i \frac{\partial p_i}{\partial \alpha_k} - \frac{\partial}{\partial \alpha_k}\sum_{i=1}^{n} q_i p_i' \equiv \sum_{i=1}^{n} \frac{\partial p_i}{\partial \alpha_k} q_i' - \sum_{i=1}^{n} \frac{\partial q_i}{\partial \alpha_k} p_i', \tag{2}$$

as is readily verified by carrying out the differentiations indicated in the left member. If the values of the p_i' and q_i' from Eqs. (161.5) are substituted in the right member, then, by virtue of Eq. (1), Eq. (2) becomes

$$\frac{d}{dt}\sum_{i=1}^{n} q_i \frac{\partial p_i}{\partial \alpha_k} - \frac{\partial}{\partial \alpha_k}\sum_{i=1}^{n} q_i p_i' = \frac{\partial H}{\partial \alpha_k}, \qquad k = 1, \cdots, 2n. \tag{3}$$

On the other hand, if by any means it is known that Eq. (3) holds, then, by virtue of Eqs. (1) and (2), it can be shown that the variables p_i and q_i satisfy Eqs. (161.5). Suppose this is the case, and it is known that Eq. (3) holds for a set of variables p_i and q_i. Then, in view of Eq. (2),

$$\frac{\partial H}{\partial \alpha_k} = \sum_{i=1}^{n} \frac{\partial p_i}{\partial \alpha_k} q_i' - \sum_{i=1}^{n} \frac{\partial q_i}{\partial \alpha_k} p_i'. \tag{4}$$

On subtracting Eqs. (1) from Eqs. (4), there results

$$\sum_{i=1}^{n}\left(q_i' - \frac{\partial H}{\partial p_i}\right)\frac{\partial p_i}{\partial \alpha_k} - \sum_{i=1}^{n}\left(p_i' + \frac{\partial H}{\partial q_i}\right)\frac{\partial q_i}{\partial \alpha_k} = 0, \qquad k = 1, \cdots, 2n. \tag{5}$$

These equations are linear and homogeneous in the quantities $\left(q_i' - \frac{\partial H}{\partial p_i}\right)$ and $\left(p_i' + \frac{\partial H}{\partial q_i}\right)$ and the determinant is not zero, for it is the functional determinant of the p's and q's with respect to the α's; and it is not zero by hypothesis.

Therefore

$$q_i' = \frac{\partial H}{\partial p_i}, \qquad \text{and} \qquad p_i' = -\frac{\partial H}{\partial q_i}, \qquad i = 1, \cdots, n, \tag{6}$$

which are Eqs. (161.5).

It follows that Eqs. (3) and Eqs. (6) are equivalent, since each implies the other.

164. Contact Transformations.—If a transformation is made from the variables p_i and q_i to a new set of variables P_i and Q_i, and if the two sets of variables satisfy a relation of the form

$$\sum_{i=1}^{n} q_i\, dp_i - \sum_{i=1}^{n} Q_i\, dP_i = dS, \tag{1}$$

where dS is an exact differential, the transformation was called by Sophus Lie a contact transformation.

As an example, suppose

$$Q_i = p_i, \qquad P_i = -q_i, \qquad i = 1, \cdots, n. \tag{2}$$

Then

$$\begin{aligned} \sum q_i\, dp_i - \sum Q_i\, dP_i &= -\sum P_i\, dQ_i - \sum Q_i\, dP_i \\ &= -d\left(\sum P_i Q_i\right), \end{aligned}$$

which is an exact differential, and the transformation is a contact transformation.

As a second example, suppose

$$\left.\begin{aligned} p_i &= \sqrt{Q_i + f_i(P_i)}\, e^{P_i} \\ q_i &= \sqrt{Q_i + f_i(P_i)}\, e^{-P_i} \end{aligned}\right\} i = 1, \cdots, k,$$

$$\left.\begin{aligned} p_i &= P_i \\ q_i &= Q_i \end{aligned}\right\} i = k + 1, \cdots, n.$$

where $f_i(P_i)$ is an arbitrary, but integrable, function of P_i. It is found that

$$q_i\, dp_i - Q_i\, dP_i = \tfrac{1}{2}\, dQ_i + \tfrac{1}{2} \frac{\partial f_i}{\partial P_i} dP_i + f_i(P_i)\, dP_i$$
$$i = 1, \cdots, k,$$

and equal to zero for the other values of i. Hence, if

$$S = \sum_{i=1}^{k} \left(\tfrac{1}{2} Q_i + \tfrac{1}{2} f_i(P_i) + \int f_i\, dP_i \right),$$

it is evident that

$$\sum_{i=1}^{n} q_i\, dp_i - \sum_{i=1}^{n} Q_i\, dp_i = dS,$$

and the transformation is a contact transformation whatever the $f_i(P_i)$ may be.

As an example of linear transformations, let

$$Q_i = \sum_{j=1}^{n} a_{ij}q_j,$$

$$P_i = \sum_{k=1}^{n} b_{ik}p_k, \qquad i = 1, \cdots, n,$$

where the coefficients a_{ij} and b_{ik} are constants. Let Δ be the determinant of the letters a_{ij}, and Δ_{ij} the minor of the element a_{ij} in Δ. Suppose also that

$$b_{ij} = \frac{\Delta_{ij}}{\Delta};$$

then

$$\sum P_iQ_i = \sum p_iq_i.$$

Since dP_i are related to the dp_j by the same equations that relate the P_i to the p_j, it is evident that

$$\sum Q_i\,dP_i - \sum q_i\,dp_i = 0,$$

which is exact, and therefore the transformation is a contact transformation.

Suppose finally that $F(q_j, P_j)$ is any function of the $2n$ variables $q_1, \ldots, q_n; P_1, \ldots, P_n$, and that the transformation of variables is defined by the equations

$$p_i = \frac{\partial F}{\partial q_i}, \qquad Q_i = \frac{\partial F}{\partial P_i}, \qquad i = 1, \cdots, n.$$

Then

$$\begin{aligned}\sum_i q_i\,dp_i - \sum_i Q_i\,dP_i = \\ &\sum_i q_i\,dp_i + \sum_i p_i\,dq_i - \sum_i p_i\,dq_i - \sum_i Q_i\,dP_i \\ &= d\left(\sum_i p_iq_i\right) - dF,\end{aligned}$$

since

$$\sum_i p_i\,dq_i + \sum_i Q_i\,dP_i = \sum_i \frac{\partial F}{\partial q_i}dq_i + \sum_i \frac{\partial F}{\partial P_i}dP_i = dF.$$

Hence,

$$\sum_i q_i\, dp_i - \sum_i Q_i\, dP_i = d\Big(\sum_i p_i q_i - F\Big)$$

is an exact differential, and the transformation so defined is a contact transformation. With one exception, namely the transformation

$$p_i = C_i Q_i, \qquad q_i = -\frac{P_i}{C_i},$$

all contact transformations can be derived in this manner. This method is due to Jacobi.

165. Contact Transformations Leave the Canonical Form of the Differential Equations Unaltered.—Suppose the transformation is from the p_i and q_i to the variables P_i and Q_i and that the relation

$$\sum q_i\, dp_i - \sum Q_i\, dP_i = dS \tag{1}$$

is satisfied, where dS is an exact differential, the time if it occurs explicitly being regarded as a variable. Suppose also that the p_i and q_i satisfy the canonical equations

$$q_i' = \frac{\partial H}{\partial p_i}, \qquad p_i' = -\frac{\partial H}{\partial q_i}. \tag{2}$$

From Eqs. (1) it follows that

$$\sum_i q_i p_i' - \sum_i Q_i P_i' = \frac{dS}{dt},$$

and also that

$$\sum_i q_i \frac{\partial p_i}{\partial \alpha_k} - \sum_i Q_i \frac{\partial P_i}{\partial \alpha_k} = \frac{\partial S}{\partial \alpha_k}.$$

Let the first of these equations be differentiated with respect to α_k and the second with respect to t. The right members being the same, the two left members are equal. Hence

$$\frac{d}{dt}\sum_i q_i \frac{\partial p_i}{\partial \alpha_k} - \frac{\partial}{\partial \alpha_k}\sum_i q_i p_i' = \frac{d}{dt}\sum_i Q_i \frac{\partial p_i}{\partial \alpha_k} - \frac{\partial}{\partial \alpha_k}\sum_i Q_i P_i', \tag{3}$$

or, on account of Eq. (163.3),

$$\frac{d}{dt}\sum_i Q_i \frac{\partial P_i}{\partial \alpha_k} - \frac{\partial}{\partial \alpha_k}\sum_i Q_i P_i' = \frac{\partial H}{\partial \alpha_k};$$

but this is merely Eq. (163.3) in the new variables. Hence, by Sec. 163,

$$Q_i' = \frac{\partial H}{\partial P_i}, \qquad P_i' = -\frac{\partial H}{\partial Q_i}; \tag{4}$$

the change of variables is canonical, and it is necessary merely to transform H from the variables p_i, q_i to the variables P_i, Q_i.

It will be observed that in these transformations the time t has been left unaltered. If the time, too, is transformed, so that the transformation is

$$q_i = q_i(Q_j, P_j; T), \qquad p_i = p_i(Q_j, P_j; T), \qquad t = t(Q_j, P_j; T);$$

and if the relation

$$\sum q_i\, dp_i - \sum Q_i\, dP_i = dS + \left(\sum_i \frac{\partial p_i}{\partial T} - \frac{\partial S}{\partial T}\right) dT, \tag{5}$$

where S is some function (arbitrary) of Q_j, P_j, and T, is satisfied, the transformation is still a contact transformation with the new Hamiltonian function

$$H_1 = -\sum_i q_i \frac{dp_i}{dT} + H\frac{\partial t}{\partial T} - \frac{\partial S}{\partial T}. \tag{6}$$

The term *contact transformation* as here used is a generalization to space of n-dimensions of the contact transformation of Sophus Lie. A contact transformation is independent of the Hamiltonian function, as will be observed.

A transformation is said to be *canonical* if the Roman letters x_i, y_i, t, are replaced by the Greek letters ξ_j, η_j, τ, in the transformation

$$x_i = x_i(\xi_j, \eta_j; \tau), \qquad y_i = y_i(\xi_j, \eta_j; \tau), \qquad t = t\,(\xi_j, \eta_j; \tau); \tag{7}$$

if *first*, the functional determinant

$$\frac{\partial(x_i, y_i; t)}{\partial(\xi_j, \eta_j; \tau)} \neq 0,$$

and if, *second*, there exist three functions

$$H_1(\xi_j, \eta_j; \tau), \qquad H(x_i, y_i; t), \qquad S(x_i, y_i; t)$$

for which the relation

$$\sum_j \eta_j \, d\xi_j - H_1 \, d\tau = \sum_i y_i \, dx_i - H \, dt + dS$$

is satisfied identically by virtue of Eqs. (7); and such transformations leave the canonical form of the differential equations unaltered. The above contact transformations are therefore canonical transformations, but canonical transformations, in general, are relative to the H function, and therefore, in general, are not contact transformations.[1]

166. Hamilton's Partial Differential Equation.—Suppose the differential equations

$$\left.\begin{aligned} q_i' &= \frac{\partial H}{\partial p_i}, \qquad p_i' = -\frac{\partial H}{\partial q_i}, \qquad i = 1, \cdots, n, \\ H &= \sum_i p_i q_i' - L, \qquad \text{and} \qquad L = T + U, \end{aligned}\right\} \tag{1}$$

have been completely integrated, and that the solution is

$$q_i = q_i(t; c_1, c_2, \cdots, c_{2n}),$$
$$p_i = p_i(t; c_1, c_2, \cdots, c_{2n}),$$

where $c_1, c_2, \ldots, c_{2n}$ are the $2n$ constants of integration. If these values are substituted in H, then H becomes a function of t and the $2n$ constants $c_1, c_2, \ldots, c_{2n}$; that is

$$H = H(t; c_1, c_2, \cdots, c_{2n}).$$

Let c_k be any one of these constants. Then

$$\begin{aligned} \frac{\partial H}{\partial c_k} &= \sum_i \frac{\partial H}{\partial p_i}\frac{\partial p_i}{\partial c_k} + \sum_i \frac{\partial H}{\partial q_i}\frac{\partial q_i}{\partial c_k} \\ &= \sum_i q_i'\frac{\partial p_i}{\partial c_k} - \sum_i p_i'\frac{\partial q_i}{\partial c_k} \qquad \text{by Eqs. (1);} \\ &= \frac{\partial}{\partial c_k}\sum_i p_i q_i' - \frac{d}{dt}\sum_i p_i \frac{\partial q_i}{\partial c_k} \qquad \text{(identity),} \end{aligned}$$

[1] For a discussion of the general canonical transformation the reader is referred to Chap. 5, by C. Carathéodory, of Riemann-Weber's Differential gleichungen der Physik. Vol. 1, edited by Dr. Richard v. Mises (1925).

and since

$$\frac{\partial}{\partial c_k}\sum_i p_i q_i' - \frac{\partial H}{\partial c_k} = \frac{\partial L}{\partial c_k} = \frac{\partial}{\partial c_k}(T + U), \qquad \text{by Eqs. (1);}$$

it is seen that

$$\frac{\partial}{\partial c_k}(T + U) = \frac{d}{dt}\sum_i p_i \frac{\partial q_i}{\partial c_k},$$

from which it follows, by integration, that

$$\frac{\partial}{\partial c_k}\int_{t_0}^{t}(T + U)\,dt = \sum_i p_i \frac{\partial q_i}{\partial c_k} - \sum_i p_{i0}\frac{\partial q_{i0}}{\partial c_k}, \tag{2}$$

where p_{i0} and q_{i0} are the values of p_i and q_i for $t = t_0$.

The function

$$S = \int_{t_0}^{t}(T + U)\,dt \tag{3}$$

was called by Hamilton *the principal function* of motion of a system, because, as he remarked "The variation of this definite integral S has therefore the double property, of giving the differential equations of motion for any transformed coordinates when the extreme positions are regarded as fixed (Hamilton's principle), and of giving the integrals of those differential equations when the extreme positions are treated as varying." The function S is not unique, however, in this respect, as he gave two other, though allied, functions which will serve the same purpose.

Regarding S and the coordinates q_i as functions of the time t and the $2n$ constants of integrations $c_1, c_2, \ldots, c_{2n}$, it is evident that these functions vary with the variations of the constants. In accordance with the notation of the calculus of variations these variations will be denoted by the symbol δ. These variations are related to the variations of the constants by the equations

$$\delta S = \sum_k \frac{\partial S}{\partial c_k}\delta c_k, \qquad \delta q_i = \sum_k \frac{\partial q_i}{\partial c_k}\delta c_k. \tag{4}$$

Now let Eq. (2) be multiplied by δc_k and then summed with respect to the letter k. In view of Eqs. (4), there results

$$\delta S = \sum_i p_i \delta q_i - \sum_i p_{i0}\delta q_{i0}, \tag{5}$$

and in these variations the time is not changed, or varied. Expressed in terms of t and the constants of integration

$$\begin{aligned} q_i &= q_i(t; c_1, c_2, \cdots, c_{2n}), \\ q_{i0} &= q_{i0}(t_0; c_1, c_2, \cdots, c_{2n}), \qquad i = 1, \cdots, n. \\ S &= S(t; c_1, c_2, \cdots, c_{2n}). \end{aligned}$$

The first $2n$ of these equations can be thought of as solved for $c_1, \ldots, c_{2n}$ in terms of $q_1, q_{10}, \ldots, q_n, q_{n0}$, and t, and these results substituted in the last equation; so that

$$S = S(t; q_1, \cdots, q_n; q_{10}, \cdots, q_{n0}). \tag{6}$$

If this expression is varied (t and t_0 fixed), the variation of S takes the form

$$\delta S = \sum_i \frac{\partial S}{\partial q_i}\delta q_i + \sum_i \frac{\partial S}{\partial q_{i0}}\delta q_{i0}. \tag{7}$$

A comparison of Eqs. (5) and (7) shows that

$$\frac{\partial S}{\partial q_i} = p_i, \qquad \text{and} \qquad \frac{\partial S}{\partial q_{i0}} = -p_{i0}, \qquad i = 1, \cdots, n, \tag{8}$$

since the variations δq_i and δq_{i0} are entirely arbitrary. Equations (8) form a complete set of integrals of the differential equations, for the equations

$$\frac{\partial S}{\partial q_{i0}} = -p_{i0}, \qquad i = 1, \cdots, n,$$

could be solved for $q_1, \ldots, q_n$ in terms of t and the initial values q_{i0} and p_{i0}; and these values of the q_i substituted in the equations

$$\frac{\partial S}{\partial q_i} = p_i,$$

would give the p_i as functions of the same arguments.

The problem can be solved therefore if the S function, or the principal function, can be found. As a step in this direction, let Eq. (6) be differentiated totally with respect to the time. There results

$$
\begin{aligned}
S' &= \frac{\partial S}{\partial t} + \sum_i \frac{\partial S}{\partial q_i} q_i' \\
&= \frac{\partial S}{\partial t} + \sum_i p_i q_i';
\end{aligned}
$$

and, since by its definition [Eq. (3)],

$$S' = T + U = L, \qquad \text{and} \qquad \Sigma p_i q_i' = L + H,$$

by Eq. (161.3), it follows that

$$\frac{\partial S}{\partial t} + H(t; q_1, \cdots, q_n; p_1, \cdots, p_n) = 0. \tag{9}$$

If the p_i in this expression for H are replaced by their equals $\partial S/\partial q_i$, Eq. (9) becomes

$$\frac{\partial S}{\partial t} + H\left(t; q_1, \cdots, q_n; \frac{\partial S}{\partial q_1}, \cdots, \frac{\partial S}{\partial q_n}\right) = 0, \tag{10}$$

which is a partial differential equation of the first order and second degree, since the H function is a quadratic in $p_1, \ldots, p_n$. Hamilton's S function, therefore, satisfies this partial differential equation.

167. Hamilton's Principle.—The functions $q_1, \ldots, q_n$ can be regarded as the coordinates of a point in space of n-dimensions. Consider the curve described by this point in the interval of time $t_0 \cdots t_1$. Let the initial point be P_0 and let the terminal point be P_1. All along this curve the differential equations are satisfied. Passing through the fixed points P_0 and P_1 are infinitely many other geometrically possible, but dynamically impossible, curves whose coordinates $q_i + \delta q_i$ can be represented parametrically as functions of the time, for example,

$$q_i + \delta q_i = q_i(t) + \epsilon_i(t - t_0)(t_1 - t)\varphi_i(t).$$

At the instants t_0 and t_1 these points on the varied curves coincide with P_0 and P_1, and for other values of the time will differ from the point on the dynamical curve by as little as may be desired, if the φ_i are continuous in the interval, though otherwise arbitrary, and if the constants ϵ_i are taken sufficiently small.

With the limitation that they vanish at t_0 and t_1 the δq_i are entirely arbitrary. No restriction is placed upon velocities along these curves other than that just mentioned, so that δp_i which are linear combinations of the $\delta q_i'$ also can be regarded as arbitrary. Furthermore, as is easily seen,

$$(\delta q_i)' = \delta q_i'.$$

Hamilton's principle asserts that the principal function S has a stationary value in passing from one infinitely close geometrical curve through the dynamical curve to another infinitely close geometrical curve. In other words,

$$\delta S = \int_{t_0}^{t_1} \delta(T + U)\, dt = 0. \tag{1}$$

Furthermore, the differential equations of motion can be derived from the assumption that this condition is satisfied, whatever the coordinate system may be.

From the definition of H,

$$H = \sum_i p_i q_i' - (T + U),$$

it is seen that the variation of S can also be written

$$\delta S = \delta \int_{t_0}^{t_1} \left(\sum_i p_i q_i' - H \right) dt. \tag{2}$$

From the two identities

$$\delta \sum_i p_i q_i' \equiv \sum_i p_i \delta q_i' + \sum_i q_i' \delta p_i,$$

and

$$\left(\sum_i p_i \delta q_i \right)' \equiv \sum_i p_i \delta q_i' + \sum_i p_i' \delta q_i,$$

it is found by subtraction that

$$\delta \sum_i p_i q_i' = \sum_i q_i' \delta p_i - \sum_i p_i' \delta q_i + \left(\sum_i p_i \delta q_i \right)';$$

and since

$$\int_{t_0}^{t_1} \left(\sum_i p_i \delta q_i \right)' dt = \left[\sum_i p_i \delta q_i \right]_{t_0}^{t_1} = 0,$$

which is true by virtue of the fact that $\delta q_i = 0$ at both limits, it is seen that Eq. (2) can also be written

$$\delta S = \int_{t_0}^{t_1} \sum_i \left(q_i' \delta p_i - p_i' \delta q_i - \frac{\partial H}{\partial q_i} \delta q_i - \frac{\partial H}{\partial p_i} \delta p_i \right) dt,$$

or

$$\delta S = \int_{t_0}^{t_1} \sum_i \left[\left(q_i' - \frac{\partial H}{\partial p_i}\right)\delta p_i - \left(p_i' + \frac{\partial H}{\partial q_i}\right)\delta q_i\right] dt. \quad (3)$$

From this form of the variation of S, Hamilton's principle follows at once. If the differential equations are

$$q_i' = \frac{\partial H}{\partial p_i}, \qquad p_i' = -\frac{\partial H}{\partial q_i},$$

the variation vanishes since the integrand vanishes identically; and if $\delta S = 0$ for all variations of the p_i and q_i, it is necessary that

$$q_i' = \frac{\partial H}{\partial p_i}, \qquad p_i' = -\frac{\partial H}{\partial q_i},$$

which are the differential equations of motion. It will be observed that in all of these variations the time is regarded as a constant.

Since the potential function U is the negative of the potential energy V, and since

$$\frac{1}{t_1 - t_0}\int_{t_0}^{t_1} (T - V)\, dt$$

is the average value with respect to the time of the difference between the kinetic and potential energies, it is seen that Hamilton's principle asserts that in the motion that actually occurs the time average of the difference between the kinetic and the potential energies has a stationary value when compared with any other infinitely near motion between the same two points, provided the time interval and the potential functions are the same for both motions.

168. Jacobi's Extension of Hamilton's Partial Differential Equation Theorem.—Given the function H expressed in terms of the variables $t;\ q_1, \ldots, q_n;\ p_1, \ldots, p_n$,

$$H(t;\ q_1, \ldots, q_n;\ p_1, \ldots, p_n),$$

and the differential equations

$$q_i' = \frac{\partial H}{\partial p_i}, \qquad p_i' = -\frac{\partial H}{\partial q_i};$$

the principal function

$$S = \int_{t_0}^{t_1} (T + U)\,dt$$

satisfies the partial differential equation

$$\frac{\partial S}{\partial t} + H\left(t;\, q_1, \, \cdots, \, q_n;\, \frac{\partial S}{\partial q_1}, \, \cdots, \, \frac{\partial S}{\partial q_n}\right) = 0, \qquad (1)$$

which is formed merely by replacing the p_j in H by $\partial S/\partial q_j$, adding the term $\partial S/\partial t$, and equating the result to zero. Hamilton imagined the function S expressed in terms of the time, the coordinates $q_1, \ldots, q_n$, and their initial values $q_{10}, \ldots, q_{n0}$, and then showed that a complete set of integrals of the differential equations could be obtained by writing

$$p_i = \frac{\partial S}{\partial q_i}, \qquad p_{i0} = -\frac{\partial S}{\partial q_{i0}}, \qquad i = 1, \cdots, n,$$

where the new constants p_{i0} are the initial values of the p_i, Sec. 166.

Jacobi advanced the matter an additional step by showing that if

$$S(t;\, q_1, \ldots, q_n;\, \alpha_1, \ldots, \alpha_n)$$

is any complete solution of Eq. (1), a complete set of integrals of the equations of motion can be derived from it by writing

$$p_i = \frac{\partial S}{\partial q_i}, \qquad \beta_i = \frac{\partial S}{\partial \alpha_i}, \qquad i = 1, \cdots, n. \qquad (2)$$

By a complete solution is meant a function S that, in addition to the arguments $t;\, q_1, \ldots, q_n$, contains n arbitrary constants $\alpha_1, \ldots, \alpha_n$, which when substituted in Eq. (1) reduces it to an identity. Of course, if S is a solution, so also is $S + C$ a solution, where C is any constant. The constants $\alpha_1, \ldots, \alpha_n$ are independent of C and independent of one another in the sense that $\partial S/\partial \alpha_i$ form a set of n independent functions of the arguments $q_1, \ldots, q_n$, so that their functional determinant

$$\left| \frac{\partial^2 S}{\partial \alpha_i\, \partial q_j} \right| \neq 0. \qquad (3)$$

From the symmetry of this functional determinant in the arguments α_i and q_j, it could equally well be stated that the α_i

are independent constants in the sense that the partial derivatives $\partial S/\partial q_i$ form a set of n independent functions of the arguments $\alpha_1, \cdot \cdot \cdot , \alpha_n$, for the condition that this should be so also is the non-vanishing of the determinant [Eq. (3)].

Suppose a complete solution S of Eq. (1) is known, and the functions p_i and the constants β_i are defined as in Eqs. (2). If the second set of Eqs. (2) are differentiated totally with respect to the time, there results

$$\frac{\partial^2 S}{\partial \alpha_i\, \partial t} + \sum_j \frac{\partial^2 S}{\partial \alpha_i\, \partial q_j} q_j' = 0, \tag{4}$$

since the α's and β's are constants.

If the first set of Eqs. (2) are substituted in Eq. (1), there results

$$\frac{\partial S}{\partial t} + H(t; q_1, \cdot \cdot \cdot , q_n; p_1, \cdot \cdot \cdot , p_n) = 0; \tag{5}$$

and if this equation is differentiated with respect to α_i, it is found that

$$\frac{\partial^2 S}{\partial t\, \partial \alpha_i} + \sum_j \frac{\partial H}{\partial p_j} \frac{\partial p_j}{\partial \alpha_i} = 0,$$

since the constants α_i enter the H function of Eq. (5) only through the p's. On account of Eqs. (2), this equation can also be written

$$\frac{\partial^2 S}{\partial t\, \partial \alpha_i} + \sum_j \frac{\partial H}{\partial p_j} \frac{\partial^2 S}{\partial q_j\, \partial \alpha_i} = 0. \tag{6}$$

On forming the difference between Eqs. (4) and (6), there is obtained

$$\sum_j \left(q_j' - \frac{\partial H}{\partial p_j} \right) \frac{\partial^2 S}{\partial q_j\, \partial \alpha_i} = 0, \qquad i = 1, \cdot \cdot \cdot , n.$$

This is a set of linear equations that is homogeneous in the quantities

$$\left(q_j' - \frac{\partial H}{\partial p_j} \right).$$

The determinant

$$\left| \frac{\partial^2 S}{\partial q_j \, \partial \alpha_i} \right| \neq 0,$$

by hypothesis. It follows therefore that

$$q_j' = \frac{\partial H}{\partial p_j}, \qquad j = 1, \cdot \cdot \cdot , n, \tag{7}$$

which is the first half of Hamilton's set of equations.

In order to obtain the second half, differentiate the first set of Eqs. (2) with respect to the time. The result is

$$p_i' = \frac{\partial^2 S}{\partial q_i \, \partial t} + \sum_j \frac{\partial^2 S}{\partial q_i \, \partial q_j} q_j',$$

which, in view of Eqs. (7), can be written

$$p_i' = \frac{\partial^2 S}{\partial q_i \, \partial t} + \sum \frac{\partial^2 S}{\partial q_i \, \partial q_j} \frac{\partial H}{\partial p_j}. \tag{8}$$

On differentiating Eq. (5) with respect to q_i and bearing in mind that, on account of Eqs. (2), the p's are functions of the q's, there results

$$0 = \frac{\partial^2 S}{\partial q_i \, \partial t} + \frac{\partial H}{\partial q_i} + \sum \frac{\partial^2 S}{\partial q_i \, \partial q_j} \frac{\partial H}{\partial p_j}, \tag{9}$$

and by subtracting Eqs. (9) from Eqs. (8), it is found that

$$p_i' = -\frac{\partial H}{\partial q_i}, \qquad i = 1, \cdot \cdot \cdot , n.$$

which is the second half of Hamilton's equations.

It is true, therefore, that if

$$S(t; q_1, \ . \ . \ . \ , q_n; \alpha_1, \ . \ . \ . \ , \alpha_n)$$

is any complete solution of Hamilton's partial differential equation,

$$\frac{\partial S}{\partial t} + H\left(t; q_1, \cdot \cdot \cdot , q_n; \frac{\partial S}{\partial q_1}, \cdot \cdot \cdot , \frac{\partial S}{\partial q_n}\right) = 0,$$

a complete set of integrals of the differential equations can be obtained by writing

$$p_i = \frac{\partial S}{\partial q_i}, \qquad \beta_i = \frac{\partial S}{\partial \alpha_i}, \qquad i = 1, \cdot \cdot \cdot , n.$$

If the second set of these equations is then solved for $q_1, \ldots, q_n$, a complete solution

$$q_i = q_i(t; \alpha_1, \cdots, \alpha_n; \beta_1, \cdots, \beta_n)$$

will be obtained in which the q_i are expressed as functions of the time and the $2n$ arbitrary constants $\alpha_1, \ldots, \alpha_n; \beta_1, \ldots, \beta_n$.

169. The Restricted Case in Which the Time Does Not Occur Explicitly.—If the time does not occur explicitly in H, it is possible to take

$$S = -\alpha_1 t + S_1(q_1, \cdots, q_n; \alpha_1, \cdots, \alpha_n), \tag{1}$$

and Hamilton's partial differential equation becomes

$$H\left(q_1, \cdots, q_n; \frac{\partial S_1}{\partial q_1}, \cdots \frac{\partial S_1}{\partial q_n}\right) = \alpha_1, \tag{2}$$

which does not contain the time explicitly. It is sufficient then to find a function S_1 of the arguments $q_1, \ldots, q_n$ which in addition to the constant α_1 contains $n - 1$ new constants $\alpha_2, \ldots, \alpha_n$. The set of integrals becomes

$$\begin{aligned} \beta_1 &= \frac{\partial S_1}{\partial \alpha_1} - t, & \beta_i &= \frac{\partial S_1}{\partial \alpha_i}, \\ p_1 &= \frac{\partial S_1}{\partial q_1}, & p_i &= \frac{\partial S_1}{\partial q_i}, \end{aligned} \qquad i = 2, \cdots, n, \tag{3}$$

or, on taking $\beta_1 = -t_0$,

$$t - t_0 = \frac{\partial S_1}{\partial \alpha_1}. \tag{4}$$

This situation arises, in particular, when the system is a conservative one, for then

$$H = \sum_i p_i q_i' - (T + U) = 2T - (T + U) = T - U,$$

which is the energy. On replacing $\partial S_1/\partial \alpha_j$ by p_j in Eq. (2), it is seen that

$$H(q_1, \cdots, q_n; p_1, \cdots, p_n) = \alpha_1;$$

and therefore α_1 is the energy constant.

Another procedure has been used by Poincaré. Suppose a function $S_1(q_1, \ldots, q_n; \alpha_1, \ldots, \alpha_n)$ has been found, which when substituted in the left member of Eq. (2) reduces it to a constant. This constant will be a function of $\alpha_1, \ldots, \alpha_n$, say

$$H\left(q_1, \cdots, q_n; \frac{\partial S_1}{\partial q_1}, \cdots, \frac{\partial S_1}{\partial q_n}\right) = \varphi(\alpha_1, \cdots, \alpha_n). \quad (5)$$

As before, take

$$p_i = \frac{\partial S_1}{\partial q_i}, \qquad \beta_i = \frac{\partial S_1}{\partial \alpha_i}, \quad (6)$$

without, however, making any hypothesis as to the nature of the β's. Equations (6) can then be regarded as defining a transformation from the variables p_i, q_i to the variables α_i, β_i, and by Sec. 164, this transformation is canonical; that is

$$\beta_i' = \frac{\partial H}{\partial \alpha_i}, \qquad \alpha_i' = -\frac{\partial H}{\partial \beta_i}. \quad (7)$$

In the new variables

$$H = \varphi(\alpha_1, \cdots, \alpha_n),$$

so that Eqs. (7) become

$$\beta_i' = \frac{\partial \varphi}{\partial \alpha_i}, \qquad \alpha_i' = 0. \quad (8)$$

Again it is evident that the α_i's are constants, but the β_i's are linear functions of the time. If the partial derivatives $\partial\varphi/\partial\alpha_i$ are denoted by φ_i, it is clear that the φ_i are constants and that

$$\beta_i = \varphi_i t + \beta_{i0},$$

where the β_{i0} are n constants of integration.

170. Example: The Compound Pendulum.—The compound pendulum was discussed in detail in Sec. 61, and the notation of that article will be adopted here. Let the angle between the vertical plane through the axis of suspension of the body and the plane through the axis of suspension and the center of gravity of the body be θ. Let the mass of the body be M, its radius of gyration with respect to the axis of suspension be k_1, and the perpendicular distance from the center of gravity to the axis of suspension be l_1. The energy equation is then

$$H = \tfrac{1}{2}Mk_1^2\theta'^2 - Mgl_1 \cos\theta = \alpha,$$

and since the body has but one degree of freedom subscripts on the variables are not necessary. On taking,

$$p = \frac{\partial H}{\partial \theta'} = Mk_1^2\theta',$$

it is found that

$$H = \frac{p^2}{2Mk_1^2} - Mgl_1 \cos \theta = \alpha. \tag{1}$$

Since the time does not occur explicitly,

$$S = -\alpha t + S_1(\theta),$$

and Hamilton's partial differential equation is

$$\frac{1}{2Mk_1^2}\left(\frac{\partial S_1}{\partial \theta}\right)^2 - Mgl_1 \cos \theta = \alpha, \tag{2}$$

which is obtained by replacing p in Eq. (1) by $\partial S_1/\partial \theta$.

As θ is the only variable in this equation, it is an ordinary differential equation of the first order. Its solution is

$$S_1 = \sqrt{2Mk_1^2}\int \sqrt{\alpha + Mgl_1 \cos \theta}\, d\theta.$$

Then, by Eq. (169.4),

$$\frac{\partial S_1}{\partial \alpha} = t - t_0 = \frac{1}{2}\int \frac{\sqrt{2Mk_1^2}\, d\theta}{\sqrt{\alpha + Mgl_1 \cos \theta}}.$$

On substituting

$$\alpha = -Mgl_1 \cos \theta_0,$$

it becomes

$$t - t_0 = \frac{1}{2}\sqrt{\frac{k_1^2}{gl_1}}\int \frac{d\theta}{\sqrt{\sin^2 \frac{1}{2}\theta_0 - \sin^2 \frac{1}{2}\theta}};$$

and the further substitutions,

$$\sin \frac{1}{2}\theta = k \sin \varphi, \qquad k = \sin \frac{1}{2}\theta_0,$$

put it in the normal form of Legendre

$$t - t_0 = \sqrt{\frac{k_1^2}{gl_1}}\int \frac{d\varphi}{\sqrt{1 - k^2 \sin^2 \varphi}}.$$

On taking $k_1^2 = ll_1$, it is seen that this is the integral for the simple pendulum of length l (I, **319**).

171. Lagrange's Case of a Spinning Body.—As a second example of the use of canonical variables, consider the problem of spinning tops in which one point of the body is fixed, the ellipsoid of inertia at the fixed point is a spheroid, and the center of gravity is on the axis of this spheroid.

In terms of the angular velocities and moments of inertia at the fixed point the kinetic energy is [Eq. (86.5)]

$$T = \tfrac{1}{2}(A\omega_i^2 + B\omega_j^2 + C\omega_k^2),$$

and the potential energy is

$$-U = +Mgl \cos \theta,$$

where l is the distance from the fixed point to the center of gravity; hence

$$H = T - U = \tfrac{1}{2}(A\omega_i^2 + B\omega_j^2 + C\omega_k^2) + Mgl \cos \theta.$$

The angular velocities in terms of Euler's angles and their derivatives are [Eq. (85.4)]

$$\left.\begin{aligned} \omega_i &= \psi' \sin \theta \cos \varphi + \theta' \cos \varphi, \\ \omega_j &= \psi' \sin \theta \sin \varphi - \theta' \sin \varphi, \\ \omega_k &= \psi' \cos \theta \qquad\qquad + \varphi'; \end{aligned}\right\} \tag{1}$$

and, since $A = B$, the expression for H becomes

$$\tfrac{1}{2}\{A\psi'^2 \sin^2 \theta + A\theta'^2 + C(\varphi' + \psi' \cos \theta)^2\} + Mgl \cos \theta. \tag{2}$$

Then on associating p_1 with θ, p_2 with φ, p_3 with ψ, it is found that

$$\frac{\partial H}{\partial \theta'} = p_1 = A\theta',$$

$$\frac{\partial H}{\partial \varphi'} = p_2 = C(\varphi' + \psi' \cos \theta),$$

$$\frac{\partial H}{\partial \psi'} = p_3 = A\psi' \sin^2 \theta + C(\varphi' + \psi' \cos \theta) \cos \theta;$$

from which it follows that

$$\left.\begin{aligned} \theta' &= \frac{p_1}{A}, \\ \varphi' + \psi' \cos \theta &= \frac{p_2}{C}, \\ \psi' \sin^2 \theta &= \frac{p_3 - p_2 \cos \theta}{A}. \end{aligned}\right\} \tag{3}$$

In terms of the canonical variables, therefore,

$$H = \frac{1}{2}\left\{\frac{p_1^2}{A} + \frac{p_2^2}{C} + \frac{(p_3 - p_2 \cos \theta)^2}{A \sin^2 \theta}\right\} + Mgl \cos \theta = \alpha_1,$$

where α_1 is the energy constant. Hamilton's partial differential equation is, therefore,

$$\frac{1}{A}\left(\frac{\partial S}{\partial \theta}\right)^2 + \frac{1}{C}\left(\frac{\partial S}{\partial \varphi}\right)^2 + \frac{1}{A \sin^2 \theta}\left(\frac{\partial S}{\partial \psi} - \cos \theta \frac{\partial S}{\partial \varphi}\right)^2 + 2Mgl \cos \theta = 2\alpha_1. \quad (4)$$

Since this equation does not contain either t, φ, or ψ explicitly, it is sufficient to take

$$S = -\alpha_1 t + \alpha_2 \varphi + \alpha_3 \psi + S_1(\theta),$$

where α_2 and α_3 are two new constants, and $S_1(\theta)$ is a function of θ alone; and the substitution of this form in Eq. (4) reduces it to the ordinary differential equation

$$\left(\frac{dS_1}{d\theta}\right)^2 = \left(2A\alpha_1 - \frac{A}{C}\alpha_2^2 - 2AMgl \cos \theta\right) - \frac{1}{\sin^2 \theta}(\alpha_3 - \alpha_2 \cos \theta)^2. \quad (5)$$

If the substitution

$$\cos \theta = u, \qquad \left(\frac{\partial S_1}{\partial \theta}\right)^2 = (1 - u^2)\left(\frac{\partial S_1}{\partial u}\right)^2$$

is made, and if, for brevity of notation,

$$\left(2A\alpha_1 - \frac{A}{C}\alpha_2^2 - 2AMglu\right)(1 - u^2) - (\alpha_3 - \alpha_2 u)^2 = f(u),$$

it is found, on integrating that

$$S_1(\theta) = \int \frac{\sqrt{f(u)}}{1 - u^2} du. \quad (6)$$

Then

$$\frac{\partial S_1}{\partial \alpha_1} = t - t_0 = \int \frac{A\, du}{\sqrt{f(u)}}, \quad (7)$$

$$\frac{\partial S}{\partial \alpha_2} = \beta_2 = \varphi - \frac{A\alpha_2}{C}\int \frac{du}{\sqrt{f(u)}} + \int \frac{u(\alpha_3 - \alpha_2 u)}{1 - u^2}\frac{du}{\sqrt{f(u)}}, \quad (8)$$

$$\frac{\partial S}{\partial \alpha_3} = \beta_3 = \psi - \int \frac{\alpha_3 - \alpha_2 u}{1 - u^2}\frac{du}{\sqrt{f(u)}}. \quad (9)$$

In order to bring the notation used here into agreement with that used in Sec. 104, it is necessary to take

$$\alpha_1 = \tfrac{1}{2}h, \qquad 2Mgl = Aa,$$
$$\alpha_2 = Ab\omega_k, \qquad l = \zeta,$$
$$\alpha_3 = Ab\omega_k u_4, \qquad b = \frac{C}{A}.$$

Equation (7) gives u as a function of the time, and Eqs. (8) and (9) give φ and ψ as functions of u. Since u is equivalent to θ, the solution of the problem is complete.

172. Poisson's Brackets.—Suppose

$$\omega(q_1, \cdots, q_n; p_1, \cdots, p_n; t) = C$$

is an integral of the canonical differential equations

$$q_i' = \frac{\partial H}{\partial p_i}, \qquad p_i' = -\frac{\partial H}{\partial q_i}. \tag{1}$$

Differentiation of this integral with respect to the time gives

$$\frac{\partial \omega}{\partial t} + \sum_i \frac{\partial \omega}{\partial q_i} q_i' + \sum \frac{\partial \omega}{\partial p_i} p_i' = 0,$$

which, by the use of Eqs. (1), can be written

$$\frac{\partial \omega}{\partial t} + \sum_i \left(\frac{\partial \omega}{\partial q_i}\frac{\partial H}{\partial p_i} - \frac{\partial \omega}{\partial p_i}\frac{\partial H}{\partial q_i} \right) \equiv 0; \tag{2}$$

that is, this expression vanishes whatever values p_i, q_i, and t may have. Conversely, if ω satisfies this relation ω = constant is an integral.

Suppose ψ is a second function of the same arguments, the notation

$$[\psi, \omega] = \sum_i \left(\frac{\partial \psi}{\partial q_i}\frac{\partial \omega}{\partial p_i} - \frac{\partial \psi}{\partial p_i}\frac{\partial \omega}{\partial q_i} \right) \tag{3}$$

was adopted by Poisson, and the symbol $[\psi, \omega]$ is called *Poisson's bracket*. Some of its more evident properties are:

(*a*) If c is a constant, $\qquad [c, \omega] = 0.$

(*b*) $\qquad [\psi, \omega] = -[\omega, \psi], \qquad [-\psi, \omega] = -[\psi, \omega],$

(c) If

$$\psi = \sum_j \psi_j, \qquad \text{then} \qquad [\psi, \omega] = \sum_j [\psi_j, \omega].$$

If ψ and ω contain the time explicitly,

$$\frac{\partial}{\partial t}[\psi, \omega] = \sum_i \left(\frac{\partial(\partial\psi/\partial t)}{\partial q_i} \frac{\partial \omega}{\partial p_i} - \frac{\partial(\partial\psi/\partial t)}{\partial p_i} \frac{\partial \omega}{\partial q_i} \right) + \sum_i \left(\frac{\partial \psi}{\partial q_i} \frac{\partial(\partial\omega/\partial t)}{\partial p_i} - \frac{\partial \psi}{\partial p_i} \frac{\partial(\partial\omega/\partial t)}{\partial q_i} \right),$$

or

$$\frac{\partial}{\partial t}[\psi, \omega] = \left[\frac{\partial \psi}{\partial t}, \omega \right] + \left[\psi, \frac{\partial \omega}{\partial t} \right]. \tag{4}$$

173. Poisson's Identity.—For still further brevity, let Eq. (172.3)

$$\alpha = [\psi, \omega] = \sum_i \alpha_i.$$

Then

$$[\varphi, \alpha] = \sum_j \sum_i \left(\frac{\partial \varphi}{\partial q_j} \frac{\partial \alpha_i}{\partial p_j} - \frac{\partial \varphi}{\partial p_j} \frac{\partial \alpha_i}{\partial q_j} \right) = [\varphi, [\psi, \omega]].$$

Now

$$\frac{\partial \alpha_i}{\partial p_j} = \frac{\partial \omega}{\partial p_i} \frac{\partial^2 \psi}{\partial q_i\, \partial p_j} - \frac{\partial \omega}{\partial q_i} \frac{\partial^2 \psi}{\partial p_i\, \partial p_j} + \frac{\partial \psi}{\partial q_i} \frac{\partial^2 \omega}{\partial p_i\, \partial p_j} - \frac{\partial \psi}{\partial p_i} \frac{\partial^2 \omega}{\partial q_i\, \partial p_j},$$

and

$$\frac{\partial \alpha_i}{\partial q_j} = \frac{\partial \omega}{\partial p_i} \frac{\partial^2 \psi}{\partial q_i\, \partial q_j} - \frac{\partial \omega}{\partial q_i} \frac{\partial^2 \varphi}{\partial p_i\, \partial q_j} + \frac{\partial \psi}{\partial q_i} \frac{\partial^2 \omega}{\partial p_i\, \partial q_j} - \frac{\partial \psi}{\partial p_i} \frac{\partial^2 \omega}{\partial q_i\, \partial q_j}.$$

On multiplying the first of these expressions by $\partial\varphi/\partial q_j$, the second by $-\partial\varphi/\partial p_j$, and then taking the double sum, there results

$$[\varphi[\psi, \omega]] = \sum_j \sum_i \tag{1}$$

$$\left\{ \frac{\partial \omega}{\partial p_i} \frac{\partial \varphi}{\partial q_j} \frac{\partial^2 \psi}{\partial q_i\, \partial p_j} - \frac{\partial \omega}{\partial p_i} \frac{\partial \varphi}{\partial p_j} \frac{\partial^2 \psi}{\partial q_i\, \partial q_j} - \frac{\partial \omega}{\partial q_i} \frac{\partial \varphi}{\partial q_j} \frac{\partial^2 \psi}{\partial p_i\, \partial p_j} + \frac{\partial \omega}{\partial q_i} \frac{\partial \varphi}{\partial p_j} \frac{\partial^2 \psi}{\partial p_i\, \partial q_j} + \frac{\partial \varphi}{\partial q_i} \frac{\partial \psi}{\partial q_j} \frac{\partial^2 \omega}{\partial p_i\, \partial p_j} - \frac{\partial \varphi}{\partial p_i} \frac{\partial \psi}{\partial q_j} \frac{\partial^2 \omega}{\partial q_i\, \partial p_j} - \frac{\partial \varphi}{\partial q_i} \frac{\partial \psi}{\partial p_j} \frac{\partial^2 \omega}{\partial p_i\, \partial q_j} + \frac{\partial \varphi}{\partial p_i} \frac{\partial \psi}{\partial p_j} \frac{\partial^2 \omega}{\partial q_i\, \partial q_j} \right\},$$

except that in the last line the subscripts i and j have been interchanged. This is permissible since the sum is taken with respect to both i and j, and the interchange can be made on any of the terms.

On permuting the letters φ, ψ, ω circularly twice in Eq. (1) and then adding, it is found that the right member vanishes identically, that is,

$$[\varphi, [\psi, \omega]] + [\psi, [\omega, \varphi]] + [\omega, [\varphi, \psi]] \equiv 0, \tag{2}$$

which is Poisson's identity.

174. Poisson's Theorem on Integrals.—Suppose

$$\left.\begin{aligned} \psi(q_1, \cdots, q_n; p_1, \cdots, p_n; t) &= c_1 \\ \omega(q_1, \cdots, q_n; p_1, \cdots, p_n; t) &= c_2 \end{aligned}\right\} \tag{1}$$

are two integrals of Eqs. (172.1). Then, by Eq. (172.2),

$$\left.\begin{aligned} [\psi, H] + \frac{\partial \psi}{\partial t} &= 0, \\ \text{and} \qquad [\omega, H] + \frac{\partial \omega}{\partial t} &= 0. \end{aligned}\right\} \tag{2}$$

Also, by Poisson's identity, Eq. (173.2),

$$[H, [\psi, \omega]] + [\psi, [\omega, H]] + [\omega, [H, \psi]] \equiv 0. \tag{3}$$

For simplicity of notation, let

$$[\psi, \omega] = \varphi(q_1, \cdots, q_n; p_1, \cdots, p_n; t);$$

then, by Eq. (172.4),

$$\left[\frac{\partial \psi}{\partial t}, \omega\right] + \left[\psi, \frac{\partial \omega}{\partial t}\right] = \frac{\partial \varphi}{\partial t}.$$

From Eqs. (2) and (3), it is found that

$$[H, \varphi] - \left[\psi, \frac{\partial \omega}{\partial t}\right] + \left[\omega, \frac{\partial \psi}{\partial t}\right] = 0,$$

or

$$[\varphi, H] + \frac{\partial \varphi}{\partial t} = 0; \tag{4}$$

that is, by Eq. (172.2),

$$\varphi = c_3 \tag{5}$$

also is an integral. For example, if Eqs. (1) are two of the integrals of momentum in the problem of n bodies, it will be found that Eq. (5) is the third integral of momentum.

It is natural to assume that Eq. (5) is a new integral, but, it will be observed, the theorem does not say this. It merely says that Eq. (5) is an integral. It may be a function of the integrals in Eqs. (1), or it may be merely a trivial identity. Notwithstanding the fact that Poisson's theorem gives an interesting relation among integrals, it cannot be said that it has led to integrals that were not already known. As a matter of fact it has been singularly sterile.

Another interesting relationship is found when H does not contain the time explicitly. In this event $H = c_1$ is the energy integral. Suppose $\varphi(q_k; p_k; t) = c_2$ is a second integral; then by the above theorem

$$[H, \varphi] = c_3 \tag{6}$$

also is an integral. But since $\varphi = c_2$ is an integral,

$$[\varphi, H] + \frac{\partial \varphi}{\partial t} = 0,$$

which, by Eq. (6), becomes

$$\frac{\partial \varphi}{\partial t} = c_3.$$

Thus if $\varphi = c_2$ is an integral that contains the time explicitly, $\partial\varphi/\partial t = c_3$ is a second integral; and similarly $\partial^2\varphi/\partial t^2 = c_4$ is a third integral, and so on: but, if φ does not contain the time, $c_3 = 0$, and

$$[H, \varphi] \equiv 0. \tag{7}$$

175. Lagrange's Brackets.—Another set of brackets, different from those of Poisson, is due to Lagrange, although the setting in which it is found here is due to Poincaré.

Suppose the canonical equations [Eqs. (172.1)] have been integrated, so that the q_i and the p_i are expressed as functions of the time t and $2n$ constants of integration $\alpha_1, \ldots, \alpha_{2n}$. The brackets

$$(\alpha_j, \alpha_k) = \sum_i \left(\frac{\partial q_i}{\partial \alpha_j}\frac{\partial p_i}{\partial \alpha_k} - \frac{\partial q_i}{\partial \alpha_k}\frac{\partial p_i}{\partial \alpha_j}\right) \tag{1}$$

are called *Lagrange's brackets.*

It was shown in Eqs. (163.3) that, as a consequence of the differential equations, the following relations hold:

$$\frac{d}{dt}\sum_i q_i\frac{\partial p_i}{\partial \alpha_k} - \frac{\partial}{\partial \alpha_k}\sum q_i p_i' = \frac{\partial H}{\partial \alpha_k}, \qquad k = 1, \cdots, 2n,$$

which can also be written

$$\frac{d}{dt}\sum_i q_i\frac{\partial p_i}{\partial \alpha_k} = \frac{\partial}{\partial \alpha_k}\left(H - \sum_i q_i\frac{\partial H}{\partial q_i}\right), \tag{2}$$

and similarly

$$\frac{d}{dt}\sum_i q_i\frac{\partial p_i}{\partial \alpha_j} = \frac{\partial}{\partial \alpha_j}\left(H - \sum_i q_i\frac{\partial H}{\partial q_i}\right). \tag{3}$$

If Eq. (2) is differentiated with respect to α_j, Eq. (3) with respect to α_k, and the second result is then subtracted from the first, it is found that

$$\frac{d}{dt}\left(\frac{\partial}{\partial \alpha_j}\sum_i q_i\frac{\partial p_i}{\partial \alpha_k} - \frac{\partial}{\partial \alpha_k}\sum_i q_i\frac{\partial p_i}{\partial \alpha_j}\right) = \frac{d}{dt}\sum_i\left(\frac{\partial q_i}{\partial \alpha_j}\frac{\partial p_i}{\partial \alpha_k} - \frac{\partial q_i}{\partial \alpha_k}\frac{\partial p_i}{\partial \alpha_j}\right) = 0,$$

or

$$\frac{d}{dt}(\alpha_j, \alpha_k) = 0, \qquad j, k = 1, \cdots, 2n. \tag{4}$$

It follows therefore that a Lagrange bracket is independent of the time and therefore a function of the constants α only. In addition to the obvious relations

$$(\alpha_j, \alpha_j) = 0, \qquad (\alpha_j, \alpha_k) = -(\alpha_k, \alpha_j),$$

among the Lagrange brackets, there exists the identity

$$\frac{\partial(\alpha_j, \alpha_k)}{\partial \alpha_i} + \frac{\partial(\alpha_k, \alpha_i)}{\partial \alpha_j} + \frac{\partial(\alpha_i, \alpha_j)}{\partial \alpha_k} \equiv 0, \tag{5}$$

for any three of the $2n$ constants $\alpha_1, \ldots, \alpha_{2n}$. As has just been seen, at Eq. (4) and above,

$$(\alpha_j, \alpha_k) = \frac{\partial}{\partial \alpha_j}\sum_h q_h \frac{\partial p_h}{\partial \alpha_k} - \frac{\partial}{\partial \alpha_k}\sum_h q_h \frac{\partial p_h}{\partial \alpha_j},$$

$$(\alpha_k, \alpha_i) = \frac{\partial}{\partial \alpha_k}\sum_h q_h \frac{\partial p_h}{\partial \alpha_i} - \frac{\partial}{\partial \alpha_i}\sum_h q_h \frac{\partial p_h}{\partial \alpha_k},$$

$$(\alpha_i, \alpha_j) = \frac{\partial}{\partial \alpha_i}\sum_h q_h \frac{\partial p_h}{\partial \alpha_j} - \frac{\partial}{\partial \alpha_j}\sum_h q_h \frac{\partial p_h}{\partial \alpha_i}.$$

If the first of these equations is differentiated with respect to α_i, the second with respect to α_j, the third with respect to α_k, and the sum is then taken, it is seen that the right member vanishes identically, and there remains the identity, Eq. (5).

176. The Method of Variation of Parameters.—The solution of the problem of two bodies shows that each of the two bodies describes an ellipse (or, in general, a conic) about their common center of gravity; or, if preferred, each describes an ellipse (or conic) about the other. When a third or fourth body is introduced into the system, none of the bodies describes a conic, that is to say, conic section motion does not satisfy the differential equations. Notwithstanding this fact, it is true, however, that the orbits of the planets about the sun continue to be elliptical in character and the motion Keplerian. The constants that define the elliptical orbit, namely, a the major semiaxis, e the eccentricity, Ω the longitude of the node, $\bar{\omega}$ the longitude of perihelion from the node, i the inclination of the plane of the orbit, and, finally, T the time of perihelion passage, are not exactly the same from year to year, but the changes are small. As a consequence, the astronomers continued to think of the planetary orbits as ellipses about the sun even when the perturbations of the other planets were taken into account. The elements of the orbit, a, e, i, Ω, $\bar{\omega}$, and T, were regarded as varying slowly with the time, but the motion in the ellipse at any moment was Keplerian. From the point of view of differential equations, the constants of integration of the two-body problem were to be regarded as variables for the solution of the perturbation problem. The success of the method is due to the fact that the perturbative function, as it is called, is small and remains small. Evidently the method is available for the solution of other mechanical problems that exhibit similar characteristics, and the method is known as *variation of parameters.* It was developed extensively by Lagrange for planetary theory, and the properties of Lagrange's brackets were known to every astronomer.

Suppose the differential equations are canonical, and that they are

$$q_i' = \frac{\partial H}{\partial p_i}, \qquad p_i' = -\frac{\partial H}{\partial q_i}, \qquad i = 1, \cdots, n. \tag{1}$$

Suppose further that the function H can be broken up into two parts

$$H = H_0 + H_1,$$

in which H_1 is small as compared with H_0. In the planetary theory H_0 is the Hamiltonian function for the two-body problem and H_1 is the ensemble of terms that must be added to H_0 when the perturbative action of the planets is taken into account. Suppose, finally, that it is known how to solve the equations

$$q_i' = \frac{\partial H_0}{\partial p_i}, \qquad p_i' = -\frac{\partial H_0}{\partial q_i}, \qquad i = 1, \cdots, n. \tag{2}$$

That is to say, a function

$$S(q_1, \ldots, q_n; \beta_1, \ldots, \beta_n; t)$$

can be found, in which $\beta_1, \ldots, \beta_n$ are n independent, arbitrary constants, that satisfies the partial differential equation

$$\frac{\partial S}{\partial t} + H_0\left(q_1, \cdots, q_n; \frac{\partial S}{\partial q_1}, \cdots, \frac{\partial S}{\partial q_n}; t\right) = 0.$$

The integrals of Eq. (2) are then defined by the relations

$$p_i = \frac{\partial S}{\partial q_i}, \qquad \alpha_i = \frac{\partial S}{\partial \beta_i}, \qquad i = 1, \cdots, n, \tag{3}$$

where the α_i are new arbitrary constants.

The $2n$ equations, Eqs. (3), can be solved for the p_i and q_i as functions of the $2n$ constants α_i, β_i, and the time t; that is

$$\left.\begin{aligned} p_i &= p_i(\alpha_1, \cdots, \alpha_n; \beta_1, \cdots, \beta_n; t), \\ q_i &= q_i(\alpha_1, \cdots, \alpha_n; \beta_1, \cdots, \beta_n; t), \end{aligned}\right\} \tag{4}$$

and these expressions substituted in Eqs. (2) reduce the differential equations to an identity.

Equations (4) can be regarded, however, not as solutions of Eqs. (2) which, of course they are, but as equations of transformation from the letters p_i and q_i of Eqs. (1) to the letters α_i and β_i. On account of Eqs. (3), it is seen that

$$\sum_{i} q_i\,dp_i - \sum_{-i} \alpha_i\,d\beta_i \equiv \left(\sum_{-i} q_i\,dp_i + \sum_{-i} p_i\,dq_i\right) - \left(\sum_{i} p_i\,dq_i + \sum_{i} \alpha_i\,d\beta_i\right)$$

$$= d\sum_{i}(p_iq_i) - \sum_{i}\left(\frac{\partial S}{\partial q_i}dq_i + \frac{\partial S}{\partial \beta_i}d\beta_i\right)$$

$$= d(\Sigma p_iq_i - S),$$

which is an exact differential. The transformation of variables therefore is a canonical one, and

$$\alpha_i' = \frac{\partial H_1}{\partial \beta_i}, \qquad \beta_i' = -\frac{\partial H_1}{\partial \alpha_i}, \qquad i = 1, \cdots, n.$$

The term H_0 disappears from the Hamiltonian function by virtue of the fact that if $H_1 = 0$, the α_i and β_i are constants, that is

$$\alpha_i' = \beta_i' = 0.$$

It is necessary only to transform the function H_1 from the letters p_i and q_i to the letters α_i and β_i by means of Eqs. (4).

Application of this method to the problems of the perturbations of the planets and to the theory of the rotation of the earth taking into account the actions of the sun and the moon will be found in Vols. 1 and 2 respectively of Tisserand's "Mécanique Céleste." In Vol. 3 is given a résumé of Delaunay's theory of the motion of the moon in which this change of variables is made over and over again, each time cutting out one term from the perturbative function. Hamilton himself adopted this method of developing the S function, separating it into two parts, $S = S_0 + S_1$ just as H is separated into two parts, $H = H_0 + H$.

Problems

1. Derive Lagrange's equations of motion by means of Hamilton's principle.

2. Show that

$$\frac{\partial p_i}{\partial \alpha_k} = \frac{\partial \beta_k}{\partial q_i}, \qquad \frac{\partial p_i}{\partial \beta_k} = -\frac{\partial \alpha_k}{\partial q_i}$$

$$\frac{\partial q_i}{\partial \beta_k} = \frac{\partial \alpha_k}{\partial p_i}, \qquad \frac{\partial q_i}{\partial \alpha_k} = -\frac{\partial \beta_k}{\partial p_i}.$$

3. Given the canonical equations

$$x_i' = \frac{\partial H}{\partial y_i}, \qquad y_i' = -\frac{\partial H}{\partial x_i}.$$

If X is Hamilton's principal function

$$\frac{\partial X}{\partial t} + H\left(x_j; \frac{\partial X}{\partial x_j}\right) = 0.$$

Suppose there is a canonical change of variables from the letters x_i y_i to the letters q_i, p_i, so that

$$q_i' = \frac{\partial H}{\partial p_i}, \qquad p_i' = -\frac{\partial H}{\partial q_i};$$

and if Q is the principal function

$$\frac{\partial Q}{\partial t} + H\left(q_i; \frac{\partial Q_i}{\partial q_i}\right) = 0.$$

Show that, in general, the function Q is not merely the transform of the function X.

4. Given the canonical equations

$$q_i' = \frac{\partial H}{\partial p_i}, \qquad p_i' = -\frac{\partial H}{\partial q_i}, \qquad i = 1, \cdots, n,$$

in which

$$H(q_1, \ldots, q_n; p_1, \ldots, p_n; t)$$

contains the time explicitly. Show that H can be replaced by

$$H_1 = H(q_1, \cdots, q_n; p_1, \cdots, p_n; q_{n+1}) + p_{n+1},$$

which is simply H with t replaced by q_{n+1} and p_{n+1} is then added, and the equations are still canonical

$$q_i' = \frac{\partial H_1}{\partial p_i}, \qquad p_i' = -\frac{\partial H_1}{\partial q_i}, \qquad i = 1, \cdots, n+1.$$

The time t does not occur explicitly in H_1, but evidently

$$q_{n+1} = t,$$

since

$$q_{n+1}' = \frac{\partial H}{\partial p_{n+1}} = 1.$$

Thus a system in which the time occurs explicitly can always be replaced by another system, but with one more degree of freedom, in which the time does not occur explicitly. Also interpret the new variable p_{n+1}.

5. Suppose the set of differential equations

$$\begin{aligned} q_i' &= Q_i(q_1, \cdots, q_n; p_1, \cdots, p_n; t), \\ p_i' &= P_i(q_1, \cdots, q_n; p_1, \cdots, p_n; t), \qquad i = 1, \cdots, n, \end{aligned}$$

admits two known integrals

$$\varphi_1 = c_1, \qquad \varphi_2 = c_2.$$

Show that the differential equations can be expressed in the canonical form.

6. *Liouville's Theorem.*—Suppose A_i, B_i, and U_i are functions of q_i alone, for each i; that

$$2T = (A_1 + A_2 + \cdots + A_n)(B_1 q_1'^2 + B_2 q_2'^2 + \cdots + B_n q_n'^2),$$

and that

$$U = \frac{U_1 + U_2 + \cdots + U_n}{A_1 + A_2 + \cdots + A_n}.$$

Show that the problem can be reduced to quadratures.

7. *Staeckel's Theorem.*—Given n^2 functions φ_{ij} such that the function φ_{ij} is a function of q_j alone, for each j. Let

$$\Delta = |\varphi_{ij}|$$

be the determinant of these functions, and let Φ_{ij} be the minor of Δ for the element φ_{ij}. If

$$2T = \Delta \sum_j \frac{q_j'^2}{\Phi_{1j}}, \qquad U = \frac{\sum \Phi_{1j} U_j}{\Delta},$$

where U_j is a function of q_j only, the problem can be reduced to quadratures. Show that Liouville's theorem is a particular case of Staeckel's theorem.

8. Show that Hamilton's principal function also satisfies the partial differential equation

$$\frac{\partial S}{\partial t} + H\left(t; \frac{\partial S}{\partial q_{10}}, \cdots \frac{\partial S}{\partial q_{n0}}; q_{10}, \cdots q_{n0}\right) = 0,$$

where the q_{i0} is the initial value of q_i, and that

$$p_{i0} = -\frac{\partial S}{\partial q_{i0}}.$$

CHAPTER XII

THE METHOD OF PERIODIC SOLUTIONS

177. Introduction.—It was doubtless perceived early in the study of mechanics that in many problems, perhaps one might say in most problems, of mechanics the differential equations of motion cannot be integrated. This statement is understood to mean that integrals that are algebraic in character, or even simply transcendental, in sufficient number to form a complete system, cannot be found.

This fact has led to the development of solutions that are expressible in infinite series of one kind or another. For example, if the initial values of the variables are such that the differential equations are regular (in the sense of the complex variable theory) a solution can be developed in powers of the time. The series so obtained are convergent for values of the time sufficiently small, and they satisfy the differential equations. They are, therefore, solutions of the problem in a mathematical sense, but, in general, have very little value in a mechanical sense in that they do not reveal the essential, or interesting, properties of the motion.

In numerical cases, by a process known as *mechanical quadrature*, the motion can be followed step by step for as long a period of time as may be desired; although, as a matter of practice, the time so desired is rather short on account of the great labor which the method requires. This method has been used by the astronomers, particularly in the determination of perturbations, but, like the previous method, it does not give any general theorems about the motion. The information which it gives is limited to the particular solution that is followed and to the particular interval of time that is used.

A third method is the development of solutions in powers of a parameter. The parameter or parameters, in powers of which the expansions are made, may occur naturally in the differential equations, or they may be introduced into the differential equations intentionally for purposes of expansion. This method has the advantage that the series which represent the solutions are convergent for any assigned interval of time provided the parameters are sufficiently small; that is, the question of convergence is thrown onto the parameters, and the interval of time is left free. The coefficients of the various powers of the parameter, or parameters, are functions of the time and these functions, in general, become very complicated as the powers of the parameters increase. But suppose the initial values of the variables can be chosen in such a way that at the expiration of the time P all of the dependent variables have returned to their initial values. It is evident then, if the time does not occur explicitly in the differential equations, or if it does occur explicitly it does so in a form that is periodic with the period P, that the motion is periodic with the period P; for, by virtue of the differential equations, not only have the variables returned to their initial values but all of their derivatives have done likewise. These series, when expressed in a periodic form are convergent, if the parameters are sufficiently small, for all values of the time in the interval $0 \leqq t \leqq P$, and are therefore convergent for all finite values of the time. The properties of the motion revealed for one cycle are thus made known for all values of the time; and it is this fact that gives to the method of periodic solutions the high position that it occupies in modern analysis.

It is the purpose of the present chapter to show how these series can be constructed; but before this is done it is necessary to establish the legitimacy of the processes that are used: in other words to lay a logical foundation for the construction of the series. This requires certain theorems in the domains of implicit function and of differential equations; in particular, there is given a complete theory of linear differential equations with constant coefficients that is due to W. Bartky, a method that depends upon the theory of matrices.

I. CERTAIN THEOREMS CONCERNING IMPLICIT FUNCTIONS

178. Solutions of Simultaneous Equations as Power Series in a Parameter.—Suppose there are given n analytic functions

$$F_i(\alpha_1, \cdots, \alpha_n; \mu) = 0,$$

which have the following properties:

(a) $\qquad F_i(0, 0, \cdots, 0; 0) = 0. \qquad i = 1, \cdots, n;$

(*b*) the functional determinant,

$$\left|\frac{\partial F_i}{\partial \alpha_j}\right|,$$

does not vanish at the origin, that is for

$$\alpha_1 = \alpha_2 = \cdots = \alpha_n = \mu = 0;$$

and finally,

(*c*) the partial derivatives $\partial F_i/\partial \mu$ are not all zero at the origin.

The functions F_i are expansible in the neighborhood of the origin in powers of $\alpha_1, \ldots, \alpha_n$, and μ. For compactness of notation the letter μ will be denoted by α_0. Then, on taking the terms that are linear in $\alpha_1, \ldots, \alpha_n$ to the left side of the equation, these expansions have the form

$$\sum_{j=1}^{n} f_j^{(i)}\alpha_j = f_0^{(i)}\alpha_0 + \sum_{j=0}^{n}\sum_{k=0}^{j} f_{jk}^{(i)}\alpha_j\alpha_k + \sum_{j=0}^{n}\sum_{k=0}^{j}\sum_{l=0}^{k} f_{jkl}^{(i)}\alpha_j\alpha_k\alpha_l + \cdots, \tag{1}$$

in which the letters f are constants, and $i = 1, \cdots, n$. By hypothesis, the determinant $|f_j^{(i)}|$, which is the functional determinant at the origin, is not zero; and, also, not every $f_0^{(i)}$ is zero.

By the method of undetermined coefficients, Eqs. (1) can be formally satisfied by taking

$$\alpha_j = \sum_{s=1}^{\infty} \beta_{js}\alpha_0^s, \qquad j = 0, 1, \cdots, n, \tag{2}$$

in which, of course, since $\alpha_0 = \alpha_0$,

$$\beta_{01} = 1, \qquad \text{and} \qquad \beta_{0s} = 0, \qquad s = 2, \cdots, \infty,$$

while the remaining β's are constants to be determined in such a way that Eqs. (1) are reduced to identities.

If Eqs. (2) are substituted in Eqs. (1), there results

$$\sum_{j=1}^{n}\sum_{s=1}^{\infty} f_j^{(i)}\beta_{js}\alpha_0^s = f_0^{(i)}\alpha_0 + \sum_{j=0}^{n}\sum_{k=0}^{j}\sum_{s=1}^{\infty}\sum_{t=1}^{\infty} f_{jk}^{(i)}\beta_{js}\beta_{kt}\alpha_0^{s+t} + \sum_{j=0}^{n}\sum_{k=0}^{j}\sum_{l=0}^{k}\sum_{s=1}^{\infty}\sum_{t=1}^{\infty}\sum_{u=1}^{\infty} f_{jkl}^{(i)}\beta_{js}\beta_{kt}\beta_{lu}\alpha_0^{s+t+u} + \cdots.$$

Since the left and right members of these equations must be identical, a comparison of the coefficients of the first, second, and third powers of α_0 give the following sets of equations, and it is evident that the process can be carried as far as is desired:

$$(1)\qquad \sum_{j=1}^{n} f_j^{(i)}\beta_{j1} = f_0^{(i)}, \qquad i = 1, \cdots, n,$$

$$(2)\qquad \sum_{j=1}^{n} f_j^{(i)}\beta_{j2} = \sum_{j=0}^{n}\sum_{k=0}^{j} f_{jk}^{(i)}\beta_{j1}\beta_{k1},$$

$$(3)\qquad \sum_{j=1}^{n} f_j^{(i)}\beta_{j3} = \sum_{j=0}^{n}\sum_{k=0}^{j} f_{jk}^{(i)}(\beta_{j2}\beta_{k1} + \beta_{j1}\beta_{k2}) + \sum_{j=0}^{n}\sum_{k=0}^{j}\sum_{l=0}^{k} f_{jkl}^{(i)}\beta_{j1}\beta_{k1}\beta_{l1}.$$

In set (1) the β_{j1} are the only unknowns; the equations are linear in these letters and the determinant is not zero. The equations have therefore a unique solution for the β_{j1}, and since, by hypothesis, not all of the $f_0^{(i)}$ are zero, not all of the β_{j1} are zero.

In the left members of the second set the letters β_{j2} enter just as the letters β_{j1} do in the first set, and therefore have the same determinant. The right members contain only known quantities, since the β_{j1} are all known. This set of equations therefore determine the letters β_{j2} uniquely.

In general, the mth set of equations determine the letters β_{jm}, for these letters are in the left members only. They enter linearly, and the determinant is $|f_j^{(i)}|$ which is independent of m. Since $\beta_{j1}, \beta_{j2}, \cdots, \beta_{j,m-1}$ enter in the right members and are all known, the right members can all be regarded as known. Thus the series, Eqs. (2), can be developed step by step, and the development can be carried as far as may be desired.

It is a simple matter to extend the solution to cover many parameters instead of only one, if the functional determinant is not zero.

179. Convergence of the Solutions.—For purely theoretic purposes the above equations can be simplified by making a linear change of variables. If the substitutions

$$\sum_{j=1}^{n} f_j^{(i)}\alpha_j = a_i, \qquad \alpha_0 = a_0, \tag{1}$$

be made, Eqs. (178.1) take the form

$$a_i = p_0^{(i)}a_0 + \sum_{j=0}^{n}\sum_{k=0}^{j} p_{jk}^{(i)}a_ja_k + \sum_{j=0}^{n}\sum_{k=0}^{j}\sum_{l=0}^{k} p_{jkl}a_ja_ka_l, + \cdots, \tag{2}$$

which by the substitution

$$a_j = \sum_{s=1}^{\infty} b_{js}a_0^s, \qquad j = 0, \cdots, n, \tag{3}$$

with

$$b_{01} = 1, \qquad \text{and} \qquad b_{0s} = 0, \qquad s = 2, \cdots, \infty,$$

becomes

$$\sum_{s=1}^{\infty} b_{is}a_0^s = p_0^{(i)} + \sum_{j=0}^{n}\sum_{k=0}^{j}\sum_{s=1}^{\infty}\sum_{t=1}^{\infty} p_{jk}^{(i)}b_{js}b_{kt}a_0^{s+t} + \cdots. \tag{4}$$

A comparison of the coefficients on the two sides of these equations gives the results

$$\left.\begin{aligned} b_{i1} &= p_0^{(i)}, \qquad\qquad i = 1, \cdots, n, \\ b_{i2} &= \sum_{j=0}^{n}\sum_{k=0}^{j} p_{jk}^{(i)}b_{j1}b_{j2}, \\ b_{i3} &= \sum_{j=0}^{n}\sum_{k=0}^{j} p_{jk}^{(i)}(b_{j2}b_{k1} + b_{k2}b_{j1}) + \sum_{j=0}^{n}\sum_{k=0}^{j}\sum_{l=0}^{k} p_{jkl}^{(i)}b_{j1}b_{k1}b_{l1}, \end{aligned}\right\} \tag{5}$$

and so on. These equations are already solved for the letters b_{is} and are therefore simpler for purposes of comparison.

It should be remarked that Eqs. (2) converge if Eqs. (178.1) converge, since the substitution from the α's to the a's is linear. Since the determinant $| f_j^{(i)} |$ is not zero, Eqs. (1) can be solved for the α's in terms of the a's. Let this solution be

$$\alpha_i = \sum_{j=1}^{n} g_j^{(i)}a_j.$$

Then, if the series

$$a_j = \sum_{s=1}^{\infty} b_{js}a_0^s \tag{6}$$

converges, the series

$$\alpha_i = \sum_{j=1}^{n}\sum_{s=1}^{\infty} g_j^{(i)}b_{js}\alpha_0^s \tag{7}$$

also will converge. It is necessary, therefore, to show that the series in Eqs. (6) converge.

If the series, Eqs. (2), converge for

$$|a_j| \leqq r, \qquad j = 0, \cdots, n,$$

where r is some positive number, it can be assumed without loss of generality that $r = 1$, for the substitution $a_j = h_j r$ would give a series convergent for $|h_j| \leqq 1$. It is assumed therefore that Eqs. (2) converge for $|a_j| \leqq 1$, and therefore there is a maximum value of the coefficients in these series. Let M be a positive number larger than this maximum value. Then the equations

$$x_i = Mx_0 + M\sum_{j=2}^{\infty}(x_0 + x_1 + \cdots + x_n)^j, \qquad i = 1, \cdots, n, \quad (8)$$

dominate Eqs. (2); that is, the coefficient of each term in the right members of Eqs. (8) is positive and numerically greater than the corresponding coefficient in Eqs. (2). They can be solved just as Eqs. (2) were solved; that is, by substituting

$$x_j = \sum_{s=1}^{\infty} c_{js} x_0^s \qquad (9)$$

and equating coefficients, there results a series of equations corresponding to Eqs. (5) that determine the coefficients c_{js} successively. It will be observed that in Eqs. (5) only positive signs occur. The terms in the right members of the c_{js} are all positive and dominate the corresponding terms in the b_{js} equations. Hence, for every s and every j,

$$c_{js} > |b_{js}|.$$

It follows therefore that if the series Eqs. (9) converge so also do Eqs. (3) converge. Equations (8), however, can be solved in another manner. Let

$$y = x_0 + x_1 + \cdots + x_n,$$

and let the sum of the n equations in (8) be taken. There results

$$\begin{aligned} y &= (Mn + 1)x_0 + Mn\sum_{j=2}^{\infty} y^j, \\ &= (Mn + 1)x_0 + Mn\frac{y^2}{1 - y}; \end{aligned}$$

whence, on setting $Mn + 1 = m$ and clearing of fractions,

$$my^2 - (1 + mx_0)y + mx_0 = 0.$$

The solution of this equation that vanishes with x_0 is

$$y = \frac{1 + mx_0}{2m}\left[1 - \sqrt{1 - \frac{4m^2x_0}{(1 + mx_0)^2}}\right],$$

which, evidently, is expansible in powers of x_0; and this expansion, for $m > 1$, is convergent if $|x_0| < 1/m$.

Since Eqs. (8) are all alike it is clear that

$$x_1 = x_2 = \cdots = x_n,$$

and if x is the common value of these quantities,

$$x = \frac{y - x_0}{n},$$

which also is expansible as a convergent power series in x_0, and therefore the series in Eqs. (8) are convergent. Since Eqs. (9) dominate Eqs. (3), it follows that Eqs. (3) also are convergent; and likewise Eqs. (7).

180. The Functional Determinant Vanishes, but Not All of Its First Minors.—If the functional determinant vanishes at the origin without the vanishing of all of its first minors, it is possible to solve $n - 1$ of Eqs. (178.1), say for $\alpha_2, \alpha_3, \ldots, \alpha_n$ as power series in α_0 and α_1, α_1 playing merely the rôle of another parameter. If the values of $\alpha_2, \ldots \alpha_n$, so obtained are substituted in the nth equation, the result, if it is not an identity, is an equation in α_1 and α_0, $f(\alpha_1, \alpha_0) = 0$, but the linear term in α_1 will be missing since its coefficient is the functional determinant, which is zero. Other terms of low degree in α_1 and α_0 also may be missing. This equation is solvable for α_1 in terms of α_0, but the power series expansion may be in fractional powers of α_0 instead of integral powers.

In the discussion of this equation in α_1 and α_0 the following theorem,[1] which is a variation of the Weierstrass theorem on the factorization of a power series, will be useful:

[1] MacMillan, *Bulletin of the American Mathematical Society*, Vol. 17, p. 116 (1910).

Theorem.—If $f(y; x_1, \ldots, x_p)$ is a convergent power series in $y; x_1, \ldots, x_p$ such that $f(y; 0, 0, \ldots, 0)$ begins with a term of degree n, there exists a convergent power series $\varphi(y; x_1, \ldots, x_p)$ with a constant term different from zero, such that the product

$$f \cdot \varphi = p^{(n)} = -y^n + a_1 y^{n-1} + a_2 y^{n-2} + \cdots + a_n$$

is a polynomial in y of degree n in which the coefficient of y^n is minus one and the coefficients of the remaining powers of y, $a_1, \ldots, a_n$, are convergent power series in $x_1, \ldots, x_p$ that vanish for $x_1 = x_2 = \cdots = x_p = 0$.

For the purpose of determining the coefficients of the series, it will simplify the notation to put $x_i = \xi_i x$ and then arrange in powers of x. The series f, φ, and $p^{(n)}$ can be written

$$\begin{aligned} f &= -y^n(1 - b_0) + b_1 x + b_2 x^2 + \cdots, \\ \varphi &= c_0 + c_1 x + c_2 x^2 + \cdots, \\ p^{(n)} &= -y^n + p_1 x + p_2 x^2 + \cdots, \end{aligned}$$

where the coefficients b_k are known power series in y and are homogeneous of degree k in the ξ_i, b_0 being a power series in y alone that vanishes for y equal to zero. The coefficients c_k are power series in y whose coefficients are to be determined, and the p_k are polynomials in y, also to be determined, of degree $n - 1$.

By taking the product of f and φ it is found that

$$\begin{aligned} f \cdot \varphi = -c_0(1 - b_0)y^n &+ [-(1 - b_0)c_1 y^n + b_1 c_0]x - \\ &+ [-(1 - b_0)c_2 y^n + b_1 c_1 + b_2 c_0]x^2 \\ &+ \cdots\cdots\cdots\cdots \\ &+ \left[-(1 - b_0)c_k y^n + \sum_{j=1}^{k} b_j c_{k-j}\right]x^k \\ &+ \cdots\cdots\cdots\cdots, \end{aligned}$$

and this is equal to

$$-y^n + p_1 x + p_2 x^2 + \cdots + p_k x^k + \cdots.$$

A comparison of the coefficients of the various powers of x in these two expressions gives the equations

$$\begin{aligned} (1 - b_0)c_0 y^n &= y^n, \\ (1 - b_0)c_1 y^n &= b_1 c_0 - p_1, \\ (1 - b_0)c_2 y^n &= b_1 c_1 + b_2 c_0 - p_2, \\ &\cdots\cdots\cdots\cdots \end{aligned}$$

$$(1 - b_0)c_k y^n = \sum_{j=1}^{k} b_j c_{k-j} - p_k,$$

. . . .

These equations can be solved successively for the p's and c's. From the first follows at once

$$c_0 = \frac{1}{1 - b_0}.$$

Since c_0 and b_1 are known power series in y, it is seen from the second equation that p_1 can be chosen uniquely in such a way that $b_1 c_0 - p_1 = \beta_1 y^n$ is divisible by y^n. The solution for c_1 is then

$$c_1 = \frac{\beta_1}{1 - b_0}.$$

Similarly p_2 can be chosen uniquely so that

$$b_1 c_1 + b_2 c_0 - p_2 = \beta_2 y^n$$

is divisible by y^n, and then

$$c_2 = \frac{\beta_2}{1 - c_0},$$

and so on to as high a degree in x as may be desired. The proof of convergence is by dominant series, but it will be omitted here. The reader will find it in the article above cited.

Since

$$f \cdot \varphi = p^{(n)} = 0,$$

and φ does not vanish in the neighborhood of the origin, since it has a constant term, the roots of $p^{(n)}$ are identical with the roots of f in the neighborhood of the origin. By the fundamental theorem of algebra, the equation $p^{(n)} = 0$ has n roots, all of which vanish with x. The same is true, therefore, of the equation $f = 0$.

181. The Determination of the Series for Two Variables.— For the actual determination of the series for α_1, in integral or fractional powers of μ, that satisfy the equation

$$f(\alpha_1, \mu) = 0, \tag{1}$$

it is not necessary to form the corresponding algebraic equation. The introduction of the Weierstrass theorem was merely for the purpose of establishing the number of solutions. Since the linear term in α_1 alone is not present, there are at least two solutions; if the terms in α_1^2 alone also are missing, there are at least three solutions; and so on. The vanishing of the functional determinant therefore indicates the existence of multiple solutions.

In order to find the expansions for these solutions, Newton's parallelogram[1] will be found most useful. In this scheme the terms that occur in the power series expansion of Eq. (1) are plotted as points in a coordinate system. For example, if the term $a_{ij}\alpha_1^j\mu^i$ occurs, that is the coefficient a_{ij} is not zero, it is plotted as the point (i, j). The value of a_{ij}, provided it is not zero, is quite immaterial. If m is the smallest value of i for which j is zero, and n is the smallest value of j for which i is zero, draw a dotted straight line through the points $(0, n)$ and $(m, 0)$, and plot all of the terms of Eq. (1) that are below, or to the left of, this line. Since its equation is

$$my + nx = mn,$$

for all points (i, j) above or to the right $mj + ni > mn$, and these points play no rôle. The terms for which $mj + ni \leqq mn$ are the important ones, and these all lie in the first quadrant below and to the left of the dotted line. Imagine these plotted points to be pins or pegs in the plane and a string tied to the pin $(0, n)$. Let the string initially coincide with the j-axis. Then let it be moved to the right under a slight tension until it touches the point $(0, m)$. In the final position either it coincides with the dotted line or it forms a broken line by contact with other pins. *It is the segments of this broken line and the points that lie on it that are essential.*

Suppose, for example, with coefficients omitted,

$$f(\alpha_1, \mu) = \alpha_1^5 + \mu\alpha_1^4 + (\mu + \mu^2)\alpha_1^3 + (\mu^2 + \mu^3)\alpha_1^2 + (\mu^3 + \mu^4)\alpha_1 + \mu^6 + H,$$

where H includes all of the terms that lie above the dotted line. The algebraic theory shows that there are five solutions for α_1 that vanish with μ, and the Newton parallelogram (Fig. 80)

[1] Chrystal's "Algebra," Vol. 2, p. 362.

shows three segments of the broken line, on each of which there are at least two points, and on the middle one three points.

With each segment there is associated a group of solutions, in number equal to the difference in the ordinates of the end points of the segment. In the above example there are two solutions associated with the upper segment, two with the middle, and one with the lower—five altogether.

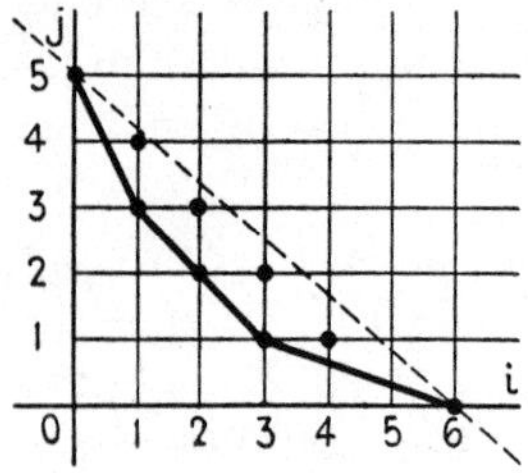

FIG. 80.

If m_k, n_k are the coordinates of the upper end point of any segment, and m_l, n_l are the coordinates of the lower end point of the same segment, the equation of the line in which the segment lies is

$$(m_l - m_k)y + (n_k - n_l)x = m_l n_k - n_l m_k,$$

in which x and y are the running coordinates of the line. Except the points that lie on the segment, all of the points that belong to $f(\alpha_1, \mu)$ lie above and to the right of this line. Therefore, if i and j are the exponents of any term $\alpha_1{}^j\mu^i$ of f, it is true that

$$(m_l - m_k)j + (n_k - n_l)i \geqq m_l n_k - n_l m_k,$$

or, if,

$$\sigma = \frac{n_k - n_l}{m_l - m_k};$$

$$j + \sigma i \geqq \frac{m_l n_k - n_l m_k}{m_l - m_k} = m;$$

where σ, evidently, is the tangent of the acute angle which the segment makes with the j-axis, and m is a perfectly definite number.

Now let the variable α_1 be replaced by α by the substitution

$$\alpha_1 = \alpha\mu^\sigma. \tag{2}$$

The equation

$$f(\alpha_1, \mu) = \sum^{\infty}\sum^{\infty} a_{ij}\alpha_1{}^j\mu^i = 0$$

becomes

$$\sum^{\infty}\sum^{\infty} a_{ij}\alpha^j\mu^{j+\sigma i} = 0;$$

and since for every i and j

$$j + \sigma i \geqq m,$$

a factor μ^m can be divided out, leaving

$$\sum^{\infty}\sum^{\infty} a_{ij}\alpha^i\mu^{j+\sigma i-m} = 0.$$

In this expression the exponents of μ are integral multiples of $1/(m_l - m_k)$; hence, if the substitution

$$\nu = \mu^{\frac{1}{m_l - m_k}} \tag{3}$$

is made, the above equation becomes

$$\varphi(\alpha, \nu) = \sum^{\infty}\sum^{\infty} a_{kj}\alpha^i\nu^k = 0, \tag{4}$$

in which only integral powers of ν occur. For $\nu = 0$ the series $\varphi(\alpha, \nu)$ reduces to the terms whose plotted points lie on the segment under discussion, namely

$$a_{m_kn_k}\alpha^{n_k} + \cdot \cdot \cdot + a_{m_ln_l}\alpha^{n_l} = 0, \tag{5}$$

or

$$a_{m_kn_k}\alpha^{n_l}(\alpha - r_1)(\alpha - r_2) \cdot \cdot \cdot (\alpha - r_{n_k - n_l}) = 0,$$

where the r's are the $n_k - n_l$ roots of Eq. (5) that are distinct from zero; the n_l zero roots are without interest here. Let r_k be any one of these roots, and let the substitution

$$\alpha = \beta + r_k \tag{6}$$

be made. Equation (5) then becomes a polynomial in β in which the linear term in β is present, if r_k is a simple root. Assuming that this is the case, the series $\varphi(\alpha, \nu)$ [Eq. (4)] becomes a series $\psi(\beta, \nu)$ which contains only integral powers of β and ν and in which the linear term in β is present. It can therefore be solved in a unique manner for β in powers of ν, and, going back through the substitutions, Eqs. (6), (3), and (2), α_1 is expressed finally as a power series in fractional powers of μ that vanishes with μ.

There is one such expansion for each non-vanishing, simple root of Eq. (5), or $n_k - n_l$ altogether. If r_k is a multiple root of Eq. (5), the power series $\psi(\beta, \nu)$ will not contain a linear term in β, and the entire process must be repeated for $\psi(\beta, \nu)$ just as for the original series $f(\alpha_1, \mu)$. Since there are $n_k - n_l$ expansions for each segment and $n_k - n_l$ is the difference in the ordinates of the end points of the segments, it is evident that there are

$$\Sigma(n_k - n_l) = n$$

expansions altogether, as there should be.

182. All of the First Minors Vanish.—The cases in which the functional determinant does not vanish, or, if it does, not all of its first minors vanish, are particular cases of a general situation in which n functions $x_1, \ldots, x_n$ are defined by means of n equations in $x_1, \ldots x_n$, and k parameters $\mu_1, \ldots, \mu_k$. A separate treatment of these two cases is justified by their simplicity and by their frequent occurrence. If all of the first minors vanish, it is best to proceed at once to the general case. The method of treatment rests upon a generalization of the theorem in Sec. 180.[1]

Suppose

$$F_i(x_1, \cdots, x_n; \mu) = 0, \qquad i = 1, \cdots, n,$$

are n analytic functions in $x_1, \ldots, x_n$, and μ which vanish with these variables. The function F_i is said to be of order d_i if, for $\mu = 0$ in the power series expansion of $F_i(x_1, \ldots, x_n; \mu)$ in the neighborhood of the origin, the homogeneous polynomial f_i which is composed of the aggregate of terms of lowest degree that actually occur in $F_i(x_1, \ldots, x_n; 0)$ is of degree d_i in $x_1, \ldots, x_n$; and f_i is called the *characteristic polynomial* of F_i. An *eliminating determinant* is a determinant that arises in the process of forming the eliminant of the f_i by Caley's method.[2] Let d be a positive integer defined as follows:

$$d = \Sigma d_i - n.$$

The theorem that is of interest here is the following:

Theorem.—If

$$F_i(x_1, \cdots, x_n; \mu) \qquad i = 1, \cdots, n$$

[1] MacMillan, "A Reduction of a System of Power Series to an Equivalent System of Polynomials," *Mathematische Annalen*, Vol. 72, p. 157 (1912).

[2] Caley, *Cambridge and Dublin Mathematical Journal*, Vol. 3, p. 116 (1848). See also Salmon, "Modern Higher Algebra," p. 87.

is a system of power series in $x_1, \ldots, x_n$ and μ, vanishing with these variables, of order d_i, and characteristic polynomials f_i which have an eliminating determinant different from zero, then multipliers

$$\Phi_{ij}(x_1, \cdots, x_n; \mu), \qquad i, j = 1, \cdots, n,$$

that vanish with $x_1, \ldots, x_n$, and μ, and polynomials

$$P_i(x_1, \ldots, x_n; \mu),$$

of degree d and order d_i, exist such that

$$\begin{aligned}
(1 + \Phi_{11})F_1 + \quad \Phi_{12}F_2 + \cdots + \quad \Phi_{1n}F_n &= P_1,\\
\Phi_{21}F_1 + (1 + \Phi_{22})F_2 + \cdots + \quad \Phi_{2n}F_n &= P_2,\\
\cdots\cdots\cdots\cdots\cdots\cdots\cdots\cdots\cdots\cdots\cdots\cdots &\\
\Phi_{n1}F_1 + \quad \Phi_{n2}F_2 + \cdots + (1 + \Phi_{nn})F_n &= P_n.
\end{aligned}$$

Since the determinant of the coefficients of the F's of the left member does not vanish in the neighborhood of the origin, it follows that the system of equations

$$P_1 = P_2 = \cdots = P_n = 0,$$

is equivalent to the system of equations

$$F_1 = F_2 = \cdots = F_n = 0,$$

in the sense that they define $x_1, \ldots, x_n$ as the same functions of the parameter μ in the neighborhood of the origin, and the number of the solutions that vanish with μ is Πd_i.

Just as in the case of the single equation in two variables, the above theorem gives the number of solutions in any particular case. It is not necessary to form the polynomials P_i. In order to obtain the expansions of the x_i in powers of μ, or fractional powers as the case may be, the procedure is similar to that of the single equation, namely, by the use of Newton parallelograms,[1] but the proof is too long to be given here. The reader is referred to the papers cited.

II. THE SOLUTIONS OF DIFFERENTIAL EQUATIONS AS POWER SERIES IN A PARAMETER

183. Formal Solutions of Differential Equations of Type I.— The set of differential equations

$$x_i' = \mu f_i(x_1, \cdots, x_n; \mu; t), \qquad i = 1, \cdots, n, \tag{1}$$

[1] MacMillan, "A Method of Determining the Solutions of a System of Analytic Functions in the Neighborhood of a Branch Point," *Mathematische Annalen*, Vol. 72, p. 180 (1912).

are said to be of type I when the right members carry the parameter μ as a factor and the f_i are analytic in $x_1, \ldots, x_n, \mu$ and t and are regular at the point $x_i = a_i$, $\mu = 0$, for all values of the time that lie in the interval $0 \leqq t \leqq T$. Under these conditions the functions f_i are expansible in powers of $(x_i - a_i)$ and μ, and these power series are convergent for all values of t that lie in the interval specified provided

$$|x_i - a_i| \leqq r_i \quad \text{and} \quad |\mu| < \rho,$$

where r_i and ρ are certain positive numbers, not zero.

The differential equations of mechanics are usually of the second order, but, as has been seen in the chapter on Hamilton's equations, they can always be reduced to a set each of which is of the first order.

In order to show that Eqs. (1) can be solved formally as a power series in the parameter, let the dependent variables x_i be changed to ξ_i by the substitution

$$x_i - a_i = \xi_i,$$

and, for compactness of notation let $\mu = \xi_0$. After expansion of the right members of Eqs. (1) in powers of ξ_j and μ, but not in powers of t, Eqs. (1) become

$$\xi_i' = \xi_0 \left[\varphi_{i0} + \sum_{j=0}^{n} \varphi_{ij}\xi_j + \sum_{j=0}^{n} \sum_{k=0}^{j} \varphi_{ijk}\xi_j\xi_k + \cdots \right], \tag{2}$$

where the coefficients φ are functions of the time, or, if the time does not occur explicitly, are constants.

Under the assumption that the ξ_i can be expanded as a power series in ξ_0, the time, of course, occurring in the coefficients, let

$$\xi_i = \sum_{r=1}^{\infty} \xi_{ir}\xi_0{}^r, \tag{3}$$

with the understanding that $\xi_{01} = 1$, and $\xi_{0r} = 0$ if $r > 1$, since necessarily, $\xi_0 = \xi_0$. Let Eqs. (3) be substituted in Eqs. (2) and the series then arranged according to powers of ξ_0, namely

$$\sum_{r=1}^{\infty} \xi_{ir}'\xi_0{}^r = \varphi_{i0}\xi_0 + \sum_{r=1}^{\infty} \sum_{j=0}^{n} \varphi_{ij}\xi_{jr}\xi_0{}^{r+1}$$
$$+ \sum_{r=1}^{\infty} \sum_{s=1}^{\infty} \sum_{j=0}^{n} \sum_{k=0} \varphi_{ijk}\xi_{jr}\xi_{ks}\xi_0{}^{r+s+1} + \cdots. \tag{4}$$

Since this equation is an identity in ξ_0, the coefficients of the same power of ξ_0 in the left and right members are equal. Hence sequentially,

$$\left.\begin{aligned}
\xi_{i1}' &= \varphi_{i0}, \qquad i = 1, \cdots, n. \\
\xi_{i2}' &= \sum_{j=0}^{n} \varphi_{ij}\xi_{j1}, \\
\xi_{i3}' &= \sum_{j=0}^{n} \varphi_{ij}\xi_{j2} + \sum_{j=0}^{n} \sum_{k=0}^{j} \varphi_{ijk}\xi_{j1}\xi_{k1}, \\
&\cdots\cdots\cdots\cdots\cdots\cdots\cdots\cdots\cdots\cdot
\end{aligned}\right\} \tag{5}$$

If, whatever μ may be, the initial values of the x_i are the a_i, it is necessary that the initial values of the ξ_i be zero, and since this is true whatever μ may be, it is necessary that every ξ_{ir}, $r = 1, \cdots, \infty$, $i = 1, \cdots, n$, should vanish. The constants of integration of Eqs. (5), therefore, must be chosen so as to satisfy this condition. Since the φ_{i0} are known functions of the time, the coefficients ξ_{i1} are determined by a quadrature; and if

$$\Phi_{i1}(t) = \int_0^t \varphi_{i0}(t)\,dt,$$

then

$$\xi_{i1} = \Phi_{i1}(t).$$

With the ξ_{i1} as known functions of t, the right members of the second set are known functions of the time. Hence, if

$$\Phi_{i2} = \int_0^t \sum_{j=0}^{n} \varphi_{ij}\Phi_{j1}\,dt, \qquad i = 1, \cdots, n,$$

it is evident that

$$\xi_{i2} = \Phi_{i2}(t);$$

and so on, as far as may be desired. Hence, formally, the differential equations [Eqs. (1)] can be satisfied by solutions of the form

$$x_i = a_i + \sum_{r=1}^{\infty} \Phi_{ir}(t)\mu^r, \tag{6}$$

which, if convergent, reduce at $t = 0$ to

$$x_i(0) = a_i,$$

as was desired, and it will be observed that the process everywhere is unique.

184. The Solutions Are Convergent for μ Sufficiently Small.—It is no essential restriction upon the differential equations to assume that the right members of Eqs. (183.2) are convergent for

$$|\xi_j| = 1, \qquad j = 0, \cdots, n,$$

provided t lies in the interval $0 \leqq t \leqq T$; for, if it were not so, the substitutions

$$\xi_j = r_j\eta_j, \qquad \nu = \rho\mu,$$

would result in equations of the same type in which assumption was true. As it simplifies the notation, this assumption will be made. It follows that for all values of t in the interval specified the coefficients in the right members of Eqs. (183.2) are bounded, say each one is less than a certain positive number M. Consider the comparison set of equations

$$\eta_i' = \frac{M\mu}{(1-\mu)\left(1 - \sum_{i=1}^{n} \eta_i\right)}, \qquad i = 1, \cdots, n. \tag{1}$$

The right members of these equations also can be expanded in powers of the η_i and μ. Furthermore in these expansions every coefficient is positive and numerically greater than the corresponding coefficient of Eqs. (183.2).

Equations (1) can be solved by the method of Sec. 184, and since the right members of the equations which correspond to Eqs. (184.5) are greater than are those of Eqs. (184.5), it follows that if the solutions of Eqs. (1) converge so also will the solutions of Eqs. (184.2) converge. Equations (1) can be integrated otherwise, however. The right members of Eqs. (1) are all alike, and the initial values of the η_i are all zero, and therefore all alike. Consequently

$$\eta_1 = \eta_2 = \cdots = \eta_n$$

for all values of the time. If their common value is denoted by the letter η, it is seen that, from Eqs. (1),

$$\eta' = \frac{M\mu}{(1-\mu)(1-n\eta)} \tag{2}$$

or

$$(1 - n\eta)\eta' = M\frac{\mu}{1-\mu}.$$

After integration and determination of the constant of integration so that η vanishes with t, it is found that

$$\eta - \frac{n}{2}\eta^2 = \frac{M\mu t}{1-\mu}, \tag{3}$$

which, solved for η, gives

$$\eta = \frac{1}{n}\left[1 - \sqrt{1 - \frac{2Mn\mu t}{1-\mu}}\right], \tag{4}$$

the minus sign being taken before the radical since η vanishes with t, and also with μ.

Equation (4) is expansible in powers of μ, and this expansion is convergent for all values of the time in the interval $0 \leqq t \leqq T$ provided

$$\left|\frac{2Mn\mu t}{1-\mu}\right| < 1,$$

that is, provided

$$|\mu| < \frac{1}{1 + 2MnT} = \mu_0.$$

Since the solution of Eqs. (2) by the method of Sec. 183 is unique, the solution so obtained is the same as the expansion of Eq. (4); it is convergent, provided $|\mu| < \mu_0$. The same is true therefore of the solutions of Eqs. (183.2), and the series Eqs. (183.6) are therefore convergent, provided $|\mu|$ is sufficiently small.

185. Formal Solution of Differential Equations of Type II.— Suppose the differential equations have the form

$$x_i' = g_i(x_1, \cdots, x_n; t) + \mu f_i(x_1, \cdots, x_n; \mu; t) \qquad i = 1, \cdots, n, \tag{1}$$

in which the functions g_i are not identically zero; if the g_i were all identically zero, the equations would reduce to type I. Suppose further that $x_i = x_{i0}(t)$ is a known solution of the differential equations for $\mu = 0$; that is, the functions $x_{i0}(t)$ satisfy the differential equations

$$x_{i0}' = g_i(x_{10}, \cdots x_{n0}; t) \qquad i = 1, \cdots, n,$$

and, for $t = 0$, reduce to $x_{i0}(0) = a_i$.

In what follows, it will be assumed that the functions g_i are expansible in powers of $x_i - x_{i0}$, and that the f_i are expansible in powers of $x_i - x_{i0}$ and μ, and it is desired to find solutions of Eqs. (1) that are expansible in powers of μ and that reduce for $t = 0$ to the same initial values $x_i = a_i$.

For this purpose, let

$$x_i - x_{i0} = \xi_i, \qquad i = 1, \cdots, n,$$

and for compactness of notation let $\mu = \xi_0$; the functions g_i and f_i are then, by hypothesis, expansible in powers of the ξ_j, and the differential equations (1) become

$$\left.\begin{aligned} \xi_i' = \sum_{j=1}^{n} g_{ij}\xi_j + \sum_{j=1}^{n}\sum_{k=1}^{j} g_{ijk}\xi_j\xi_k + \cdots \\ + \xi_0 f_{i0} + \xi_0 \sum_{j=0}^{n} f_{ij}\xi_j + \xi_0 \sum_{j=0}^{n}\sum_{k=0}^{j} f_{ijk}\xi_j\xi_k + \cdots, \end{aligned}\right\} \tag{2}$$

in which the coefficients $g_{i\ldots}$ and $f_{i\ldots}$ are, in general, functions of t.

In order to show formally that solutions in powers of $\mu = \xi_0$ can be derived, let

$$\xi_i = \sum_{r=1}^{\infty} \xi_{ir}\xi_0^r, \qquad i = 0, \cdots, n,$$

with

$$\xi_{01} = 1 \qquad \text{and} \qquad \xi_{0r} = 0, \qquad r > 1, \qquad \text{as before.}$$

If these expressions are substituted in Eqs. (2), it is found that

$$\begin{aligned} \sum_{r=1}^{\infty}\left(\xi_{ir}' - \sum_{j=1}^{n} g_{ij}\xi_{jr}\right)\xi_0^r = \xi_0 f_{i0} + \sum_{r=1}^{\infty}\sum_{j=0}^{n} f_{ij}\xi_{jr}\xi_0^{r+1} \\ + \sum_{r=1}^{\infty}\sum_{s=1}^{\infty}\sum_{j=1}^{n}\sum_{k=1}^{j} (g_{ijk} + \xi_0 f_{ijk})\xi_{jr}\xi_{ks}\xi_0^{r+s} + \cdots. \end{aligned} \tag{3}$$

A comparison of the coefficients of the first power of ξ_0 in the left and right members of these equations, then the second power, the third, and so on gives the following sets of equations:

$$\left.\begin{aligned}
&\xi_{i1}' - \sum_{j=1}^{n} g_{ij}\xi_{j1} = f_{i0}, \qquad i = 1, \cdots, n. \\
&\xi_{i2}' - \sum_{j=1}^{n} g_{ij}\xi_{j2} = \sum_{j=0}^{n} f_{ij}\xi_{j1} + \sum_{j=1}^{n}\sum_{k=1}^{j} g_{ijk}\xi_{j1}\xi_{k1}, \\
&\cdots\cdots\cdots\cdots\cdots\cdots\cdots\cdots\cdots\cdots \\
&\xi_{ir}' - \sum_{j=1}^{n} g_{ij}\xi_{jr} = \Phi_{ir}(\xi_{k1}, \cdots, \xi_{k,r-1}; t), \\
&\cdots\cdots\cdots\cdots\cdots\cdots\cdots\cdots\cdots\cdots .
\end{aligned}\right\} \tag{4}$$

These equations exhibit the following properties:

(*a*) The left members are linear and homogeneous in the ξ_{jr} and their derivatives.

(*b*) The coefficients of the left members are the same from one set to another, that is, they are independent of the subscript r.

(*c*) The right members contain only the letters ξ_{js} for which s is less than the corresponding subscript r of the left members.

The differential equations to be solved at each step are linear and non-homogeneous, and the difference in these equations from one set to another is in the right members only. If the equations are solved step by step, in every case the right members are known functions of t; the left members are the same at every step and, of course, are known. The form of the general solution of the linear, non-homogeneous differential equations

$$\xi_i' - \sum_{j=1}^{n} g_{ij}\xi_j = \Phi_i(t)$$

is

$$\xi_i = \sum_{j=1}^{n} A_j\varphi_{ij}(t) + F_i(t),$$

in which the A_j are constants of integration, the $\varphi_{ij}(t)$ are functions of t whose determinant $|\varphi_{ij}|$ is not zero, and the $F_i(t)$ are functions that depend upon the Φ_i.

In the solutions of Eqs. (4) it is necessary to choose the constants of integration in such a way that every $\xi_{ir} = 0$ at $t = 0$. Since the determinant $|\varphi_{ij}(0)|$ does not vanish, this condition can be satisfied, and then every ξ_{ir} becomes a definite function of the time,

$$\xi_{ir} = \psi_{ir}(t).$$

It follows, therefore, that the series

$$x_i = x_{i0} + \sum_{r=1}^{\infty} \psi_{ir}\mu^r \tag{5}$$

formally satisfies Eqs. (1).

186. The Formal Solution is Convergent.—Before proceeding to the proof that the series Eq. (185.5) is convergent for values of μ sufficiently small, it is desirable to prove the following lemma:

Lemma.—If

$$\xi_i' = \sum g_{ij}(t)\xi_j + h_i(t) \qquad i = 1, \cdots, n$$

is a set of linear differential equations for which the functions $g_{ij}(t)$ *and* $h_i(t)$ *have no singularities in the interval* $0 \leqq t \leqq T$, *the solution that vanishes with* t, *i.e.*, $\xi_1 = \xi_2 = \cdots = \xi_n = 0$ *for* $t = 0$, *is dominated by the solution that vanishes with* t *of the differential equations*

$$\eta_i' = M\sum \eta_i + M, \qquad i = 1, \cdots, n,$$

where M *is a positive number greater than* $|g_{ij}|$ *and* $|h_i|$ *for every* t *in the interval* $0 \leqq t \leqq T$.

By Picard's method of successive approximations[1] a series of sets of functions $\xi_i^{(0)}, \xi_i^{(1)}, \ldots \xi_i^{(k)}, \ldots$ and $\eta_i^{(0)}, \eta_i^{(1)}, \ldots, \eta_i^{(k)}, \ldots$ are defined as follows:

$$\xi_i^{(0)} = \int_0^t f_{i0}\,dt,$$

$$\eta_i^{(0)} = \int_0^t M\,dt,$$

$$\xi_i^{(1)} = \int_0^t \sum_{j=1}^{n} g_{ij}\xi_j^{(0)} + \int_0^t f_{i0}\,dt,$$

$$\eta_i^{(1)} = \int_0^t \sum_{j=1}^{n} M\eta_j^{(0)} + \int_0^t M\,dt,$$

. . . .

$$\xi_i^{(k)} = \int_0^t \sum g_{ij}\xi_j^{(k-1)} + \int_0^t f_{i0}\,dt,$$

$$\eta_i^{(k)} = \int_0^t \sum M\eta_j^{(k-1)} + \int_0^t M\,dt,$$

. . . .

[1] PICARD'S, "Traité d'Analyse," Vol. 2, p. 340 (1905).

It is readily seen from these series that for every t in the assigned interval

$$\eta_i^{(0)} > |\xi_i^{(0)}|;$$

and then from the second set that

$$\eta_i^{(1)} > |\xi_i^{(1)}|;$$

and, in general, that

$$\eta_i^{(k)} > |\xi_i^{(k)}|.$$

By Picard's theorem $\lim_{k=\infty} \xi_i^{(k)} = \xi_i$ and $\lim_{k=\infty} \eta_i^{(k)} = \eta_i$ for a sufficiently restricted range of t, which in the present case is the original interval $0 \leqq t \leqq T$, since the equations are linear. It follows therefore that

$$\eta_i > |\xi_i|$$

throughout the same interval, which proves the lemma. One of the hypotheses with regard to Eqs. (185.1) is that the power series expansions, Eqs. (185.2), are convergent for the interval $0 \leqq t \leqq T$ provided $|\xi_j| < r_j$, $j = 0, \cdots, n$, where r_j is some fixed positive number. Just as before, it is no essential restriction to assume that $r_j = 1$ for every j, since the substitution $\xi_j = r_j x_j$ would result in series of the same type that are convergent for $|x_j| = 1$. Hence it is assumed that this is true for the series in Eqs. (2), and that $r_j = 1$. Since the series, Eqs. (185.2), are convergent for $|\xi_j| = 1$, it follows that for $0 \leqq t \leqq T$ there is a maximum value of the coefficients. Let M be a positive number that exceeds this maximum value, and let the comparison equations be

$$\eta_i' = M\frac{(\eta_0 + \eta_1 + \cdots + \eta_n)}{1 - (\eta_0 + \eta_1 + \cdots + \eta_n)}, \qquad \text{where} \qquad \eta_0 = \mu. \qquad (1)$$

If the right member of this equation is expanded, it will be a power series in the η_j that will dominate Eq. (185.2). It can be solved in the same manner, that is, by taking

$$\eta_i = \sum_{r=1}^{\infty} \eta_{ir}\eta_0^r,$$

there will result a series of sets of differential equations similar to Eqs. (185.4) but which dominate them. If the η_i vanish at $t = 0$, every η_{ir} also vanishes. It follows from the lemma, therefore, that the solutions η_{ir} dominate the corresponding solutions ξ_{ir}, and therefore the series

$$\eta_i = \sum_{r=1}^{\infty} \eta_{ir}\eta_0^r \tag{2}$$

dominates the series

$$\xi_i = \sum_{r=1}^{\infty} \xi_{ir}\xi_0^r. \tag{3}$$

Hence if the first series converges, the second also will converge.

It will be observed that the differential Equations, Eqs. (1), for the η_i are all alike, and, since they have the same initial value, that

$$\eta_1 = \eta_2 = \cdot \cdot \cdot = \eta_n$$

for all values of t. Let

$$\zeta = \eta_1 + \eta_2 + \cdot \cdot \cdot + \eta_n, \qquad \text{and} \qquad nM = N.$$

The sum of the Eqs. (1) is then the single equation

$$\zeta' = N\frac{\zeta + \mu}{1 - (\zeta + \mu)},$$

and the solution that vanishes with t is

$$\log\left(1 + \frac{\zeta}{\mu}\right) - \zeta = Nt,$$

or

$$\zeta = \mu(e^{\zeta}e^{Nt} - 1).$$

Expanded in powers of ζ this expression becomes

$$\zeta = \frac{(l^{Nt} - 1)}{1 - \mu e^{Nt}}\mu + \frac{\mu e^{Nt}}{1 - \mu e^{Nt}}\left(\frac{1}{2!}\zeta^2 + \frac{1}{3!}\xi^3 + \cdot \cdot \cdot\right),$$

which, expanded in powers of μ, is convergent for all values of ζ and for $|\mu| < e^{-Nt}$. By the principles of Sec. 178, this equation admits a unique solution for ζ as a power series in μ that converges for every t in the interval $0 \leqq t \leqq T$, provided $|\mu|$ is sufficiently small. Finally, since

$$\eta_1 = \eta_2 = \cdots = \eta_n = \frac{\zeta}{n},$$

a unique solution for η_i as a power series in μ that converges for $|\mu|$ sufficiently small has been derived. By virtue of the uniqueness, this solution is the same as that in Eq. (2), which dominates Eqs. (3). It follows that Eqs. (3) converge and therefore Eqs. (185.5) also.

III. THEOREMS ON MATRICES AND LINEAR DIFFERENTIAL EQUATIONS

187. Definitions and the Algebra of Square Matrices.—A matrix is a rectangular array, or table, of numbers. It is called an $m \times n$ matrix if the array has m rows and n columns, and a square matrix if m and n are equal; thus

$$\begin{Vmatrix} \kappa_{11} & \kappa_{12} & \cdots & \kappa_{1n} \\ \kappa_{21} & \kappa_{22} & \cdots & \kappa_{2n} \\ \cdot & \cdot & \cdots & \cdot \\ \kappa_{n1} & \kappa_{n2} & \cdots & \kappa_{nn} \end{Vmatrix}$$

is a square matrix, since it has n rows and n columns. If n is equal to one, the matrix reduces to a single number. The notation

$$\| \kappa_{ij} \| \qquad i, j = 1, \cdots, n,$$

can be used to denote a matrix, or, even more briefly, the single Greek letter, κ.

If

$$\kappa^{(1)} = \| \kappa_{ij}^{(1)} \|, \qquad \kappa^{(2)} = \| \kappa_{ij}^{(2)} \|, \qquad i, j = 1, \cdots, n \tag{1}$$

are two square matrices, they are equal, if and only if,

$$\kappa_{ij}^{(1)} = \kappa_{ij}^{(2)} \tag{2}$$

for every i and j. Their sum is the matrix in which each element is the sum of the corresponding elements in $\kappa^{(1)}$ and $\kappa^{(2)}$, so that

$$\kappa^{(1)} + \kappa^{(2)} = \| (\kappa_{ij}^{(1)} + \kappa_{ij}^{(2)}) \| = \| (\kappa_{ij}^{(2)} + \kappa_{ij}^{(1)}) \| = \kappa^{(2)} + \kappa^{(1)}. \tag{3}$$

For example,

$$\begin{Vmatrix} 1 & 2 \\ 3 & 4 \end{Vmatrix} + \begin{Vmatrix} 5 & 6 \\ 7 & 8 \end{Vmatrix} = \begin{Vmatrix} 6 & 8 \\ 10 & 12 \end{Vmatrix}.$$

The product of a scalar and a matrix is a matrix in which each element is the product of the corresponding element of the given matrix by the given scalar. Thus if s is a scalar and κ is a matrix,

$$s\kappa = s \| \kappa_{ij} \| = \| (s\kappa_{ij}) \|. \tag{4}$$

Hence

$$\kappa - \kappa = \kappa + (-1)\kappa = \begin{Vmatrix} 0 & 0 & \cdots & 0 \\ 0 & 0 & \cdots & 0 \\ \cdot & \cdot & \cdots & \cdot \\ 0 & 0 & & 0 \end{Vmatrix} = \| 0 \|,$$

in which each element is zero, is called the $n \times n$ zero matrix.

The product of two matrices $\kappa^{(1)}$ and $\kappa^{(2)}$ in the order given is

$$\begin{aligned} \kappa^{(1)}\kappa^{(2)} &= \| (\kappa_{i1}{}^{(1)}\kappa_{1j}{}^{(2)} + \kappa_{i2}{}^{(1)}\kappa_{2j}{}^{(2)} + \cdots + \kappa_{in}{}^{(1)}\kappa_{nj}{}^{(2)}) \| \\ &= \left\| \sum_{r=1}^{n} \kappa_{ir}{}^{(1)}\kappa_{rj}{}^{(2)} \right\|, \end{aligned} \tag{5}$$

just as in the product of two determinants; thus

$$\kappa^{(1)}\kappa^{(2)} = \underset{\text{rows}}{\begin{Vmatrix} 1 & 2 \\ 3 & 4 \end{Vmatrix}} \underset{\text{col's}}{\begin{Vmatrix} 3 & 4 \\ 5 & 6 \end{Vmatrix}} = \begin{Vmatrix} 1 \cdot 3 + 2 \cdot 5 & 1 \cdot 4 + 2 \cdot 6 \\ 3 \cdot 3 + 4 \cdot 5 & 3 \cdot 4 + 4 \cdot 6 \end{Vmatrix} = \begin{Vmatrix} 13 & 16 \\ 29 & 36 \end{Vmatrix},$$

and

$$\kappa^{(2)}\kappa^{(1)} = \underset{\text{rows}}{\begin{Vmatrix} 3 & 4 \\ 5 & 6 \end{Vmatrix}} \underset{\text{col's}}{\begin{Vmatrix} 1 & 2 \\ 3 & 4 \end{Vmatrix}} = \begin{Vmatrix} 3 \cdot 1 + 4 \cdot 3 & 3 \cdot 2 + 4 \cdot 4 \\ 5 \cdot 1 + 6 \cdot 3 & 5 \cdot 2 + 6 \cdot 4 \end{Vmatrix} = \begin{Vmatrix} 15 & 22 \\ 23 & 34 \end{Vmatrix};$$

from which it is evident that the order of multiplication is important, and, generally speaking,

$$\kappa^{(1)}\kappa^{(2)} \neq \kappa^{(2)}\kappa^{(1)}.$$

For the product of a scalar and a matrix, however,

$$s\kappa = \| (s\kappa_{ij}) \| = \| (\kappa_{ij}s) \| = \kappa s,$$

and the order is not important.

The *identity matrix* is defined to be

$$\delta = \begin{Vmatrix} 1 & 0 & \cdots & 0 \\ 0 & 1 & \cdots & 0 \\ \cdots & \cdots & \cdots & \cdots \\ 0 & 0 & \cdots & 1 \end{Vmatrix},$$

that is, ones down the main diagonal and zero elsewhere. If δ and κ are each n^2 matrices, it is readily verified that

$$\delta\kappa = \kappa\delta = \kappa.$$

If $\kappa^{(1)}$, $\kappa^{(2)}$, and $\kappa^{(3)}$ are three $n \times n$ matrices,

$$(\kappa^{(1)} + \kappa^{(2)})\kappa^{(3)} = \kappa^{(1)}\kappa^{(3)} + \kappa^{(2)}\kappa^{(3)}.$$

From these examples it is evident that the associative, distributive and commutative laws hold for addition and scalar multiplication of matrices. The associative and distributive laws hold for multiplication of matrices, but the commutative law does not hold in general.

Finally, the *derivative of a matrix* whose elements are functions of a variable, say t, is defined to be

$$\frac{d\kappa}{dt} = \kappa' = \begin{Vmatrix} \kappa_{11}' & \kappa_{21}' & \cdots & \kappa_{n1}' \\ \kappa_{21}' & \kappa_{22}' & \cdots & \kappa_{n2}' \\ \cdots & \cdots & \cdots & \cdots \\ \kappa_{n1}' & \kappa_{n2}' & \cdots & \kappa_{nn}' \end{Vmatrix}.$$

which is obtained from κ by differentiating each element of κ.

188. The Determinant of a Matrix.—The determinant

$$\begin{vmatrix} \kappa_{11} & \kappa_{12} & \cdots & \kappa_{1n} \\ \kappa_{21} & \kappa_{22} & \cdots & \kappa_{2n} \\ \cdots & \cdots & \cdots & \cdots \\ \kappa_{n1} & \kappa_{n2} & \cdots & \kappa_{nn} \end{vmatrix}, \qquad (1)$$

evaluated in the usual manner, is called the determinant of the matrix κ, and is written det κ. While the matrix is an array of numbers, its determinant is a scalar, that is, a single number.

The cofactor of the element κ_{ij} in Eq. (1) is the determinant obtained from Eq. (1) by suppressing the ith row and the jth column and then multiplying by $(-1)^{i+j}$. Let it be denoted by K_{ji} (observe the transposition of subscripts). The matrix

$$K = \begin{Vmatrix} K_{11} & K_{12} & \cdots & K_{1n} \\ K_{21} & K_{22} & \cdots & K_{2n} \\ \cdots & \cdots & \cdots & \cdots \\ K_{n1} & K_{n2} & \cdots & K_{nn} \end{Vmatrix}$$

is called the *adjoint matrix* of the matrix κ. The effect of the transposition of subscripts is merely to change rows into columns in K. Since, from the theory of determinants,

$$\sum_{r=1}^{n} \kappa_{ir} K_{rj} = \begin{matrix} \det \kappa, & \text{if} & i = j, \\ 0, & \text{if} & i \neq j, \end{matrix}$$

it follows that

$$\kappa K = \begin{Vmatrix} \kappa_{11} & \kappa_{12} & \cdots & \kappa_{1n} \\ \kappa_{21} & \kappa_{22} & \cdots & \kappa_{2n} \\ \cdots & \cdots & \cdots & \cdots \\ \kappa_{n1} & \kappa_{n2} & \cdots & \kappa_{nn} \end{Vmatrix} \times \begin{Vmatrix} K_{11} & K_{12} & \cdots & K_{1n} \\ K_{21} & K_{22} & \cdots & K_{2n} \\ \cdots & \cdots & \cdots & \cdots \\ K_{n1} & K_{n2} & \cdots & K_{nn} \end{Vmatrix}$$

$$= \begin{Vmatrix} (\det \kappa) & 0 & \cdots & 0 \\ 0 & (\det \kappa) & \cdots & 0 \\ \cdots & \cdots & \cdots & \cdots \\ 0 & 0 & \cdots & (\det \kappa) \end{Vmatrix} = \det \kappa \cdot \delta,$$

where δ is the identity matrix.

189. Matrix Polynomials—The Characteristic Equation.—Since the product of two matrices is a matrix, it is possible to have

$$\kappa\kappa = \kappa^2, \qquad \kappa\kappa\kappa = \kappa^3, \qquad \cdots,$$

and thus build up a polynomial

$$p(\kappa) = a_m\kappa^m + a_{m-1}\kappa^{m-1} + \cdots + a_1 k + a_0\delta,$$

which also is a matrix, since it is merely a sum of matrices. It is readily verified that the product of two powers of κ is commutative; that is

$$\kappa^s\kappa^r = \kappa^r\kappa^s = \kappa^{r+s}.$$

Let $p(s)$ be the corresponding scalar polynomial. Just as the scalar polynomial

$$p(s) = a_m(s - s_1)(s - s_2) \cdots (s - s_m)$$

is factorable, so also is the matrix polynomial factorable, and

$$p(\kappa) = a_m(\kappa - s_1\delta)(\kappa - s_2\delta) \cdots (\kappa - s_m\delta),$$

since the coefficients and exponents obey the same laws in the two cases.

Suppose

$$p(\lambda) = (-1)^n \det (\kappa - \lambda\delta)$$

$$= (-1)^n \begin{vmatrix} \kappa_{11} - \lambda & \kappa_{12} & \cdots & \kappa_{1n} \\ \kappa_{21} & \kappa_{22} - \lambda & \cdots & \kappa_{2n} \\ \cdots & \cdots & \cdots & \cdots \\ \kappa_{n1} & \kappa_{n2} & \cdots & \kappa_{nn} - \lambda \end{vmatrix}$$

$$= \lambda^n + a_{n-1}\lambda^{n-1} + \cdots + a_1\lambda + a_0. \quad (1)$$

The equation

$$p(\lambda) = 0 \quad (2)$$

is called the *characteristic equation* of the matrix κ, and its roots λ_i are the *characteristic numbers* for κ. If Eq. (1) has r distinct roots and each λ_i is a root of multiplicity m_i, then

$$\sum_{i=1}^{r} m_i = n,$$

and the polynomial can be written

$$p(\lambda) = \prod_{i=1}^{r} (\lambda - \lambda_i)^{m_i}. \quad (3)$$

The matrix

$$\begin{Vmatrix} \kappa_{11} - \lambda & \kappa_{12} & \cdots & \kappa_{1n} \\ \kappa_{21} & \kappa_{22} - \lambda & \cdots & \kappa_{2n} \\ \cdots & \cdots & \cdots & \cdots \\ \kappa_{n1} & \kappa_{n2} & \cdots & \kappa_{nn} - \lambda \end{Vmatrix}$$

can be written $\kappa - \lambda\delta$, or simply $\kappa(\lambda)$, with $\kappa(0) = \kappa$. If $K(\lambda)$ is its adjoint matrix, then, by Sec. 188 and Eq. (1),

$$\kappa(\lambda)K(\lambda) = [\det \kappa(\lambda)]\delta \quad (4)$$

$$= (-1)^n p(\lambda)\delta.$$

The elements K_{ij} of the matrix K are polynomials in λ of degree not greater than $n - 1$. Hence the matrix K can be written in the form

$$K(\lambda) = \sum_{i=0}^{n-1} K^{(i)}\lambda^i,$$

where $K^{(i)}$ are matrices that do not contain λ; and this expression substituted in Eq. (4) gives, since $\kappa(\lambda) = \kappa - \lambda\delta$,

$$\kappa \sum_{i=0}^{n-1} K^{(i)}\lambda^i - \lambda \sum_{i=0}^{n-1} K^{(i)}\lambda^i = (-1)^n(a_0 + a_1\lambda + a_2\lambda^2 + \cdots + \lambda^n)\delta. \tag{5}$$

Since this equation is true for every λ, the corresponding coefficients of the left and right members are equal. Hence

$$\begin{aligned} \kappa K^{(0)} \phantom{- K^{(0)}} &= (-1)^n a_0 \delta, \\ \kappa K^{(1)} - K^{(0)} &= (-1)^n a_1 \delta, \\ \kappa K^{(2)} - K^{(1)} &= (-1)^n a_2 \delta, \\ &\cdots\cdots\cdots\cdots \\ \kappa K^{(n-1)} - K^{(n-2)} &= (-1)^n a_{n-1} \delta, \\ -K^{(n-1)} &= (-1)^n \delta. \end{aligned}$$

If the first of these equations is multiplied by δ, the second by κ, the third by κ^2, and so on, and the equations are then added, it is found that the left member is the zero matrix and the right member is $(-1)^n p(\kappa)\delta$. Hence

$$p(\kappa) = \kappa^n + a_{n-1}\kappa^{n-1} + \cdots + a_1\kappa + a_0\delta = \| 0 \|, \tag{6}$$

or again [Eq. (3)]

$$p(\kappa) = \prod_{i=1}^{r} (\kappa - \lambda_i\delta)^{m_i} = \| 0 \|. \tag{7}$$

This shows that the matrix satisfies its own characteristic equation, a theorem due to Sylvester.

Example.—If

$$\kappa = \begin{Vmatrix} 3 & -1 \\ 1 & 5 \end{Vmatrix}, \qquad \text{then} \qquad \kappa - \lambda\delta = \kappa(\lambda) = \begin{Vmatrix} 3 - \lambda & -1 \\ 1 & 5 - \lambda \end{Vmatrix},$$

and

$$p(\lambda) = \lambda^2 - 8\lambda + 16 = (\lambda - 4)^2;$$

so that $\lambda = 4$ is a double root. Consequently

$$(\kappa(4))^2 = \begin{Vmatrix} -1 & -1 \\ +1 & +1 \end{Vmatrix} \times \begin{Vmatrix} -1 & -1 \\ +1 & +1 \end{Vmatrix} = \begin{Vmatrix} 0 & 0 \\ 0 & 0 \end{Vmatrix} = \| 0 \|.$$

It is evident that if

$$P(\kappa) = \kappa^m + b_{m-1}\kappa^{m-1} + \cdots + b_1\kappa + b_0\delta, \qquad m > n, \tag{8}$$

is any other polynomial in κ of degree greater than n, it can be reduced by means of Eq. (6) to a polynomial of degree not higher than $n - 1$, that is, it can be written in the form

$$P(\kappa) = c_{n-1}\kappa^{n-1} + c_{n-2}\kappa^{n-2} + \cdots + c_1\kappa + c_0\delta.$$

190. Bartky's Identity.—Before proceeding to the formulation of this reduction it is desirable to establish an identity that is due to W. Bartky.

Let E_i be an operator with the definition

$$E_i = 1 + \frac{\lambda - \lambda_i}{1!}\frac{d}{d\mu} + \cdots + \frac{(\lambda - \lambda_i)^{m_i-1}}{(m_i - 1)!}\frac{d^{m_i-1}}{d\mu^{m_i-1}}$$
$$= \sum_{k=0}^{m_i-1} \frac{(\lambda - \lambda_i)^k}{k!}\frac{d^k}{d\mu^k},$$

and let R_i, S_i be functions of λ and μ respectively with the definitions

$$\left.\begin{aligned} R_i(\lambda) &= \prod_{j=1}^{r}{}' (\lambda - \lambda_j)^{m_j}, \qquad j \neq i, \\ S_i(\mu) &= \prod_{j=1}^{r}{}' (\mu - \lambda_j)^{-m_j}, \qquad j \neq i. \end{aligned}\right\} \tag{0}$$

It is assumed that if i and j are distinct $\lambda_i \neq \lambda_j$; that the m_i are positive integers and that no m_i is zero; and finally, that

$$\sum_{i=1}^{r} m_i = n;$$

so that the R_i are polynomials of degree not higher than $n - 1$. If the λ_i's are all equal, $R = S = 1$, and $m = n$, the subscript being useless.

Bartky's polynomial $Q(\lambda)$ is then defined to be

$$Q(\lambda) = \sum_{i=1}^{r} R_i(E_iS_i)_{\mu=\lambda_i} = \sum_{i=1}^{r} Q_i, \tag{1}$$

and it is readily seen that its degree in λ is not higher than $n - 1$. It will be shown that

$$Q(\lambda) \equiv 1. \tag{2}$$

It is fairly evident that for any t

$$Q(\lambda_t) = 1, \tag{3}$$

since $R_i(\lambda_t) = 0$, if $i \neq t$; while for $i = t$, $E_i(\lambda_t) = 1$, so that

$$Q(\lambda_t) = R_t(\lambda_t)S_t(\lambda_t) = 1.$$

When E_i in Eq. (1) is replaced by its definition, the polynomial $Q(\lambda)$ becomes

$$Q(\lambda) = \sum_{i=1}^{r} \sum_{k=0}^{m_i-1} R_i(\lambda)\frac{(\lambda - \lambda_i)^k}{k!}S_i^{(k)}(\lambda_i) = \sum_{i=1}^{r} Q_i,$$

where $S_i^{(k)}(\lambda_i)$ is the kth derivative of $S_i(\mu)$ for the value $\mu = \lambda_i$. The pth derivative of Q with respect to λ is

$$Q^{(p)}(\lambda) = \sum_{i=1}^{r} Q_i^{(p)}(\lambda);$$

and, for $\lambda = \lambda_t$ and $p < m_t$,

$$Q^{(p)}(\lambda_t) = Q_t^{(p)}(\lambda_t), \tag{4}$$

since, for $i \neq t$, Q_i has the factor $(\lambda - \lambda_t)^{m_t}$.

In the neighborhood of λ_t, $S_t(\lambda)$ can be expanded in the Taylor series

$$S_t(\lambda) = \sum_{k=0}^{\infty} \frac{(\lambda - \lambda_t)^k}{k!}S_t^{(k)}(\lambda_t);$$

and therefore

$$Q_t(\lambda) = \sum_{k=0}^{m_t-1} R_t(\lambda)\frac{(\lambda - \lambda_t)^k}{k!}S_t^{(k)}(\lambda_t)$$

becomes

$$Q_t(\lambda) = R_t(\lambda)S_t(\lambda) - \sum_{k=m_t}^{\infty} R_t(\lambda)\frac{(\lambda - \lambda_t)^k}{k!}S_t^{(k)}(\lambda_t).$$

The first term in the right member, R_tS_t, is equal to unity, and the second term, the infinite series, carries $(\lambda - \lambda_t)^{m_t}$ as a factor. Hence, by Eq. (4),

$$Q^{(p)}(\lambda_t) = Q_t^{(p)}(\lambda_t) = 0, \qquad \text{provided} \qquad 0 < p < m_t.$$

Since $Q(\lambda) - 1$ and its first $m_t - 1$ derivatives vanish for $\lambda = \lambda_t$, it follows that $(\lambda - \lambda_t)^{m_t}$ is a factor of $Q(\lambda) - 1$; also that

$$\prod_{t=1}^{r} (\lambda - \lambda_t)^{m_t}$$

is a factor. Since $Q(\lambda) - 1$ is of degree $n - 1$ at most and $\Sigma m_t = n$, it follows that

$$Q(\lambda) - 1 \equiv 0;$$

therefore

$$Q(\lambda) \equiv 1.$$

The corresponding matrix polynomial is

$$Q(\kappa) = \delta; \tag{5}$$

that is

$$Q(\kappa) = \sum_{i=1}^{r} \sum_{k=0}^{m_i - 1} \frac{R_i(\kappa)\kappa_i^k}{k!} S_i^{(k)}(\lambda_i) \equiv \delta, \tag{6}$$

in which

$$\kappa_i = (\kappa - \lambda_i\delta), \qquad \kappa_i^0 = \delta,$$

and

$$R_i(\kappa) = \prod_{j=1}^{r}{}' (\kappa - \lambda_j\delta)^{m_j} = \prod_{j=1}^{r}{}' \kappa_j^{m_j}, \qquad j \neq i.$$

If now the λ_i are the characteristic numbers of κ, and the m_i their multiplicities, then, since the matrix κ satisfies its own characteristic equation [Eq. (189.7)], it is evident that

$$\prod_{j=1}^{r} (\kappa - \lambda_j\delta)^{m_j} = \prod_{j=1}^{r} \kappa_j^{m_j} \equiv \| 0 \|, \tag{7}$$

and the summation with respect to k in Eq. (6) can be continued to infinity, for all of the succeeding terms vanish. Furthermore, this sum can be written symbolically

$$\sum_{k=0}^{\infty} \frac{\kappa_i^k}{k!} D_\mu^k = e^{\kappa_i D_\mu},$$

where $D_\mu \equiv d/d\mu$, and therefore

$$Q(\kappa) = \sum_{i=1}^{r} R_i(\kappa)(e^{\kappa_i D_\mu} S_i)_{\mu=\lambda_i} = \sum_{i=1}^{r} Q_i. \tag{8}$$

Since Q_i carries $R_i(\kappa)$ as a factor, it is evident from Eq. (7) that

$$\kappa_i^{m_i} Q_i = \| 0 \|. \tag{9}$$

From this fact and the fact that Q_j carries $\kappa_i^{m_i}$ as a factor in $R_j(\kappa)$, it is readily seen that

$$Q_i Q_j = \| 0 \|, \tag{10}$$

when $i \neq j$; and on multiplying the identity Eq. (5),

$$\sum_{j=1}^{r} Q_j \equiv \delta,$$

through by Q_i, and then applying Eq. (10), that

$$Q_i Q_i = \delta Q_i = Q_i, \qquad i = 1, \cdots, r. \tag{11}$$

191. Functions of a Matrix.—Suppose κ is a given matrix with characteristic numbers λ_i of multiplicity m_i, and that

$$P_q(\lambda), \qquad q = 1, 2, 3, \cdots,$$

is a sequence of polynomials in λ of degree n_q, not necessarily constant. Suppose further that

$$\lim_{q=\infty} P_q(\lambda_i) = F(\lambda_i),$$

$$\lim_{q=\infty} \frac{d^s}{d\lambda^s} P_q(\lambda) \bigg|_{\lambda=\lambda_i} = F^{(s)}(\lambda_i), \qquad s = 1, 2, \cdots, m_i - 1.$$

For example,

$$P_0(\lambda) = 1, \qquad P_1(\lambda) = 1 - \frac{\lambda^2}{2!}, \qquad P_2(\lambda) = 1 - \frac{\lambda^2}{2!} + \frac{\lambda^4}{4!}, \quad \cdots.$$

Evidently

$$F(\lambda_i) = \cos \lambda_i.$$

Let $P_q(\kappa)$ be the corresponding sequence of matrix polynomials. Then

Theorem A.—The limit for q equal to infinity of $P_q(\kappa)$ is a matrix, $F(\kappa)$; and, if $\Sigma m_i = n$, $F(\kappa)$ can be expressed as a polynomial in κ of degree not greater than $n - 1$.

Since, by Eq. (190.5),

$$Q(\kappa) = \Sigma Q_i = \delta,$$

$P_q(\kappa)$ can be written

$$P_q(\kappa) = \sum_{i=1}^{r} Q_i P_q(\kappa). \tag{1}$$

For each i, $P_q(\lambda)$ can be expanded by Taylor's theorem in the neighborhood of the characteristic number λ_i. That is,

$$P_q(\lambda) = P_q(\lambda_i) + \frac{(\lambda - \lambda_i)}{1!} P_q^{(1)}(\lambda_i) + \cdots + \frac{(\lambda - \lambda_i)^{n_q}}{n_q!} P_q^{(n_q)}(\lambda_i);$$

hence

$$P_q(\kappa) = \sum_{i=1}^{r} Q_i \left[P_q(\lambda_i) + \frac{\kappa_i}{1!} P_q^{(1)}(\lambda_i) + \cdots + \frac{\kappa_i^{n_q}}{n_q!} P_q^{(n_q)}(\lambda_i) \right]. \tag{2}$$

Now, as was observed in Eq. (190.9),

$$Q_i \kappa_i^{m_i} = \| 0 \|. \tag{3}$$

It is not necessary, therefore, to carry the expansion by Taylor's theorem in Eq. (2) beyond the $(m_i - 1)$th term, since all of the higher terms vanish. Hence, whatever n_q may be,

$$P_q(\kappa) = \sum_{i=1}^{r} Q_i \sum_{k=0}^{m_i = 1} \frac{\kappa_i^k}{k!} P_q^{(k)}(\lambda_i), \tag{4}$$

which is a polynomial in κ of degree not higher than $n - 1$; for the factor

$$R_i(\kappa) = \prod_{j=1}^{r}{}' (\kappa - \lambda_j \delta)^{m_j}$$

of Q_i, which contains the κ, is of degree $n - m_i$ and therefore $Q_i \kappa_i^k$ is of degree $n - m_i + k$, for $k \leqq m_i - 1$. On letting q pass to the limit, there results the desired formula

$$F(\kappa) = \sum_{i=1}^{r} Q_i \sum_{k=0}^{m_i - 1} \frac{\kappa_i^k}{k!} F^{(k)}(\lambda_i), \tag{5}$$

in which $F(\kappa)$ is represented as a polynomial in κ of degree not greater than $n - 1$.

If for each i the finite sequence of numbers $F(\lambda_i), F^{(1)}(\lambda_i), \ldots, F^{(m_i-1)}(\lambda_i)$, defined at the beginning of this section, be extended in any desired manner to an infinite sequence of numbers $F_i^{(m_i)}(\lambda_i), \ldots$, then, since, by Eq. (3),

$$Q_i\kappa_i^{m_i+s} = Q_i\kappa_i^{m_i}\kappa^s = \| 0 \|, \qquad s = 0, 1, 2, \cdots, \tag{6}$$

Eq. (5) can be written

$$F(\kappa) = \sum_{i=1}^{r} Q_i \sum_{k=0}^{\infty} \frac{\kappa_i^k}{k!} F^{(k)}(\lambda_i),$$

or symbolically,

$$F(\kappa) = \sum_{i=1}^{r} Q_i e^{\kappa_i \Omega_i} F(\lambda_i), \tag{7}$$

where Ω_i^k operates on $F(\lambda_i)$ to give $F^{(k)}(\lambda_i)$. From Eq. (190.8)

$$Q_i = R_i(\kappa)(e^{\kappa_i D\mu} S_i(\mu))_{\mu=\lambda_i}, \tag{8}$$

and Eq. (7) becomes

$$F(\kappa) = \sum_{i=1}^{r} R_i(\kappa)(e^{\kappa_i(\Omega_i + D\mu)} S_i(\mu) F(\lambda_i))_{\mu=\lambda_i}, \tag{9}$$

in which Ω_i operates only on $F(\lambda_i)$ and D_μ operates only on $S_i(\mu)$. The expression of the exponential operator need be continued to and including the term $\kappa_i^{m_i-1}$ only, since the terms of degree m_i and higher vanish.

When the sequence of polynomials $P_q(\lambda)$ converges in a region that contains $\lambda_1, \ldots, \lambda_r$, to a function $F(\lambda)$, and the kth derivatives of the polynomials converge on the same interval to the kth derivatives of $F(\lambda)$, and this will be the case in the following sections, the numbers $F^{(k)}(\lambda_i)$ can be taken to be

$$\Omega_i^{(k)} F(\lambda_i) = F^{(k)}(\lambda_i) = \frac{d^k}{d\lambda^k} F(\lambda)\Big|_{\lambda=\lambda_i}, \qquad k = 1, 2, 3, \cdots,$$

and then Eq. (9) becomes

$$F(\kappa) = \sum_{i=1}^{r} R_i(\kappa)(e^{\kappa_i(D_\lambda + D\mu)} S_i(\mu) F(\lambda))_{\lambda=\mu=\lambda_i}. \tag{10}$$

In this case the matrix $F(\kappa)$ is called *the matrix associated with the function* $F(\lambda)$.

Theorem B.—If

$$F(\lambda) = a_1F_1(\lambda) + a_2F_2(\lambda)$$

for λ *in a region containing* $\lambda_1, \ldots, \lambda_r$, *then*

$$F(\kappa) = a_1F_1(\kappa) + a_2F_2(\kappa),$$

as is readily seen from Eq. (10).

Theorem C.—If

$$F(\lambda) = F_1(\lambda)F_2(\lambda)$$

or λ *in a region containing* $\lambda_1, \ldots, \lambda_r$, *then*

$$F(\kappa) = F_1(\kappa)F_2(\kappa).$$

By Eq. (7)

$$F_1(\kappa) = \sum_{i=1}^{r} Q_i(e^{\kappa_i D_\lambda}F_1(\lambda))_{\lambda=\lambda_i}$$

$$F_2(\kappa) = \sum_{j=1}^{r} Q_j(e^{\kappa_j D_\mu}F_2(\mu))_{\mu=\lambda_j}.$$

On taking the product and bearing in mind that

$$Q_iQ_i = Q_i \qquad \text{and} \qquad Q_iQ_j = \| 0 \|, \qquad \text{if} \qquad j \neq i,$$

it is found that

$$F_1(\kappa)F_2(\kappa) = \sum_{i=1}^{r} Q_i\{e^{\kappa_i(D_\lambda + D_\mu)}F_1(\lambda)F_2(\mu)\}_{\lambda=\mu=\lambda_i};$$

and since

$$[(D_\lambda + D_\mu)^s F_1(\lambda)F_2(\mu)]_{\lambda=\mu=\lambda_i} = [D_\lambda{}^s F_1(\lambda)F_2(\lambda)]_{\lambda=\lambda_i},$$

it follows that

$$F_1(\kappa)F_2(\kappa) = \sum_{i=1}^{r} Q_i\{e^{\kappa_i D_\lambda}F_1(\lambda)F_2(\lambda)\}_{\lambda=\lambda_i}$$
$$= F(\kappa).$$

The following theorems also are easily proved and, for brevity, the proofs will be omitted.

Theorem D.—If

$$\frac{d}{dt}F(\lambda; t) = G(\lambda; t)$$

for λ *in a region containing* $\lambda_1, \ldots, \lambda_r$, *then*

$$\frac{d}{dt}F(\kappa; t) = G(\kappa; t).$$

Theorem E.—If

$$\int_{t_0}^{t} F(\lambda; t)\,dt = I(\lambda; t)$$

for λ *in a region containing* $\lambda_1, \ldots, \lambda_r$, *then*

$$\int_{t_0}^{t} F(\kappa; t)\,dt = I(\kappa; t).$$

192. Example—the Matrix $e^{\kappa t}$.—The matrix that is associated with the function $e^{\lambda t}$ can be written $e^{\kappa t}$. Since

$$\frac{d}{dt}e^{\lambda t} = \lambda e^{\lambda t},$$

it follows from Theorem D that

$$\frac{d}{dt}e^{\kappa t} = \kappa e^{\kappa t}. \tag{0}$$

Now, by Eq. (191.10),

$$e^{\kappa t} = \sum_{i=1}^{r} R_i(\kappa)[e^{\kappa_i(D_\lambda + D_\mu)}e^{\lambda t}S_i(\mu)]_{\lambda=\mu=\lambda_i},$$

and since

$$e^{\kappa_i D_\lambda}e^{\lambda t} = e^{\lambda t}e^{\kappa_i t},$$

it follows that

$$e^{\kappa t} = \sum_i e^{\lambda_i t}R_i(\kappa)[e^{\kappa_i(t + D_\mu)}S_i(\mu)]_{\mu=\lambda_i},$$

or, in an expanded form,

$$e^{\kappa t} = \sum_i e^{\lambda_i t}R_i(\kappa)\left\{\left[\delta + \frac{\kappa_i}{1!}(t + D_\mu) + \cdots + \frac{\kappa_i^{m_i-1}}{(m_i - 1)!}(t + D_\mu)^{m_i-1}\right]S_i(\mu)\right\}_{\mu=\lambda_i}. \tag{1}$$

If the characteristic numbers are all distinct, each $m_i = 1$, and

$$e^{\kappa t} = \sum_{i=1}^{n} e^{\lambda_i t} R_i(\kappa) S_i(\lambda_i); \tag{2}$$

and if they are all equal, $m_i = n$, $\lambda_1 = \cdots = \lambda_n$, and

$$e^{\kappa t} = e^{\lambda t}\left[\delta + \frac{\kappa_1}{1!}t + \cdots + \frac{\kappa_1{}^{n-1}}{(n-1)!}t^{n-1}\right], \tag{3}$$

since, by definition for this case, $R_i = S_i = 1$.

Numerical Example.—Suppose the given matrix is

$$\kappa = \begin{Vmatrix} +1 & -1 & -1 \\ -1 & +1 & -1 \\ -1 & -1 & +1 \end{Vmatrix}, \text{ so that } \kappa(\lambda) = \begin{Vmatrix} 1-\lambda & -1 & -1 \\ -1 & 1-\lambda & -1 \\ -1 & -1 & 1-\lambda \end{Vmatrix};$$

$$\det \kappa(\lambda) = -(\lambda + 1)(\lambda - 2)^2.$$

The characteristic numbers λ_i of κ and their multiplicities m_i are

$$\lambda_1 = -1, \quad m_1 = 1; \quad \lambda_2 = 2, \quad m_2 = 2.$$

Therefore

$$\kappa - \lambda_1\delta = \kappa_1 = \begin{Vmatrix} +2 & -1 & -1 \\ -1 & +2 & -1 \\ -1 & -1 & +2 \end{Vmatrix}$$

and

$$\kappa - \lambda_2\delta = \kappa_2 = \begin{Vmatrix} -1 & -1 & -1 \\ -1 & -1 & -1 \\ -1 & -1 & -1 \end{Vmatrix}.$$

Also

$$R_1(\kappa) = \kappa_2^2, \quad S_1(\mu) = (\mu - 2)^{-2}; \quad R_2(\kappa) = \kappa_1, \quad S_2 = (\mu + 1)^{-1}.$$

Equation (1) becomes

$$\begin{aligned} e^{\kappa t} &= e^{-t}R_1(\kappa)S_1(\lambda_1) + e^{2t}R_2(\kappa)[\delta S_2(\lambda_2) + \kappa_2\{tS_2(\lambda_2) + S_2^{(1)}(\lambda_2)\}] \\ &= \tfrac{1}{9}e^{-t}\kappa_2^2 + \tfrac{1}{3}e^{2t}\kappa_1[\delta + \kappa_2(t - \tfrac{1}{3})], \end{aligned}$$

which reduces to

$$e^{\kappa t} = -\tfrac{1}{3}e^{-t}\kappa_2 + \tfrac{1}{3}e^{2t}\kappa_1,$$

since

$$\kappa_1\kappa_2 = \|0\| \quad \text{and} \quad \kappa_2^2 = -3\kappa_2.$$

193. Homogeneous Linear Differential Equations with Constant Coefficients.—Suppose κ is an $n \times n$ matrix and x is an $n \times 1$ matrix, that is a matrix with n rows and but one column. The product κx is an $n \times 1$ matrix. Suppose, for example,

$$
\begin{aligned}
y_1 &= \kappa_{11}x_1 + \kappa_{12}x_2 + \cdots + \kappa_{1n}x_n, \\
&\cdots\cdots\cdots\cdots\cdots\cdots \\
y_n &= \kappa_{n1}x_1 + \kappa_{n2}x_2 + \cdots + \kappa_{nn}x_n,
\end{aligned}
\tag{1}
$$

is a set of linear equations. The right members of these equations can be regarded as the elements of an $n \times 1$ matrix obtained by taking the product of the two matrices

$$
\kappa = \| \kappa_{ij} \| \qquad \text{and} \qquad x = \left\| \begin{matrix} x_1 \\ x_2 \\ \cdot \\ \cdot \\ \cdot \\ x_n \end{matrix} \right\|.
$$

If this product is identified with the matrix

$$
y = \left\| \begin{matrix} y_1 \\ y_2 \\ \cdot \\ \cdot \\ \cdot \\ y_n \end{matrix} \right\|,
$$

then the matrix equation,

$$
y = \kappa x, \tag{2}
$$

is equivalent to the set of linear equations in Eqs. (1).

If an $n \times 1$ matrix is called a *vector*, its elements are the components of the vector. Thus $x_1, \ldots, x_n$ are the components of the vector x, and $y_1, \ldots, y_n$ are the components of the vector y.

Suppose $x_1, \ldots, x_n$ are functions of t and that $x_1', \ldots, x_n'$ are the derivatives of these functions with respect to t. The set of linear differential equations,

$$
\left.
\begin{aligned}
x_1' &= \kappa_{11}x_1 + \kappa_{12}x_2 + \cdots + \kappa_{n1}x_n, \\
&\cdots\cdots\cdots\cdots\cdots\cdots \\
x_n' &= \kappa_{n1}x_1 + \kappa_{n2}x_2 + \cdots + \kappa_{nn}x_n,
\end{aligned}
\right\}
\tag{3}
$$

evidently, can be written in the vector form

$$x' = \kappa x, \tag{4}$$

since $x_1', \ldots, x_n'$ are the components of a vector which can be denoted by x', and this is true even though the elements of κ are themselves functions of the time t.

Suppose, however, the κ_{ij} are constants, and that

$$x(0) = a,$$

where a is a vector with the components $a_1, \ldots, a_n$.

The solution of Eq. (4) is

$$x = e^{\kappa t}a, \tag{5}$$

for by differentiating and using Eq. (192.0) it is seen that

$$x' = \kappa e^{\kappa t}a = \kappa x$$

and, for $t = 0$,

$$x(0) = a.$$

Example.—If the differential equations are

$$\begin{aligned} x_1' &= +x_1 - x_2 - x_3, \\ x_2' &= -x_1 + x_2 - x_3, \\ x_3' &= -x_1 - x_2 + x_3, \end{aligned}$$

the matrix of the coefficients of the right members is the same as κ of the numerical example in Sec. 192. Hence

$$e^{\kappa t} = -\tfrac{1}{3}e^{-t}\kappa_2 + \tfrac{1}{3}e^{2t}\kappa_1,$$

and

$$x = -\tfrac{1}{3}e^{-t}\kappa_2 a + \tfrac{1}{3}e^{2t}\kappa_1 a,$$

which, expanded, gives

$$\left.\begin{aligned} x_1 &= \tfrac{1}{3}a_1(e^{-t} + 2e^{2t}) + \tfrac{1}{3}a_2(e^{-t} - e^{2t}) + \tfrac{1}{3}a_3(e^{-t} - e^{2t}), \\ x_2 &= \tfrac{1}{3}a_1(e^{-t} - e^{2t}) + \tfrac{1}{3}a_2(e^{-t} + 2e^{2t}) + \tfrac{1}{3}a_3(e^{-t} - e^{2t}), \\ x_3 &= \tfrac{1}{3}a_1(e^{-t} - e^{2t}) + \tfrac{1}{3}a_2(e^{-t} - e^{-2t}) + \tfrac{1}{3}a_3(e^{-t} + 2e^{2t}). \end{aligned}\right\} \tag{6}$$

194. Linear Differential Equations of the Second Order.—If each of the differential equations is of the second order instead of the first, that is,

$$\begin{aligned} x_1'' &= \kappa_{11}x_1 + \cdots + \kappa_{n1}x_n, \\ &\cdots\cdots\cdots\cdots\cdots \\ x_n'' &= \kappa_{1n}x_1 + \cdots + \kappa_{nn}x_n, \end{aligned}$$

the corresponding matrix equation can be written

$$x'' = -\kappa x, \tag{1}$$

where κ is the matrix

$$\kappa = \begin{Vmatrix} -\kappa_{11} & \cdots & -\kappa_{n1} \\ \cdots & \cdots & \cdots \\ -\kappa_{1n} & \cdots & -\kappa_{nn} \end{Vmatrix},$$

and, as is easily verified, the solution is

$$x = (\cos\sqrt{\kappa}t)a + \left(\frac{\sin\sqrt{\kappa}t}{\sqrt{\kappa}}\right)b, \tag{2}$$

with the initial values

$$x(0) = a, \qquad x'(0) = b.$$

It will be observed that the vectors a and b in Eqs. (2) are multiplied on the right.

The matrices

$$\cos\sqrt{\kappa}t \qquad \text{and} \qquad \frac{\sin\sqrt{\kappa}t}{\sqrt{\kappa}}$$

are then computed by means of the general formula for the functions of a matrix [Eq. (191.10)]. If

$$\left.\begin{aligned}
\omega_{1i} &= \left[\delta - \frac{1}{8}\frac{t^2}{\lambda_i}\kappa_i^2 + \frac{1}{16}\frac{t^2}{\lambda_i^2}\kappa_i^3 + \cdots\right],\\
\omega_{2i} &= \frac{1}{\sqrt{\lambda_i}}\left[-\frac{t}{2}\kappa_i + \frac{1}{8}\frac{t}{\lambda_i}\kappa_i^2 - \frac{1}{48}\left(\frac{3t}{\lambda_i^2} - \frac{t^3}{\lambda_i}\right)\kappa_i^3 + \cdots\right],\\
\psi_{1i} &= \frac{1}{\sqrt{\lambda_i}}\left[\delta - \frac{1}{2\lambda_i}\kappa_i + \left(\frac{3}{8}\frac{1}{\lambda_i^2} - \frac{1}{8}\frac{t^2}{\lambda_i}\right)\kappa_i^2 + \right.\\
&\qquad\qquad \left.\left(-\frac{15}{16}\frac{1}{\lambda_i^3} + \frac{1}{8}\frac{t^2}{\lambda_i^2}\right)\kappa_i^3 + \cdots\right],\\
\psi_{2i} &= \left[\frac{t}{2\lambda_i}\kappa_i - \frac{3}{8}\frac{t}{\lambda_i^2}\kappa_i^2 + \left(\frac{5}{16}\frac{t}{\lambda_i^3} - \frac{1}{48}\frac{t^3}{\lambda_i^2}\right)\kappa_i^3 + \cdots\right],
\end{aligned}\right\} \tag{3}$$

it is found that, for $\lambda = \lambda_i$,

$$\left.\begin{aligned}
e^{\kappa_i D_\lambda}\cos\sqrt{\lambda}t &= \omega_{1i}\cos\sqrt{\lambda_i}t + \omega_{2i}\sin\sqrt{\lambda_i}t,\\
e^{\kappa_i D_\lambda}\left(\frac{\sin\sqrt{\lambda}t}{\sqrt{\lambda}}\right) &= \psi_{1i}\sin\sqrt{\lambda_i}t + \psi_{2i}\cos\sqrt{\lambda_i}t;
\end{aligned}\right\} \tag{4}$$

and then

$$\cos \sqrt{\kappa}t = \sum_{i=1}^{r} (\omega_{1i} \cos \sqrt{\lambda_i}t + \omega_{2i} \sin \sqrt{\lambda_i}t) R_i(\kappa) (e^{\kappa_i D_\mu} S_i(\mu))_{\mu=\lambda_i},$$

$$\frac{\sin \sqrt{\kappa}t}{\sqrt{\kappa}} = \sum_{i=1}^{r} (\psi_{1i} \sin \sqrt{\lambda_i}t + \psi_{2i} \cos \sqrt{\lambda_i}t) R_i(\kappa) (e^{\kappa_i D_\mu} S_i(\mu))_{\mu=\lambda_i}. \tag{5}$$

If $\lambda_i = 0$ is a characteristic number of κ of multiplicity m_i, the det κ also is zero, and therefore there exist constants α_{ij}, $i = 1, \cdots, m_i$, such that the m_i independent relations

$$\alpha_{i1}x_1'' + \alpha_{i2}x_2'' + \cdots + \alpha_{in}x_n'' = 0. \qquad i = 1, \cdots, m_i \tag{6}$$

exist; and by integration

$$\alpha_{i1}x_1 + \alpha_{i2}x_2 + \cdots + \alpha_{in}x_n = c_{i0} + c_{i1}t. \tag{7}$$

By means of these relations the order of the differential equations can be reduced by m_i. The reduced equations have a matrix for which zero is not a characteristic number and they can be solved by the above method, although they are non-homogeneous.

Numerical Example.—Suppose the differential equations are

$$\begin{aligned} x_1'' &= +x_1 - x_2 - x_3, \\ x_2'' &= -x_1 + x_2 - x_3, \\ x_3'' &= -x_1 - x_2 + x_3; \end{aligned}$$

and therefore

$$\kappa = \begin{Vmatrix} -1 & +1 & +1 \\ +1 & -1 & +1 \\ +1 & +1 & -1 \end{Vmatrix}, \qquad \kappa(\lambda) = \begin{Vmatrix} -1-\lambda & +1 & +1 \\ +1 & -1-\lambda & +1 \\ +1 & +1 & -1-\lambda \end{Vmatrix}.$$

Then

$$\det \kappa(\lambda) = -(\lambda - 1)(\lambda + 2)^2,$$

and

$$\kappa_1 = \begin{Vmatrix} -2 & +1 & +1 \\ +1 & -2 & +1 \\ +1 & +1 & -2 \end{Vmatrix}, \qquad \kappa_2 = \begin{Vmatrix} +1 & +1 & +1 \\ +1 & +1 & +1 \\ +1 & +1 & +1 \end{Vmatrix},$$

if the notation is chosen so that

$$\lambda_1 = +1, \qquad m_1 = 1; \qquad \lambda_2 = -2, \qquad m_2 = 2.$$

It is easily verified that

$$\kappa_1^2 = -3\kappa_1, \qquad \kappa_2^2 = +3\kappa_2, \qquad \kappa_1\kappa_2 = \| 0 \|;$$

also that

$$R_1(\kappa) = \kappa_2^2 = 3\kappa_2, \qquad R_2(\kappa) = \kappa_1,$$
$$S_1(\mu) = (\mu + 2)^{-2}, \qquad S_2(\mu) = (\mu - 1)^{-1}$$

The application of Eqs. (5) now gives

$$\cos\sqrt{\kappa}t = \delta\cos t \cdot 3\kappa_2 \cdot \frac{1}{9} + \left(\cosh\sqrt{2}t - \frac{t}{2\sqrt{2}}\kappa_2 \sinh\sqrt{2}t\right)\kappa_1\left(-\frac{1}{3} - \frac{1}{9}\kappa_2\right),$$
$$= \left(\frac{1}{3}\cos t\right)\kappa_2 - \left(\frac{1}{3\sqrt{2}}\cosh\sqrt{2}t\right)\kappa_1,$$

$$\frac{\sin\sqrt{\kappa}t}{\sqrt{\kappa}} = \delta\sin t \cdot 3\kappa_2 \cdot \frac{1}{9} + \frac{1}{4}\left(\frac{1}{\sqrt{2}}\sinh\sqrt{2}t - t\kappa_2\cosh\sqrt{2}t\right)\kappa_1\left(-\frac{1}{3} - \frac{1}{9}\kappa_2\right)$$
$$= \left(\frac{1}{3}\sin t\right)\kappa_2 - \left(\frac{1}{3\sqrt{2}}\sinh\sqrt{2}t\right)\kappa_1.$$

Hence

$$x = \left[\left(\frac{1}{3}\cos t\right)\kappa_2 - \left(\frac{1}{3\sqrt{2}}\cosh\sqrt{2}t\right)\kappa_1\right]a + \left[\left(\frac{1}{3}\sin t\right)\kappa_2 - \left(\frac{1}{3\sqrt{2}}\sinh\sqrt{2}t\right)\kappa_1\right]b;$$

or, in the expanded form,

$$3x_1 = a_1(\cos t + 2\cosh\sqrt{2}t) + a_2(\cos t - \cosh\sqrt{2}t) + a_3(\cos t - \cosh\sqrt{2}t)$$
$$+ b_1(\sin t + \sqrt{2}\sinh\sqrt{2}t) + b_2\left(\sin t - \frac{1}{\sqrt{2}}\sinh\sqrt{2}t\right) + b_3\left(\sin t - \frac{1}{\sqrt{2}}\sinh\sqrt{2}t\right),$$
$$3x_2 = a_1(\cos t - \cosh\sqrt{2}t) + a_2(\cos t + 2\cosh\sqrt{2}t) + a_3(\cos t - \cosh\sqrt{2}t)$$
$$+ b_1\left(\sin t - \frac{1}{\sqrt{2}}\sinh\sqrt{2}t\right) + b_2(\sin t + \sqrt{2}\sinh\sqrt{2}t) + b_3\left(\sin t - \frac{1}{\sqrt{2}}\sinh\sqrt{2}t\right),$$
$$3x_3 = a_1(\cos t - \cosh\sqrt{2}t) + a_2(\cos t - \cosh\sqrt{2}t) + a_3(\cos t + 2\cosh\sqrt{2}t)$$
$$+ b_1\left(\sin t - \frac{1}{\sqrt{2}}\sinh\sqrt{2}t\right) + b_2\left(\sin t - \frac{1}{\sqrt{2}}\sinh\sqrt{2}t\right) + b_3(\sin t + \sqrt{2}\sinh\sqrt{2}t).$$

195. Non-homogeneous Linear Differential Equations.—If the differential equations are non-homogeneous, they can be written

$$x' = \kappa x + \varphi(t), \tag{1}$$

where $\varphi(t)$ is a vector with the components $\varphi_1(t)$, $\varphi_2(t)$, . . . , $\varphi_n(t)$. By the substitution

$$x = e^{\kappa t}y, \tag{2}$$

where y is a new vector, Eq. (1) becomes, by this substitution,

$$y' = e^{-\kappa t}\varphi;$$

and, by integration,

$$y = a + \int_0^t e^{-\kappa t}\varphi \, dt. \tag{3}$$

This value of y substituted in Eq. (2) gives

$$x = e^{\kappa t}a + e^{\kappa t}\int_0^t e^{-\kappa t}\varphi \, dt, \tag{4}$$

which for $t = 0$ gives

$$x(0) = a.$$

Since φ is a vector and $e^{-\kappa t}$ is a matrix, their product is a vector. The integral of this vector also is a vector whose components are the integrals of the components of the vector $e^{-\kappa t}\varphi$. Let ψ be this vector with the components $\psi_1(t)$, . . . , $\psi_n(t)$. The complete solution of Eq. (1) is then

$$x = e^{\kappa t}(a + \psi). \tag{5}$$

Suppose, for example,

$$x' = \kappa x + \varphi(t),$$

where κ is the same as in the example of Sec. 193, and therefore

$$\kappa_1^2 = 3\kappa_1, \qquad \kappa_2^2 = -3\kappa_2, \qquad \kappa_1\kappa_2 = \| 0 \|.$$

As was shown in Sec. 192,

$$e^{+\kappa t} = -\tfrac{1}{3}e^{-t}\kappa_2 + \tfrac{1}{3}e^{2t}\kappa_1.$$

Therefore, by changing the sign of t,

$$e^{-\kappa t} = -\tfrac{1}{3}e^{t}\kappa_2 + \tfrac{1}{3}e^{-2t}\kappa_1.$$

Hence

$$\int e^{-\kappa t}\varphi_i \, dt = -\tfrac{1}{3}\kappa_2\int_0^t e^{t}\varphi_i(t) \, dt + \tfrac{1}{3}\kappa_1\int_0^t e^{-2t}\varphi_i(t) \, dt = \psi_i(t),$$

and

$$e^{\kappa t}\int_0^t e^{-\kappa t}\varphi(t)\,dt = (-\tfrac{1}{3}e^{-t}\kappa_2 + \tfrac{1}{3}e^{2t}\kappa_1)\Big(-\tfrac{1}{3}\kappa_2\int_0^t e^t\varphi(t)\,dt + \tfrac{1}{3}\kappa_1\int_0^t e^{-2t}\varphi(t)\,dt\Big)$$
$$= -\tfrac{1}{3}\kappa_2 e^{-t}\int_0^t e^t\varphi\,dt + \tfrac{1}{3}\kappa_1 e^{2t}\int_0^t e^{-2t}\varphi\,dt.$$

If

$$W_{i1} = e^{-t}\int_0^t \varphi_i\,dt \qquad \text{and} \qquad W_{i2} = e^{2t}\int_0^t e^{-2t}\varphi_i\,dt,$$

the terms to be added to the solution given in Eqs. (193.6) are

$$\begin{aligned} x_1 &= \tfrac{1}{3}(W_{11} + W_{21} + W_{31} + 2W_{12} - W_{22} - W_{32}),\\ x_2 &= \tfrac{1}{3}(W_{11} + W_{21} + W_{31} - W_{12} + 2W_{22} - W_{32}),\\ x_3 &= \tfrac{1}{3}(W_{11} + W_{21} + W_{31} - W_{12} - W_{22} + 2W_{32}). \end{aligned}$$

Of course the expression

$$F(\kappa) = e^{\kappa t}\int_0^t e^{-\kappa t}\varphi_i(t)\,dt$$

can be evaluated by the general formula for the functions of a matrix [Eq. (191.10)].

IV. THE EXISTENCE AND CONSTRUCTION OF PERIODIC SOLUTIONS[1]

196. The Differential Equations.—Consider the differential equations

$$y_i' = f_i(y_i, \cdots, y_n; \mu), \qquad i = 1, \cdots, n, \tag{1}$$

in which the f_i are analytic functions of its arguments. Suppose that when the parameter μ is zero, Eqs. (1) admit the known periodic solution

$$y_i = y_i^{(0)}(t), \qquad i = 1, \cdots, n,$$

in which y_i are either constants or periodic functions of the time. Without loss of generality the period can be taken equal to 2π, for it can always be made 2π by a suitable change of the independent variable.

[1] MacMillan, "An Existence Theorem for Periodic Solutions," *Transactions of the American Mathematical Society*, Vol. 13, p. 146 (1912).

In order to discuss the solutions of Eqs. (1) when μ is distinct from zero, and there may be more than one such parameter, let

$$y_i = y_i^{(0)}(t) + x_i, \qquad i = 1, \cdots, n,$$

and suppose that the f_i are regular for

$$y_i - y_i^{(0)}(t) = \mu = 0,$$

for all values of t in the interval zero to 2π. If for convenience of notation the parameter μ is denoted by x_0, Eqs. (1) become, on expanding in powers of the x_j,

$$\begin{aligned} x_i' + \sum_{j=1}^{n} \theta_j^{(i)} x_j = \theta_0^{(i)} x_0 &+ \sum_{j=0}^{n} \sum_{k=0}^{j} \theta_{jk}^{(i)} x_j x_k \\ &+ \sum_{j=0}^{n} \sum_{k=0}^{j} \sum_{l=0}^{k} \theta_{jkl}^{(i)} x_j x_k x_l + \cdots, \end{aligned} \tag{2}$$

in which the coefficients $\theta_{j\ldots}^{(i)}$ are either constants or continuous, periodic functions of t with the period 2π.

Before integrating Eqs. (2), consider the linear equations

$$x_i' = \Sigma \theta_j^{(i)} x_j = 0, \tag{3}$$

that are obtained by setting the left members of Eqs. (2) equal to zero. These equations are linear and homogeneous with periodic coefficients. Their solution can be written in the form[1]

$$x_i = \sum_{j=1}^{n} A_j \xi_j^{(i)}(t), \tag{4}$$

in which the A_j are constants of integration and the functions $\xi_j^{(i)}$ can be so taken that the determinant

$$\Delta = | \xi_j^{(i)}(0) | = 1.$$

Expanded according to the elements of its ith line

$$\Delta = \sum_{j=1}^{n} \Delta_j^{(i)} \xi_j^{(i)}(0) = 1, \tag{5}$$

where $\Delta_j^{(i)}$ is the minor obtained by suppressing the ith line and the jth column of Δ and multiplying by $(-1)^{i+j}$.

[1] See Moulton and MacMillan, *American Journal of Mathematics*, Vol. 33, pp. 63–96 (1911).

197. Integration of the Differential Equations as a Power Series in the Initial Values.—If the initial values of the x_i are denoted by α_i, and $x_0 = \mu$ by α_0, it follows from Cauchy's existence theorem[1] that the solutions of Eqs. (196.2) are expansible as power series in the α_j, reducing for $t = 0$ to

$$x_i(0) = \alpha_i,$$

and from Poincaré's extension[2] of Cauchy's theorem that these solutions converge for all values of t in any preassigned range for which the right members of Eqs. (196.2) converge, provided the moduli of the α_i are sufficiently small. That is, the solutions of Eqs. (196.2) can be written

$$x_i = \sum_{j=0}^{n} x_j^{(i)}\alpha_j + \text{higher degree terms}, \qquad i = 1, \cdots, n, \tag{1}$$

where

$$x_i^{(i)}(0) = 1, \tag{2}$$

and all of the other coefficients vanish at $t = 0$. On substituting Eqs. (1) in Eqs. (196.2), it is found that the differential equations for the linear terms in $\alpha_1, \ldots, \alpha_n$ are

$$\frac{dx_j^{(i)}}{dt} + \sum_{k=1}^{n} \theta_k^{(i)} x_j^{(k)} = 0, \qquad i, j = 1, \cdots, n. \tag{3}$$

These equations are the same as Eqs. (196.3), and the solutions are therefore

$$x_j^{(i)} = \sum_{k=1}^{n} A_k^{(j)} \xi_k^{(i)}(t), \qquad i, j = 1, \cdots, n.$$

From the initial conditions, Eqs. (2), it follows that

$$x_j^{(i)}(0) = \delta_{ij},$$

where

$$\delta_{jj} = 1 \qquad \text{and} \qquad \delta_{ij} = 0, \qquad (i \neq j).$$

Hence

$$\sum_{k=1}^{n} A_k^{(j)} \xi_k^{(i)}(0) = \delta_{ij}.$$

[1] Collected Works, 1st series, Vol. 7.

[2] *Les Méthodes Nouvelles de la Mécanique Céleste*, Vol. 1, p. 55.

Since the determinant of the left members is equal to unity, the solutions of these equations are

$$A_k^{(j)} = \Delta_k^{(i)},$$

and therefore

$$x_j^{(i)} = \sum_{k=1}^{n} \Delta_k^{(j)} \xi_k^{(i)}(t), \qquad i, j = 1, \cdots, n. \tag{4}$$

Since $x_0 = \mu = \alpha_0$, the coefficients of α_0 are linear but not homogeneous. They are

$$\frac{dx_0^{(i)}}{dt} + \sum_{k=1}^{n} \theta_k^{(i)} x_0^{(k)} = \theta_0^{(i)}(t), \qquad i = 1, \cdots, n. \tag{5}$$

The general solution of these non-homogeneous equations can be denoted by

$$x_0^{(i)} = m_i(t) + \sum_{k=1}^{n} A_k^{(0)} \xi_k^{(i)}, \tag{6}$$

in which $m_i(t)$ is the particular solution and the $A_k^{(0)}$ are the constants of integration.

From the initial conditions,

$$x_0^{(i)}(0) = 0,$$

it follows that

$$\sum_{k=1}^{n} A_k^{(0)} \xi_k^{(i)}(0) = -m_i(0).$$

Hence

$$A_k^{(0)} = -\sum_{j=1}^{n} \Delta_k^{(j)} m_j(0), \qquad k = 1, \cdots, n,$$

and

$$x_0^{(i)} = m_i(t) - \sum_{k=1}^{n} \sum_{j=1}^{n} \Delta_k^{(j)} m_j(0) \xi_k^{(i)}(t), \qquad i = 1, \cdots, n. \tag{7}$$

The linear terms of the solutions as power series in the α's are therefore

$$\sum_{j=0}^{n} x_j^{(i)} \alpha_j = \sum_{k=1}^{n} \left[\sum_{j=1}^{n} \Delta_k^{(j)} [\alpha_j - m_i(0)\alpha_0] \right] \xi_k^{(i)}(t) + m_i(t)\alpha_0. \tag{8}$$

198. A Change of Parameters.—It is convenient now to change the parameters by the linear substitutions

$$\alpha_0 = \beta_0, \qquad \sum_{j=1}^{n} \Delta_k^{(j)}[\alpha_j - m_i(0)\alpha_0] = \beta_k, \qquad k = 1, \cdots, n, \quad (1)$$

which can be solved for the α's in terms of the β's, since the determinant $|\Delta_k^{(j)}|$ has the value unity. The result is

$$\alpha_0 = \beta_0, \qquad \alpha_j = m_j(0)\beta_0 + \sum_{k=1}^{n} \xi_k^{(j)}(0)\beta_k, \qquad j = 1, \cdots, n. \quad (2)$$

Since Eqs. (1) as power series in $\alpha_0, \ldots, \alpha_n$ converge if the moduli of the α_j are sufficiently small, the solutions of Eqs. (196.2) can also be developed as power series in the β_j which converge if the moduli of the β_j are sufficiently small; and for $t = 0$ will reduce to [Eqs. (197.7)] the linear terms

$$x_i(0) = m_i(0)\beta_0 + \sum_{k=1}^{n} \xi_k^{(i)}(0)\beta_k, \qquad i = 1, \cdots, n. \quad (3)$$

For, the transformation, Eqs. (1), are linear and homogeneous, and the coefficient of every α of degree higher than the first vanishes at $t = 0$. The same will be true, therefore, for the series in the β's.

Expressed in terms of the β's, the solutions of Eqs. (196.2) can be written

$$x_i = m_i(t)\beta_0 + \sum_{j=1}^{n} \xi_j^{(i)}(t)\beta_j + \sum_{j=0}^{n}\sum_{k=0}^{j} x_{jk}^{(i)}\beta_j\beta_k + \sum_{j=0}^{n}\sum_{k=0}^{j}\sum_{l=0}^{k} x_{jkl}^{(i)}\beta_j\beta_k\beta_l + \cdots. \quad (4)$$

Since $\beta_1, \ldots, \beta_n$ are arbitrary, it is seen that they are merely the constants of integration of the linear terms [Eqs. (196.3)].

Hence the following theorem, since the periodic properties of Eqs. (196.1) have not been used:

Theorem.—If

$$(A) \qquad \frac{dx_i}{dt} = f_i(x_1, \cdots, x_n; \mu; t), \qquad i = 1, \cdots, n$$

is a system of differential equations in which the f_i are analytic functions of $x_1, \ldots, x_n$; and μ, regular for all t in the interval $0 \leqq t \leqq T$, and vanish for $x_1 = x_2 = \cdots = x_n = \mu = 0$, and if the f_i are uniform and continuous in the interval $0 \leqq t \leqq T$; and if

$$(B) \qquad \frac{dx_i}{dt} + \sum \theta_j^{(i)} x_j = 0$$

are the linear terms of (*A*) *equated to zero, then the solutions of* (*A*) *are expansible as power series in* μ *and the constants of integration of the solutions of* (*B*), *and these solutions converge in the interval* $0 \leqq t \leqq T$ *provided the moduli of* μ *and the constants of integration are sufficiently small.*

For homogeneity of notation, Eqs. (4) will hereafter be written

$$x_i = \sum_{j=0}^{n} x_j^{(i)}\beta_j + \sum_{j=0}^{n}\sum_{k=0}^{j} x_{jk}^{(i)}\beta_j\beta_k + \sum_{j=0}^{n}\sum_{k=0}^{j}\sum_{l=0}^{k} x_{jkl}^{(i)}\beta_j\beta_k\beta_l + \cdots, \qquad (5)$$

though it should be observed that the $x_j^{(i)}$ are the same as the linear terms in Eqs. (4) and are not the same as the $x_j^{(i)}$ used in Sec. 197.

On substituting Eqs. (5) in Eqs. (196.2) and rearranging as power series in $\beta_0, \ldots, \beta_n$, it is found that the terms of the second degree in the β's are

$$\left.\begin{aligned}
&\sum_{j=0}^{n}\sum_{k=0}^{j}\left[\frac{dx_{jk}^{(i)}}{dt} + \sum_{l=1}^{n}\theta_l^{(i)}x_{jk}^{(l)}\right]\beta_j\beta_k = \\
&\quad \sum_{j=0}^{n}\sum_{k=0}^{j}\theta_{jk}^{(i)}\left(\sum_{n=0}^{n}x_r^{(i)}\beta_r\right)\left(\sum_{s=0}^{n}x_s^{(k)}\beta_s\right) = \\
&\qquad \sum_{r=0}^{n}\sum_{s=0}^{r}e_{rs}\left(\sum_{j=0}^{n}\sum_{k=0}^{j}\theta_{jk}^{(i)}(x_r^{(j)}x_s^{(k)} + x_r^{(k)}x_s^{(j)})\right)\beta_r\beta_s = \\
&\qquad \sum_{j=0}^{n}\sum_{k=0}^{j}e_{jk}\left(\sum_{r=0}^{n}\sum_{s=0}^{r}\theta_{rs}^{(i)}(x_j^{(r)}x_k^{(s)} + x_j^{(s)}x_k^{(r)})\right)\beta_j\beta_k,
\end{aligned}\right\} \qquad (6)$$

in which $e_{jk} = 1$ if j and k are different and $e_{jj} = \frac{1}{2}$. Hence

$$\frac{dx_{jk}^{(i)}}{dt} + \sum_{l=1}^{n}\theta_l^{(i)}x_{jk}^{(l)} = e_{jk}\sum_{r=0}^{n}\sum_{s=0}^{r}\theta_{rs}^{(i)}(x_j^{(r)}x_k^{(s)} + x_j^{(s)}x_k^{(r)}),$$
$$i = 1, \cdots, n. \qquad (7)$$

Since the linear terms are known, the right numbers of these equations are known functions of the time. The equations are therefore linear and non-homogeneous in the $x_{jk}^{(i)}$. If a particular solution is $\varphi_{jk}^{(i)}(t)$, the general solution of Eqs. (7) is

$$x_{jk}^{(i)} = \varphi_{jk}^{(i)}(t) + \sum_{l=1}^{n} A_{jk}^{(l)}\xi_l^{(i)}, \qquad i = 1, \cdots, n. \tag{8}$$

In order to satisfy the initial condition, it is necessary that

$$\sum_{l=1}^{n} A_{jk}^{(l)}\xi_l^{(i)}(0) = -\varphi_{jk}^{(i)}(0),$$

whence

$$A_{jk}^{(l)} = -\sum_{h=1}^{n}\Delta_l^{(h)}\varphi_{jk}^{(h)}(0);$$

so that Eqs. (7) become

$$x_{jk}^{(i)} = \varphi_{jk}^{(i)}(t) - \sum_{l=1}^{n}\sum_{h=1}^{n}\Delta_l^{(h)}\varphi_{jk}^{(h)}(0)\,\xi_l^{(i)}(t). \tag{9}$$

Thus the terms of the second degree become known.

In a similar manner there is obtained for the terms of third degree

$$\left.\begin{aligned}
&\sum_{j=0}^{n}\sum_{k=0}^{j}\sum_{l=0}^{k}\left[\frac{dx_{jkl}^{(i)}}{dt}+\sum_{m=1}^{n}\theta_m^{(i)}x_{jkl}^{(m)}\right]\beta_j\beta_k\beta_l = \\
&\quad\sum_{p=0}^{n}\sum_{q=0}^{p}\sum_{r=0}^{q}\theta_{pqr}^{(i)}\left(\sum_{j=0}^{n}x_j^{(p)}\beta_j\right)\left(\sum_{k=0}^{n}x_k^{(q)}\beta_k\right)\times \\
&\quad\quad\left(\sum_{l=0}^{n}x_l^{(r)}\beta_l\right)+\sum_{p=0}^{n}\sum_{q=0}^{p}\theta_{pq}^{(i)}\left\{\left(\sum_{j=0}^{n}x_j^{(q)}\beta_j\right)\right. \\
&\quad\quad\left(\sum_{j=0}^{n}\sum_{k=0}^{j}x_{jk}^{(p)}\beta_j\beta_k\right)+\left(\sum_{j=0}^{n}x_j^{(p)}\beta_j\right)\times \\
&\quad\quad\left.\left(\sum_{j=0}^{n}\sum_{k=0}^{j}x_{jk}^{(q)}\beta_j\beta_k\right)\right\} = \sum_{j=0}^{n}\sum_{k=0}^{j}\sum_{l=0}^{k} \\
&\left[\sum_{p=0}^{n}\sum_{q=0}^{p}\sum_{r=0}^{q}e_{jkl}\theta_{pqr}^{(i)}\left\{\begin{aligned}&+(x_j^{(p)}x_k^{(q)}+x_k^{(p)}x_j^{(q)})x_l^{(r)}\\&+(x_j^{(p)}x_l^{(q)}+x_l^{(p)}x_j^{(q)})x_k^{(r)}\\&+(x_k^{(p)}x_l^{(q)}+x_l^{(p)}x_k^{(q)})x_j^{(r)}\end{aligned}\right\}+\right. \\
&\quad\left.\sum_{p=0}^{n}\sum_{q=0}^{p}\delta_{jkl}\theta_{pq}^{(i)}\left\{\begin{aligned}&+(x_{jk}^{(p)}x_l^{(q)}+x_{jk}^{(q)}x_l^{(p)})\\&+(x_{jl}^{(p)}x_k^{(q)}+x_{jl}^{(q)}x_k^{(p)})\\&+(x_{kl}^{(p)}x_j^{(q)}+x_{kl}^{(q)}x_j^{(p)})\end{aligned}\right\}\right]\beta_j\beta_k\beta_l.
\end{aligned}\right\} \tag{10}$$

The symbol e_{jkl} is 1 if j, k, and l are all different; $\frac{1}{2}$ if two are alike and different from the third; and $\frac{1}{6}$ if all three are alike. The symbol δ_{jkl} means that when two of the three letters j, k and l are equal only one of two like terms are to be taken, and when all three are alike, only one of three like terms is to be taken.

The right members of the differential equations in Eqs. (10) are known since the $x_j^{(i)}$ and $x_{jk}^{(i)}$ are all known functions of the time. If $\varphi_{jkl}^{(i)}$ is a particular solution, the general solution is

$$x_{jkl}^{(i)} = \varphi_{jkl}^{(i)}(t) + \sum_{m=1}^{n} A_{jkl}^{(m)}\xi_m^{(i)}(t),$$

and when the constants of integration are determined so that every $x_{jkl}^{(i)}$ vanishes with t, the solution is

$$x_{jkl}^{(i)} = \varphi_{jkl}^{(i)}(t) - \sum_{g=1}^{n}\sum_{h=1}^{n}\Delta_g^{(h)}\varphi_{jkl}^{(h)}(0)\xi_g^{(i)}(t). \qquad (11)$$

The integration, evidently, can be carried as far as may be desired.

199. The Integration as Power Series in μ Alone.—Without specifying the initial values of the x_i and without regard to the convergence of the series so derived, the differential equations can be integrated formally as power series in μ, or any root of μ, say $\mu^{1/p}$. The integration will be carried out here as a power series in μ, and the constants of integration arising at each step left undetermined.

Let the assumed series

$$x_i = x_1^{(i)}\mu + x_2^{(i)}\mu^2 + x_3^{(i)}\mu^3 + \cdots, \qquad i = 1, \cdots, n. \qquad (1)$$

be substituted in the differential equations, Eqs. 196.2, and these series then arranged in powers of μ. From the coefficients of the first power of μ it is found that

$$\frac{dx_1^{(i)}}{dt} + \sum_{j=1}^{n}\theta_j^{(i)}x_1^{(j)} = \theta_0^{(i)}(t), \qquad i = 1, \cdots, n. \qquad (2)$$

These differential equations are the same as Eqs. (197.5) and have therefore the same solutions, Eqs. (197.6), namely

$$x_1^{(i)} = m_i(t) + \sum_{j=1}^{n} A_j^{(i)}\xi_j^{(i)}(t) \qquad i = 1, \cdots, n, \qquad (3)$$

which can be written

$$x_1^{(i)} = \sum_{j=0}^{n} A_j^{(1)} x_j^{(i)}, \tag{4}$$

the $x_j^{(i)}$ being the same functions of t as in Eqs. (198.5), and $A_0^{(1)} = 1$.

The coefficients of μ^2 give the equations

$$\frac{dx_2^{(i)}}{dt} + \sum_{j=1}^{n} \theta_j^{(i)} x_2^{(j)} = \sum_{j=0}^{n} \sum_{k=0}^{j} \theta_{jk}^{(i)} \left(\sum_{p=0}^{n} A_p^{(1)} x_p^{(j)} \right) \times \left(\sum_{q=0}^{n} A_q^{(1)} x_q^{(k)} \right), \quad i = 1, \cdots, n. \tag{5}$$

The right members of these equations differ from those in Eqs. (198.6) only in that $A_p^{(1)}$ is substituted for β_p. The solutions are therefore, Eqs. (198.7),

$$x_2^{(i} = \sum_{j=0}^{n} \sum_{k=0}^{j} \varphi_{jk}^{(i)}(t) A_j^{(1)} A_k^{(1)} + \sum_{l=1}^{n} B_l^{(2)} \xi_l^{(i)}(t).$$

It is proposed to leave the constants of integration undetermined, but it will be observed that if $B_l^{(2)}$ is given the form

$$B_l^{(2)} = -\sum_{h=1}^{n} \Delta_l^{(h)} \sum_{j=0}^{n} \sum_{k=0}^{j} \varphi_{jk}^{(h)}(0) A_j^{(1)} A_k^{(1)} + A_l^{(2)},$$

where the $A_l^{(2)}$ are undetermined, the solution of Eqs. (5) takes the form

$$\left. \begin{aligned} x_2^{(i)} = \sum_{j=0}^{n} \sum_{k=0}^{j} \left[\varphi_{jk}^{(i)}(t) - \sum_{l=1}^{n} \sum_{h=1}^{n} \Delta_l^{(h)} \varphi_{jk}^{(h)}(0) \xi_l^{(i)}(t) \right] A_j^{(1)} A_k^{(1)} \\ + \sum_{j=1}^{n} A_j^{(2)} \xi_j^{(i)} = \sum_{j=0}^{n} \sum_{k=0}^{j} x_{jk}^{(i)} A_j^{(1)} A_k^{(1)} + \sum_{j=0}^{n} A_j^{(2)} x_j^{(i)}, \end{aligned} \right\} \tag{6}$$

where $A_0^{(2)}$ is zero. The initial value of $x_2^{(i)}$ is then

$$x_2^{(i)}(0) = \sum_{j=0}^{n} A_j^{(2)} x_j^{(i)}(0),$$

which is undetermined, since all of the $A_j^{(2)}$ are undetermined.

From the coefficients of μ^3 it is found that

$$\frac{dx_3^{(i)}}{dt} + \sum_{j=1}^{n} \theta_j^{(i)} x_3^{(j)} = \sum_{p=0}^{n} \sum_{q=0}^{p} \sum_{r=0}^{q} \theta_{pqr}^{(i)} \left(\sum_{j=0}^{n} A_j^{(1)} x_j^{(p)} \right) \left(\sum_{k=0}^{n} A_k^{(1)} x_k^{(q)} \right) \left(\sum_{l=0}^{n} A_l^{(1)} x_l^{(r)} \right) + \sum_{p=0}^{n} \sum_{q=0}^{p} \theta_{pq}^{(i)} \left\{ \sum_{j=0}^{n} A_j^{(1)} x_j^{(p)} \left[\sum_{k=0}^{n} \sum_{l=0}^{k} A_k^{(1)} A_l^{(1)} x_{kl}^{(q)} + \sum_{k=0}^{n} A_k^{(2)} x_k^{(q)} \right] + \sum_{j=0}^{n} A_j^{(1)} x_j^{(q)} \left[\sum_{k=0}^{n} \sum_{l=0}^{k} A_k^{(1)} A_l^{(1)} x_{kl}^{(p)} + \sum_{k=0}^{n} A_k^{(2)} x_k^{(p)} \right] \right\}$$

which becomes, on rearranging the right members,

$$\frac{dx_3^{(i)}}{dt} + \sum_{j=1}^{n} \theta_j^{(i)} x_3^{(j)} = \sum_{j=0}^{n} \sum_{k=0}^{j} \sum_{l=0}^{k} \left[\sum_{p=0}^{n} \sum_{q=0}^{p} \sum_{r=0}^{q} e_{jkl} \theta_{pqr}^{(i)} \begin{Bmatrix} + (x_j^{(p)} x_k^{(q)} + x_j^{(q)} x_k^{(q)}) x_l^{(r)} \\ + (x_j^{(p)} x_l^{(q)} + x_j^{(q)} x_l^{(p)}) x_k^{(r)} \\ + (x_k^{(p)} x_l^{(q)} + x_k^{(q)} x_l^{(p)}) x_j^{(r)} \end{Bmatrix} + \sum_{p=0}^{n} \sum_{q=0}^{p} \delta_{jkl} \theta_{pq}^{(i)} \begin{Bmatrix} + (x_{jk}^{(p)} x_l^{(q)} + x_{jk}^{(q)} x_l^{(p)}) \\ + (x_{jl}^{(p)} x_k^{(q)} + x_{jl}^{(q)} x_k^{(p)}) \\ + (x_{kl}^{(p)} x_j^{(q)} + x_{kl}^{(q)} x_j^{(p)}) \end{Bmatrix} \right] A_j^{(1)} A_k^{(1)} A_l^{(1)} + \sum_{j=0}^{n} \sum_{k=0}^{j} \left[\sum_{p=0}^{n} \sum_{q=0}^{p} e_{jk} \theta_{pq}^{(i)} (x_j^{(p)} x_k^{(q)} + x_j^{(q)} x_k^{(p)}) \right] [A_j^{(1)} A_k^{(2)} + A_j^{(2)} A_k^{(1)}].$$

On comparing these equations with Eqs. (198.10) and (198.6), it is seen that the solution is

$$x_3^{(i)} = \sum_{j=0}^{n} \sum_{k=0}^{j} \sum_{l=0}^{k} \varphi_{jkl}^{(i)} A_j^{(1)} A_k^{(1)} A_l^{(1)} + \sum_{j=0}^{n} \sum_{k=0}^{j} \varphi_{jk}^{(i)} [A_j^{(1)} A_k^{(2)} + A_j^{(2)} A_k^{(1)}] + \sum_{g=1}^{n} B_g^{(3)} \xi_g^{(i)};$$

and if the constants of integration are given the form

$$B_g^{(3)} = -\sum_{h=1}^{n}\Delta_g^{(h)}\left[\sum_{j=0}^{n}\sum_{k=0}^{j}\sum_{l=0}^{k}\varphi_{jkl}^{(h)}(0)A_j^{(1)}A_k^{(1)}A_l^{(1)} + \sum_{j=0}^{n}\sum_{k=0}^{j}\varphi_{jk}^{(h)}(0)[A_j^{(1)}A_k^{(2)} + A_k^{(1)}A_j^{(2)}]\right] + A_g^{(3)},$$

they become

$$x_3^{(i)} = \sum_{j=0}^{n}\sum_{k=0}^{j}\sum_{l=0}^{k}\left[\varphi_{jkl}^{(i)} - \sum_{g=1}^{n}\sum_{h=1}^{n}\Delta_g^{(h)}\varphi_{jkl}^{(h)}(0)\xi_g^{(i)}\right] + \sum_{j=0}^{n}\sum_{k=0}^{j}\left[\varphi_{jk}^{(i)} - \sum_{g=1}^{n}\sum_{h=1}^{n}\Delta_g^{(h)}\varphi_{jk}^{(h)}(0)\xi_g^{(i)}\right][A_j^{(1)}A_k^{(2)} + A_k^{(1)}A_j^{(2)}] + \sum_{j=1}^{n}A_j^{(3)}x_j^{(i)};$$

or, more simply,

$$x_3^{(i)} = \sum_{j=0}^{n}\sum_{k=0}^{j}\sum_{l=0}^{k}x_{jkl}^{(i)}A_j^{(1)}A_k^{(1)}A_l^{(1)} + \sum_{j=0}^{n}\sum_{k=0}^{j}x_{jk}^{(i)}(A_j^{(1)}A_k^{(2)} + A_k^{(1)}A_j^{(2)}) + \sum_{j=0}^{n}A_j^{(3)}x_j^{(i)},$$

in which $A_j^{(3)}$ are the constants of integration, $A_0^{(3)}$ is zero, and $x_{jk}^{(i)}$, $x_{jkl}^{(i)}$ are the same functions of t that occur in Eqs. (198.9) and (198.11). Since these functions vanish with t, the initial values of $x_3^{(i)}$ are

$$x_3^{(i)}(0) = \sum_{j=0}^{n}A_j^{(3)}x_j^{(i)}(0).$$

The coefficients of the higher powers of μ can be determined in a similar manner. So far as they have been worked out, the solutions as power series in μ are

$$\left.\begin{aligned} x_i = {} & \left[\sum_{j=0}^{n}A_j^{(1)}x_j^{(i)}\right]\mu + \left[\sum_{j=0}^{n}\sum_{k=0}^{j}x_{jk}^{(i)}A_j^{(1)}A_k^{(1)} + \sum_{j=0}^{n}A_j^{(2)}x_j^{(i)}\right]\mu^2 + \left[\sum_{j=0}^{n}\sum_{k=0}^{j}\sum_{l=0}^{k}x_{jkl}^{(i)}A_j^{(1)}A_k^{(1)}A_l^{(1)} + \right. \\ & \sum_{j=0}^{n}\sum_{k=0}^{j}x_{jk}^{(i)}(A_j^{(1)}A_k^{(2)} + \\ & \left. A_k^{(1)}A_j^{(2)}) + \sum_{j=0}^{n}A_j^{(3)}x_j^{(i)}\right]\mu^3 + \cdots, \end{aligned}\right\} \quad (7)$$

in which $A_0^{(1)} = 1$ and $A_0^{(p)} = 0$, $p > 1$. All of the other $A_j^{(p)}$ are undetermined.

A comparison of Eqs. (7) with Eqs. (198.5) shows that Eqs. (7) could have been derived from Eqs. (198.5) by taking

$$\beta_0 = \mu \quad \text{and} \quad \beta_j = A_j^{(1)}\mu + A_j^{(2)}\mu^2 + A_j^{(3)}\mu^3 + \cdots . \tag{8}$$

This, of course, was to have been expected; for if $0 < A_j^{(p)} < M$, where M is a positive constant, the substitution, Eqs. (8), converges for all $\mu < 1$. Therefore the substitution of Eqs. (8) will give solutions of the differential equations as power series in μ which converge for μ sufficiently small, and which, at $t = 0$, reduce to

$$x_i(0) = \sum_{k=1}^{\infty} \sum_{j=0}^{n} A_j^{(k)} x_j^{(i)}(0)\mu^k.$$

But these are exactly the conditions under which Eqs. (7) were developed. The two series are therefore identical.

200. Conditions for Periodic Solutions.—From the hypothesis on the coefficients $\theta_{j\ldots}^{(i)}$ in the differential equations, *i.e.*, that they are constants or periodic functions of t with the period 2π, it follows that sufficient conditions that the solutions shall be periodic with the period $2k\pi$ (k an integer) are

$$x_i(2k\pi) = x_i(0). \qquad i = 1, \cdots, n.$$

If the x_i all return to their original values, it is obvious from the differential equations that their first derivatives retake their initial values, and therefore all higher derivatives do likewise. Consequently, under these conditions,

$$x_i(t + 2k\pi) \equiv x_i(t) \qquad i = 1, \cdots, n.$$

If the difference between the value of a function at $t = 2k\pi$ and at $t = 0$ is denoted by a dash over the letter representing the function, for example,

$$\bar{x}_i \equiv x_i(2k\pi) - x_i(0),$$

the conditions for periodicity as derived from Eqs. (198.5) are

$$0 = \sum_{j=0}^{n} \bar{x}_j^{(i)}\beta_j + \sum_{j=0}^{n} \sum_{k=0}^{j} \bar{x}_{jk}^{(i)}\beta_j\beta_k + \sum_{=0}^{n} \sum_{k=0}^{j} \sum_{l=0}^{k} \bar{x}_{jkl}^{(i)}\beta_j\beta_k\beta_l + \cdots , \tag{1}$$

and as derived from Eqs. (199.7),

$$
\left.\begin{aligned}
0 \underset{\mu}{\equiv} &\left[\sum_{j=0}^{n} A_j^{(1)}\bar{x}_j^{(i)}\right]\mu + \left[\sum_{j=0}^{n}\sum_{k=0}^{j}\bar{x}_{jk}^{(i)}A_j^{(1)}A_k^{(1)} + \right. \\
&\left.\sum_{j=0}^{n} A_j^{(2)}\bar{x}_j^{(i)}\right]\mu^2 + \left[\sum_{j=0}^{n}\sum_{k=0}^{j}\sum_{l=0}^{k}\bar{x}_{jkl}^{(i)}A_j^{(1)}A_k^{(1)}A_l^{(1)} + \right. \\
&\sum_{j=0}^{n}\sum_{k=0}^{j}\bar{x}_{jk}^{(i)}(A_j^{(1)}A_k^{(2)} + A_k^{(1)}A_j^{(2)}) + \\
&\qquad\qquad\qquad \left.\sum_{j=0}^{n} A_j^{(3)}\bar{x}_j^{(i)}\right]\mu^3 + \cdots .
\end{aligned}\right\} \quad (2)
$$

Since the second set of conditions, Eqs. (2), can be derived from the first set, Eqs. (1), by the substitution Eqs. (199.8), it is clear that if the constants $A_j^{(p)}$ can be determined so as to satisfy Eqs. (2), then the values of the β_j as defined in Eqs. (199.8) will also satisfy Eqs. (1). That is, the determination of the constants $A_j^{(p)}$ in such a way as to make the series Eqs. (199.7) periodic is equivalent to a solution of the equations of condition Eqs. (1). The convergence of the series so derived is assured by the general theorem in Sec. 182. For any sort of series for the β's in integral or fractional powers of μ, that vanishes with μ, and satisfies Eqs. (1) is convergent if the modulus of μ is sufficiently small, provided the determination of the constants becomes unique at some stage of the process and remains so.

It should be stated however that Eqs. (1) may admit solutions that are not of the form Eqs. (199.8), which contains only integral powers of μ. There may exist solutions in fractional powers of μ, and none in integral powers. If this is true it is necessary to have Eqs. (1), and Eqs. (1) can be obtained from Eqs. (2) by the substitution

$$A_j^{(1)}\mu = \beta_j, \qquad A_j^{(p)} = 0 \qquad p > 1.$$

These results are embodied in the following theorem:

Theorem.—If

$$\frac{dx_i}{dt} = f_i(x_1, \cdots, x_n; \mu; t), \qquad i = 1, \cdots, n,$$

is a system of differential equations in which the f_i are expansible as power series in $x_1, \ldots, x_n$ and μ, *vanishing for*

$$x_1 = \cdots = x_n = \mu = 0,$$

with coefficients which are uniform, continuous, and periodic functions of t with the period 2π, and if the f_i converge for $0 \leqq t \leqq 2\pi$ when $x_i < \rho_i$, $\mu < r$, then the $x_i(t)$ are expansible as power series in μ, or any fractional power of μ, which converge for all values of t in the interval $0 \leqq t \leqq 2\pi$ provided $|\mu|$ is sufficiently small. If the constants of integration that arise at each stage of the process can be determined so that the series are formally periodic, then the solution so determined will be periodic and will converge for all finite values of t provided $|\mu|$ is sufficiently small.

It has been assumed for simplicity that there is but one parameter μ. There may be several and the course of the argument is not altered. Suppose δ is a second parameter and is available for making the series periodic. If δ can be determined as a power series in μ in such a way as to make the series periodic, the equations of condition, Eqs. (1), will be satisfied and the series so derived will converge.

V. ILLUSTRATIVE EXAMPLES

201. The Rocking Pendulum without Friction.—In Sec. 67 the problem of the rocking pendulum was discussed and, for the case in which there is no friction, the energy equation [Eq. (67.5)] gave

$$\left(\frac{d\theta}{dt}\right)^2 = 2gl\frac{\cos\theta - \cos\theta_0}{\rho^2 + l^2\sin^2\theta}, \tag{1}$$

where θ is the angle which the axis of the pendulum makes with the vertical, l is the distance of the center of gravity from the axis of the rolling cylinder, ρ is the radius of gyration at the center of gravity, and θ_0 is the amplitude of the oscillation.

Equation (1) requires but a single integration to effect a solution, but as an integral in terms of known functions cannot be found, resort to integration by series is necessary. The problem of the simple pendulum (I, **319**) suggests the notation

$$\mu = \sin\tfrac{1}{2}\theta_0, \qquad \lambda^2 = \frac{4l^2}{\rho^2}, \tag{2}$$

and the substitution

$$\sin\tfrac{1}{2}\theta = \mu\sin\varphi. \tag{3}$$

With these changes Eq. (1) becomes

$$\left(\frac{d\varphi}{dt}\right)^2 = \frac{gl}{\rho^2}\frac{1 - \mu^2\sin^2\varphi}{1 + \lambda^2\mu^2\sin^2\varphi(1 - \mu^2\sin^2\varphi)}, \tag{4}$$

a form that is suitable for expansion in powers of μ. A second parameter λ also occurs, but for a given pendulum λ is a definite constant, and therefore is not available for making the solution periodic in form.

For $\mu = 0$ the solution of Eq. (4) is simply

$$\varphi = \sqrt{\frac{gl}{\rho^2}}\, t,$$

if φ vanishes with t. It is seen from Eq. (3) that as φ runs from zero to 2π the pendulum makes a complete oscillation. Therefore, for $\mu = 0$, the limit of the period of the pendulum is

$$P = 2\pi\sqrt{\frac{\rho^2}{gl}}.$$

Presumably, the period of the pendulum depends upon the amplitude of the oscillation, and this fact suggests a change of the independent variable from t to τ by the substitution

$$\sqrt{\frac{gl}{\rho^2}}\, t = (1 + \delta)\tau, \tag{5}$$

where δ is a new parameter that will be available for making the solution periodic in τ with the fixed period 2π. If this can be done, the period in t will be

$$P = 2\pi(1 + \delta)\sqrt{\frac{\rho^2}{gl}}. \tag{6}$$

Since δ vanishes with μ, it is seen that for $\mu = 0$, $\varphi = \tau$. Hence, in general, that is, for $\mu \neq 0$,

$$\varphi = \tau + \psi,$$

where ψ is some function of τ that vanishes with μ. On introducing these new variables and using accents to indicate differentiation with respect to τ, Eq. (4) becomes

$$(1 + \psi')^2 = (1 + \delta)^2 \frac{1 - \mu^2 \sin^2 (\tau + \psi)}{1 + \lambda^2\mu^2 \sin^2 (\tau + \psi)[1 - \mu^2 \sin^2 (\tau + \psi)]}. \tag{7}$$

Since μ occurs in this equation only in the form μ^2, it will be assumed that the solution is a power series in μ^2, and therefore that

and

$$\left.\begin{aligned} \psi &= \psi_2\mu^2 + \psi_4\mu^4 + \psi_6\mu^6 + \cdots, \\ \delta &= \delta_2\mu^2 + \delta_4\mu^4 + \delta_6\mu^6 + \cdots. \end{aligned}\right\} \tag{8}$$

The coefficients ψ_j of the first series are functions of τ to be determined by the differential equations, and the coefficients δ_j are constants to be determined by the condition that the ψ_i be periodic in τ with the period 2π.

If Eqs. (8) are substituted in Eq. (7) and the series are then arranged in powers of μ^2, it is found that

$$\begin{aligned} 2\psi_2'\mu^2 + 2\psi_4'\mu^4 + 2\psi_6'\mu^6 + \cdots \underset{\mu}{\equiv}\, & [2\delta_2 - \tfrac{1}{2}(1 + \lambda^2) + \tfrac{1}{2}(1 + \lambda^2)\cos 2\tau]\mu^2 \\ & + [2\delta_4 + \delta_2^2 + \delta_2(1 + \lambda^2)(-1 + \cos 2\tau) - \psi_2'^2 \\ & + (2\lambda^2 + \lambda^4)(\tfrac{3}{8} - \tfrac{1}{2}\cos 2\tau + \tfrac{1}{8}\cos 4\tau) - \psi_2(1 + \lambda^2 \sin 2\tau]\mu^4 \\ & + [2\delta_6 + 2\delta_2\delta_4 + (\delta_4 + \tfrac{1}{2}\delta_2^2)(1 + \lambda^2)(-1 + \cos 2\tau) \\ & + 2\delta_2(2\lambda^2 + \lambda^4)(\tfrac{3}{8} - \tfrac{1}{2}\cos 2\tau + \tfrac{1}{8}\cos 4\tau) - \\ & \qquad 2\delta_2\psi_2(1 + \lambda^2)\sin 2\tau \\ & + (\lambda^2 + 3\lambda^4 + \lambda^6)(-\tfrac{5}{16} + \tfrac{15}{32}\cos 2\tau - \tfrac{3}{16}\cos 4\tau + \tfrac{1}{32}\cos 6\tau) \\ & - (1 + \lambda^2)\psi_2^2 \cos 2\tau + (2\lambda^2 + \lambda^4)\psi_2 \sin 2\tau \\ & \quad - (\tfrac{1}{2}\lambda^2 + \tfrac{1}{4}\lambda^4)\psi_2 \sin 4\tau - (1 + \lambda^2)\psi_4 \sin 2\tau - 2\psi_2'\psi_4']\mu^6 \\ & + \cdots\cdots . \end{aligned}$$

A comparison of the coefficients of the two members of this equation shows that:

Coefficients of μ^2.

$$\psi_2' = \delta_2 - \tfrac{1}{4}(1 + \lambda^2) + \tfrac{1}{4}(1 + \lambda^2)\cos 2\tau.$$

In order that the solution of this equation may be periodic, it is necessary that the constant term in the right member shall be zero. This condition requires that

$$\delta_2 = \tfrac{1}{4}(1 + \lambda^2),$$

and it is then found that

$$\psi_2 = \tfrac{1}{8}(1 + \lambda^2)\sin 2\tau,$$

if the constant of integration is chosen so that ψ_2 vanishes with τ.

Coefficient of μ^4.

$$\begin{aligned} 2\psi_4' = {} & 2\delta_4 + \delta_2^2 + \delta_2(1 + \lambda^2)(-1 + \cos 2\tau) - \psi_2'^2 \\ & + (2\lambda^2 + \lambda^4)(\tfrac{3}{8} - \tfrac{1}{2}\cos 2\tau + \tfrac{1}{8}\cos 4\tau) - \psi_2(1 + \lambda^2)\sin 2\tau. \end{aligned}$$

If the values of ψ_2 and δ_2 that have just been determined are substituted in the right member of this equation, it becomes

$$2\psi_4' = (2\delta_4 - \tfrac{9}{32} + \tfrac{3}{16}\lambda^2 + \tfrac{3}{64}\lambda^4) + (\tfrac{1}{4} - \tfrac{1}{2}\lambda^2 - \tfrac{1}{4}\lambda^4)\cos 2\tau +$$
$$(\tfrac{1}{32} + \tfrac{5}{16}\lambda^2 + \tfrac{5}{32}\lambda^4)\cos 4\tau.$$

The condition that the constant term be zero requires that

$$\delta_4 = \tfrac{9}{64} - \tfrac{3}{32}\lambda^2 - \tfrac{3}{64}\lambda^4,$$

and then, by integration,

$$\psi_4 = (\tfrac{1}{16} - \tfrac{1}{8}\lambda^2 - \tfrac{1}{16}\lambda^4)\sin 2\tau + (\tfrac{1}{256} + \tfrac{5}{128}\lambda^2 + \tfrac{5}{256}\lambda^4)\sin 4\tau.$$

Coefficients of μ^6.

It is found in an entirely similar manner from the coefficients of μ^6 that

$$\delta_6 = \tfrac{1}{256}(25 - 5\lambda^2 + 15\lambda^4 + 5\lambda^6),$$

and

$$\psi_6 = (83 + \lambda^2 + 237\lambda^4 + 79\lambda^6)\frac{\sin 2\tau}{2048} +$$
$$(1 - 3\lambda^2 - 15\lambda^4 - 5\lambda^6)\frac{\sin 4\tau}{256}$$
$$+ (1 + 27\lambda^2 + 63\lambda^4 + 21\lambda^6)\frac{\sin 6\tau}{6144}.$$

The details of the computation will be left as an exercise. It is evident that the term $2\delta_{2j}$ occurs in the constant term in the coefficient of μ^{2j}, and the condition that this term must vanish determines δ_{2j} for every j. Integration then gives ψ_{2j}, and if the constant of integration is chosen so that ψ_{2j} vanishes with τ it is evident that the expression for ψ_{2j} contains only terms that are sines of even multiples of τ, and the entire series vanishes with τ.

The solution for φ is therefore

$$\left.\begin{aligned}
\varphi = \tau &+ [\tfrac{1}{8}(1 + \lambda^2)\sin 2\tau]\mu^2 \\
&+ [(\tfrac{1}{16} - \tfrac{1}{8}\lambda^2 - \tfrac{1}{16}\lambda^4)\sin 2\tau + \\
&\qquad (\tfrac{1}{256} + \tfrac{5}{128}\lambda^2 + \tfrac{5}{256}\lambda^4)\sin 4\tau]\mu^4 \\
&+ \Big[\,(83 + \lambda^2 + 237\lambda^4 + 79\lambda^6)\frac{\sin 2\tau}{2048} + \\
&\qquad (1 - 3\lambda^2 - 15\lambda^4 - 5\lambda^6)\frac{\sin 4\tau}{256} \\
&+ (1 + 27\lambda^2 + 63\lambda^4 + 21\lambda^6)\frac{\sin 6\tau}{6144}\Big]\mu^6 + \cdots.
\end{aligned}\right\} \quad (9)$$

$$\delta = \tfrac{1}{4}(1 + \lambda^2)\mu^2 + (\tfrac{9}{64} - \tfrac{3}{32}\lambda^2 - \tfrac{3}{64}\lambda^4)\mu^4 +$$
$$\tfrac{5}{256}(5 - \lambda^2 + 3\lambda^4 + \lambda^6)\mu^6 + \cdots.$$

If it is borne in mind that the origin of time is arbitrary, it is seen that Eqs. (9) are the complete solution of the problem.

AN UNSYMMETRICAL TOP

202. The Differential Equations.—Suppose a rigid body is moving about a fixed point O that is located on a principal axis of the central ellipsoid of inertia at a distance h from the center of mass. This line also is a principal axis of inertia at the point O (Sec. 22). Let it be taken as the **k**-axis of a rectangular system of coordinates, **i, j, k** with the origin at O, and the **i**- and **j**-axes coinciding with the other principal axes at O. It will be assumed that the center of mass lies on the positive end of the **k**-axis, and therefore h is positive.

If, aside from the constraint at O, the only force acting is its weight, the equations of motion are [Eqs. (85.3)]

$$\left.\begin{aligned} A\omega_i' &= (B - C)\omega_j\omega_k + mgh\gamma_2, \\ B\omega_j' &= (C - A)\omega_k\omega_i - mgh\gamma_1, \\ C\omega_k' &= (A - B)\omega_i\omega_j + 0; \end{aligned}\right\} \tag{1}$$

in which ω_i, ω_j, and ω_k are the angular velocities, and γ_1, γ_2, and γ_3 are the direction cosines of the k-axis with respect to a set of rectangular axes that are fixed in space with the z-axis vertical.

In terms of Euler's angles [Eqs. (85.4) and Sec. 52]

$$\left.\begin{aligned} \omega_i &= \psi' \sin\theta \sin\varphi + \theta' \cos\varphi, & \gamma_1 &= \sin\theta \sin\varphi, \\ \omega_j &= \psi' \sin\theta \cos\varphi - \theta' \sin\varphi, & \gamma_2 &= \sin\theta \cos\varphi, \\ \omega_k &= \psi' \cos\theta + \varphi', & \gamma_3 &= \cos\theta. \end{aligned}\right\} \tag{2}$$

The direction cosines γ_j satisfy the differential equations (Problem 9, Chapter VI)

$$\left.\begin{aligned} \gamma_1' &= \omega_k\gamma_2 - \omega_j\gamma_3, \\ \gamma_2' &= \omega_i\gamma_3 - \omega_k\gamma_1, \\ \gamma_3' &= \omega_j\gamma_1 - \omega_i\gamma_2. \end{aligned}\right\} \tag{3}$$

On dividing Eqs. (1) by A, B, and C respectively and then taking

$$a = \frac{B - C}{A}, \qquad b = \frac{A - C}{B}, \qquad c = \frac{A - B}{C},$$

$$h_1 = \frac{mgh}{A}, \qquad h_2 = \frac{mgh}{B},$$

they become

$$\left.\begin{aligned} \omega_i' &= \quad a\omega_j\omega_k + h_1\gamma_2, \\ \omega_j' &= -b\omega_k\omega_i - h_2\gamma_1, \\ \omega_k' &= \quad c\omega_i\omega_j + 0. \end{aligned}\right\} \tag{4}$$

The constants a, b, and c are not independent. They satisfy the relation

$$b = \frac{a + c}{1 + ac},$$

and therefore (Problem 22, Chap. II)

$$A = (1 + c)D, \qquad B = (1 + ac)D, \qquad C = (1 - a)D$$

with

$$-1 < a < +1, \qquad -1 < c < +1.$$

The moments of inertia related to points in the ac-plane have the following order of magnitude:

$$\left.\begin{array}{lll} \text{First quadrant,} & a > 0, c > 0, & A > B > C, \\ \text{Second quadrant,} & a < 0, c > 0, & A > C > B, \quad \text{if } a + c > 0, \\ & & C > A > B, \quad \text{if } a + c < 0, \\ \text{Third quadrant,} & a < 0, c < 0, & C > B > A, \\ \text{Fourth quadrant,} & a > 0, c < 0, & B > A > C, \quad \text{if } a + c > 0, \\ & & B > C > A, \quad \text{if } a + c < 0. \end{array}\right\} \tag{5}$$

The integrals of energy and moment of momentum [Eqs. (86.5) and (86.7)] become

$$\left.\begin{aligned} &(1 + c)\omega_i^2 + (1 + ac)\omega_j^2 + (1 - a)\omega_k^2 \\ &\qquad\qquad = \frac{2mgh}{D}\gamma_3 + \text{constant}, \\ &(1 + c)\omega_i\gamma_1 + (1 + ac)\omega_j\gamma_2 + (1 - a)\omega_k\gamma_3 = \text{constant}, \\ &\text{and, of course,} \\ &\qquad\qquad \gamma_1^2 + \gamma_2^2 + \gamma_3^2 = 1. \end{aligned}\right\} \tag{6}$$

On account of the third of Eqs. (6), it is seen that Eqs. (3) and (4) are really of the fifth order only, and not the sixth which is the order of the complete set of differential equations. Since the γ's depend only upon the angles φ and θ, the angles φ and θ are defined as soon as γ_1 and γ_2 are known. The third of Eqs. (85.5),

$$\sin\theta\,\psi' = \omega_i \sin\varphi + \omega_j \cos\varphi, \tag{7}$$

is necessary to complete the set of differential equations. Equations (3) and (4) however are independent of Eq. (7), since they do not contain the angle ψ, or its derivatives, explicitly. After these equations have been solved, the angle ψ is obtained from Eq. (7) by a quadrature.

203. The Equations of Variation.—Equations (202.3) and (202.4) admit two simple particular solutions. They are: First,

$$\omega_i = \omega_j = \gamma_1 = \gamma_2 = 0, \qquad \omega_3 = n, \qquad \gamma_3 = \pm 1; \tag{1}$$

in which n is arbitrary. In this case the body turns about a principal axis that coincides permanently with the vertical. Second,

$$\left.\begin{array}{lll} & \omega_i = +\omega_0 \cos \beta t, & \gamma_1 = +\sin\theta_0 \cos\beta t, \\ c = 0, & \omega_j = -\omega_0 \sin\beta t, & \gamma_2 = -\sin\theta_0 \sin\beta t, \\ \therefore a = b, & \omega_k = n, & \gamma_3 = +\cos\theta_0, \end{array}\right\} \tag{2}$$

$$\begin{aligned} n &= \frac{\omega_0 \cos\theta_0}{(1-a)\sin\theta_0} + \frac{h_0 \sin\theta_0}{(1-a)\omega_0}, \\ \beta &= \frac{a}{1-a}\,\frac{\omega_0\cos\theta_0}{\sin\theta_0} + \frac{h_0\sin\theta_0}{(1-a)\omega_0}, \end{aligned} \qquad h_0 = h_1 = h_2,$$

and θ_0 and ω_0 are arbitrary. In this solution the principal axis of the body describes a right circular cone about a vertical axis with an arbitrary rate of spin.

Either of these particular solutions can be regarded as a generating solution for a family of periodic solutions of the problem. The first will be selected here as the simpler, since it does not contain the time, and therefore leads to expansions with constant coefficients.

Let μ be an arbitrary parameter, and let new variables v_1, . . . , v_5 be introduced by the relations

$$\left.\begin{array}{ll} \gamma_1 = \mu v_1, & \omega_i = \mu v_3, \\ \gamma_2 = \mu v_2, & \omega_j = \mu v_4, \\ \gamma_3 = \sqrt{1-(v_1^2+v_2^2)\mu^2}, & \omega_\kappa = n + \mu v_5, \end{array}\right\} \tag{3}$$

with the condition upon the solution that initially

$$v_1^2 + v_2^2 = 1, \qquad \text{and therefore} \qquad \mu = \sin\theta_0,$$

where θ_0 is the initial value of the angle θ. For $\mu = 0$ it is evident that Eqs. (3) reduce to Eqs. (1), and therefore Eqs. (1) are the generating solution for the family of solutions, Eqs. (3).

After the substitutions and the removal of a factor μ, the differential equations, Eqs. (202.3) and (202.4), become

$$\begin{aligned} v_1' - nv_2 + v_4 &= +v_2v_5\mu + v_4[1 - \sqrt{1 - (v_1^2 + v_2^2)\mu^2}], \\ v_2' + nv_1 - v_3 &= -v_1v_5\mu - v_3[1 - \sqrt{1 - (v_1^2 + v_2^2)\mu^2}], \\ v_3' - h_1v_2 - anv_4 &= +av_4v_5\mu, \\ v_4' + h_2v_1 + bnv_3 &= -bv_3v_5\mu, \\ v_5' &= cv_3v_4\mu; \end{aligned} \qquad (4)$$

and the last of Eqs. (202.3) can be discarded, since

$$\gamma_3 = \sqrt{1 - (v_1^2 + v_2^2)\mu^2}.$$

For $\mu = 0$, Eqs. (4) reduce to the linear equations

$$\left.\begin{aligned} v_1' - nv_2 + v_4 = 0, \qquad v_3' - h_1v_2 - anv_4 = 0, \\ v_2' + nv_1 - v_3 = 0, \qquad v_4' + h_2v_1 + bnv_3 = 0, \\ v_5' = 0, \end{aligned}\right\} \qquad (5)$$

which are known as the equations of variation.

204. The Characteristic Equation.—It follows from the last of Eqs. (203.5) that v_5 is a constant. The characteristic equation (Sec. 189) of the remaining equations is

$$\begin{vmatrix} \lambda & -n & 0 & 1 \\ n & \lambda & -1 & 0 \\ 0 & -h_1 & \lambda & -an \\ h_2 & 0 & bn & \lambda \end{vmatrix} = 0,$$

or

$$\lambda^4 + [(1 + ab)n^2 - (h_1 + h_2)]\lambda^2 + (an^2 + h_1)(bn^2 + h_2) = 0. \qquad (1)$$

This is an equation in λ^2, a property that is characteristic of the equations of mechanics.[1] The roots therefore occur in pairs and the two members of the pairs differ only in sign. Regarded as a quadratic in λ^2, the roots are real or complex according as the discriminant

$$D_\lambda = [(1 + ab)n^2 - (h_1 + h_2)]^2 - 4(an^2 + h_1)(bn^2 + h_2) \qquad (2)$$

is positive or negative. As the character of these roots is fundamental in the problem, it is necessary to examine this discriminant

[1] POINCARÉ, "Méthodes Nouvelles de la Mécanique Céleste," 1, p. 193.

with care. For this purpose, let the notation be changed by taking

$$a = x, \qquad c = y, \qquad b = \frac{x + y}{1 + xy}, \qquad \frac{h_2}{h_1} = \frac{1 + y}{1 + xy}, \qquad \frac{n^2}{h_1} = z,$$
$$-1 < x < +1, \qquad -1 < y < +1, \qquad z > 0.$$

The characteristic equation then becomes

$$\lambda^4 + \left[\frac{1 + 2xy + x^2}{1 + xy} z + \frac{2 + y + xy}{1 + xy}\right]\lambda^2 h_1 + \frac{1 + xz}{1 + xy}(1 + y + yz + xz)h_1^2, \quad (3)$$

and its discriminant

$$D_\lambda = \frac{h_1^2}{(1 + xy)^2}\{[(1 + 2xy + x^2)z - (2 + y + xy)]^2 - 4(1 + xy)(1 + xz)(1 + y + xz + yz)\}. \quad (4)$$

The discriminant vanishes on the surface

$$(S) \; [(1 + 2xy + x^2)z - (2 + y + xy)]^2 - 4(1 + xy)(1 + xz)(1 + y + xz + yz) = 0; \quad (5)$$

but only that portion of the surface that lies inside of the square cylinder, C, whose edges are parallel to the z-axis and pass through the points $+1, +1$; $-1, +1$; $-1, -1$; and $+1, -1$, and for which $z > 0$, is of interest in the present problem.

Arranged according to powers of y the surface S is

$$[(1 - x)^2 - 8zx(1 + x)]y^2 - 2z(1 + x)^2(3 + x)y + (1 + x)^2[(1 - x^2)^2z^2 - 4z] = 0.$$

This equation is not only quadratic in y, it is also quadratic in z. Thus for a given point x, y there are either two values of z or none. In the hatched area of Fig. 81 the values of z are complex and therefore the surface S lies over the remainder of the square. Since both values of z are positive (or zero along the lines $y = 0$, and $x = +1$) there is a volume below S and above the xy-plane within which D_λ is positive. Inside of S, D_λ is negative, and the two roots λ^2 are complex. Above the second sheet of S, D is again positive. The contour lines of S for $z = 1, 2, 3$, and 4 are given in Fig. 81. The surface S has a cuspidal edge along the straight line $x = -1$, $y = 0$ from $z = 0$ to $z = +1$, and the contour line for every z passes through the point $+1, -1$. As z increases the contour lines, which are hyperbolas, tend toward coincidence inside of C with the straight line $x = +1$. Thus for every point x, y, with z sufficiently large, D_λ is positive and the two roots λ^2 are real.

Inside of C and outside of S, D is positive, and the two values of λ^2 are real. Thus the four roots λ are real or purely imaginary. If all four roots are purely imaginary, the motion is said to be

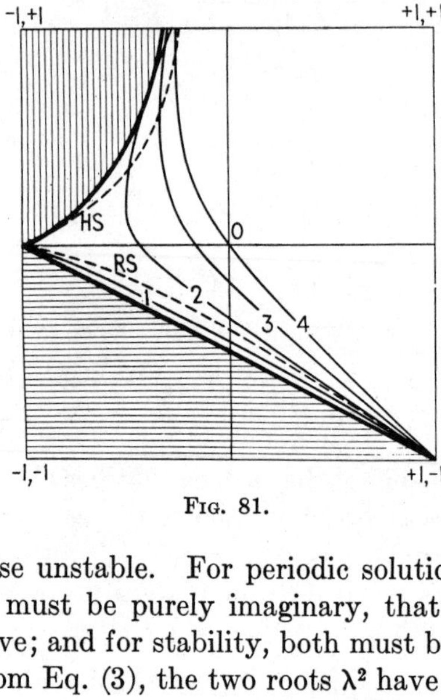

FIG. 81.

stable, otherwise unstable. For periodic solutions at least two of the roots λ must be purely imaginary, that is, one root λ^2 must be negative; and for stability, both must be negative.

As is seen from Eq. (3), the two roots λ^2 have the same sign if

$$(1 + xz)(1 + y + xz + yz) > 0,$$

and opposite signs if this product is negative. One of the roots changes sign if the point $p(x, y, z)$ crosses the hyperbolic cylinder

$$(H) \qquad 1 + xz = 0,$$

or the ruled surface

$$(R) \qquad 1 + y + xz + yz = 0.$$

The intersection of the surfaces S and H with the plane $y = +1$ is shown in Fig. 82. The surfaces S and R intersect in the plane $y = 0$ along the hyperbola $1 + xz = 0$.

It is easy to find the lines of intersection of H and S; for if p is on both R and S it is necessary that

$$1 + xz = 0,$$

and, as is seen from Eq. (5), that

$$(1 + 2xy + x^2)z - (2 + y + xy) = 0.$$

These equations give the line

$$(HS) \qquad x = -\frac{1}{z}, \qquad y = \frac{(z-1)^2}{3z-1}; \qquad (6)$$

and similarly, for the intersection of R and S,

$$(RS) \qquad x = \frac{z^2 - z - 1}{z(2-z)},$$

$$y = \frac{-(z-1)^2}{(1+z)(2-z)}. \qquad (7)$$

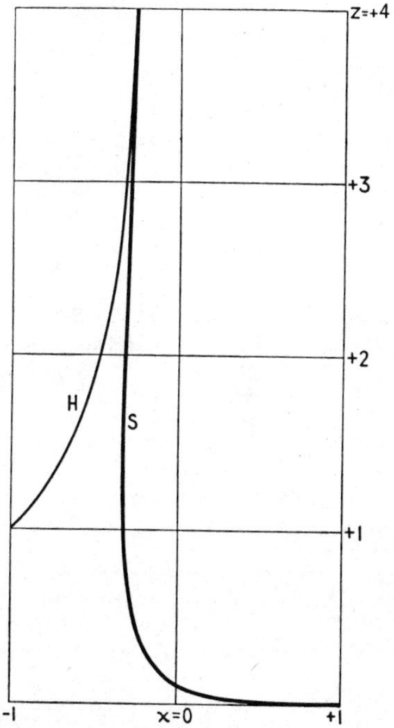

FIG. 82.

The projections of these lines on the xy-plane are shown as dotted lines in Fig. 81. It is easy to see from Eq. (5) that the surfaces H and R have contact of the second order with S and therefore do not cut through it. For the discriminant D_λ has the form

$$D_\lambda = F^2 - 4EG.$$

On the surface S, $D_\lambda = 0$, and on the surfaces H and R either $E = 0$ or $G = 0$. If a point p moves along either H or R

$$D_\lambda = F^2,$$

which is positive except along the lines of contact where it vanishes. It follows that H lies entirely on one side of the surface S, and R likewise.

The lines HS and RS, Eqs. (6) and (7), can also be regarded as the intersection of the surface S with the surface

$$F = 0, \qquad \text{where} \qquad F = (1 + 2xy + x^2)z - (2 + y + xy).$$

205. The Roots of the Characteristic Equation.—It is now possible to discuss the character of the roots of the characteristic equation, and this will be done by quadrants.

In the first quadrant

$$x > 0, \qquad y > 0, \qquad \text{and} \qquad A > B > C,$$

as is seen by Eq. (202.5). In the volume above the xy-plane but below the first sheet of S, both roots λ^2 are positive; and in the volume above the second sheet, both roots are negative. In either of these volumes

$$D_\lambda > 0, \qquad H > 0, \qquad \text{and} \qquad R > 0,$$

if it is permitted to write H and R for the functions $1 + xz$ and $1 + y + xz + yz$ respectively. But above S the function $F > 0$, and below S, $F < 0$.

The second quadrant, $x < 0$, $y > 0$, is more complicated since it is cut by both the surfaces H and R. Also [Eq. (202.5)]

$$A > C > B, \qquad \text{if} \qquad x + y > 0,$$

and

$$C > A > B, \qquad \text{if} \qquad x + y < 0.$$

Since R intersects S in the plane $y = 0$ in the hyperbola $H = 0$, R lies inside of H in the second quadrant. Also H touches S in the line HS. Outside of H and S and below the line HS

$$D_\lambda > 0, \qquad H > 0, \qquad R > 0$$

and both roots λ^2 are positive. On crossing the surface H one of the roots becomes negative, and on crossing the surface R also both roots are negative. In this region, which is inside of H and to the left of R, and in which both roots are negative,

$$D_\lambda > 0, \qquad H < 0, \qquad R < 0.$$

But if the point p after entering H passes upward, and leaves H above the line HS, it is above the surface S, and

$$D_\lambda > 0, \qquad H > 0, \qquad R > 0,$$

and again both roots λ^2 are negative. There are therefore two distinct regions in the second quadrant in which both roots are negative.

The third quadrant also is crossed by both H and R, but in this quadrant R is outside of H. For z sufficiently small both roots λ^2 are positive, and

$$D_\lambda > 0, \qquad R > 0, \qquad H > 0.$$

Between R and H one root is positive and one is negative. Inside of H both roots are negative, and

$$D_\lambda > 0, \qquad R < 0, \qquad H < 0;$$

or, passing outside of R again above the surface $F = 0$, both roots are negative and

$$D_\lambda > 0, \qquad R > 0, \qquad H > 0, \qquad F > 0.$$

Thus again there are two distinct regions in which both roots are negative.

In the fourth quadrant there is but one region in which both roots are negative, namely,

$$D_\lambda > 0, \qquad R > 0, \qquad H > 0, \qquad F > 0.$$

The surface H does not cross this quadrant, but R does. The region indicated is to the right of R and outside of S above the dotted line RS.

Thus in each quadrant there are regions in which both roots λ^2 are negative, but certainly not everywhere.

206. Solution of the Equations of Variation.—It will be assumed that both λ^2 roots of the characteristic equation are negative, and therefore all four λ roots are pure imaginaries. The constants a and c (which correspond to x and y of the last two sections) depend upon the body and the point O about which it turns. They are therefore fixed constants, but n^2/h_1, which corresponds to z, is determined by the rate of spin. In a general way, though not always, it is true, if the spin is sufficiently great, that all four λ roots are pure imaginaries as is here assumed to be the case, namely,

$$+i\lambda_1, \qquad -i\lambda_1, \qquad +i\lambda_2, \qquad -i\lambda_2, \qquad i = \sqrt{-1}.$$

A particular solution of the equations of variation [Eqs. (203.5)]

$$\left.\begin{aligned} v_1' - nv_2 + v_4 &= 0, \qquad & v_3' - h_1v_2 - anv_4 &= 0,\\ v_2' + nv_1 - v_3 &= 0, \qquad & v_4' + h_2v_1 + bnv_3 &= 0,\end{aligned}\right\} \tag{1}$$

can be obtained by taking

$$\left.\begin{aligned} v_1 &= A_1 \cos \lambda_1 t, & v_3 &= A_3 \cos \lambda_1 t, \\ v_2 &= A_2 \sin \lambda_1 t, & v_4 &= A_4 \sin \lambda_1 t. \end{aligned}\right\} \qquad (2)$$

On substituting Eqs. (2) in Eq. (1), it is found that the constants A_j must satisfy the linear equations

$$\left.\begin{aligned} -\lambda_1 A_1 - nA_2 + 0A_3 + 1A_4 &= 0, \\ nA_1 + \lambda_1 A_2 - 1A_3 + 0A_4 &= 0, \\ 0A_1 - h_1 A_2 - \lambda_1 A_3 - anA_4 &= 0, \\ h_2 A_1 + 0A_2 + bnA_3 + \lambda_1 A_4 &= 0. \end{aligned}\right\} \qquad (3)$$

The determinant of the left members, Δ, is the characteristic equation [Eq. (204.1)] for $\lambda = i\lambda_1$, and therefore vanishes. Then, on omitting the last equation, it is found that

$$A_1 = Aa_1, \qquad A_2 = Aa_2, \qquad A_3 = Aa_3, \qquad A_4 = Aa_4,$$

where

$$\left.\begin{aligned} \Delta_{41} = a_1 &= -\lambda_1^2 - an^2 - h_1, \\ -\Delta_{42} = a_2 &= +n(1 + a)\lambda_1, \\ \Delta_{43} = a_3 &= +n(a\lambda_1^2 - an^2 - h_1), \\ -\Delta_{44} = a_4 &= -\lambda_1(\lambda_1^2 - n^2 + h_1), \end{aligned}\right\} \qquad (4)$$

and A is an arbitrary constant.

A second particular solution is obtained from the first by increasing t by a quarter period. A third and fourth solution is obtained by using λ_2 instead of λ_1. Thus a complete solution of the equations of variation is

$$\left.\begin{aligned} v_1 &= Aa_1 \cos \lambda_1 t + Ba_1 \sin \lambda_1 t + Cc_1 \cos \lambda_2 t + Dc_1 \sin \lambda_2 t, \\ v_2 &= Aa_2 \sin \lambda_1 t - Ba_2 \cos \lambda_1 t + Cc_2 \sin \lambda_2 t - Dc_2 \cos \lambda_2 t, \\ v_3 &= Aa_3 \cos \lambda_1 t + Ba_3 \sin \lambda_1 t + Cc_3 \cos \lambda_2 t + Dc_3 \sin \lambda_2 t, \\ v_4 &= Aa_4 \sin \lambda_1 t - Ba_4 \cos \lambda_1 t + Cc_4 \sin \lambda_2 t - Dc_4 \cos \lambda_2 t, \end{aligned}\right\} \qquad (5)$$

in which A, B, C, and D are constants of integration, and c_j is obtained from a_j by replacing λ_1 by λ_2.

207. The Non-homogeneous Equations.—Instead of the right members of Eqs. (1) being all zero, suppose they were

$$m_1 \sin k\lambda_1 t, \quad m_2 \cos k\lambda_1 t, \quad m_3 \sin k\lambda_1 t, \quad \text{and} \quad m_4 \cos k\lambda_1 t \qquad (1)$$

respectively, k being a positive integer. The particular solution that depends upon these terms is obtained by assuming that

$$\left.\begin{aligned} v_1 &= l_1 \cos k\lambda_1 t, & v_3 &= l_3 \cos k\lambda_1 t, \\ v_2 &= l_2 \sin k\lambda_1 t, & v_4 &= l_4 \sin k\lambda_1 t, \end{aligned}\right\} \qquad (2)$$

substituting in the differential equations, and solving the resulting algebraic equations. These equations are similar to Eqs. (206.3) except that the A's are replaced by the l's, λ_1 is replaced by $k\lambda_1$, and the right members are m_1, m_2, m_3, and m_4, respectively. The determinant of the left members is now not zero, since $k\lambda_1$ is not a root of the characteristic equation, unless $k = 1$, or $k\lambda_1 = \lambda_2$. The equations can therefore be solved, and the particular solution has the form given in Eqs. (2).

If $k = 1$, the solution in general is not periodic. A periodic solution of the form Eq. (2) with $k = 1$ exists, if the constants m_i satisfy the relation

$$\sum_i (-1)^i \Delta_{i1} m_i = 0, \tag{3}$$

where Δ_{i1} is the minor obtained from Δ by suppressing the ith row and the first column.

Assuming that $k = 1$, the substitution of Eqs. (2) in the differential Eqs. (206.1) with the right members as in (1), there results

$$\begin{aligned}
-\lambda_1 l_1 - nl_2 + 0l_3 + \quad l_4 &= m_1,\\
+nl_1 + \lambda_1 l_2 - \quad l_3 + 0l_4 &= m_2,\\
0l_1 - h_1 l_2 - \lambda_1 l_3 - anl_4 &= m_3,\\
+h_2 l_1 + 0l_2 + bnl_3 + \lambda_1 l_4 &= m_4.
\end{aligned}$$

The determinant Δ of the left members is zero, but the equations are consistent by virtue of the assumption (3). Not all the first minors of Δ are zero, however, since its roots are simple roots, or, at least they are in general. It is assumed here that they are simple, and therefore not all of the first minors are zero. Suppose $\Delta_{41} \neq 0$; suppress the last equation and rewrite the other three equations as follows,

$$\begin{aligned}
- nl_2 + 0l_3 + \quad l_4 &= m_1 + \lambda_1 l_1,\\
+\lambda_1 l_2 - \quad l_3 + 0l_4 &= m_2 - nl_1,\\
-h_1 l_2 - \lambda l_3 - anl_4 &= m_3 + 0l_1.
\end{aligned}$$

If $D = \Delta_{41}$ is the determinant of the left members and D_{ij} are its first minors, the solution is

$$\begin{aligned}
Dl_2 &= [+D_{11}m_1 - D_{21}m_2 + D_{31}m_3] + [\ \ \lambda_1 D_{11} + nD_{21}]l_1,\\
Dl_3 &= [-D_{12}m_1 + D_{22}m_2 - D_{32}m_3] + [-\lambda_1 D_{12} - nD_{22}]l_1,\\
Dl_4 &= [+D_{13}m_1 - D_{23}m_2 + D_{33}m_3] + [\ \ \lambda_1 D_{13} + nD_{23}]l_1,
\end{aligned}$$

in which l_1 is arbitrary. The coefficients of l_1 in the right members are a_2, a_3, and a_4, of Eqs. 4, and D is a_1. Hence, by taking

$$l_1 = la_1,$$

it is seen that

$$l_1 = la_1, \qquad l_3 = p_3 + la_3,$$
$$l_2 = p_2 + la_2, \qquad l_4 = p_4 + la_4,$$

in which l is arbitrary, and p_2, p_3, and p_4 are functions of the m's as defined above. Equations (2) then become

$$\left.\begin{aligned} v_1 &= la_1 \cos \lambda_1 t, & v_3 &= (p_3 + la_3) \cos \lambda_1 t,\\ v_2 &= (p_2 + la_2) \sin \lambda_1 t, & v_4 &= (p_4 + la_4) \sin \lambda_1 t.\end{aligned}\right\} \tag{4}$$

The terms which carry l as a factor, however, are merely terms of the complementary function [Eqs. (206.5)], and therefore, without loss of generality, l can be taken equal to zero.

208. A Periodic Solution of the General Equations.—It will now be shown that the differential equations of motion [Eqs. (203.4)] can be satisfied by power series of the following form:

$$\left.\begin{aligned} v_1 &= \cos \lambda_1\tau + [v_{12}^{(1)} \cos \lambda_1\tau + v_{12}^{(3)} \cos 3\lambda_1\tau]\mu^2 + \cdots,\\ v_2 &= r_2 \sin \lambda_1\tau + [v_{22}^{(1)} \sin \lambda_1\tau + v_{22}^{(3)} \sin 3\lambda_1\tau]\mu^2 + \cdots,\\ v_3 &= r_3 \cos \lambda_1\tau + [v_{32}^{(1)} \cos \lambda_1\tau + v_{32}^{(3)} \cos 3\lambda_1\tau]\mu^2 + \cdots,\\ v_4 &= r_4 \sin \lambda_1\tau + [v_{42}^{(1)} \sin \lambda_1\tau + v_{42}^{(3)} \sin 3\lambda_1\tau]\mu^2 + \cdots,\\ v_5 &= [v_{51}^{(0)} + v_{51}^{(2)} \cos 2\lambda_1\tau]\mu +\\ &\qquad [v_{53}^{(0)} + v_{53}^{(2)} \cos 2\lambda_1\tau + v_{53}^{(4)} \cos 4\lambda_1\tau]\mu^3 + \cdots, \end{aligned}\right\} \tag{1}$$

in which the $v_{ij}^{(k)}$ are constants and τ is a new independent variable defined by the relations

$$t = (1 + \delta)\tau,$$

and

$$\delta = \delta_2\mu^2 + \delta_4\mu^4 + \cdots . \tag{2}$$

This form of the solution is suggested by the following properties of the differential equations: If v_1, v_2, v_3, and v_4 are even functions of μ, and v_5 is an odd function, all of the terms of the first four of the differential equations [Eqs. (203.4)] are even in μ, and all of the terms of the last equation are odd. If v_1, v_3, and v_5 are even functions of t, and v_2 and v_4 are odd functions, all of the terms of the first, third, and fifth equations are odd in t, and all of the terms of the second and fourth are even functions of t. It will be observed that if τ is increased by a quarter of the period, $\pi/(2\lambda_1)$, the property of evenness and oddness in the time is reversed in the series of Eqs. (1), with the exception of the last. The same is true in the differential equations.

In order to effect a solution of the differential equations after the change in the independent variable from t to τ, let

$$\begin{aligned} v_1 &= v_{10} + v_{12}\mu^2 + v_{14}\mu^4 + \cdots, \\ v_2 &= v_{20} + v_{22}\mu^2 + v_{24}\mu^4 + \cdots, \\ v_3 &= v_{30} + v_{32}\mu^2 + v_{34}\mu^4 + \cdots, \\ v_4 &= v_{40} + v_{42}\mu^2 + v_{44}\mu^4 + \cdots, \\ v_5 &= v_{51}\mu + v_{53}\mu^3 + v_{55}\mu^5 + \cdots, \end{aligned} \tag{3}$$

in which the v_{ij} are functions of the time to be determined, be substituted, and the differential equations then arranged in powers of μ.

The Terms of Degree Zero.—The terms that are independent of μ are the same as the equations of variation [Eqs. (206.1)] and their solutions are therefore Eqs. (206.5), except that the independent variable is τ instead of t. The period in τ that has been chosen is $2\pi/\lambda_1$; the terms that contain the period $2\pi/\lambda_2$ are made to disappear by taking the constants C and D equal to zero, and, for simplicity, B also is taken equal to zero, although this last is not necessary. There remain only the terms that have A as a factor.

It will be remembered that at Eqs. (203.3) the condition was imposed upon the variables that for all values of μ

$$v_1^2 + v_2^2 = 1.$$

It follows therefore that A is the reciprocal of a_1, the minor of Δ, that by hypothesis is not zero. Then, by taking

$$r_k = \frac{a_k}{a_1},$$

there is obtained

$$\left.\begin{aligned} v_{10} &= \cos\lambda_1\tau, & v_{30} &= r_3\cos\lambda_1\tau, \\ v_{20} &= r_2\sin\lambda_1\tau, & v_{40} &= r_4\sin\lambda_1\tau. \end{aligned}\right\} \tag{4}$$

which agrees with the first terms of Eqs. (1).

The Term of First Degree.—There is but one term of the first degree in μ, namely,

$$\frac{dv_{51}}{d\tau} = cv_{30}v_{40},$$

or, after substitution from Eqs. (4),

$$\frac{dv_{51}}{d\tau} = \frac{1}{2}cr_3r_4 \sin 2\lambda_1\tau.$$

The first term n of ω_k is arbitrary. It will be assumed, therefore, that the initial value of v_5 is zero, whatever μ may be. Therefore, on integrating and choosing the constant of integration so that this condition is satisfied, it is found that

$$v_{51} = \frac{c}{4\lambda_1}r_3r_4(1 - \cos 2\lambda_1\tau). \tag{5}$$

Terms of the Second Degree.—When the values of v_{i0} and v_{51} that have been determined [Eqs. (4) and (5)] are used, it is found that the differential equations for v_{i2} are

$$\left.\begin{aligned}
&\frac{dv_{12}}{d\tau} - nv_{22} + v_{42} = \\
&\qquad [(nr_2 - r_4)\delta_2 + m_{12}^{(1)}] \sin \lambda_1\tau + m_{12}^{(3)} \sin 3\lambda_1\tau, \\
&\frac{dv_{22}}{d\tau} + nv_{12} - v_{32} = \\
&\qquad [(-n + r_3)\delta_2 + m_{22}^{(1)}] \cos \lambda_1\tau + m_{22}^{(3)} \cos 3\lambda_1\tau, \\
&\frac{dv_{32}}{d\tau} - h_1v_{22} - anv_{42} = \\
&\qquad [(h_1r_2 + anr_4)\delta_2 + m_{32}^{(1)}] \sin \lambda_1\tau + m_{32}^{(3)} \sin 3\lambda_1\tau, \\
&\frac{dv_{42}}{d\tau} + h_2v_{12} + bnv_{32} = \\
&\qquad [-(h_2 + bnr_3)\delta_2 + m_{42}^{(1)}] \cos \lambda_1\tau + m_{42}^{(3)} \cos 3\lambda_1\tau,
\end{aligned}\right\} \tag{6}$$

in which the $m_{ij}^{(k)}$ are constants that are not computed here. The explicit values of the coefficients of δ_2 are given, as their values are necessary in order to show that the periodicity condition stated in Eq. (207.3) can be satisfied.

This condition, stated explicitly, is

$$\begin{aligned}
[(nr_2-r_4)\Delta_{11}-(-n+r_3)\Delta_{21}+(h_1r_2+anr_4)\Delta_{31}+(h_2+bnr_3)\Delta_{41}]\delta_2 \\
+ [m_{12}^{(1)}\Delta_{11} + m_{22}^{(1)}\Delta_{21} + m_{32}^{(1)}\Delta_{31} - m_{42}^{(1)}\Delta_{41}] = 0;
\end{aligned}$$

and δ_2 can be chosen so that the condition is satisfied provided the coefficient of δ_2 is not zero. Since $\Delta = 0$, this coefficient can be expressed in the form

$$-2\lambda_1^2\{[(1 + 2a + ab)n^2 + (h_1 - h_2)]\lambda_1^2 - (an^2 + h_1)[(1 + 2b + ab)n^2 - (h_1 - h_2)]\},$$

and, by the elimination of λ_1^2, finally in the form

$$-2(1 + a)(1 + b)n^2\lambda_1^2 D_{\lambda_1},$$

where D_λ is the λ discriminant defined at Eq. (204.4). The root of the characteristic equation, λ, vanishes on one of the two surfaces H and R, D_λ only on the surface S, and the other factors on the walls and floor of the square cylinder C. The coefficient of δ_2 does not vanish in the interior of the prescribed regions, and in these regions the periodicity condition can always be satisfied.

The solution of Eqs. (6) then is, bearing in mind the discussion in Sec. 207,

$$\left.\begin{aligned} v_{12} &= (\;0 + l_2)\cos\lambda_1\tau + v_{12}^{(3)}\cos 3\lambda_1\tau,\\ v_{22} &= (p_2 + l_2)\sin\lambda_1\tau + v_{22}^{(3)}\sin 3\lambda_1\tau,\\ v_{32} &= (p_3 + l_2)\cos\lambda_1\tau + v_{32}^{(3)}\cos 3\lambda_1\tau,\\ v_{42} &= (p_4 + l_2)\sin\lambda_1\tau + v_{42}^{(3)}\sin 3\lambda_1\tau.\end{aligned}\right\} \quad (7)$$

It is still subject to the condition that, for $\tau = 0$,

$$v_1^2 + v_2^2 \underset{\mu}{\equiv} 1.$$

Since v_{22} vanishes with τ, the constant of integration l_2 must be chosen so that v_{12} vanishes with τ; that is

$$l_2 = -v_{12}^{(3)}.$$

If this value of l_2 is substituted in Eqs. (7), it is seen that the expressions given in Eqs. (7) agree in form with the coefficients of μ^2 in Eqs. (1).

Terms of Higher Degrees.—As developed thus far, v_1, v_3 and v_5 are even functions of τ, while v_2 and v_4 are even functions. From the properties of the differential equations already mentioned it is seen that this property persists: v_{1k} v_{3k} and v_{5k} are always even functions, while v_{2k} and v_{4k} are odd functions. Furthermore, v_{1k} and v_{3k} contain only cosines of odd multiples of $\lambda_1\tau$, while v_{5k} contains only even multiples; and v_{2k} and v_{4k} contain only sines of odd multiples of τ.

Since the derivative of v_{5k} is odd in τ, it has no constant term and the periodicity condition is satisfied automatically. The constant arising in the integration can always be chosen so that v_{5k} vanishes at $\tau = 0$.

The integration of the coefficients of the even powers of μ is quite similar to that of the second degree. The periodicity condition is the same, and δ_k occurs in this condition with precisely the same coefficient as in the terms of the second degree, already discussed. Hence δ_k can always be chosen so as to satisfy this condition, and the constant of integration then arising can always be chosen so that v_{1k} vanishes with τ, and therefore, at $\tau = 0$,

$$v_1^2 + v_2^2 \underset{\mu}{\equiv} 1.$$

The solution therefore can be carried as far as may be desired; and by the general theorems, the series are convergent if $|\mu|$ is sufficiently small.

By changing the origin of τ, these series will lose the property of evenness and oddness with respect to τ. Such series could have been developed from the beginning, but as they are less simple and add nothing essential to the solution, it is better to develop the series as has been done here.

209. The Eulerian Angles.—From the second column of Eqs. (202.2) it is seen that

$$\tan\varphi = \frac{\gamma_1}{\gamma_2}, \qquad \sin\theta = \sqrt{\gamma_1^2 + \gamma_2^2},$$

and therefore, in terms of the series developed in the last section,

$$\sin\varphi = \frac{v_1}{\sqrt{v_1^2 + v_2^2}}, \qquad \cos\varphi = \frac{v_2}{\sqrt{v_1^2 + v_2^2}},$$
$$\sin\theta = \mu\sqrt{v_1^2 + v_2^2}, \qquad \cos\theta = \sqrt{1 - (v_1^2 + v_2^2)\mu^2}.$$

At $\tau = 0$,

$$v_1 = +1, \qquad v_2 = v_4 = v_5 = 0,$$
$$v_3 = r_3 + [v_{32}^{(1)} + v_{32}^{(3)}]\mu^2 + \cdots;$$

at $\tau = \pi/2\lambda_1$, the quarter period,

$$v_1 = v_3 = 0, \qquad v_2 = r_2 + [v_{22}^{(1)} - v_{22}^{(3)}]\mu^2 + \cdots,$$
$$v_4 = r_4 + [v_{42}^{(1)} - v_{42}^{(3)}]\mu^2 + \cdots,$$
$$v_5 = [v_{51}^{(0)} - v_{51}^{(2)}]\mu + [v_{53}^{(0)} - v_{53}^{(2)} + v_{53}^{(4)}]\mu^3 + \cdots,$$

and at $\tau = \pi/\lambda_1$, the half period,

$$v_j\left(\frac{\pi}{\lambda_1}\right) = -v_j(0).$$

Thus φ, which initially is $\pi/2$, increases by π during the half period, and by 2π during the complete period. That is the body makes one complete turn per period.

The initial value of $\sin\theta$ is μ. At the expiration of a quarter period its value is

$$r_2\mu + [v_{22}^{(1)} - v_{22}^{(3)}]\mu^3 + \cdots,$$

which is a maximum or a minimum value, since the derivative vanishes at $\tau = \pi/2\lambda_1$. At the expiration of a half period, $\sin\theta$ has returned to its initial value. Thus the principal axis, the **k**-axis, describes a curve on the unit sphere that always lies between two parallels of latitude as in Figs. 60, 61, and 62.

The rate of precession [Eq. (202.7)] is

$$\psi' = \frac{v_1v_3 + v_2v_4}{v_1^2 + v_2^2}.$$

At $\tau = 0$, the value of ψ' is r_3, and at the quarter period its value is

$$\frac{v_4}{v_2} = \frac{r_4 + [v_{42}^{(1)} - v_{42}^{(3)}]\mu^2 + \cdots}{r_2 + [v_{22}^{(1)} - v_{22}^{(3)}]\mu^2 + \cdots}.$$

210. Concluding Remarks.—The solution just derived contains four arbitrary constants, n, μ, ψ_0, and τ_0, since the initial values of ψ and τ can be regarded as arbitrary. It is a particular solution, inasmuch as the differential equations are of the sixth order, and therefore six arbitrary constants are needed for a complete solution. In this respect it differs from the problem first considered, the rocking pendulum.

It will be observed that the method of periodic solutions is long and difficult. It is not possible therefore to multiply examples here. A collection of problems in which this method has been used will be found in a volume entitled "Periodic Orbits," by F. R. Moulton and others, published by the Carnegie Institution of Washington, Publication 161; and many others are to be found in the literature. As remarked by its originator, H. Poincaré, it is the only worth-while method that is known for a wide class of problems.

Problems

1. Prove that the matrices $\cos \kappa t$ and $\sin \kappa t/\kappa$ satisfy the matrix identity

$$(\cos \kappa t)^2 + \kappa^2 \left(\frac{\sin \kappa t}{\kappa}\right)^2 = \delta.$$

2. Given that $\det \kappa \neq 0$. Show that Eq. (191.10) defines at least one matrix κ^n whatever the value of the scalar n (real or complex) may be. For $n = -1$,

$$\kappa^{-1} = \frac{K}{\det \kappa},$$

where K is the adjoint of κ, is the reciprocal of the matrix κ.

Then show that the solution of the set of linear equations

$$\kappa x = y, \qquad x = (x_1, \cdot \cdot \cdot , x_n),$$

is

$$x = \kappa^{-1} y, \qquad y = (y_1, \cdot \cdot \cdot , y_n).$$

3. If $\det \kappa \neq 0$ and $n = \frac{1}{2}$, the matrix $\kappa^{\frac{1}{2}} = \sqrt{\kappa}$ is a square root of κ, that is

$$\sqrt{\kappa}\sqrt{\kappa} = \kappa.$$

How many such square roots are obtainable from Eq. (191.10)?

Ans. $2r$, where r is the number of distinct characteristic values of κ.

4. The matrix

$$\eta = \begin{vmatrix} a & -a \\ a - \frac{1}{a} & -a \end{vmatrix}$$

satisfies the equation

$$\eta^2 = \delta.$$

Is η obtainable from Eq. (191.10)?

5. Prove that, if η is a matrix and m is an integer,

$$\det (e^{m\eta}) = (\det e^{\eta})^m.$$

Generalize this result for m a rational fraction.

[Let

$$\det e^{\eta} = e^s,$$

then from the identity

$$\begin{aligned} e^{sm} &= \det (e^{m\eta}) \\ &= \det \left(\delta + \frac{m\eta}{1!} + \frac{m^2\eta^2}{2!} + \cdot \cdot \cdot\right) \end{aligned}$$

show that

$$\begin{aligned} s &= \text{coefficient of } m \text{ in } \det (\delta + m\eta) \\ &= \text{sum of diagonal terms of } \eta]. \end{aligned}$$

6. If the scalar μ is sufficiently small, there exists a matrix

$$\begin{aligned}\eta(\mu) &= -\log(\delta - \mu\kappa)\\ &= \mu\kappa + \tfrac{1}{2}\mu^2\kappa^2 + \tfrac{1}{3}\mu^3\kappa^3 + \cdots,\end{aligned}$$

such that

$$\delta - \mu\kappa = e^{\eta(\mu)}.$$

7. Let O stand for the operation of taking the sum of the diagonal terms of a matrix; then show that

$$\begin{aligned}\det|\delta - \mu\kappa| &= e^{O\eta(\mu)},\\ &= e^{-\left(\mu O(\kappa) + \frac{\mu^2}{2}O(\kappa^2) + \cdots\right)},\\ &= e^{+\mu O[\log(\delta - \mu\kappa)]}.\end{aligned}$$

From this identity develop a method of finding the characteristic equation, $\det|\kappa - \lambda\delta|$ from the sum of the diagonal terms of $\kappa, \kappa^2, \kappa^3, \ldots, \kappa^{n-1}$.

8. Consider the non-homogeneous differential equation

$$\frac{dx}{dt} - \kappa x = e^{\lambda_0 t}C,$$

where C is a constant vector. Show that for $\det|\kappa - \lambda_0\delta| \neq 0$, a particular solution is

$$x = e^{\lambda_0 t}(-\kappa + \lambda_0\delta)^{-1}C,$$

and for $\lambda_0 = \lambda_1$, a characteristic root of κ of multiplicity m_1, a particular solution is

$$x = e^{\lambda_1 t}\left\{\sum_{s=1}^{m}\frac{t^s}{s!}(\kappa - \lambda_1\delta)^{s-1}\frac{R_1(\kappa)}{R_1(\lambda_1)} + T(\kappa)\right\}C,$$

where

$$R_1(\lambda) = (-1)^n\frac{\det(\kappa - \lambda\delta)}{(\lambda - \lambda_1)^{m_1}},$$

and

$$T(\lambda) = \frac{R_1(\lambda) - R_1(\lambda_1)}{(\lambda - \lambda_1)R(\lambda_1)}.$$

9. Solve for the vector x the differential equation

$$\frac{d^2x}{dt^2} + \kappa x = \varphi(t)$$

with the initial values

$$x(0) = a, \qquad \frac{dx}{dt}(0) = b,$$

where κ is a matrix.

Ans.

$$x = \cos\sqrt{\kappa}t\, y^{(1)} + \frac{\sin\sqrt{\kappa}t}{\sqrt{\kappa}}y^{(2)},$$

where

$$\begin{aligned}y^{(1)} &= a + \int_0^t \frac{\sin\sqrt{\kappa}t}{\sqrt{\kappa}}\varphi(t)\,dt,\\ y^{(2)} &= b - \int_0^t \cos\sqrt{\kappa}t\,\varphi(t)\,dt.\end{aligned}$$

10. Let D denote the operation of differentiating with respect to t. Express the matrix operator $F(\kappa, \delta D)$ in terms of the scalar operators $F^{(i)}(\lambda_i, D)$ multiplied by polynomials in the matrix κ. Show that in terms of this operational notation a solution of the equation

$$\frac{d^2x}{dt^2} + \kappa x = \varphi(t),$$

is

$$x = \frac{1}{+\kappa + \delta D^2}\varphi(t).$$

11. Develop the solution of the simple pendulum by the method of periodic solutions.

12. Develop the solution of the rocking pendulum with friction by the method of periodic solutions.

BIBLIOGRAPHY

Out of the vast literature on the subject of mechanics the author has selected the following list of books that will be of interest to the students of this subject:

NEWTON, "Principia" (1686), Andrew Motte's translation, edited by Florian Cajori, University of California Press. (1934.)

EULER, "Mechanica," 2 vols. (1736.)

LAGRANGE, "Mécanique Analytique," rev. ed. (1811–1815.)

POISSON, "Traité de Mécanique," 2 vols., Paris. (1833.)

JACOBI, "Vorlesungen über Mechanik," Gesammelte Werke, Supplement. (1884.)

THOMSON and TAIT, "Treatise on Natural Philosophy," Oxford. (1873.)

ROUTH, "Dynamics of a System of Rigid Bodies," Elementary Part, 5th ed. (1891); Advanced Part, 5th ed. (1892). London.

"Analytical Statics," 2 vols., Cambridge. (1891.)

MINCHIN, "Treatise on Statics," 2 vols., Oxford, 4th ed. (1890.)

TISSERAND, "Mécanique Céleste," 4 vols., Paris. (1889–1896.)

HELMHOLTZ, "Vorlesungen über die Dynamik Discrete Massenpunkte," Leipzig. (1898.)

POINCARÉ, "Les Méthodes Nouvelles de la Mécanique Céleste," 3 vols., Paris. (1892–1899.)

BALL, "Theory of Screws," Cambridge. (1900.)

KLEIN and SOMMERFELD, "Theorie des Kreisels," Leipzig. (1903.)

APPELL, "Traité de Mécanique Rationelle," 4 vols., 4th ed. (1919–1924.)

WHITTAKER, "Analytical Dynamics," 3d ed., Edinburgh. (1927.)

WEBSTER, "The Dynamics of Particles, and of Rigid, Elastic, and Fluid Bodies," Leipzig. (1904.)

LEVI CIVITA, "Lezioni di Mecanica Razionale," 3 vols., Bologna. (1922–1927.)

PAINLEVÉ, "Cours de Mécanique," Vol. I, Paris. (1930.)

AUTHOR INDEX

SUBJECT INDEX

CATALOGUE OF DOVER BOOKS

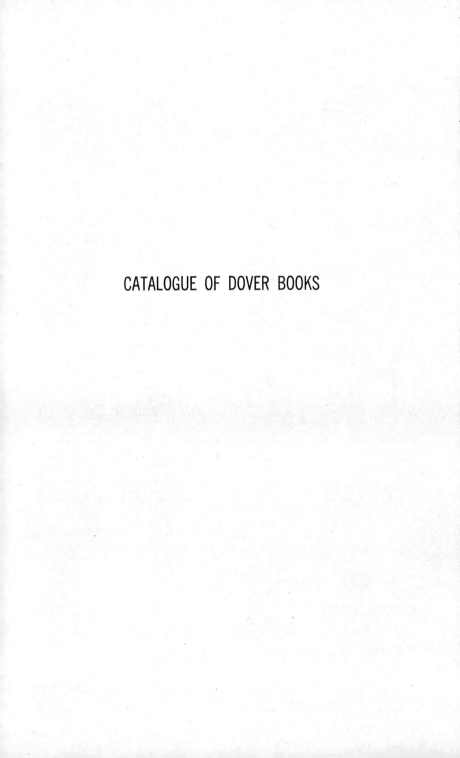

PHYSICS

General physics

FOUNDATIONS OF PHYSICS, R. B. Lindsay & H. Margenau. Excellent bridge between semi-popular works & technical treatises. A discussion of methods of physical description, construction of theory; valuable for physicist with elementary calculus who is interested in ideas that give meaning to data, tools of modern physics. Contents include symbolism, mathematical equations; space & time foundations of mechanics; probability; physics & continua; electron theory; special & general relativity; quantum mechanics; causality. "Thorough and yet not overdetailed. Unreservedly recommended," NATURE (London). Unabridged, corrected edition. List of recommended readings. 35 illustrations. xi + 537pp. 5⅜ x 8.
S377 Paperbound **$2.75**

FUNDAMENTAL FORMULAS OF PHYSICS, ed. by D. H. Menzel. Highly useful, fully inexpensive reference and study text, ranging from simple to highly sophisticated operations. Mathematics integrated into text—each chapter stands as short textbook of field represented. Vol. 1: Statistics, Physical Constants, Special Theory of Relativity, Hydrodynamics, Aerodynamics, Boundary Value Problems in Math. Physics; Viscosity, Electromagnetic Theory, etc. Vol. 2: Sound, Acoustics, Geometrical Optics, Electron Optics, High-Energy Phenomena, Magnetism, Biophysics, much more. Index. Total of 800pp. 5⅜ x 8. Vol. 1 S595 Paperbound **$2.00**
Vol. 2 S596 Paperbound **$2.00**

MATHEMATICAL PHYSICS, D. H. Menzel. Thorough one-volume treatment of the mathematical techniques vital for classic mechanics, electromagnetic theory, quantum theory, and relativity. Written by the Harvard Professor of Astrophysics for junior, senior, and graduate courses, it gives clear explanations of all those aspects of function theory, vectors, matrices, dyadics, tensors, partial differential equations, etc., necessary for the understanding of the various physical theories. Electron theory, relativity, and other topics seldom presented appear here in considerable detail. Scores of definitions, conversion factors, dimensional constants, etc. "More detailed than normal for an advanced text . . . excellent set of sections on Dyadics, Matrices, and Tensors," JOURNAL OF THE FRANKLIN INSTITUTE. Index. 193 problems, with answers. x + 412pp. 5⅜ x 8. S56 Paperbound **$2.00**

THE SCIENTIFIC PAPERS OF J. WILLARD GIBBS. All the published papers of America's outstanding theoretical scientist (except for "Statistical Mechanics" and "Vector Analysis"). Vol I (thermodynamics) contains one of the most brilliant of all 19th-century scientific papers—the 300-page "On the Equilibrium of Heterogeneous Substances," which founded the science of physical chemistry, and clearly stated a number of highly important natural laws for the first time; 8 other papers complete the first volume. Vol II includes 2 papers on dynamics, 8 on vector analysis and multiple algebra, 5 on the electromagnetic theory of light, and 6 miscellaneous papers. Biographical sketch by H. A. Bumstead. Total of xxxvi + 718pp. 5⅝ x 8⅜.
S721 Vol I Paperbound **$2.50**
S722 Vol II Paperbound **$2.00**
The set **$4.50**

BASIC THEORIES OF PHYSICS, Peter Gabriel Bergmann. Two-volume set which presents a critical examination of important topics in the major subdivisions of classical and modern physics. The first volume is concerned with classical mechanics and electrodynamics: mechanics of mass points, analytical mechanics, matter in bulk, electrostatics and magnetostatics, electromagnetic interaction, the field waves, special relativity, and waves. The second volume (Heat and Quanta) contains discussions of the kinetic hypothesis, physics and statistics, stationary ensembles, laws of thermodynamics, early quantum theories, atomic spectra, probability waves, quantization in wave mechanics, approximation methods, and abstract quantum theory. A valuable supplement to any thorough course or text.
Heat and Quanta: Index. 8 figures. x + 300pp. 5⅜ x 8½. S968 Paperbound **$1.75**
Mechanics and Electrodynamics: Index. 14 figures. vii + 280pp. 5⅜ x 8½.
S969 Paperbound **$1.75**

THEORETICAL PHYSICS, A. S. Kompaneyets. One of the very few thorough studies of the subject in this price range. Provides advanced students with a comprehensive theoretical background. Especially strong on recent experimentation and developments in quantum theory. Contents: Mechanics (Generalized Coordinates, Lagrange's Equation, Collision of Particles, etc.), Electrodynamics (Vector Analysis, Maxwell's equations, Transmission of Signals, Theory of Relativity, etc.), Quantum Mechanics (the Inadequacy of Classical Mechanics, the Wave Equation, Motion in a Central Field, Quantum Theory of Radiation, Quantum Theories of Dispersion and Scattering, etc.), and Statistical Physics (Equilibrium Distribution of Molecules in an Ideal Gas, Boltzmann statistics, Bose and Fermi Distribution, Thermodynamic Quantities, etc.). Revised to 1961. Translated by George Yankovsky, authorized by Kompaneyets. 137 exercises. 56 figures. 529pp. 5⅜ x 8½. S972 Paperbound **$2.50**

ANALYTICAL AND CANONICAL FORMALISM IN PHYSICS, André Mercier. A survey, in one volume, of the variational principles (the key principles—in mathematical form—from which the basic laws of any one branch of physics can be derived) of the several branches of physical theory, together with an examination of the relationships among them. Contents: the Lagrangian Formalism, Lagrangian Densities, Canonical Formalism, Canonical Form of Electrodynamics, Hamiltonian Densities, Transformations, and Canonical Form with Vanishing Jacobian Determinant. Numerous examples and exercises. For advanced students, teachers, etc. 6 figures. Index. viii + 222pp. 5⅜ x 8½. S1077 Paperbound **$1.75**

Acoustics, optics, electricity and magnetism, electromagnetics, magnetohydrodynamics

THE THEORY OF SOUND, Lord Rayleigh. Most vibrating systems likely to be encountered in practice can be tackled successfully by the methods set forth by the great Nobel laureate, Lord Rayleigh. Complete coverage of experimental, mathematical aspects of sound theory. Partial contents: Harmonic motions, vibrating systems in general, lateral vibrations of bars, curved plates or shells, applications of Laplace's functions to acoustical problems, fluid friction, plane vortex-sheet, vibrations of solid bodies, etc. This is the first inexpensive edition of this great reference and study work. Bibliography. Historical introduction by R. B. Lindsay. Total of 1040pp. 97 figures. 5⅜ x 8.
S292, S293, Two volume set, paperbound, **$4.70**

THE DYNAMICAL THEORY OF SOUND, H. Lamb. Comprehensive mathematical treatment of the physical aspects of sound, covering the theory of vibrations, the general theory of sound, and the equations of motion of strings, bars, membranes, pipes, and resonators. Includes chapters on plane, spherical, and simple harmonic waves, and the Helmholtz Theory of Audition. Complete and self-contained development for student and specialist; all fundamental differential equations solved completely. Specific mathematical details for such important phenomena as harmonics, normal modes, forced vibrations of strings, theory of reed pipes, etc. Index. Bibliography. 86 diagrams. viii + 307pp. 5⅜ x 8. S655 Paperbound **$1.50**

WAVE PROPAGATION IN PERIODIC STRUCTURES, L. Brillouin. A general method and application to different problems: pure physics, such as scattering of X-rays of crystals, thermal vibration in crystal lattices, electronic motion in metals; and also problems of electrical engineering. Partial contents: elastic waves in 1-dimensional lattices of point masses. Propagation of waves along 1-dimensional lattices. Energy flow. 2 dimensional, 3 dimensional lattices. Mathieu's equation. Matrices and propagation of waves along an electric line. Continuous electric lines. 131 illustrations. Bibliography. Index. xii + 253pp. 5⅜ x 8.
S34 Paperbound **$2.00**

THEORY OF VIBRATIONS, N. W. McLachlan. Based on an exceptionally successful graduate course given at Brown University, this discusses linear systems having 1 degree of freedom, forced vibrations of simple linear systems, vibration of flexible strings, transverse vibrations of bars and tubes, transverse vibration of circular plate, sound waves of finite amplitude, etc. Index. 99 diagrams. 160pp. 5⅜ x 8. S190 Paperbound **$1.35**

LIGHT: PRINCIPLES AND EXPERIMENTS, George S. Monk. Covers theory, experimentation, and research. Intended for students with some background in general physics and elementary calculus. Three main divisions: 1) Eight chapters on geometrical optics—fundamental concepts (the ray and its optical length, Fermat's principle, etc.), laws of image formation, apertures in optical systems, photometry, optical instruments etc.; 2) 9 chapters on physical optics—interference, diffraction, polarization, spectra, the Rayleigh refractometer, the wave theory of light, etc.; 3) 23 instructive experiments based directly on the theoretical text. "Probably the best intermediate textbook on light in the English language. Certainly, it is the best book which includes both geometrical and physical optics," J. Rud Nielson, PHYSICS FORUM. Revised edition. 102 problems and answers. 12 appendices. 6 tables. Index. 270 illustrations. xi +489pp. 5⅜ x 8½. S341 Paperbound **$2.50**

PHOTOMETRY, John W. T. Walsh. The best treatment of both "bench" and "illumination" photometry in English by one of Britain's foremost experts in the field (President of the International Commission on Illumination). Limited to those matters, theoretical and practical, which affect the measurement of light flux, candlepower, illumination, etc., and excludes treatment of the use to which such measurements may be put after they have been made. Chapters on Radiation, The Eye and Vision, Photo-Electric Cells, The Principles of Photometry, The Measurement of Luminous Intensity, Colorimetry, Spectrophotometry, Stellar Photometry, The Photometric Laboratory, etc. Third revised (1958) edition. 281 illustrations. 10 appendices. xxiv + 544pp. 5½ x 9¼. S319 Clothbound **$10.00**

EXPERIMENTAL SPECTROSCOPY, R. A. Sawyer. Clear discussion of prism and grating spectrographs and the techniques of their use in research, with emphasis on those principles and techniques that are fundamental to practically all uses of spectroscopic equipment. Beginning with a brief history of spectroscopy, the author covers such topics as light sources, spectroscopic apparatus, prism spectroscopes and graphs, diffraction grating, the photographic process, determination of wave length, spectral intensity, infrared spectroscopy, spectrochemical analysis, etc. This revised edition contains new material on the production of replica gratings, solar spectroscopy from rockets, new standard of wave length, etc. Index. Bibliography. 111 illustrations. x + 358pp. 5⅜ x 8½. S1045 Paperbound **$2.25**

FUNDAMENTALS OF ELECTRICITY AND MAGNETISM, L. B. Loeb. For students of physics, chemistry, or engineering who want an introduction to electricity and magnetism on a higher level and in more detail than general elementary physics texts provide. Only elementary differential and integral calculus is assumed. Physical laws developed logically, from magnetism to electric currents, Ohm's law, electrolysis, and on to static electricity, induction, etc. Covers an unusual amount of material; one third of book on modern material: solution of wave equation, photoelectric and thermionic effects, etc. Complete statement of the various electrical systems of units and interrelations. 2 Indexes. 75 pages of problems with answers stated. Over 300 figures and diagrams. xix +669pp. 5⅜ x 8. S745 Paperbound **$2.75**

MATHEMATICAL ANALYSIS OF ELECTRICAL AND OPTICAL WAVE-MOTION, Harry Bateman. Written by one of this century's most distinguished mathematical physicists, this is a practical introduction to those developments of Maxwell's electromagnetic theory which are directly connected with the solution of the partial differential equation of wave motion. Methods of solving wave-equation, polar-cylindrical coordinates, diffraction, transformation of coordinates, homogeneous solutions, electromagnetic fields with moving singularities, etc. Index. 168pp. 5⅜ x 8. S14 Paperbound **$1.75**

PRINCIPLES OF PHYSICAL OPTICS, Ernst Mach. This classical examination of the propagation of light, color, polarization, etc. offers an historical and philosophical treatment that has never been surpassed for breadth and easy readability. Contents: Rectilinear propagation of light. Reflection, refraction. Early knowledge of vision. Dioptrics. Composition of light. Theory of color and dispersion. Periodicity. Theory of interference. Polarization. Mathematical representation of properties of light. Propagation of waves, etc. 279 illustrations, 10 portraits. Appendix. Indexes. 324pp. 5⅜ x 8. S178 Paperbound **$2.00**

THE THEORY OF OPTICS, Paul Drude. One of finest fundamental texts in physical optics, classic offers thorough coverage, complete mathematical treatment of basic ideas. Includes fullest treatment of application of thermodynamics to optics; sine law in formation of images, transparent crystals, magnetically active substances, velocity of light, apertures, effects depending upon them, polarization, optical instruments, etc. Introduction by A. A. Michelson. Index. 110 illus. 567pp. 5⅜ x 8. S532 Paperbound **$2.45**

ELECTRICAL THEORY ON THE GIORGI SYSTEM, P. Cornelius. A new clarification of the fundamental concepts of electricity and magnetism, advocating the convenient m.k.s. system of units that is steadily gaining followers in the sciences. Illustrating the use and effectiveness of his terminology with numerous applications to concrete technical problems, the author here expounds the famous Giorgi system of electrical physics. His lucid presentation and well-reasoned, cogent argument for the universal adoption of this system form one of the finest pieces of scientific exposition in recent years. 28 figures. Index. Conversion tables for translating earlier data into modern units. Translated from 3rd Dutch edition by L. J. Jolley. x + 187pp. 5½ x 8¾. S909 Clothbound **$6.00**

ELECTRIC WAVES: BEING RESEARCHES ON THE PROPAGATION OF ELECTRIC ACTION WITH FINITE VELOCITY THROUGH SPACE, Heinrich Hertz. This classic work brings together the original papers in which Hertz—Helmholtz's protegé and one of the most brilliant figures in 19th-century research—probed the existence of electromagnetic waves and showed experimentally that their velocity equalled that of light, research that helped lay the groundwork for the development of radio, television, telephone, telegraph, and other modern technological marvels. Unabridged republication of original edition. Authorized translation by D. E. Jones. Preface by Lord Kelvin. Index of names. 40 illustrations. xvii + 278pp. 5⅜ x 8½. S57 Paperbound **$1.75**

PIEZOELECTRICITY: AN INTRODUCTION TO THE THEORY AND APPLICATIONS OF ELECTROMECHANICAL PHENOMENA IN CRYSTALS, Walter G. Cady. This is the most complete and systematic coverage of this important field in print—now regarded as something of scientific classic. This republication, revised and corrected by Prof. Cady—one of the foremost contributors in this area—contains a sketch of recent progress and new material on Ferroelectrics. Time Standards, etc. The first 7 chapters deal with fundamental theory of crystal electricity. 5 important chapters cover basic concepts of piezoelectricity, including comparisons of various competing theories in the field. Also discussed: piezoelectric resonators (theory, methods of manufacture, influences of air-gaps, etc.); the piezo oscillator; the properties, history, and observations relating to Rochelle salt; ferroelectric crystals; miscellaneous applications of piezoelectricity; pyroelectricity; etc. "A great work," W. A. Wooster, NATURE. Revised (1963) and corrected edition. New preface by Prof. Cady. 2 Appendices. Indices. Illustrations. 62 tables. Bibliography. Problems. Total of 1 + 822pp. 5⅜ x 8½.
S1094 Vol. I Paperbound **$2.50**
S1095 Vol. II Paperbound **$2.50**
Two volume set Paperbound **$5.00**

MAGNETISM AND VERY LOW TEMPERATURES, H. B. G. Casimir. A basic work in the literature of low temperature physics. Presents a concise survey of fundamental theoretical principles, and also points out promising lines of investigation. Contents: Classical Theory and Experimental Methods, Quantum Theory of Paramagnetism, Experiments on Adiabatic Demagnetization. Theoretical Discussion of Paramagnetism at Very Low Temperatures, Some Experimental Results, Relaxation Phenomena. Index. 89-item bibliography. ix + 95pp. 5⅜ x 8. S943 Paperbound **$1.25**

SELECTED PAPERS ON NEW TECHNIQUES FOR ENERGY CONVERSION: THERMOELECTRIC METHODS; THERMIONIC; PHOTOVOLTAIC AND ELECTRICAL EFFECTS; FUSION, Edited by Sumner N. Levine. Brings together in one volume the most important papers (1954-1961) in modern energy technology. Included among the 37 papers are general and qualitative descriptions of the field as a whole, indicating promising lines of research. Also: 15 papers on thermoelectric methods, 7 on thermionic, 5 on photovoltaic, 4 on electrochemical effect, and 2 on controlled fusion research. Among the contributors are: Joffe, Maria Telkes, Herold, Herring, Douglas, Jaumot, Post, Austin, Wilson, Pfann, Rappaport, Morehouse, Domenicali, Moss, Bowers, Harman, Von Doenhoef. Preface and introduction by the editor. Bibliographies. xxviii + 451pp. 6⅛ x 9¼. S37 Paperbound **$3.00**

SUPERFLUIDS: MACROSCOPIC THEORY OF SUPERCONDUCTIVITY, Vol. I, Fritz London. The major work by one of the founders and great theoreticians of modern quantum physics. Consolidates the researches that led to the present understanding of the nature of superconductivity. Prof. London here reveals that quantum mechanics is operative on the macroscopic plane as well as the submolecular level. Contents: Properties of Superconductors and Their Thermodynamical Correlation; Electrodynamics of the Pure Superconducting State; Relation between Current and Field; Measurements of the Penetration Depth; Non-Viscous Flow vs. Superconductivity; Micro-waves in Superconductors; Reality of the Domain Structure; and many other related topics. A new epilogue by M. J. Buckingham discusses developments in the field up to 1960. Corrected and expanded edition. An appreciation of the author's life and work by L. W. Nordheim. Biography by Edith London. Bibliography of his publications. 45 figures. 2 Indices. xviii + 173pp. 5⅝ x 8⅜. S44 Paperbound **$1.45**

SELECTED PAPERS ON PHYSICAL PROCESSES IN IONIZED PLASMAS, Edited by Donald H. Menzel, Director, Harvard College Observatory. 30 important papers relating to the study of highly ionized gases or plasmas selected by a foremost contributor in the field, with the assistance of Dr. L. H. Aller. The essays include 18 on the physical processes in gaseous nebulae, covering problems of radiation and radiative transfer, the Balmer decrement, electron temperatives, spectrophotometry, etc. 10 papers deal with the interpretation of nebular spectra, by Bohm, Van Vleck, Aller, Minkowski, etc. There is also a discussion of the intensities of "forbidden" spectral lines by George Shortley and a paper concerning the theory of hydrogenic spectra by Menzel and Pekeris. Other contributors: Goldberg, Hebb, Baker, Bowen, Ufford, Liller, etc. viii + 374pp. 6⅛ x 9¼. S60 Paperbound **$2.95**

THE ELECTROMAGNETIC FIELD, Max Mason & Warren Weaver. Used constantly by graduate engineers. Vector methods exclusively: detailed treatment of electrostatics, expansion methods, with tables converting any quantity into absolute electromagnetic, absolute electrostatic, practical units. Discrete charges, ponderable bodies, Maxwell field equations, etc. Introduction. Indexes. 416pp. 5⅜ x 8. S185 Paperbound **$2.00**

THEORY OF ELECTRONS AND ITS APPLICATION TO THE PHENOMENA OF LIGHT AND RADIANT HEAT, H. Lorentz. Lectures delivered at Columbia University by Nobel laureate Lorentz. Unabridged, they form a historical coverage of the theory of free electrons, motion, absorption of heat, Zeeman effect, propagation of light in molecular bodies, inverse Zeeman effect, optical phenomena in moving bodies, etc. 109 pages of notes explain the more advanced sections. Index. 9 figures. 352pp. 5⅜ x 8. S173 Paperbound **$1.85**

FUNDAMENTAL ELECTROMAGNETIC THEORY, Ronold P. King, Professor Applied Physics, Harvard University. Original and valuable introduction to electromagnetic theory and to circuit theory from the standpoint of electromagnetic theory. Contents: Mathematical Description of Matter—stationary and nonstationary states; Mathematical Description of Space and of Simple Media—Field Equations, Integral Forms of Field Equations, Electromagnetic Force, etc.; Transformation of Field and Force Equations; Electromagnetic Waves in Unbounded Regions; Skin Effect and Internal Impedance—in a solid cylindrical conductor, etc.; and Electrical Circuits—Analytical Foundations, Near-zone and quasi-near zone circuits, Balanced two-wire and four-wire transmission lines. Revised and enlarged version. New preface by the author. 5 appendices (Differential operators: Vector Formulas and Identities, etc.). Problems. Indexes. Bibliography. xvi + 580pp. 5⅜ x 8½. S1023 Paperbound **$2.75**

Hydrodynamics

A TREATISE ON HYDRODYNAMICS, A. B. Basset. Favorite text on hydrodynamics for 2 generations of physicists, hydrodynamical engineers, oceanographers, ship designers, etc. Clear enough for the beginning student, and thorough source for graduate students and engineers on the work of d'Alembert, Euler, Laplace, Lagrange, Poisson, Green, Clebsch, Stokes, Cauchy, Helmholtz, J. J. Thomson, Love, Hicks, Greenhill, Besant, Lamb, etc. Great amount of documentation on entire theory of classical hydrodynamics. Vol I: theory of motion of frictionless liquids, vortex, and cyclic irrotational motion, etc. 132 exercises. Bibliography. 3 Appendixes. xii + 264pp. Vol II: motion in viscous liquids, harmonic analysis, theory of tides, etc. 112 exercises, Bibliography. 4 Appendixes. xv + 328pp. Two volume set. 5⅜ x 8.

S724 Vol I Paperbound **$1.75**
S725 Vol II Paperbound **$1.75**
The set **$3.50**

HYDRODYNAMICS, Horace Lamb. Internationally famous complete coverage of standard reference work on dynamics of liquids & gases. Fundamental theorems, equations, methods, solutions, background, for classical hydrodynamics. Chapters include Equations of Motion, Integration of Equations in Special Gases, Irrotational Motion, Motion of Liquid in 2 Dimensions, Motion of Solids through Liquid-Dynamical Theory, Vortex Motion, Tidal Waves, Surface Waves, Waves of Expansion, Viscosity, Rotating Masses of liquids. Excellently planned, arranged; clear, lucid presentation. 6th enlarged, revised edition. Index. Over 900 footnotes, mostly bibliographical. 119 figures. xv + 738pp. 6⅛ x 9¼. S256 Paperbound **$3.75**

HYDRODYNAMICS, H. Dryden, F. Murnaghan, Harry Bateman. Published by the National Research Council in 1932 this enormous volume offers a complete coverage of classical hydrodynamics. Encyclopedic in quality. Partial contents: physics of fluids, motion, turbulent flow, compressible fluids, motion in 1, 2, 3 dimensions; viscous fluids rotating, laminar motion, resistance of motion through viscous fluid, eddy viscosity, hydraulic flow in channels of various shapes, discharge of gases, flow past obstacles, etc. Bibliography of over 2,900 items. Indexes. 23 figures. 634pp. 5⅜ x 8. S303 Paperbound **$2.75**

Mechanics, dynamics, thermodynamics, elasticity

MECHANICS, J. P. Den Hartog. Already a classic among introductory texts, the M.I.T. professor's lively and discursive presentation is equally valuable as a beginner's text, an engineering student's refresher, or a practicing engineer's reference. Emphasis in this highly readable text is on illuminating fundamental principles and showing how they are embodied in a great number of real engineering and design problems: trusses, loaded cables, beams, jacks, hoists, etc. Provides advanced material on relative motion and gyroscopes not usual in introductory texts. "Very thoroughly recommended to all those anxious to improve their real understanding of the principles of mechanics." MECHANICAL WORLD. Index. List of equations. 334 problems, all with answers. Over 550 diagrams and drawings. ix + 462pp. 5⅜ x 8. S754 Paperbound **$2.00**

THEORETICAL MECHANICS: AN INTRODUCTION TO MATHEMATICAL PHYSICS, J. S. Ames, F. D. Murnaghan. A mathematically rigorous development of theoretical mechanics for the advanced student, with constant practical applications. Used in hundreds of advanced courses. An unusually thorough coverage of gyroscopic and baryscopic material, detailed analyses of the Coriolis acceleration, applications of Lagrange's equations, motion of the double pendulum, Hamilton-Jacobi partial differential equations, group velocity and dispersion, etc. Special relativity is also included. 159 problems. 44 figures. ix + 462pp. 5⅜ x 8. S461 Paperbound **$2.25**

THEORETICAL MECHANICS: STATICS AND THE DYNAMICS OF A PARTICLE, W. D. MacMillan. Used for over 3 decades as a self-contained and extremely comprehensive advanced undergraduate text in mathematical physics, physics, astronomy, and deeper foundations of engineering. Early sections require only a knowledge of geometry; later, a working knowledge of calculus. Hundreds of basic problems, including projectiles to the moon, escape velocity, harmonic motion, ballistics, falling bodies, transmission of power, stress and strain, elasticity, astronomical problems. 340 practice problems plus many fully worked out examples make it possible to test and extend principles developed in the text. 200 figures. xvii + 430pp. 5⅜ x 8. S467 Paperbound **$2.00**

THEORETICAL MECHANICS: THE THEORY OF THE POTENTIAL, W. D. MacMillan. A comprehensive, well balanced presentation of potential theory, serving both as an introduction and a reference work with regard to specific problems, for physicists and mathematicians. No prior knowledge of integral relations is assumed, and all mathematical material is developed as it becomes necessary. Includes: Attraction of Finite Bodies; Newtonian Potential Function; Vector Fields, Green and Gauss Theorems; Attractions of Surfaces and Lines; Surface Distribution of Matter; Two-Layer Surfaces; Spherical Harmonics; Ellipsoidal Harmonics; etc. "The great number of particular cases . . . should make the book valuable to geophysicists and others actively engaged in practical applications of the potential theory," Review of Scientific Instruments. Index. Bibliography. xiii + 469pp. 5⅜ x 8. S486 Paperbound **$2.25**

THEORETICAL MECHANICS: DYNAMICS OF RIGID BODIES, W. D. MacMillan. Theory of dynamics of a rigid body is developed, using both the geometrical and analytical methods of instruction. Begins with exposition of algebra of vectors, it goes through momentum principles, motion in space, use of differential equations and infinite series to solve more sophisticated dynamics problems. Partial contents: moments of inertia, systems of free particles, motion parallel to a fixed plane, rolling motion, method of periodic solutions, much more. 82 figs. 199 problems. Bibliography. Indexes. xii + 476pp. 5⅜ x 8. S641 Paperbound **$2.00**

MATHEMATICAL FOUNDATIONS OF STATISTICAL MECHANICS, A. I. Khinchin. Offering a precise and rigorous formulation of problems, this book supplies a thorough and up-to-date exposition. It provides analytical tools needed to replace cumbersome concepts, and furnishes for the first time a logical step-by-step introduction to the subject. Partial contents: geometry & kinematics of the phase space, ergodic problem, reduction to theory of probability, application of central limit problem, ideal monatomic gas, foundation of thermo-dynamics, dispersion and distribution of sum functions. Key to notations. Index. viii + 179pp. 5⅜ x 8. S147 Paperbound **$1.50**

ELEMENTARY PRINCIPLES IN STATISTICAL MECHANICS, J. W. Gibbs. Last work of the great Yale mathematical physicist, still one of the most fundamental treatments available for advanced students and workers in the field. Covers the basic principle of conservation of probability of phase, theory of errors in the calculated phases of a system, the contributions of Clausius, Maxwell, Boltzmann, and Gibbs himself, and much more. Includes valuable comparison of statistical mechanics with thermodynamics: Carnot's cycle, mechanical definitions of entropy, etc. xvi + 208pp. 5⅜ x 8. S707 Paperbound **$1.45**

PRINCIPLES OF MECHANICS AND DYNAMICS, Sir William Thomson (Lord Kelvin) and Peter Guthrie Tait. The principles and theories of fundamental branches of classical physics explained by two of the greatest physicists of all time. A broad survey of mechanics, with material on hydrodynamics, elasticity, potential theory, and what is now standard mechanics. Thorough and detailed coverage, with many examples, derivations, and topics not included in more recent studies. Only a knowledge of calculus is needed to work through this book. Vol. I (Preliminary): Kinematics; Dynamical Laws and Principles; Experience (observation, experimentation, formation of hypotheses, scientific method); Measures and Instruments; Continuous Calculating Machines. Vol. II (Abstract Dynamics): Statics of a Particle—Attraction; Statics of Solids and Fluids. Formerly Titled "Treatise on Natural Philosophy." Unabridged reprint of revised edition. Index. 168 diagrams. Total of xlii + 1035pp. 5⅜ x 8½.
Vol. I: S966 Paperbound **$2.35**
Vol. II: S967 Paperbound **$2.35**
Two volume Set Paperbound **$4.70**

INVESTIGATIONS ON THE THEORY OF THE BROWNIAN MOVEMENT, Albert Einstein. Reprints from rare European journals. 5 basic papers, including the Elementary Theory of the Brownian Movement, written at the request of Lorentz to provide a simple explanation. Translated by A. D. Cowper. Annotated, edited by R. Fürth. 33pp. of notes elucidate, give history of previous investigations. Author, subject indexes. 62 footnotes. 124pp. 5⅜ x 8.
S304 Paperbound **$1.25**

MECHANICS VIA THE CALCULUS, P. W. Norris, W. S. Legge. Covers almost everything, from linear motion to vector analysis: equations determining motion, linear methods, compounding of simple harmonic motions, Newton's laws of motion, Hooke's law, the simple pendulum, motion of a particle in 1 plane, centers of gravity, virtual work, friction, kinetic energy of rotating bodies, equilibrium of strings, hydrostatics, sheering stresses, elasticity, etc. 550 problems. 3rd revised edition. xii + 367pp. 6 x 9. S207 Clothbound **$4.95**

THE DYNAMICS OF PARTICLES AND OF RIGID, ELASTIC, AND FLUID BODIES; BEING LECTURES ON MATHEMATICAL PHYSICS, A. G. Webster. The reissuing of this classic fills the need for a comprehensive work on dynamics. A wide range of topics is covered in unusually great depth, applying ordinary and partial differential equations. Part I considers laws of motion and methods applicable to systems of all sorts; oscillation, resonance, cyclic systems, etc. Part 2 is a detailed study of the dynamics of rigid bodies. Part 3 introduces the theory of potential; stress and strain, Newtonian potential functions, gyrostatics, wave and vortex motion, etc. Further contents: Kinematics of a point; Lagrange's equations; Hamilton's principle; Systems of vectors; Statics and dynamics of deformable bodies; much more, not easily found together in one volume. Unabridged reprinting of 2nd edition. 20 pages of notes on differential equations and the higher analysis. 203 illustrations. Selected bibliography. Index. xi + 588pp. 5⅜ x 8. S522 Paperbound **$2.45**

A TREATISE ON DYNAMICS OF A PARTICLE, E. J. Routh. Elementary text on dynamics for beginning mathematics or physics student. Unusually detailed treatment from elementary definitions to motion in 3 dimensions, emphasizing concrete aspects. Much unique material important in recent applications. Covers impulsive forces, rectilinear and constrained motion in 2 dimensions, harmonic and parabolic motion, degrees of freedom, closed orbits, the conical pendulum, the principle of least action, Jacobi's method, and much more. Index. 559 problems, many fully worked out, incorporated into text. xiii + 418pp. 5⅜ x 8.
S696 Paperbound **$2.25**

DYNAMICS OF A SYSTEM OF RIGID BODIES (Elementary Section), E. J. Routh. Revised 7th edition of this standard reference. This volume covers the dynamical principles of the subject, and its more elementary applications: finding moments of inertia by integration, foci of inertia, d'Alembert's principle, impulsive forces, motion in 2 and 3 dimensions, Lagrange's equations, relative indicatrix, Euler's theorem, large tautochronous motions, etc. Index. 55 figures. Scores of problems. xv + 443pp. 5⅜ x 8. S664 Paperbound **$2.50**

DYNAMICS OF A SYSTEM OF RIGID BODIES (Advanced Section), E. J. Routh. Revised 6th edition of a classic reference aid. Much of its material remains unique. Partial contents: moving axes, relative motion, oscillations about equilibrium, motion. Motion of a body under no forces, any forces. Nature of motion given by linear equations and conditions of stability. Free, forced vibrations, constants of integration, calculus of finite differences, variations, precession and nutation, motion of the moon, motion of string, chain, membranes. 64 figures. 498pp. 5⅜ x 8. S229 Paperbound **$2.45**

DYNAMICAL THEORY OF GASES, James Jeans. Divided into mathematical and physical chapters for the convenience of those not expert in mathematics, this volume discusses the mathematical theory of gas in a steady state, thermodynamics, Boltzmann and Maxwell, kinetic theory, quantum theory, exponentials, etc. 4th enlarged edition, with new material on quantum theory, quantum dynamics, etc. Indexes. 28 figures. 444pp. 6⅛ x 9¼.
S136 Paperbound **$2.65**

THE THEORY OF HEAT RADIATION, Max Planck. A pioneering work in thermodynamics, providing basis for most later work, Nobel laureate Planck writes on Deductions from Electrodynamics and Thermodynamics, Entropy and Probability, Irreversible Radiation Processes, etc. Starts with simple experimental laws of optics, advances to problems of spectral distribution of energy and irreversibility. Bibliography. 7 illustrations, xiv + 224pp. 5⅜ x 8.
S546 Paperbound **$1.50**

FOUNDATIONS OF POTENTIAL THEORY, O. D. Kellogg. Based on courses given at Harvard this is suitable for both advanced and beginning mathematicians. Proofs are rigorous, and much material not generally avaliable elsewhere is included. Partial contents: forces of gravity, fields of force, divergence theorem, properties of Newtonian potentials at points of free space, potentials as solutions of Laplace's equations, harmonic functions, electrostatics, electric images, logarithmic potential, etc. One of Grundlehren Series. ix + 384pp. 5⅜ x 8.
S144 Paperbound **$1.98**

THERMODYNAMICS, Enrico Fermi. Unabridged reproduction of 1937 edition. Elementary in treatment; remarkable for clarity, organization. Requires no knowledge of advanced math beyond calculus, only familiarity with fundamentals of thermometry, calorimetry. Partial Contents: Thermodynamic systems; First & Second laws of thermodynamics; Entropy; Thermodynamic potentials: phase rule, reversible electric cell; Gaseous reactions: van't Hoff reaction box, principle of LeChatelier; Thermodynamics of dilute solutions: osmotic & vapor pressures, boiling & freezing points; Entropy constant. Index. 25 problems. 24 illustrations. x + 160pp. 5⅜ x 8. S361 Paperbound **$1.75**

THE THERMODYNAMICS OF ELECTRICAL PHENOMENA IN METALS and A CONDENSED COLLECTION OF THERMODYNAMIC FORMULAS, P. W. Bridgman. Major work by the Nobel Prizewinner: stimulating conceptual introduction to aspects ot the electron theory of metals, giving an intuitive understanding of fundamental relationships concealed by the formal systems of Onsager and others. Elementary mathematical formulations show clearly the fundamental thermodynamical relationships of the electric field, and a complete phenomenological theory of metals is created. This is the work in which Bridgman announced his famous "thermomotive force" and his distinction between "driving" and "working" electromotive force. We have added in this Dover edition the author's long unavailable tables of thermodynamic formulas, extremely valuable for the speed of reference they allow. Two works bound as one. Index. 33 figures. Bibliography. xviii + 256pp. 5⅜ x 8. S723 Paperbound **$1.65**

TREATISE ON THERMODYNAMICS, Max Planck. Based on Planck's original papers this offers a uniform point of view for the entire field and has been used as an introduction for students who have studied elementary chemistry, physics, and calculus. Rejecting the earlier approaches of Helmholtz and Maxwell, the author makes no assumptions regarding the nature of heat, but begins with a few empirical facts, and from these deduces new physical and chemical laws. 3rd English edition of this standard text by a Nobel laureate. xvi + 297pp. 5⅜ x 8. S219 Paperbound **$1.75**

THE MATHEMATICAL THEORY OF ELASTICITY, A. E. H. Love. A wealth of practical illustration combined with thorough discussion of fundamentals—theory, application, special problems and solutions. Partial Contents: Analysis of Strain & Stress, Elasticity of Solid Bodies, Elasticity of Crystals, Vibration of Spheres, Cylinders, Propagation of Waves in Elastic Solid Media, Torsion, Theory of Continuous Beams, Plates. Rigorous treatment of Volterra's theory of dislocations, 2-dimensional elastic systems, other topics of modern interest. "For years the standard treatise on elasticity," AMERICAN MATHEMATICAL MONTHLY. 4th revised edition. Index. 76 figures. xviii + 643pp. 6⅛ x 9¼. S174 Paperbound **$3.00**

STRESS WAVES IN SOLIDS, H. Kolsky, Professor of Applied Physics, Brown University. The most readable survey of the theoretical core of current knowledge about the propagation of waves in solids, fully correlated with experimental research. Contents: Part I—Elastic Waves: propagation in an extended plastic medium, propagation in bounded elastic media, experimental investigations with elastic materials. Part II—Stress Waves in Imperfectly Elastic Media: internal friction, experimental investigations of dynamic elastic properties, plastic waves and shock waves, fractures produced by stress waves. List of symbols. Appendix. Supplemented bibliography. 3 full-page plates. 46 figures. x + 213pp. 5⅜ x 8½.
S1098 Paperbound **$1.55**

Relativity, quantum theory, atomic and nuclear physics

SPACE TIME MATTER, Hermann Weyl. "The standard treatise on the general theory of relativity" (Nature), written by a world-renowned scientist, provides a deep clear discussion of the logical coherence of the general theory, with introduction to all the mathematical tools needed: Maxwell, analytical geometry, non-Euclidean geometry, tensor calculus, etc. Basis is classical space-time, before absorption of relativity. Partial contents: Euclidean space, mathematical form, metrical continuum, relativity of time and space, general theory. 15 diagrams. Bibliography. New preface for this edition. xviii + 330pp. 5⅜ x 8.
S267 Paperbound **$2.00**

ATOMIC SPECTRA AND ATOMIC STRUCTURE, G. Herzberg. Excellent general survey for chemists, physicists specializing in other fields. Partial contents: simplest line spectra and elements of atomic theory, building-up principle and periodic system of elements, hyperfine structure of spectral lines, some experiments and applications. Bibilography. 80 figures. Index. xii + 257pp. 5⅜ x 8. S115 Paperbound **$2.00**

THE PRINCIPLE OF RELATIVITY, A. Einstein, H. Lorentz, H. Minkowski, H. Weyl. These are the 11 basic papers that founded the general and special theories of relativity, all translated into English. Two papers by Lorentz on the Michelson experiment, electromagnetic phenomena. Minkowski's SPACE & TIME, and Weyl's GRAVITATION & ELECTRICITY. 7 epoch-making papers by Einstein: ELECTROMAGNETICS OF MOVING BODIES, INFLUENCE OF GRAVITATION IN PROPAGATION OF LIGHT, COSMOLOGICAL CONSIDERATIONS, GENERAL THEORY, and 3 others. 7 diagrams. Special notes by A. Sommerfeld. 224pp. 5⅜ x 8.
S81 Paperbound **$1.75**

EINSTEIN'S THEORY OF RELATIVITY, Max Born. Revised edition prepared with the collaboration of Gunther Leibfried and Walter Biem. Steering a middle course between superficial popularizations and complex analyses, a Nobel laureate explains Einstein's theories clearly and with special insight. Easily followed by the layman with a knowledge of high school mathematics, the book has been thoroughly revised and extended to modernize those sections of the well-known original edition which are now out of date. After a comprehensive review of classical physics, Born's discussion of special and general theories of relativity covers such topics as simultaneity, kinematics, Einstein's mechanics and dynamics, relativity of arbitrary motions, the geometry of curved surfaces, the space-time continuum, and many others. Index. Illustrations, vii + 376pp. 5⅜ x 8. S769 Paperbound **$2.00**

ATOMS, MOLECULES AND QUANTA, Arthur E. Ruark and Harold C. Urey. Revised (1963) and corrected edition of a work that has been a favorite with physics students and teachers for more than 30 years. No other work offers the same combination of atomic structure and molecular physics and of experiment and theory. The first 14 chapters deal with the origins and major experimental data of quantum theory and with the development of conceptions of atomic and molecular structure prior to the new mechanics. These sections provide a thorough introduction to atomic and molecular theory, and are presented lucidly and as simply as possible. The six subsequent chapters are devoted to the laws and basic ideas of quantum mechanics: Wave Mechanics, Hydrogenic Atoms in Wave Mechanics, Matrix Mechanics, General Theory of Quantum Dynamics, etc. For advanced college and graduate students in physics. Revised, corrected republication of original edition, with supplementary notes by the authors. New preface by the authors. 9 appendices. General reference list. Indices. 228 figures. 71 tables. Bibliographical material in notes, etc. Total of xxiii + 810pp. 5⅜ x 8⅜.
S1106 Vol. I Paperbound **$2.50**
S1107 Vol. II Paperbound **$2.50**
Two volume set Paperbound **$5.00**

WAVE MECHANICS AND ITS APPLICATIONS, N. F. Mott and I. N. Sneddon. A comprehensive introduction to the theory of quantum mechanics; not a rigorous mathematical exposition it progresses, instead, in accordance with the physical problems considered. Many topics difficult to find at the elementary level are discussed in this book. Includes such matters as: the wave nature of matter, the wave equation of Schrödinger, the concept of stationary states, properties of the wave functions, effect of a magnetic field on the energy levels of atoms, electronic spin, two-body problem, theory of solids, cohesive forces in ionic crystals, collision problems, interaction of radiation with matter, relativistic quantum mechanics, etc. All are treated both physically and mathematically. 68 illustrations. 11 tables. Indexes. xii + 393pp. 5⅜ x 8½. S1070 Paperbound **$2.25**

BASIC METHODS IN TRANSFER PROBLEMS, V. Kourganoff, Professor of Astrophysics, U. of Paris. A coherent digest of all the known methods which can be used for approximate or exact solutions of transfer problems. All methods demonstrated on one particular problem —Milne's problem for a plane parallel medium. Three main sections: fundamental concepts (the radiation field and its interaction with matter, the absorption and emission coefficients, etc.); different methods by which transfer problems can be attacked; and a more general problem—the non-grey case of Milne's problem. Much new material, drawing upon declassified atomic energy reports and data from the USSR. Entirely understandable to the student with a reasonable knowledge of analysis. Unabridged, revised reprinting. New preface by the author. Index. Bibliography. 2 appendices. xv + 281pp. 5⅜ x 8½.
S1074 Paperbound **$2.00**

PRINCIPLES OF QUANTUM MECHANICS, W. V. Houston. Enables student with working knowledge of elementary mathematical physics to develop facility in use of quantum mechanics, understand published work in field. Formulates quantum mechanics in terms of Schroedinger's wave mechanics. Studies evidence for quantum theory, for inadequacy of classical mechanics, 2 postulates of quantum mechanics; numerous important, fruitful applications of quantum mechanics in spectroscopy, collision problems, electrons in solids; other topics. "One of the most rewarding features . . . is the interlacing of problems with text," Amer. J. of Physics. Corrected edition. 21 illus. Index. 296pp. 5⅜ x 8. S524 Paperbound **$2.00**

PHYSICAL PRINCIPLES OF THE QUANTUM THEORY, Werner Heisenberg. A Nobel laureate discusses quantum theory; Heisenberg's own work, Compton, Schroedinger, Wilson, Einstein, many others. Written for physicists, chemists who are not specialists in quantum theory, only elementary formulae are considered in the text; there is a mathematical appendix for specialists. Profound without sacrifice of clarity. Translated by C. Eckart, F. Hoyt. 18 figures. 192pp. 5⅜ x 8. S113 Paperbound **$1.25**

PHYSICS, HISTORIES AND CLASSICS

A HISTORY OF PHYSICS: IN ITS ELEMENTARY BRANCHES (THROUGH 1925), INCLUDING THE EVOLUTION OF PHYSICAL LABORATORIES, Florian Cajori. Revised and enlarged edition. The only first-rate brief history of physics. Still the best entry for a student or teacher into the antecedents of modern theories of physics. A clear, non-mathematical, handy reference work which traces in critical fashion the developments of ideas, theories, techniques, and apparatus from the Greeks to the 1920's. Within each period he analyzes the basic topics of mechanics, light, electricity and magnetism, sound, atomic theory and structure of matter, radioactivity, etc. A chapter on modern research: Curie, Kelvin, Planck's quantum theory, thermodynamics, Fitzgerald and Lorentz, special and general relativity, J. J. Thomson's model of an atom, Bohr's discoveries and later results, wave mechanics, and many other matters. Much bibliographic detail in footnotes. Index. 16 figures. xv + 424pp. 5⅜ x 8. T970 Paperbound **$2.00**

A HISTORY OF THE MATHEMATICAL THEORIES OF ATTRACTION AND THE FIGURE OF THE EARTH: FROM THE TIME OF NEWTON TO THAT OF LAPLACE, I. Todhunter. A technical and detailed review of the theories concerning the shape of the earth and its gravitational pull, from the earliest investigations in the seventeenth century up to the middle of the nineteenth. Some of the greatest mathematicians and scientists in history applied themselves to these questions: Newton ("Principia Mathematica"), Huygens, Maupertuis, Simpson, d'Alembert, etc. Others discussed are Poisson, Gauss, Plana, Lagrange, Boit, and many more. Particular emphasis is placed on the theories of Laplace and Legendre, several chapters being devoted to Laplace's "Mécanique Céleste" and his memoirs, and several others to the memoirs of Legendre. Important to historians of science and mathematics and to the specialist who desires background information in the field. 2 volumes bound as 1. Index. xxxvi + 984pp. 5⅜ x 8.
S148 Clothbound **$7.50**

OPTICKS, Sir Isaac Newton. In its discussions of light, reflection, color, refraction, theories of wave and corpuscular theories of light, this work is packed with scores of insights and discoveries. In its precise and practical discussion of construction of optical apparatus, contemporary understandings of phenomena it is truly fascinating to modern physicists, astronomers, mathematicians. Foreword by Albert Einstein. Preface by I. B. Cohen of Harvard University. 7 pages of portraits, facsimile pages, letters, etc. cxvi + 414pp. 5⅜ x 8.
S205 Paperbound **$2.25**

TREATISE ON LIGHT, Christiaan Huygens. The famous original formulation of the wave theory of light, this readable book is one of the two decisive and definitive works in the field of light (Newton's "Optics" is the other). A scientific giant whose researches ranged over mathematics, astronomy, and physics, Huygens, in this historic work, covers such topics as rays propagated in straight lines, reflection and refraction, the spreading and velocity of light, the nature of opaque bodies, the non-spherical nature of light in the atmosphere, properties of Iceland Crystal, and other related matters. Unabridged republication of original (1912) English edition. Translated and introduced by Silvanus P. Thompson. 52 illustrations. xii + 129pp. 5⅜ x 8. S179 Paperbound **$1.35**

FARADAY'S EXPERIMENTAL RESEARCHES IN ELECTRICITY. Faraday's historic series of papers containing the fruits of years of original experimentation in electrical theory and electrochemistry. Covers his findings in a variety of areas: Induction of electric currents, Evolution of electricity from magnetism, New electrical state or condition of matter, Explication of Arago's magnetic phenomena, New law of electric conduction, Electro-chemical decomposition, Electricity of the Voltaic Pile, Static Induction, Nature of the electric force or forces, Nature of electric current, The character and direction of the electric force of the Gymnotus, Magneto-electric spark, The magnetization of light and the illumination of magnetic lines of force, The possible relation of gravity to electricity, Sub-terraneous electro-telegraph wires, Some points of magnetic philosophy, The diamagnetic conditions of flame and gases, and many other matters. Complete and unabridged republication. 3 vols. bound as 2. Originally reprinted from the Philosophical Transactions of 1831-8. Indices. Illustrations. Total of 1463pp. 5⅜ x 8. S783-4, Clothbound **$17.50** (tentative)

REFLECTIONS ON THE MOTIVE POWER OF FIRE, Sadi Carnot, and other papers on the 2nd law of thermodynamics by E. Clapeyron and R. Clausius. Carnot's "Reflections" laid the groundwork of modern thermodynamics. Its non-technical, mostly verbal statements examine the relations between heat and the work done by heat in engines, establishing conditions for the economical working of these engines. The papers by Clapeyron and Clausius here reprinted added further refinements to Carnot's work, and led to its final acceptance by physicists. Selections from posthumous manuscripts of Carnot are also included. All papers in English. New introduction by E. Mendoza. 12 illustrations. xxii + 152pp. 5⅜ x 8.
S661 Paperbound **$1.50**

DIALOGUES CONCERNING TWO NEW SCIENCES, Galileo Galilei. This classic of experimental science, mechanics, engineering, is as enjoyable as it is important. A great historical document giving insights into one of the world's most original thinkers, it is based on 30 years' experimentation. It offers a lively exposition of dynamics, elasticity, sound, ballistics, strength of materials, the scientific method. "Superior to everything else of mine," Galileo. Trans. by H. Crew, A. Salvio. 126 diagrams. Index. xxi + 288pp. 5⅜ x 8.
S99 Paperbound **$1.75**

TREATISE ON ELECTRICITY AND MAGNETISM, James Clerk Maxwell. For more than 80 years a seemingly inexhaustible source of leads for physicists, mathematicians, engineers. Total of 1082pp. on such topics as Measurement of Quantities, Electrostatics, Elementary Mathematical Theory of Electricity, Electrical Work and Energy in a System of Conductors, General Theorems, Theory of Electrical Images, Electrolysis, Conduction, Polarization, Dielectrics, Resistance, etc. "The greatest mathematical physicist since Newton," Sir James Jeans. 3rd edition. 107 figures, 21 plates. 1082pp. 5⅜ x 8. S636-7, 2 volume set, paperbound **$4.00**

A HISTORY OF THE THEORY OF ELASTICITY AND THE STRENGTH OF MATERIALS, I. Todhunter and K. Pearson. For over 60 years a basic reference, unsurpassed in scope or authority. Both a history of the mathematical theory of elasticity from Galileo, Hooke, and Mariotte to Saint Venant, Kirchhoff, Clebsch, and Lord Kelvin and a detailed presentation of every important mathematical contribution during this period. Presents proofs of thousands of theorems and laws, summarizes every relevant treatise, many unavailable elsewhere. Practically a book apiece is devoted to modern founders: Saint Venant, Lamé, Boussinesq, Rankine, Lord Kelvin, F. Neumann, Kirchhoff, Clebsch. Hundreds of pages of technical and physical treatises on specific applications of elasticity to particular materials. Indispensable for the mathematician, physicist, or engineer working with elasticity. Unabridged, corrected reprint of original 3-volume 1886-1893 edition. Three volume set. Two indexes. Appendix to Vol. I. Total of 2344pp. 5⅜ x 8⅜. S914–916 The set, Clothbound **$15.00**

DE MAGNETE, William Gilbert. This classic work on magnetism founded a new science. Gilbert was the first to use the word "electricity", to recognize mass as distinct from weight, to discover the effect of heat on magnetic bodies; invent an electroscope, differentiate between static electricity and magnetism, conceive of the earth as a magnet. Written by the first great experimental scientist, this lively work is valuable not only as an historical landmark, but as the delightfully easy to follow record of a perpetually searching, ingenious mind. Translated by P. F. Mottelay. 25-page biographical memoir. 90 figures. lix +368pp. 5⅜ x 8. S470 Paperbound **$2.00**

ASTRONOMY

THE INTERNAL CONSTITUTION OF THE STARS, Sir A. S. Eddington. Influence of this has been enormous; first detailed exposition of theory of radiative equilibrium for stellar interiors, of all available evidence for existence of diffuse matter in interstellar space. Studies quantum theory, polytropic gas spheres, mass-luminosity relations, variable stars, etc. Discussions of equations paralleled with informal exposition of intimate relationship of astrophysics with great discoveries in atomic physics, radiation. Introduction. Appendix. Index. 421pp. 5⅜ x 8. S563 Paperbound **$2.25**

PLANETARY THEORY, E. W. Brown and C. A. Shook. Provides a clear presentation of basic methods for calculating planetary orbits for today's astronomer. Begins with a careful exposition of specialized mathematical topics essential for handling perturbation theory and then goes on to indicate how most of the previous methods reduce ultimately to two general calculation methods: obtaining expressions either for the coordinates of planetary positions or for the elements which determine the perturbed paths. An example of each is given and worked in detail. Corrected edition. Preface. Appendix. Index. xii + 302pp. 5⅜ x 8½. S1133 Paperbound **$2.25**

CANON OF ECLIPSES (CANON DER FINSTERNISSE), Prof. Theodor Ritter von Oppolzer. Since its original publication in 1887, this has been the standard reference and the most extensive single volume of data on the calculation of solar and lunar eclipses, past and future. A comprehensive introduction gives a full explanation of the use of the tables for the calculations of the exact dates of eclipses, etc. Data furnished for the calculation of 8,000 solar and 5,200 lunar eclipses, going back as far as 1200 B.C. and giving predictions up to the year 2161. Information is also given for partial and ring eclipses. All calculations based on Universal (Greenwich) Time. An unsurpassed reference work for astronomers, scientists engaged in space research and developments, historians, etc. Unabridged republication, with corrections. Preface to this edition by Donald Menzel and Owen Gingerich of the Harvard College Observatory. Translated by Owen Gingerich. 160 charts. lxx + 538pp. 8⅜ x 11¼. S114 Clothbound **$10.00**

THEORY OF THE MOTION OF THE HEAVENLY BODIES MOVING ABOUT THE SUN IN CONIC SECTIONS, Karl Friedrich Gauss. A landmark of theoretical astronomy by the great German scientist. Still authoritative and invaluable to the practicing astronomer. Part I develops the relations between the quantities on which the motion about the sun of the heavenly bodies depends—relations pertaining simply to position in the orbit, simply to position in space, between several places in orbit, and between several places in space. The calculation methods of Part II based on the groundwork of Part I include: determination of an orbit from 3 complete observations, from 4 observations (of which only two are complete), determination of an orbit satisfying as nearly as possible any number of observations whatever, and determination of orbits, taking into account the perturbations. Translation of "Theoria Motus" and with an appendix by C. H. Davis. Unabridged republication. Appendices and tables. 13 figures. xviii + 376pp. 6½ x 9¼. S1056 Paperbound **$2.95**

GEOLOGY, GEOGRAPHY, METEOROLOGY

PRINCIPLES OF STRATIGRAPHY, A. W. Grabau. Classic of 20th century geology, unmatched in scope and comprehensiveness. Nearly 600 pages cover the structure and origins of every kind of sedimentary, hydrogenic, oceanic, pyroclastic, atmoclastic, hydroclastic, marine hydroclastic, and bioclastic rock; metamorphism; erosion; etc. Includes also the constitution of the atmosphere; morphology of oceans, rivers, glaciers; volcanic activities; faults and earthquakes; and fundamental principles of paleontology (nearly 200 pages). New introduction by Prof. M. Kay, Columbia U. 1277 bibliographical entries. 264 diagrams. Tables, maps, etc. Two volume set. Total of xxxii + 1185pp. 5⅜ x 8. S686 Vol I Paperbound **$2.50**
S687 Vol II Paperbound **$2.50**
The set **$5.00**

TREATISE ON SEDIMENTATION, William H. Twenhofel. A milestone in the history of geology, this two-volume work, prepared under the auspices of the United States Research Council, contains practically everything known about sedimentation up to 1932. Brings together all the findings of leading American and foreign geologists and geographers and has never been surpassed for completeness, thoroughness of description, or accuracy of detail. Vol. 1 discusses the sources and production of sediments, their transportation, deposition, diagenesis, and lithification. Also modification of sediments by organisms and topographical, climatic, etc. conditions which contribute to the alteration of sedimentary processes. 220 pages deal with products of sedimentation: minerals, limestones, dolomites, coals, etc. Vol. 2 continues the examination of products such as gypsum and saline residues, silica, strontium, manganese, etc. An extensive exposition of structures, textures and colors of sediments: stratification, cross-lamination, ripple mark, oolitic and pisolitic textures, etc. Chapters on environments or realms of sedimentation and field and laboratory techniques are also included. Indispensable to modern-day geologists and students. Index. List of authors cited. 1733-item bibliography. 121 diagrams. Total of xxxiii + 926pp. 5⅜ x 8½.
Vol. I: S950 Paperbound **$2.50**
Vol. II: S951 Paperbound **$2.50**
Two volume set Paperbound **$5.00**

THE EVOLUTION OF THE IGNEOUS ROCKS, N. L. Bowen. Invaluable serious introduction applies techniques of physics and chemistry to explain igneous rock diversity in terms of chemical composition and fractional crystallization. Discusses liquid immiscibility in silicate magmas, crystal sorting, liquid lines of descent, fractional resorption of complex minerals, petrogenesis, etc. Of prime importance to geologists & mining engineers, also to physicists, chemists working with high temperatures and pressures. "Most important," TIMES, London. 3 indexes. 263 bibliographic notes. 82 figures. xviii + 334pp. 5⅜ x 8. S311 Paperbound **$2.00**

INTERNAL CONSTITUTION OF THE EARTH, edited by **Beno Gutenberg.** Completely revised. Brought up-to-date, reset. Prepared for the National Research Council this is a complete & thorough coverage of such topics as earth origins, continent formation, nature & behavior of the earth's core, petrology of the crust, cooling forces in the core, seismic & earthquake material, gravity, elastic constants, strain characteristics and similar topics. "One is filled with admiration . . . a high standard . . . there is no reader who will not learn something from this book," London, Edinburgh, Dublin, Philosophic Magazine. Largest bibliography in print: 1127 classified items. Indexes. Tables of constants. 43 diagrams. 439pp. 6⅛ x 9¼.
S414 Paperbound **$3.00**

HYDROLOGY, edited by **Oscar E. Meinzer.** Prepared for the National Research Council. Detailed complete reference library on precipitation, evaporation, snow, snow surveying, glaciers, lakes, infiltration, soil moisture, ground water, runoff, drought, physical changes produced by water, hydrology of limestone terranes, etc. Practical in application, especially valuable for engineers. 24 experts have created "the most up-to-date, most complete treatment of the subject," AM. ASSOC. of PETROLEUM GEOLOGISTS. Bibliography. Index. 165 illustrations. xi + 712pp. 6⅛ x 9¼. S191 Paperbound **$3.25**

SNOW CRYSTALS, W. A. Bentley and W. J. Humphreys. Over 200 pages of Bentley's famous microphotographs of snow flakes—the product of painstaking, methodical work at his Jericho, Vermont studio. The pictures, which also include plates of frost, glaze and dew on vegetation, spider webs, windowpanes; sleet; graupel or soft hail, were chosen both for their scientific interest and their aesthetic qualities. The wonder of nature's diversity is exhibited in the intricate, beautiful patterns of the snow flakes. Introductory text by W. J. Humphreys. Selected bibliography. 2,453 illustrations. 224pp. 8 x 10¼. T287 Paperbound **$2.95**

PHYSICS OF THE AIR, W. J. Humphreys. A very thorough coverage of classical materials and theories in meteorology . . . written by one of this century's most highly respected physical meteorologists. Contains the standard account in English of atmospheric optics. 5 main sections: Mechanics and Thermodynamics of the Atmosphere, Atmospheric Electricity and Auroras, Meteorological Acoustics, Atmospheric Optics, and Factors of Climatic Control. Under these headings, topics covered are: theoretical relations between temperature, pressure, and volume in the atmosphere; composition, pressure, and density; circulation; evaporation and condensation; fog, clouds, thunderstorms, lightning; aurora polaris; principal ice-age theories; etc. New preface by Prof. Julius London. 226 illustrations. Index. xviii + 676pp. 5⅜ x 8½. S1044 Paperbound **$3.00**

CHEMISTRY AND PHYSICAL CHEMISTRY

ORGANIC CHEMISTRY, F. C. Whitmore. The entire subject of organic chemistry for the practicing chemist and the advanced student. Storehouse of facts, theories, processes found elsewhere only in specialized journals. Covers aliphatic compounds (500 pages on the properties and synthetic preparation of hydrocarbons, halides, proteins, ketones, etc.), alicyclic compounds, aromatic compounds, heterocyclic compounds, organophosphorus and organometallic compounds. Methods of synthetic preparation analyzed critically throughout. Includes much of biochemical interest. "The scope of this volume is astonishing," INDUSTRIAL AND ENGINEERING CHEMISTRY. 12,000-reference index. 2387-item bibliography. Total of x + 1005pp. 5⅜ x 8. Two volume set.
S700 Vol I Paperbound **$2.00**
S701 Vol II Paperbound **$2.00**
The set **$4.00**

THE MODERN THEORY OF MOLECULAR STRUCTURE, Bernard Pullman. A reasonably popular account of recent developments in atomic and molecular theory. Contents: The Wave Function and Wave Equations (history and bases of present theories of molecular structure); The Electronic Structure of Atoms (Description and classification of atomic wave functions, etc.); Diatomic Molecules; Non-Conjugated Polyatomic Molecules; Conjugated Polyatomic Molecules; The Structure of Complexes. Minimum of mathematical background needed. New translation by David Antin of "La Structure Moleculaire." Index. Bibliography. vii + 87pp. 5⅜ x 8½. S987 Paperbound **$1.00**

CATALYSIS AND CATALYSTS, Marcel Prettre, Director, Research Institute on Catalysis. This brief book, translated into English for the first time, is the finest summary of the principal modern concepts, methods, and results of catalysis. Ideal introduction for beginning chemistry and physics students. Chapters: Basic Definitions of Catalysis (true catalysis and generalization of the concept of catalysis); The Scientific Bases of Catalysis (Catalysis and chemical thermodynamics, catalysis and chemical kinetics); Homogeneous Catalysis (acid-base catalysis, etc.); Chain Reactions; Contact Masses; Heterogeneous Catalysis (Mechanisms of contact catalyses, etc.); and Industrial Applications (acids and fertilizers, petroleum and petroleum chemistry, rubber, plastics, synthetic resins, and fibers). Translated by David Antin. Index. vi + 88pp. 5⅜ x 8½. S998 Paperbound **$1.00**

POLAR MOLECULES, Pieter Debye. This work by Nobel laureate Debye offers a complete guide to fundamental electrostatic field relations, polarizability, molecular structure. Partial contents: electric intensity, displacement and force, polarization by orientation, molar polarization and molar refraction, halogen-hydrides, polar liquids, ionic saturation, dielectric constant, etc. Special chapter considers quantum theory. Indexed. 172pp. 5⅜ x 8.
S64 Paperbound **$1.50**

THE ELECTRONIC THEORY OF ACIDS AND BASES, W. F. Luder and Saverio Zuffanti. The first full systematic presentation of the electronic theory of acids and bases—treating the theory and its ramifications in an uncomplicated manner. Chapters: Historical Background; Atomic Orbitals and Valence; The Electronic Theory of Acids and Bases; Electrophilic and Electrodotic Reagents; Acidic and Basic Radicals; Neutralization; Titrations with Indicators; Displacement; Catalysis; Acid Catalysis; Base Catalysis; Alkoxides and Catalysts; Conclusion. Required reading for all chemists. Second revised (1961) eidtion, with additional examples and references. 3 figures. 9 tables. Index. Bibliography xii + 165pp. 5⅜ x 8.
S201 Paperbound **$1.50**

KINETIC THEORY OF LIQUIDS, J. Frenkel. Regarding the kinetic theory of liquids as a generalization and extension of the theory of solid bodies, this volume covers all types of arrangements of solids, thermal displacements of atoms, interstitial atoms and ions, orientational and rotational motion of molecules, and transition between states of matter. Mathematical theory is developed close to the physical subject matter. 216 bibliographical footnotes. 55 figures. xi + 485pp. 5⅜ x 8. S95 Paperbound **$2.55**

THE PRINCIPLES OF ELECTROCHEMISTRY, D. A. MacInnes. Basic equations for almost every subfield of electrochemistry from first principles, referring at all times to the soundest and most recent theories and results; unusually useful as text or as reference. Covers coulometers and Faraday's Law, electrolytic conductance, the Debye-Hueckel method for the theoretical calculation of activity coefficients, concentration cells, standard electrode potentials, thermodynamic ionization constants, pH, potentiometric titrations, irreversible phenomena, Planck's equation, and much more. "Excellent treatise," AMERICAN CHEMICAL SOCIETY JOURNAL. "Highly recommended," CHEMICAL AND METALLURGICAL ENGINEERING. 2 Indices. Appendix. 585-item bibliography. 137 figures. 94 tables. ii + 478pp. 5⅝ x 8⅜.
S52 Paperbound **$2.45**

THE PHASE RULE AND ITS APPLICATION, Alexander Findlay. Covering chemical phenomena of 1, 2, 3, 4, and multiple component systems, this "standard work on the subject" (NATURE, London), has been completely revised and brought up to date by A. N. Campbell and N. O. Smith. Brand new material has been added on such matters as binary, tertiary liquid equilibria, solid solutions in ternary systems, quinary systems of salts and water. Completely revised to triangular coordinates in ternary systems, clarified graphic representation, solid models, etc. 9th revised edition. Author, subject indexes. 236 figures. 505 footnotes, mostly bibliographic. xii + 494pp. 5⅜ x 8. S91 Paperbound **$2.45**

THE SOLUBILITY OF NONELECTROLYTES, Joel H. Hildebrand and Robert L. Scott. The standard work on the subject; still indispensable as a reference source and for classroom work. Partial contents: The Ideal Solution (including Raoult's Law and Henry's Law, etc.); Nonideal Solutions; Intermolecular Forces; The Liquid State; Entropy of Athermal Mixing; Heat of Mixing; Polarity; Hydrogen Bonding; Specific Interactions; "Solvation" and "Association"; Systems of Three or More Components; Vapor Pressure of Binary Liquid Solutions; Mixtures of Gases; Solubility of Gases in Liquids; of Liquids in Liquids; of Solids in Liquids; Evaluation of Solubility Parameters; and other topics. Corrected republication of third (revised) edition. Appendices. Indexes. 138 figures. 111 tables. 1 photograph. iv + 488pp. 5⅜ x 8½.
S1125 Paperbound **$2.50**

TERNARY SYSTEMS: INTRODUCTION TO THE THEORY OF THREE COMPONENT SYSTEMS, G. Masing. Furnishes detailed discussion of representative types of 3-components systems, both in solid models (particularly metallic alloys) and isothermal models. Discusses mechanical mixture without compounds and without solid solutions; unbroken solid solution series; solid solutions with solubility breaks in two binary systems; iron-silicon-aluminum alloys; allotropic forms of iron in ternary system; other topics. Bibliography. Index. 166 illustrations. 178pp. 5⅝ x 8⅜. S631 Paperbound **$1.50**

THE KINETIC THEORY OF GASES, Leonard B. Loeb, University of California. Comprehensive text and reference book which presents full coverage of basic theory and the important experiments and developments in the field for the student and investigator. Partial contents: The Mechanical Picture of a Perfect Gas, The Mean Free Path—Clausius' Deductions, Distribution of Molecular Velocities, discussions of theory of the problem of specific heats, the contributions of kinetic theory to our knowledge of electrical and magnetic properties of molecules and its application to the conduction of electricity in gases. New 14-page preface to Dover edition by the author. Name, subject indexes. Six appendices. 570-item bibliography. xxxvi + 687pp. 5⅜ x 8½. S942 Paperbound **$2.95**

IONS IN SOLUTION, Ronald W. Gurney. A thorough and readable introduction covering all the fundamental principles and experiments in the field, by an internationally-known authority. Contains discussions of solvation energy, atomic and molecular ions, lattice energy, transferral of ions, interionic forces, cells and half-cells, transference of electrons, exchange forces, hydrogen ions, the electro-chemical series, and many other related topics. Indispensable to advanced undergraduates and graduate students in electrochemistry. Index. 45 illustrations. 15 tables. vii + 206pp. 5⅜ x 8½. S124 Paperbound **$1.50**

IONIC PROCESSES IN SOLUTION, Ronald W. Gurney. Lucid, comprehensive examination which brings together the approaches of electrochemistry, thermodynamics, statistical mechanics, electroacoustics, molecular physics, and quantum theory in the interpretation of the behavior of ionic solutions—the most important single work on the subject. More extensive and technical than the author's earlier work (IONS IN SOLUTION), it is a middle-level text for graduate students and researchers in electrochemistry. Covers such matters as Brownian motion in liquids, molecular ions in solution, heat of precipitation, entropy of solution, proton transfers, dissociation constant of nitric acid, viscosity of ionic solutions, etc. 78 illustrations. 47 tables. Name and subject index. ix + 275pp. 5⅜ x 8½.
S134 Paperbound **$1.75**

CRYSTALLOGRAPHIC DATA ON METAL AND ALLOY STRUCTURES, Compiled by A. Taylor and B. J. Kagle, Westinghouse Research Laboratories. Unique collection of the latest crystallographic data on alloys, compounds, and the elements, with lattice spacings expressed uniformly in absolute Angstrom units. Gathers together previously widely-scattered data from the Power Data File of the ATSM, structure reports, and the Landolt-Bornstein Tables, as well as from other original literature. 2300 different compounds listed in the first table, Alloys and Intermetallic Compounds, with much vital information on each. Also listings for nearly 700 Borides, Carbides, Hydrides, Oxides, Nitrides. Also all the necessary data on the crystal structure of 77 elements. vii + 263pp. 5⅜ x 8. S1013 Paperbound **$2.25**

MATHEMATICAL CRYSTALLOGRAPHY AND THE THEORY OF GROUPS OF MOVEMENTS, Harold Hilton. Classic account of the mathematical theory of crystallography, particularly the geometrical theory of crystal-structure based on the work of Bravais, Jordan, Sohncke, Federow, Schoenflies, and Barlow. Partial contents: The Stereographic Projection, Properties Common to Symmetrical and Asymmetrical Crystals, The Theory of Groups, Coordinates of Equivalent Points, Crystallographic Axes and Axial Ratios, The Forms and Growth of Crystals, Lattices and Translations, The Structure-Theory, Infinite Groups of Movements, Triclinic and Monoclinic Groups, Orthorhombic Groups, etc. Index. 188 figures. xii + 262pp. 5⅜ x 8½.
S1058 Paperbound **$2.00**

CLASSICS IN THE THEORY OF CHEMICAL COMBINATIONS. Edited by O. T. Benfey. Vol. I of the Classics of Science Series, G. Holton, Harvard University, General Editor. This book is a collection of papers representing the major chapters in the development of the valence concept in chemistry. Includes essays by Wöhler and Liebig, Laurent, Williamson, Frankland, Kekulé and Couper, and two by van't Hoff and le Bel, which mark the first extension of the valence concept beyond its purely numerical character. Introduction and epilogue by Prof. Benfey. Index. 9 illustrations. New translation of Kekulé paper by Benfey. xiv + 191pp. 5⅜ x 8½. S1066 Paperbound **$1.85**